F. C. STEWARD
Cornell University

GROWTH AND ORGANIZATION IN PLANTS

STRUCTURE
DEVELOPMENT
METABOLISM
PHYSIOLOGY

ADDISON-WESLEY
PUBLISHING COMPANY
Reading, Massachusetts
Menlo Park
London
Don Mills, Ontario

This book is in the
Addison-Wesley Series
in Life Science

PROLOGUE

No book such as this can ever be complete; if it seems so at one period in time, it ceases to do so in another. These chapters, essays, or expanded lectures tell their story in a highly personal way, without apology for many obvious omissions.

The author's, and indeed a customary, approach to plant physiology is deeply ingrained in the study of cells, their membranes and particulate inclusions, their metabolism and responses to stimuli. Too often the problems of growth may, therefore, be the appendix or the epilogue, not the central theme; although to leave the processes of growth and active metabolism out of the consideration of this or that physiological process is like leaving the "Prince of Denmark" out of *Hamlet*.

These essays were first organized for Summer Institutes of the Botanical Society of America and were delivered as a series of lectures on the general subject of plant growth and metabolism to an audience composed largely of college teachers of biology. In response to suggestions that the lectures would be useful if made more generally available, they were recorded on another occasion almost as they were delivered. In the delay prior to publication and in the irresistible, but probably unwise, urge to alter here and modify there, they may well have lost their spontaneity. Even so, they are now offered, belatedly, and somewhat supplemented, as one investigator's way of expressing interest in, and enthusiasm for, the great problems of plant growth, metabolism, and development. In these days when there are those who focus all their attention on a bacterium, a bacteriophage, or even on a few biologically important molecules and enzymes it may be salutory to look at the more complicated problems of flowering plants. Even the fact that they so often seem insoluble should be a challenge, not a deterrent.

Perhaps a few personal notes may be forgiven.

In presenting these essays one should first acknowledge a debt to all those teachers, colleagues and collaborators who helped to formulate a philosophy and especially to the succession of students whose lively interest has kept the sense of challenge bright.

The author began his own studies in the stimulating period that followed the first World War, when physical science became almost a religion, and somewhat crudely mechanistic hypotheses held their sway in biology. Organisms conveniently presented chemists and physicists with problems to be solved by the techniques with which they were then familiar; but by the imminence of a second World War, the limitations had become all too obvious. A renewed respect was born for biological organization, for the working dynamic machine rather than the purely equilibrium mechanism. About that time (1940) in England, the writer began an account of his own researches in a volume that has never appeared as such, but which was to have had the title "Plant Cells, Plant Growth, and Plant Nutrition." In part this present account replaces that unpublished work. However, while writing a preface in 1940 in Richmond, Surrey, England, amid the stupidity and the exhilaration of the first major aerial war, one was then impressed with the futility that uses 20th-century physical science in ways that even threaten man's destruction. By contrast Stephen Hales in the early 18th century, and but a few miles distant at Kingston, declared that, "The searching into the works of Nature . . . delights and enlarges the mind, and strikes us with the strongest assurance of the wisdom and power of the divine Architect, in framing for us so beautiful and well regulated a world. . . ."

Since 1940 the hazards have changed. The bombs over London seem insignificant as we now contemplate even more deadly weapons, and amid all the clamor about space travel. But the sense of escape and relief is still there for those who turn from the raucous turbulence engendered by the study only of the inanimate, physical, world to the contemplation of the mystery and the quiet competence of the growth of living things. Despite all the noise and blast of rocket propulsion, of soaring satellites or even megaton bombs, man cannot yet approach or emulate the coordinated, incredibly efficient growth of a fertilized egg. All the resources of the chemical industry cannot spin a cellulose wall.

It has been said, poetically, that "You are nearer God's heart in a garden than anywhere else on earth." Certainly the order and plan of organic nature and the great "garden" which is the wealth of form and structure of the plant world should inspire both the student and the teacher of plant biology, for without plants life as we know it would not for long exist. Even if physicists and engineers, studying inherently simpler systems, solve the problems of inanimate matter and energy, there will still remain great gaps in human knowledge that biologists must endeavor to fill. For those who seek to do this there is still to be found the same quiet dignity and purpose which Stephen Hales knew over two hundred years ago.

F. C. S.

Ithaca, New York
November 1967

ACKNOWLEDGMENTS

If the author were to acknowledge all his indebtedness the task would be formidable. Nevertheless one should not fail to express thanks for help of many kinds. Many publishers and editors have been especially helpful by invariably acceding to the numerous requests to re-publish figures. To all those scientists who so readily furnished the illustrations requested especial thanks are due and these go far beyond the mere acknowledgments in the text. Addison-Wesley, who had enough confidence in the work to indulge the author in what he wanted to do, has earned the author's gratitude. One should also recognize all those who, in industrial firms, in foundations, and particularly in such granting agencies as the National Institutes of Health, gave our research its needed support over the years for, without this, the present account would not have the perspective gained by firsthand experience. But there are also those whose role demands a more personal and special mention. These include Mrs. Gertrude Olsen for invaluable secretarial help; Mrs. M. O. Mapes for her work on the illustrations especially and others, who performed many helpful tasks in their role as personal assistants. Especial thanks are due to Dr. A. D. Krikorian, who gave unselfishly of his time and helped by his own infectious interest in the work. To these and to all those others who, though anonymous, helped by reading or correcting manuscript grateful thanks are due.

To Anne

CONTENTS

7
Morphogenetic Stimuli   331

8
The Onset of Flowering and Fruiting:
Contrasts in Vegetative and Reproductive Growth   372

chapter one

CONCEPTS OF GROWTH AND DEVELOPMENT: THE SCOPE OF THE PROBLEM

All aspects of biology converge in the consideration of growth, for growth may be regarded as the summation of all the physiological attributes of organisms. Any consideration of growth, organization, and metabolism in plants raises as many new problems as it solves. However, science advances when new questions are posed so that new solutions may be sought. But one may need to formulate questions about the growth of plants even though it may not always be possible to show how the problems may be investigated. The treatment in this series of chapters will therefore draw extensively upon certain researches with which the writer has been personally concerned, for these often furnish useful, though by no means unique, illustrative material.

Man's approach to the science of biology is conditioned by the fact that he is himself a part of the system that the science endeavors to interpret. As organisms ourselves, we have experienced (or are still experiencing) growth; hence the subject has an appeal to those who do not normally regard themselves as biologists. It is a deep-seated human emotion to take pleasure in watching things grow, whether these be kittens, flowers, or grandchildren! The poetic idea of the child being father to the man pays unconscious tribute to the biological concept of growth and development. Many scholarly works (e.g., D'Arcy Thompson's *Growth and Form*, first published in 1917) have approached the problems of growth from the standpoint of mathematical analysis and of the physical properties of matter. D'Arcy Thompson gave great impetus to, even if he did not initiate, the idea that organisms might be interpreted in terms of the different and stable ways in which space may be partitioned. Regular 14-sided figures (orthotetrakaidecahedra) can fill space without any "leftovers" and may, therefore, represent cells as they often exist, without air spaces, in the terminal growing points of angiosperms.

Complex Forms in Vascular and Non-Vascular Plants

Most of the ensuing discussions will be concerned with growth, development, metabolism, and nutrition of highly organized vascular plants. Nevertheless, some non-vascular plants, even non-cellular plants, may attain a surprising de-

1

FIG. 1–1. Complexity of form in some filamentous algae. A. Habit of *Halimeda tridens*, showing the jointed calcareous skeleton and rhizoids with adhering material largely composed of fragments of *Halimeda* scales. B. Habit of *Penicillus dumetosus*. C. Habit of *Udotea* sp., showing portion removed and examined at E and F. D. *Caulerpa sertulariodes*, showing portions of the thallus which superficially resemble leaves, stems, and roots. E. Portion of the thallus of *Udotea* (see C) after the calcium carbonate has been dissolved to show a tangled weft of filaments. F. Filaments of *Udotea* more highly magnified.

gree of complexity of form. These and microorganisms may, therefore, often illustrate principles that are more generally applicable. Earlier ideas that unicellular organisms are necessarily always simple, or primitive, are not perhaps so widely held as hitherto. Surprisingly complex forms may be achieved by filamentous and even non-cellular, or coenocytic plants; these may be contrasted with plants in which division of labor between different parts of the plant body is made possible by their organization into cells, tissues, and organs.

The complexity of form that is possible in plants belonging to the Thallophyta is well illustrated by certain green algae classified in the genera *Caulerpa, Halimeda, Udotea,* and *Penicillus,* which occur in warm seas and on calcareous reefs. Beneath the often calcareous skeletons, illustrated in Fig. 1–1 (A through F), lie tangled wefts of filaments which are revealed when the calcium carbonate is dissolved by acid. Thus an elaborate form, with a measure of division of labor between its parts, is not confined to higher plants which are composed of cells organized into tissues.

An organism having special features that have been used in the interpretation of complex form during growth and morphogenesis is the green alga *Acetabularia.* For most of its life cycle this organism consists of a uninucleate structure. In the course of reproduction, however, a filamentous stalk with a single basal nucleus gives rise to an umbrella-like cap into which many daughter nuclei migrate to produce cysts which, in turn, give rise to motile gametes in accordance with the life cycle illustrated in Fig. 1–2. This organism has presented an ideal system for the investigation of the role of the nucleus in morphogenesis— in this case the form and development of the cap. Some development of the cap may occur even after the basal nucleus is removed. However, the extent of this development is determined by substances which depend upon the nucleus, and is therefore limited by their formation prior to the removal of the nucleus. These relationships have been investigated by Hämmerling (1953, 1963) and those who have followed his lead. This example serves, therefore, to show the range of form and complexity (Fig. 1–3) which may be achieved in an organism that is so simple that for most of its life it exists as a single uninucleate cell.

Even though filamentous green algae exist freely suspended in liquid, their populations may nevertheless assume characteristic forms. Anyone who has observed masses of *Spirogyra* in a pond or dish will have recognized this. It is less well known, however, that even *Spirogyra* filaments, lacking mobility in the ordinary sense, will "walk" or "crawl" up an inclined glass plate in the light (cf. Lund, 1942, and references there cited). Even more striking, however, are the large spherical, i.e., "ball-shaped," masses of *Aegagropila* or other *Cladophora*-like filaments which are formed in response to water currents. Thus a somewhat complex colonial morphology may arise from simple filaments which are not even organically connected (Fig. 1–4). The ways in which the separate filaments interact to do this still present problems.

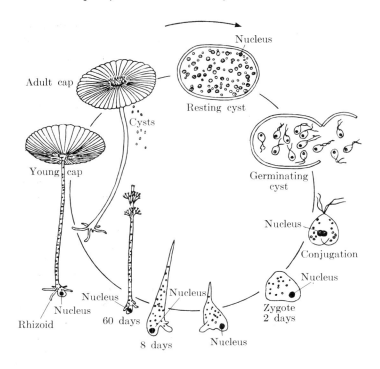

FIG. 1–2. *Acetabularia* sp. life cycle. When the cap forms, the large basal nucleus gives rise to many nuclei which spread throughout the alga including the cap, which produces resistant forms (called cysts). As the cysts germinate, motile gametes are formed and escape. After union of the gametes and the formation of a zygote, the cycle is repeated. (After Brachet, 1957.)

The Stoneworts, of which *Chara* and *Nitella* are the examples most familiar to physiologists, present examples in the algae of a highly articulated vegetative plant body. Whorls of leaf-like appendages at nodes, with long internodal segments, present a shoot-like appearance and this similarity is accentuated by the role in development of an apical cell. Nevertheless, this degree of organization is achieved by jointed multinuclear cells or coenocytic segments without benefit of a meristematic multicellular growing region, and it is also maintained without recourse to specialized tissues which are adapted for conduction. For this reason the role of the large internodal cells (see diagram p. 5) in absorption of solutes and in the nerve-like transfer of stimuli has been much investigated. These organisms also present opportunities to interpret growth and to see this in terms of the behavior of the cell wall; this opportunity has recently been seized by Green and King (1966) and by others (Probine and Preston, 1958, 1962). The growth of *Nitella* is of interest here since it illustrates how a highly articulated structure emerges from the growth of an apical cell, which is subject only to

FIG. 1–3. A number of *Acetabularia* plants growing on a shell. Note the elongate stalks and the umbrella-like caps (2 × natural size). (Material courtesy of Dr. J. M. Kingsbury, Cornell University.)

the stimuli controlling the planes of cell division and the extent and direction of the subsequent cell expansion.

Essentially *Nitella* grows in the following way: a dome-shaped apical cell expands and divides transversely to give an upper persistent apical cell and a lower cell; this lower cell divides again to give an upper nodal cell and a lower internodal cell. The internode develops by growth in length much more than by growth in circumference, and in such a way that the ratio between length and circumference is constant at about 4.5 (Green, 1963); log/log plots of length versus diameter or circumference show that this growth may be interpreted as an example of relative or heterogonic growth (cf. Chapter 9).

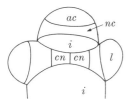

Longitudinal section through the apex of *Nitella gracilis*. (*ac*, apical cell; *cn*, central cell of node; *i*, internode; *l*, lateral of limited growth; *nc*, nodal cell.) (Redrawn from Oltmanns, 1904.)

◀FIG. 1–4. Ball of *Aegagropila* sp. This beautiful organism (A) is comprised of filaments (B, C) which organize in response to water currents. It formed as a result of some experiments done to maintain the natural shape of algal balls in culture. (From Yoshida, *Bull. Jap. Soc. Phycol.* 10, 23–27, 1962.)

The nodal cell segment (*nc* in diagram, p. 5) divides repeatedly to give the whorl of cells from which the leaf-like appendages arise. Each lateral appendage originates from an initial which behaves as an apical cell; each initiating cell grows outward, cone-like, and divides transversely at its base as it elongates at its tip. Green has described the growth of the apex of *Nitella* by the use of time-lapse photography and by an ingenious technique in which small (3 microns) particles of anion exchange resins were attached to the surfaces of the apical cell (diameter 50 μ) and of the initiating cell of the leaf-like appendage. In this way one can see how the wall must accommodate as growth occurs. The plate of Fig. 1–5, furnished by Dr. Green, illustrates dramatically the changes as they occur in space and time.

It is very clear that the upper hemispherical portion of the central apical cell retains its integrity through successive divisions which cut off, basally, the nodal and internodal segments. The growth of the apical cell of the leaf-like appendage, by contrast, forms a pointed, cone-like tip, while an intermediate segment of wall (*abef* in Fig. 1–5) is greatly expanded, especially along its outer and more curved surface. After some 24 to 36 hours two more basal segments, from which a new node and internode will arise, have fully formed and by 42 to 48 hours a new bud-like initial has made its appearance at the next level above the first. In language more appropriate to angiosperms, it may be said that in this material the "plastochron" occupies about 48 hours (cf. Chapter 8) and the cell generation time in the "apex" seems to be about 12 hours.

As Green points out, the oriented growth of *Nitella* cells and segments goes hand in hand with characteristic orientation in the anisotropic fibrillar structure of the cell walls. This is a general feature, observed equally in the contrast between the random arrangement of cellulose in primary walls of angiosperms and the spiral habit in walls of more elongated cells, and in the similar contrast between the first and the later formed wall of *Valonia* as it grows upon a naked surface of protoplasm. The wall configuration, therefore, seems to be the consequence rather than the cause of the form that the growing cells assume. The elaborate vegetative plant body of the stoneworts is, therefore, to be seen as the consequence of a pattern of controlled cell division and cell enlargement. The tip of the apical cell retains its integrity and ability to divide transversely at its base; one of a pair of basal cells grows transversely with cell divisions to form a nodal plate and gives rise at its margins to whorls of leaf-like appendages; the other grows predominantly in length, without segmentation, to form the internodal cells. But it still must be explained why such similar, adjacent, basal cells grow in such different ways when they are cut off from the apical cell.

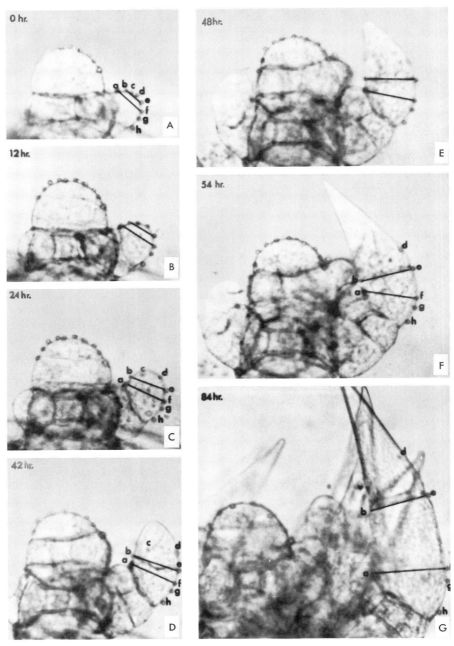

FIG. 1–5. The growth of the apical cell of *Nitella* and the origin of leaf-like appendages. The photographs were made by time-lapse photography at a magnification of ×300. The attached particles (*a* through *h*), which act as markers, are 3 μ in diameter and consist of anion-exchange resin. Parts A through G show the growth and development of an apical cell and of an apical cell of a leafy appendage at intervals during a period of 84 hours. (From photographs supplied by Dr. P. B. Green.)

The cellular slime molds are primitive organisms that nevertheless exhibit a remarkable propensity for morphogenesis, although this is achieved by aggregations of relatively unspecialized cells. These organisms, which have been extensively investigated from the standpoint of their physiology and growth by such workers as K. B. Raper, J. T. Bonner, and the Sussmans, are at the borderline between the plant and animal kingdoms, for they consist of independently living amoeboid cells in their "vegetative" state, although in the course of their fructification they aggregate to form often elaborate, more plant-like structures. The stimuli that induce this transition involve both nutritional and environmental effects. However, the interest of the slime molds in the context of this discussion is the way an elaborate morphology is created, not by the outgrowth or development from a single cell or zygote, but as a property of the population of otherwise free living cells after they have aggregated and differentiated. Thus, the cell aggregate is more than the sum of its parts. While reference may be made to papers by Kenneth B. Raper (1960, 1962), a series of figures will illustrate the essentials. These figures show for two organisms, *Dictyostelium discoideum* Raper and *Polysiphondylium pallidum* Olive, the aggregation of amoeboid cells and their convergence to form a pseudoplasmodium from which either a single stalked sorocarp, bearing spores, develops (*Dictyostelium*) or many such are borne in whorls upon a stem-like axis at definite and regular "nodes" (Fig. 1–6).

Perhaps more familiar, but nonetheless remarkable, are the elaborate fructifications achieved by many higher fungi (Basidiomycetes) by arrangement of what is essentially a weft of twisted threads or filaments (Fig. 1–7). However, these filaments may be in organic connection via the structures called clamp connections (Fig. 1–7F) which provide for the union of the contents of different filaments.

The discussion in subsequent chapters will be focused mainly upon the growth and development of angiosperms—the most highly organized plants and currently the predominant organisms on earth. The chief events of growth and development in flowering plants occur in well-defined growing regions from which a variety of organs and tissues and a great many differentiated cell types develop. The consequences of this high degree of organization will need to be considered at all levels—at the molecular and sub-cellular levels and at the level of cells, organs, and organisms.

At the outset some obvious points should be made. Higher plants have evolved a distinctive way of life. Although they have many basic attributes in common with all other living things, they make use of them in distinctive ways. The principles of chemistry and physics, the laws that govern matter and energy, apply equally in the animate and the inanimate world—to plants as well as to animals, bacteria, and viruses. But flowering plants are not merely inferior animals, nor are they merely somewhat more complicated than bacteria; their organization and the way they grow convey their distinctive attributes. Valuable as such concepts as comparative biochemistry or general physiology are, they

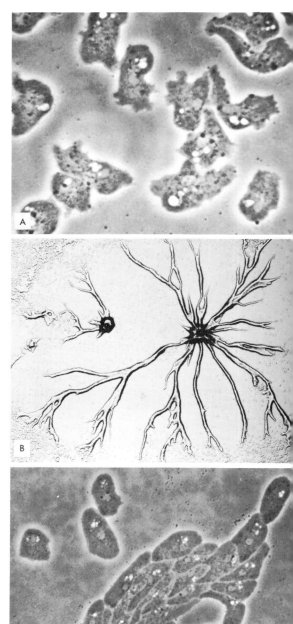

FIG. 1–6. Organization in some slime molds.   A.   *Dictyostelium discoideum* Raper in pre-aggregative stage.   Note inconstant shape, lack of uniform orientation, irregular pseudopodia, nuclei (appearing as light gray, centrally positioned areas), and white contractile vacuoles (×750).   B. A developing pseudopodium, well advanced; the smaller organization at left resulted from severance of a major stream in the larger aggregation (×18).   C.   Strongly oriented aggregating myxamoebae (×500).   D.   Diagrammatic representation of a mature sorocarp showing the expanded basal disk (4), the tapering stalk or sorophore (2, 3), and the terminal spore mass or sorus (1).   On right, detail of cellular structure at levels indicated by corresponding numerals.   E.   Early stage of the sorocarp formation (×140).   F. A developing sorocarp fixed and stained to reveal the sharp demarcation between pre-stalk cells in the apical area and the spore and pre-spore cells that comprise the main body of the sorogen (×140).   G.   *Polysiphondylium pallidum* Olive.   Typical sorocarps photographed with reflected light to reveal their natural habit and appearance (×16). (From photographs supplied by Dr. Raper.)

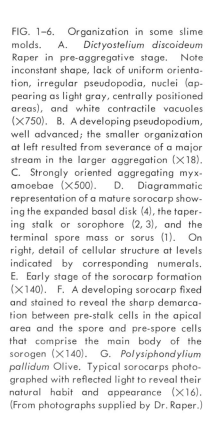

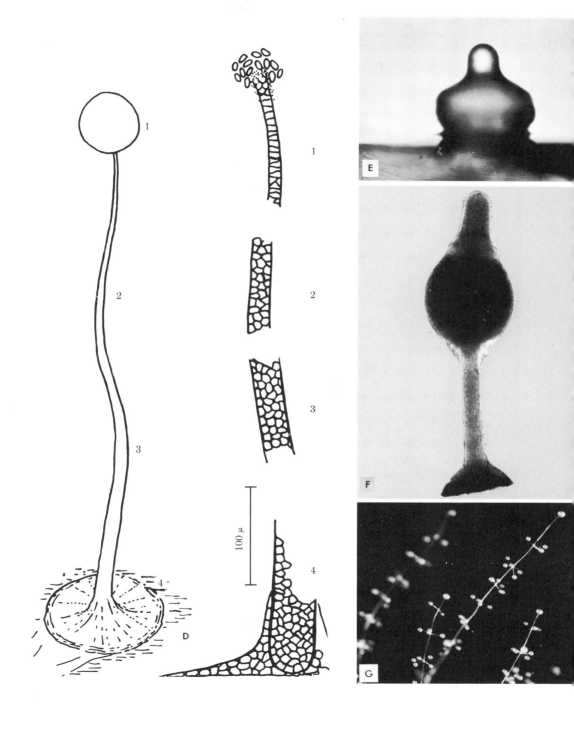

FIG. 1–7. Organization in a basidiomycete. A. Fruit bodies produced on sterile horse dung 10 days after inoculation with dicaryon mycelium. Incubated at 26°C in 12-hour day. B. Surface of gill showing tetrads of basidiospores at two levels. Each tetrad represents the four products of a meiotic division (×450). C. Oidia, uninucleate asexual spores, borne on short branches of the haploid mycelium produced by germinating basidiospores (×2000). D. Electron micrograph of septal pore connecting two adjacent haploid mycelial cells (×30,000). E. Chlamydospores of dicaryon mycelium. Upon germination these usually give rise to further dicaryotic mycelium but may form haploid, homocaryotic cells from which the parental lines may be recovered. F. Dicaryon mycelium showing characteristic clamp connections at each septum. Pores like that shown in D are present in both of the cell walls associated with each clamp. This mycelium gives rise to fruit bodies when inoculated to a suitable substrate. (From Day, *Heredity* **13**, 81–87, 1959, and Giesy and Day, *Am. J. Bot.* **52**, 287–293, 1965; photographs supplied by Dr. Day.)   ▶

alone are not sufficient to illuminate the differences between *Chlorella* and an oak tree.

Among the evident contrasts between higher plants and higher animals the following may be mentioned. Animals have highly developed organs; these acquire their special, and often seemingly irreversible, characteristics early in development, and they realize these in the "division of labor" in the animal body. The high degree of specialization in an animal body requires well-developed means to control, correlate, and integrate the behavior of its parts: there is no obvious counterpart in plants for the role of the brain, the central nervous system, and even for the blood as a circulating tissue. Even the hormonal mechanisms of animals are more localized and rigorously prescribed than their counterparts in plants. By contrast the living cells of plants often have a greater ability than animal cells to retain the general characteristics of the whole organism while they play their specialized roles, although cells are not as free to move with respect to each other in plants as in animals. Cell walls and middle lamellae of plants, which preclude the free movement of cells with respect to their neighbors, are nevertheless not to be construed as barriers that separate adjacent protoplasts. The wealth of protoplasmic connections, or plasmodesmata, that unite the protoplasts of adjacent cells may be seen in such a classical object as endosperm (Fig. 1–8). In a tissue like endosperm, which emphasizes the prior storage and later reuse of food material for the embryo, the role of plasmodesmata in the passage of solutes seems clear enough. In the general situation, the plasmodesmata which connect adjacent living cells of plants have a presumptive role in the passage of stimuli and as a means of integrating the behavior of cells *en masse* in ways that do not apply to higher animals. The later preoccupation with the challenging problems of the interpretation of growth and development of vascular plants must, therefore, pay especial attention to their organization, to their metabolism and nutrition, and to the stimuli which regulate the behavior of their cells and tissues. It should not, however, divert attention from

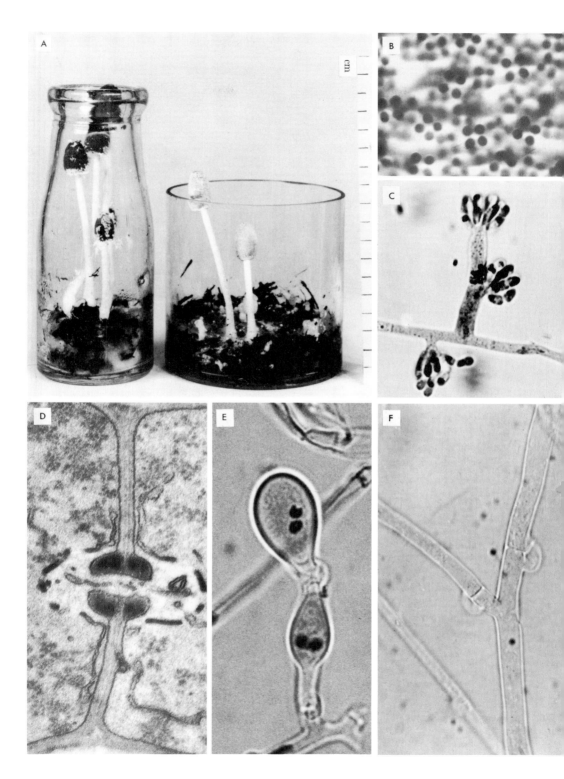

FIG. 1–8. Protoplasmic connections (plasmodesmata) in the endosperm of *Diospyros*. (Photographed from a slide by Chamberlain supplied by Dr. D. P. Voth, University of Chicago.)

the dramatic accomplishments of simpler organisms, such as those mentioned earlier in this chapter, for the interpretation of the seemingly simpler systems, which lack organized growing regions, may also shed some light on those organisms which are more complex.

Concepts of Growth: Growth as Increase of Size

Since the term "growth" is so familiar, it is well to examine our concepts. The standpoint from which we regard growth determines, in large part, the units of measurement to be used and the ideas about the process which will emerge. Growth is commonly conceived as increase of size and, so regarded, it may be measured in a variety of ways. An early memory is of growth in length, as the growing child stands against the jamb of the door, where each annual increment of growth is recorded. The newborn babe is invariably measured—usually in terms of length and of weight, or mass. At first, since all the essential organs are already laid down at birth, growth is measured by increase of weight or mass, and by the increase of size, especially in height or length.

In due course, human growth in length ceases to be the conspicuous feature; greater emphasis is placed on growth in bulk, and the scales for measuring weight, or mass, replace the tape measure for measuring length. But the attitude of mind of the football linesman and the fashion-conscious female may be quite different when they step on the scales. The football player is interested in acquisition of weight or mass, because of his bodily impact upon the opposing team. The woman, however, more concerned with visible effects, is perhaps not so much interested in her weight or mass, as her *volume*, and only inasmuch as volume and mass tend to be proportional is the method of measurement appropriate! Thus the different units—length, weight, volume—can all be used in different situations to record the increments of size which are familiarly associated with growth.

Relative Growth

It should be emphasized that in plants all organs do not grow at equal rates, and thus the concepts of relative growth need also to be recognized (Huxley, 1932). When an organism grows at equal rates in all its parts its method of growth is termed "isogonous," but when organisms grow at unequal rates in their different parts their method of growth is termed "heterogonous." A dramatic example of unequal growth rates in seedling plants is to be found in species of *Streptocarpus*, members of the Gesneriaceae (Fig. 1–9). In these plants the embryo, as

FIG. 1–9. Asymmetry in the cotyledons of *Streptocarpus*. A. *Streptocarpus grandis* N. E. Brown, a young plant with two cotyledons of unequal size. B. *Streptocarpus saundersii* Hooker, a mature plant with one cotyledon. (From photographs supplied by B. L. Burtt, Royal Botanic Garden, Edinburgh, Scotland.)

expected, has two similar cotyledons, but after they leave the seed coat, one of these may be retarded while the other increases "to an extraordinary degree and develops into a green foliage leaf lying on the ground 22 cm long and 12 cm broad. Strangely enough, many species of this genus, e.g., *Streptocarpus polyanthus*, develop no other leaves, but content themselves with the development of one cotyledon into a gigantic foliage leaf." (Kerner and Oliver, 1902).

Growth as Increase of Substance

Since organisms consist so largely of water, their increase of size, which implies accretion of substance, is very largely an increase of water. One might, however, measure growth in terms of weight by increments, not only of fresh weight, but also of dry weight, though this implies that strictly comparable samples can be used to establish the initial and final states if dry weight is to be the criterion of growth. If growth is to be traced by increase of substance, it is apparent that this increase is neither uniform in time nor invariable in composition. Both cabbages and kings change their composition as they grow and develop. Therefore growth is, in the chemical sense, also "heterogonous" and, as growth and development proceed in plants, both the organism and its organs often experience a change in their composition. Resting or dormant organs (like seeds or spores) may often have a low water content, whereas the more active ones have greater succulence and higher water content. Thus, the most actively growing systems usually have a high water content. While there is, therefore, a general trend toward a higher proportion of dry matter to water with age, this can be treated as a problem of relative growth and so may be deferred until Chapter 9. It is also a common occurrence that the internal concentration of various solutes, as, for example, potassium, may be greater in the younger and more active cells (cf. Chapter 6), and this also implies that, as they age, cells often acquire more water than dissolved substances. Also the ratios between such elements as potassium and calcium may often change during growth and development (cf. Brooks and Brooks, 1941). It is obvious, therefore, that other criteria than those of size (whether measured in units of length, mass, volume, or even by the amount of a given substance) could be used in recording the progress of growth.

Growth as Order out of Disorder

However, growth may be conceived in other terms—namely, in terms of the complexity of, or degree of order in, the substances and structures which are produced. Growth converts the random molecules of the environment (CO_2, H_2O, salts) which freely obey the laws of diffusion, into the orderly structures of the plant body, i.e., into complex molecules (cellulose, starch, proteins, etc.) and organized systems in which even the dissolved substances do not respond to diffusion in a free and unrestricted manner. Thus order appears out of disorder, and the distribution of molecules by chance, in accordance only with statistical probability, gives way to forms, structures, and arrangements the chance occurrence of which is negligible. Lecomte du Noüy (1947) estimated that it would take longer for a protein molecule to emerge by the chance assembly of atoms and molecules than the estimated age of the earth! The improbability of achieving by chance what growth accomplishes with apparent ease may be likened to scrambling the letters of the alphabet in the hope that a Shakespearean play or Tennyson's "Flower in the Crannied Wall" might emerge spontaneously! The creation during growth of this orderly pattern of molecules and substance, the material framework within which life moves, places restrictions upon the freedom of atoms and molecules as they are impressed into the pattern so established. Thus, in *What is Life?* Erwin Schrödinger (1944) pointed out that organisms evade the spontaneous approach to equilibrium that obtains in unorganized systems. Schrödinger stated that "it is by avoiding the rapid decay into the inert state of equilibrium that an organism appears so enigmatic." To create and maintain such a non-equilibrium state, work must be done and energy expended by the organism as it grows. And it is equally obvious that we must start with an organization that is capable of growing. How such organization emerged in the course of evolution is yet another great biological problem with which we are not here concerned.

The availability of energy for doing the work of organisms (which is a function of free energy, F) is not alone determined by the heat energy (H), which is itself an easily comprehensible function of molecular motion, but is also modified by a more abstract term (which involves entropy, S) that reflects certain internal properties of the system. These are, in turn, dependent upon its degree of order, or of disorder. In short they are a function of its organization. This concept may be illustrated as follows.

The effect of the internal properties of a system upon the degree to which its potential energy may be transformed into work may be demonstrated by the three simple examples shown below. In one system (a), a weight w falls freely through a height h; in (b) the same weight is on an inclined plane. Only if the plane is frictionless will the potential energy be equally convertible into work in (b) as in (a) and the presence of a drop of lubricant (c) may here have a great effect.

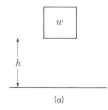

(a)

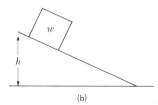

(b)

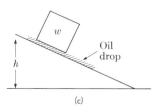

(c)

Mechanical work may be done by a falling weight and, similarly, when heat flows from a high temperature to a low temperature, heat energy may also be transformed into work. The precise measure of the convertibility of energy into useful work, in any given transaction, is the change which takes place in the "free energy" (F). If this change is to be positive, then work needs to be done on the system; if it is negative, then external work can be done by the system.

Processes can occur spontaneously if their free energy change is negative, and free energy inevitably tends in this way to reach a minimum. The change in free energy (F) is made up of the change in heat content (H) decreased by the change in a term (TS) which is the product of the absolute temperature and the entropy of (S). Thus, $F = H - TS$ and, for a given event, the changes in these quantities are $\Delta F = \Delta H - T \Delta S$. The sign of ΔS is negative whenever greater complexity is achieved and the system becomes less random (as when growth occurs); the sign of ΔS is positive whenever a more organized system becomes less organized. Putting it in another way, after Lecomte du Noüy (1947), "Entropy represents the counterpart of the available energy which has disappeared in the process and can be considered as a measure of its disorder." Another quotation from Schrödinger may also be made:

How would we express in terms of the statistical theory the marvelous faculty of the living organism, by which it delays the decay into thermodynamical equilibrium (death)? We said before, "It feeds on negative entropy," attracting as it were a stream of negative entropy upon itself to compensate the entropy increase it produces by living. . . . These (i.e., plants) of course have their most powerful supply of negative entropy in the sunlight.

Thus orderliness of molecular structure and arrangement, the inevitable concomitant of growth and molecular complexity, go hand in hand with the maintenance of that "low level of entropy" to which Schrödinger refers. As growth occurs and form is elaborated from simple substances, entropy decreases, free energy increases and is stored in a form available for conversion into work under appropriate arrangements.

Therefore, the important processes of growth require a net *increase* of free energy $(+\Delta F)$ of the system (i.e., they are *endergonic*) and they need to be coupled with some chemical or metabolic process in which the reverse occurs (i.e., with processes which are *exergonic*). In the processes of photosynthesis (a particularly endergonic process) and respiration (a characteristic exergonic process) the conspicuous change is in the heat content (H) of the substrate (sugar), but, nevertheless, the term TS has a finite value so that the free energy change per molecule of sugar synthesized, or respired, differs by a small amount from the heat released when the sugar is burned.

However, many of the changes that occur during growth involve syntheses and rearrangements of substances in which the total heat change may be small,

ganizational resistance" which accompanies "dissolution" is revealed by a renewed but temporary outburst of activity. Thus in each phase of growth the fruit may have a characteristic metabolism and respiratory behavior. The same conclusion follows from the respiratory intensity during the growth of a sunflower plant (Kidd, West, and Briggs, 1921). These data show that the respiratory intensity (measured as mg CO_2 per gm dry weight per hour) decreased from 2.90 one day after germination to 0.39 for the whole mature plant at 136 days. It is, therefore, a melancholy thought that the physiological intensity of living decreases progressively from the very beginning of growth!

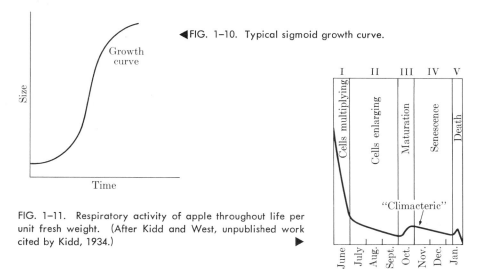

◀FIG. 1–10. Typical sigmoid growth curve.

FIG. 1–11. Respiratory activity of apple throughout life per unit fresh weight. (After Kidd and West, unpublished work cited by Kidd, 1934.) ▶

Autonomous Units Capable of Growth and Development

But what are the initial systems that are capable of growth? A distinguishing feature of the plant life cycle is that, at two main crises, the link between one generation and another is bridged by single cells. This occurs at the levels of spores and of zygotes. Spores grow characteristically without fusion with each other, but the zygote arises by the fusion of gametes, male and female, which, by themselves, normally cannot grow. The product of their fusion commonly exhibits a unique capacity for growth and development, a powerful potential which may be called its innate or "built-in" capacity for growth. In the succeeding cell divisions, all essential features of mature and complicated plants are rapidly laid down. In angiosperms the embryo reaches an advanced stage of development while it is still within the seed. In fact, it has already received, via the nucellus, the embryo sac and the endosperm, a very unique type of nutrition. In the utilization of these special nutrients, cotyledons may play a definitive role as absorbing organs (Fig. 1–12).

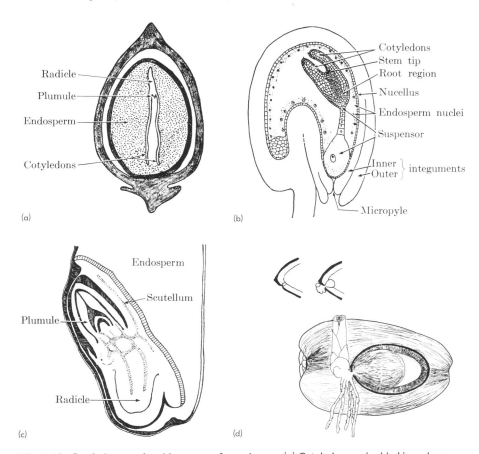

FIG. 1–12. Cotyledons as absorbing organs for embryos. (a) Cotyledons embedded in endosperm of Fagopyrum. (After Holman and Robbins, 1924.) (b) *Capsella* embryo pushed into endosperm by the suspensor. (After Holman and Robbins, 1924.) (c) Embryo of *Triticum*, showing scutellum as an absorbing organ. (After Woodhead, 1915.) (d) *Cocos nucifera* with immature embryo embedded in solid endosperm, cotyledon growing into liquid endosperm. (After Kirkwood and Gies, 1902.)

What ultimately conveys, or controls, the "built-in capacity for growth" of the zygote is a profound biological problem; modern thought credits the DNA of the nucleus with the ability to direct, if not to initiate, the growth which occurs. The "blueprint" of the pattern which emerges during growth is imprinted, as it were, in the chemical configuration of the DNA, a substance which is capable of almost infinite variation. The structure of this complex substance was interpreted by the well-known work of Watson and Crick (1953). By whatever means the coded messages of the DNA determine the way in which the built-in capacity for growth is expressed, the embryo's need for nutrition, its other responses to external stimuli, and the modifications of its growth by factors of the environment are all highly stimulating problems of modern plant physiology. It is to such problems that attention will be directed.

Centers of Growth: Growing Regions

Although the capacity to grow is first inherent—built-in—in a single cell, a spore, or a fertilized egg, the cells which result from its division quickly acquire what has been called a "division of labor." Thus the continued ability to grow remains concentrated in certain centers which, in the angiosperm plant body, are recognized as growing regions or meristematic regions. Conspicuous growing regions are those at the apex of shoot and root and the secondary growing regions of the vascular and cork cambia. But there are local centers of meristematic activity which remain behind like islands, or islets, of growth as the advancing tide of growth moves onward in the main shoot; such centers are axillary buds which continue to grow as branch shoots, or they are intercalary growing regions which remain as localized centers of activity in many stems. Similarly, behind the apex of the root, other centers may arise to form lateral roots in those regions of the root, namely the pericycle, where cells have remained capable of division and which, in some roots, though not in all, are capable of reorganizing a new growing root tip in the form of a branch or a lateral root.

It will be convenient to use the common peppermint plant (*Mentha piperita* L.) to illustrate many aspects of growth and metabolism, and the points mentioned above can be noted by reference to longitudinal and transverse sections of the shoot apex (Figs. 1–13 and 1–14) and to longitudinal sections of the root apex (Fig. 1–15). One should add, however, that the growing regions in this plant are maintained by continued vegetative propagation, for the plant is male sterile and does not therefore set seeds. This example also emphasizes that the integrity of these growing regions (i.e., the apices of the shoot), once organized, may be perpetuated by the processes of vegetative propagation. Such processes as the rooting of cuttings, again readily illustrated by the mint plant, emphasize the familiar but still profound feature that shoots often readily regenerate roots (that is, root growing points may originate from shoot tissue) although the reverse (i.e., the formation of shoot growing points on roots as shown for *Convolvulus* by Torrey, 1958) may occur less frequently.

Environmental Effects

Although the integrity of the organized growing system may be preserved through long-continued vegetative propagation, its behavior is dramatically affected by the environment. In this respect shoot apices are much more responsive than are those of roots. For example, the mint plant normally forms erect

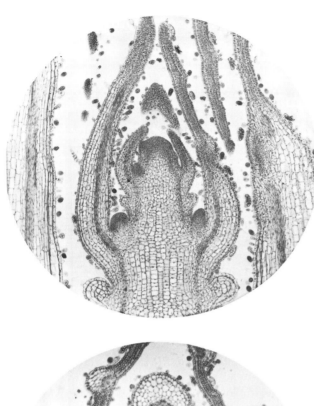

◄FIG. 1–13. Longitudinal section of the shoot apex of *Mentha piperita* L. (From Howe and Steward, 1962.)

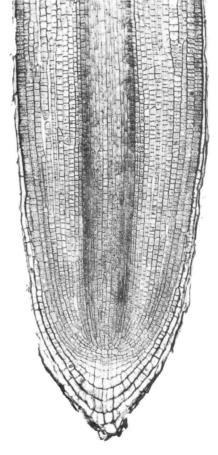

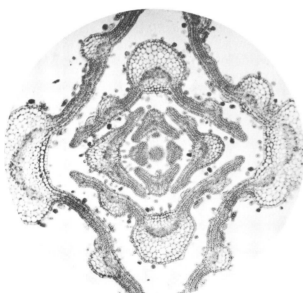

FIG. 1–14. Transverse section of the shoot apex of *Mentha piperita* L. (From Howe and Steward, 1962.)

FIG. 1–15. Median longitudinal section of the root tip of *Mentha piperita* L. (From Howe and Steward, 1962.)

FIG. 1–16. A. Mint plant (*Mentha piperita* L.) grown on long days (18 hours) for 24 days in full nutrient solution in the greenhouse. B. Plant grown on short days (8 hours) for 43 days. (From Steward, 1962.)

shoots with square stems and strongly developed leaves (Fig. 1–16A), and it flowers under long-day conditions (exceeding 12 hours of daily duration of light). Under short days (less than 12 hours) the shoot apex tends to form more pendant shoots, the axillary buds form prostrate and rounded stems, or stolons, with reduced leaves, and the plant flowers with difficulty (Fig. 1–16B). This is but one example of the numerous morphogenetic effects on growth which are imposed by variables in the external environment. These variables modify, but do not permanently change, the way the built-in capacity for growth, particularly of the shoot apex, is expressed. (For an authoritative and recent account of morphogenesis in plants, reference may be made to Sinnott, 1960.)

The Ability to Grow:
Intrinsic Properties and External Stimuli

Although relatively few of the cells of the total plant body are engaged in the production of more cells and the laying down of more tissues, events may modify this. Some cells (though by no means all) have the capacity, in response to wounding or cutting, to return to the growing state and to produce new tissue by meristematic activity. This response, which represents the ability of cells

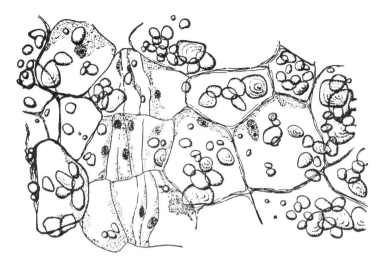

FIG. 1–17. Starch disappearance and cell division in cells near a cut surface of potato tuber tissue exposed to moist air. (From Steward, Wright, and Berry, *Protoplasma* 16, 576–611, 1932.)

which had ceased to grow, to return, at least temporarily, to the growing state, is readily seen at a cut potato surface (Fig. 1–17). Although this type of response is shown in varying degrees by many tissues that originate from cambia, it is more rare in monocotyledonous plants and even in some cells of dicotyledons, such as the tissue of mature pome fruits (e.g., the apple). If tissue explants, removed from the plant body, contain cambial tissue, they can usually be induced to grow in appropriate nutrient media by the familiar techniques of plant tissue culture; in the development of these methods White (1963 and earlier references there cited) and Gautheret (1935, 1959 and references there cited) were pioneers. However, if the tissue explanted contains no cambial tissue, but only cells already far advanced in their differentiation, certain other

FIG. 1–18. Left, cylindrical explant of carrot root phloem grown on White's nutrient medium. Right, growth from a similar explant, for the same period, on the same medium supplemented by coconut milk. (From work of Caplin and Steward.)

stimuli may be needed (Fig. 1–18), such as those which are contained in the nutrients (e.g., coconut milk) which nourish immature embryos (cf. Fig. 1–12d). In many cases, however, the means required to restore mature living cells to the actively growing state are still unknown, although many purely synthetic and highly unnatural substances can now be used to bring this event about (cf. Chapter 4).

Thus, the attempt to understand what constitutes the ability to grow and what conveys this property to a living cell quickly ends in speculation. Nevertheless, cambium cells may retain their ability to divide for very long periods, although through the year they may exhibit seasonal cycles of activity and dormancy. A near equivalency of eternal life on earth is the cambium of the giant *Sequoia* which, if not now composed of the identical cells, may contain the lineal descendants of those that functioned in the same way, in the same tree, as long as

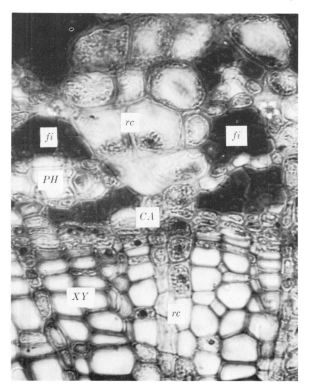

FIG. 1–19. A portion of the stem of *Tilia*, seen in transverse section, showing the cambial region (*CA*); secondary xylem (*XY*) composed of vessels, tracheids, and some parenchyma cells; medullary rays, one or two cells wide (*rc*) in the xylem but "expanding" into the secondary phloem; secondary phloem (*PH*) with groups of fibers (*fi*) alternating with thin-walled living cells consisting of phloem parenchyma, sieve tubes, and companion cells. Since both secondary xylem and phloem are laid down by similar cambial cells, the behavior of the cells derived equationally from the cambium must be closely regulated by their position.

four thousand years ago! What it is that enables this tissue and these cells of the plant body to continue, as it were indefinitely, while other cells and organisms have a life span, or rather a phase of cell multiplication, which may be severely restricted, is an interesting question. And, when one faces the physiological problems posed by the formation of one cell cut off from the cambium to form xylem and of another to form phloem, one encounters in a very dramatic way the great problem of biological differentiation (Fig. 1-19).

Some Contrasts in Organization of the Plant Body

Even a non-botanist may recognize certain obvious differences in the organization of plant bodies drawn from different parts of the plant kingdom; these differences present obvious problems in the interpretation of their growth.

There is obvious "division of labor" between the organs of flowering plants. Shoots expose green cells to light and air, whereas colorless roots are equally well adapted to maintain the contact of absorbing cells with the soil water and its dilute solutions of inorganic salts. The axis, with its stele, permits each of these organs to nourish the other, the shoot supplying essential organic and the root essential inorganic nutrients.

In more primitive plants that remained aquatic, with all their cells potentially accessible to dissolved carbon dioxide and to mineral nutrients and able to discharge all the nutritional functions, division of labor is at a minimum. But in such plants there were limitations to the size of a colony or the complexity of an organism. Neither a sort of massive aquatic "*Cladophora*-ball" (Fig. 1-4) equipped with a holdfast, nor a sort of "*Valonia*-vesicle" (Fig. 2-13) with holdfast and exposing a green surface of chloroplasts to the sea, provided a prototype on which elaborations were to be made; nor was a sort of hemispherical aerial "dome" of shoot, upon a pedestal of stem or root, as in Fig. 1-20(a), a workable plan on land. (Even so, pro-embryos often do conform, briefly, to such a seemingly simple plan, as shown in Fig. 5-18.) But vascular land plants have evolved, and, in their development, recapitulate different and presumably more efficient ways of exposing the shoot cells to light and air; there is also great diversity in the conducting or vascular tissues, i.e., the stele, of the main axis. The shoot is dissected into an elaborate system of leaves and branches, and the phyllotaxis—or the arrangement of leaves on the axis—is nature's way of saying that the functions of the shoot may be discharged in various more effective ways than the plan of Fig. 1-20(a).

When plants invaded the land and necessarily adapted to an aerial supply of gaseous carbon dioxide, at low concentration, as well as to the source of mineral nutrients at low concentrations and often in small total amounts in the soil solution, then the sharply contrasting organization of shoots and roots emerged and, with that division of labor, greater complexities were achieved and successful organisms accomplished. Much has been written about the evolution of form and reproduction in land plants (Bower, 1935); it is obvious, however, that the

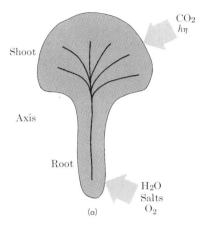

Shoot

Axis

Root

CO_2
$h\eta$

H_2O
Salts
O_2

(a)

FIG. 1–20. (a) "Division of labor" as between shoot and root. This diagram may be contrasted with parts (b), (c), and (d) for, in the efficient adjustment of the respective functions of shoot and root and the efficient utilization of light ($h\eta$), the characteristic arrangement of leaves and other appendages on an axis must have emerged. Parts (b), (c), and (d) are a diagrammatic representation of the plant body of a two-year-old dicotyledon: vertical section through plant axis (b), median longitudinal section through shoot apex (c), and root apex (d). (Drawings by M. H. Wilde; from Steward and Sutcliffe, *Plant Physiology, A Treatise*, Vol. II, Academic Press Inc., New York, 1959.)

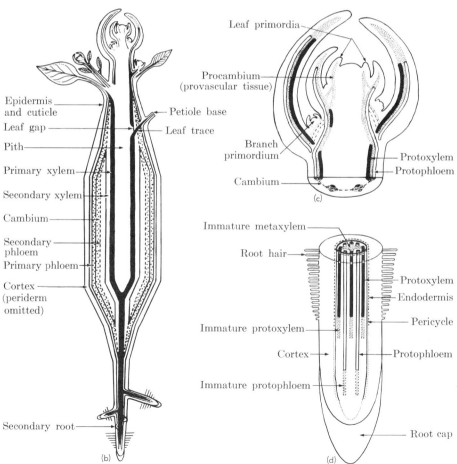

Epidermis and cuticle

Leaf gap

Pith

Primary xylem

Secondary xylem

Cambium

Secondary phloem

Primary phloem

Cortex (periderm omitted)

Secondary root

Petiole base

Leaf trace

(b)

Leaf primordia

Procambium (provascular tissue)

Branch primordium

Cambium

Protoxylem

Protophloem

(c)

Immature metaxylem

Root hair

Immature protoxylem

Cortex

Immature protophloem

Protoxylem

Endodermis

Pericycle

Protophloem

Root cap

(d)

way these plants grow must be compatible with their final form, which also imposes demands on the means to coordinate the activities of their several organs. Hence the organization of a typical angiosperm plant body should now be considered.

A schematic representation of the organization of a typical vegetative dicotyledonous plant is shown in Fig. 1–20; reference to this will be made later. The mint plant, for which the apical growing regions have been described (Figs. 1–13 and 1–14), conforms to this general plan. Here relatively few leaves are borne at a node; they tend to be broad and net-veined and by their arrangement on the axis expose a large surface to light. The axis of the shoot consists of a stem with a characteristic distribution of vascular tissue in the stele, and successive internodes commonly grow so that the leaves borne on successive nodes are well displaced from each other. Growth in girth is achieved by a vascular cambium. The tree habit is encountered in those plants (dicotyledons and gymnosperms) having a cambium which survives from year to year and which, with alternating periods of winter dormancy and spring growth, may

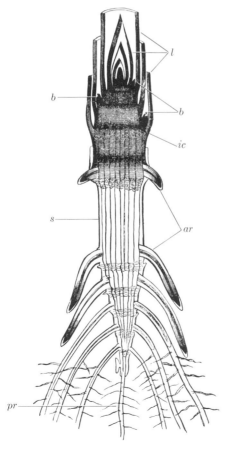

◄FIG. 1–21. Organization in a monocotyledon (*Zea mays*). (*l*, leaves with sheathing leaf bases; *b*, bud; *ar*, adventitious roots; *pr*, primary root; *ic*, intercalary growing regions; *s*, stem.) (After Sachs, 1875.)

FIG. 1–22. Sections through the shoot of a *Bambusa* sp. A. Median longitudinal section showing the nodal plates. B. Close-up of A, showing the apex and young leaf primordia. (From a slide prepared by Dr. D. W. Bierhorst, Cornell University.)   ▶

annually add to their growth. The juxtaposition of the last cambial product in the wood of one year with the first product in the next produces the familiar appearance known as an annual ring. And also in trees, provision is made for the persistence or renewal of the crop of leaves. Autumnal leaf fall, the resting of winter buds, and the spring flush of growth are familiar features of the temperate zone with its characteristically deciduous trees, though there are many dicotyledonous trees in which leaves persist throughout the year, and, in tropical or subtropical climates, their leaf fall may be determined more by rainfall than by temperature. Coniferous plants, which characteristically retain their leaves, often expose a smaller surface compared to their volume, and they often have adaptations to conserve water in the dry cold of winter.

Monocotyledonous plants, however, may have a very different organization in their shoots. Predominantly herbaceous and lacking secondary thickening in the form of wood, they grow mainly as their tissues are laid down by the apical growing regions. They commonly lack cambium to increase their girth although some, often considerable, growth is contributed by their intercalary growing regions at the base of leaves. Characteristically the leaves of mono-cotyledonous plants are linear or strap-shaped; instead of being inserted a few at each nodal level by stalk-like petioles, they are often crowded into a rosette. In fact, the axis is often composed of the encircling leaf bases so that the difference between leaf and stem is less sharp. The typical veination of monocotyledonous leaves is parallel and, since they encircle and even comprise (one within the other) the stem, it is common to find vascular bundles scattered throughout the cross section of a monocotyledonous stem. But often monocotyledons have a rosette habit, for leaves borne at successive levels are not displaced by the extensive elongation of their internodes. Associated with this very different habit of growth is the fact that many monocotyledons (grasses) will withstand mowing as in a lawn, or withstand natural "mowing" as by grazing in a pasture in a manner that can only be tolerated by those dicotyledons that can adopt a prostrate and rosette habit of growth. A typical organization of a monocotyledonous plant body is shown in Fig. 1–21, and Fig. 1–22 shows the way the shoot

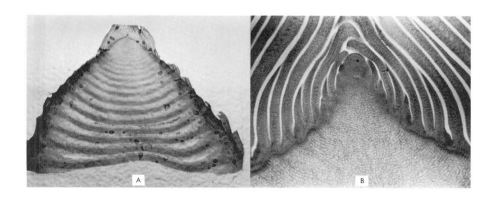

◀FIG. 1–23. Organization in *Equisetum arvense*. Longitudinal section of a subterranean bud in March. (ss, apical cell of stem; b, the leaves; K, lateral buds exposed by the section.) The subsequently very long internodes of the shoot axis are not yet formed. (After Sachs, 1875.)

FIG. 1–24. Apex of a lateral branch of *Equisetum*. The section is taken through the node at the base of the leaf sheath. Note the large apical cell with a metaphase plate. The latest derivatives of the apex are probably represented by the two cells to the right of the apical cell. The inset is an interpretive drawing of the photograph. (From a preparation by Dr. D. W. Bierhorst, Cornell University.)   ▶

may originate in such a relatively massive monocotyledon as bamboo (*Bambusa* sp.). Even in massive monocotyledons like the banana or the tree-like palms, the tissue of the entire plant body is laid down by the apical growing regions and by the intercalary meristems at the nodes and in the bases of leaves.

It will be apparent that there is much greater diversity of form in angiosperm shoots than in their roots. The contrasted organization of shoots and roots will be commented upon later. Suffice it to say here that shoots, being adapted to gas exchange and to the fixation of light energy for their nutrition, expose a great surface to the air and multiply their lateral organs superficially. They also encounter the hazards of drying out by evaporation; these, however, are minimized by cuticle, sunken stomata, and certain other increasingly xerophytic adaptations. Characteristically, however, roots make length with a relative minimum of volume, they can and often do exist in free contact with water, and their form is comparatively uninfluenced by light and unaffected by the changing seasons or fluctuations in temperature or atmospheric humidity.

Although this book is predominantly concerned with angiosperms, it is salutary to recall the very different kinds of organization of the vegetative plant body that may exist among non-flowering vascular land plants. Reference may be made to Bower's *Primitive Land Plants* (1935) to see the range of form that is encountered in such plants as horsetails and ferns which, in earlier times,

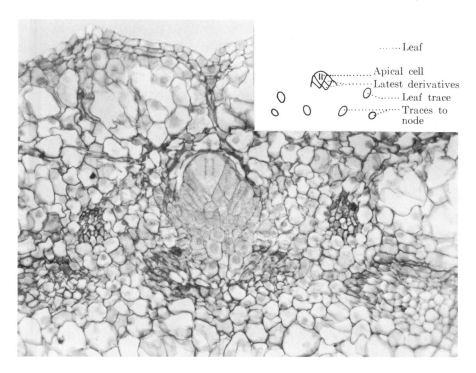

were more conspicuous features of the land flora. In these plants the organization of the shoot and of the growing tips from which it originates is very different from that of flowering plants. Figure 1–23 shows the general plan of organization of an *Equisetum,* the form of the growing region emphasizing the large pyramidal apical cell which is also illustrated in a rarely seen dividing state in the photograph shown in Fig. 1–24.

This brief excursion into the organization of the plant body should not end without a recognition that the vegetative shoot may be drastically transformed to accommodate its form to environmental and morphogenetic stimuli of all kinds. Etiolation and high insolation, aquatic, halophytic, and xerophytic habitats, the stimuli due to diurnal periodicity of light and temperature, seasonal variations and the demands of perennation in the formation of resting buds, tubers, bulbs, corms, rhizomes, etc., all make their impact upon the organization of shoots. But the great transformation is that which occurs when the indeterminate growth of vegetative shoot tips is transformed into the very different and usually strictly determined growth of its reproductive organs. The term morphogenesis is used for the transformations that occur in all these ways as the plant body responds to stimuli by changes in its form. The causal interpretations of these responses (see Chapters 6 and 8) present one of the great challenges of modern biology.

The Curve of Growth in Relation to Time

Granted a system that can grow, whether this be an organism, an organ, the cells of a microorganism, or even a population, the growth in time can often be represented by a typical sigmoid curve (Fig. 1–10). Characteristically, this growth process seems to start slowly and to gather momentum as all parts of the organism engage in growth to their maximum extent. In this interval of time the increase is exponential and obeys the so-called "Compound Interest Law," which describes the increase of substance, or "capital," as each increment of "interest" in turn becomes equally effective in growth. Such exponential growth, however, cannot continue indefinitely, for limitations of one sort or another arise and retard the growth increments with time; thus growth soon falls short of the first requirements under the Compound Interest Law.

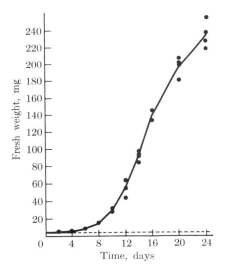

◀FIG. 1–25. Curves showing the time course of growth of explanted carrot root tissue. Growth in terms of weight (in milligrams) per explant; one mg is approximately 10,000 cells. (From Caplin and Steward, *Nature* 163, 920, 1949.)

FIG. 1–26. The time course of growth in length of (a) a root of *Vicia faba*, (b) a shoot of *Phaseolus multiflorus*.   ▶

Characteristically, the "compound interest" phase of growth gives way to one in which equal increments by growth tend to occur in equal intervals of time, instead of all parts being able to exercise their maximum capacity for growth. When this occurs the curve of growth enters a more or less linear phase. In turn, the linear phase is followed by a third phase of declining growth rate until, in fact, growth subsides and the organism, or the organ, may only maintain the size it has already achieved. Such sigmoid curves, with a more or less defined point of inflection, about which increasing growth rates give place to decreasing growth rates, are highly characteristic of many biological systems (cf. Fig. 1–25, which shows a curve for the increase in weight of explanted car-

TABLE 1-1

Growth as measured by increment of length of transverse segments
of a root (1 mm) and of a shoot (3.5 mm)

Day	*Vicia faba* Root		*Phaseolus multiflorus* Shoot	
	Final length, mm	Growth in successive days	Final length, mm	Growth in successive days
0	1.0	0	3.5	0
1	2.8	1.8	4.7	1.2
2	6.5	3.7	6.2	1.5
3	24.0	17.5	8.7	2.5
4	40.5	16.5	14.2	5.5
5	57.5	17.0	21.2	7.0
6	72.0	14.5	30.2	9.0
7	79.0	7.0	44.2	14.0
8	79.0	0	54.2	10.0
9	—	—	61.2	7.0
10	—	—	63.2	2.0

Data from J. Sachs, 1887, p. 540

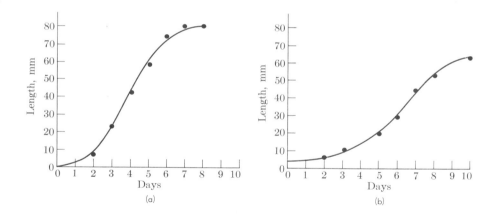

rot tissues in media supplemented with coconut milk). If the first derivative of such a curve is plotted, it is seen that the organism, organ, or cell culture passes through a period of maximum growth rate. The great German botanist, Sachs, identified this period of rapid growth rate as the "Grand Period of Growth." Even data which describe the growth of the entire plant body, although made up of the several curves which relate to organs, each of which traces out a sigmoid growth curve, may nevertheless conform *in toto* to a similar kind of growth curve. Each new organ follows its own course, and its time course may be plotted in the same way as the growth in length of a single organ, like a root or shoot (Table 1-1 and Fig. 1-26). In more recent times, and by the use of

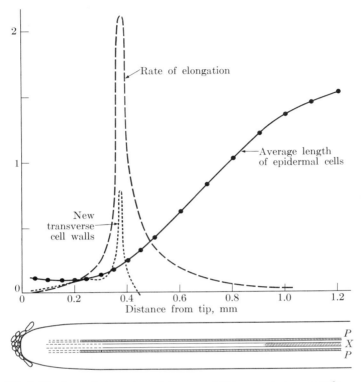

FIG. 1–27. Rate of elongation of the root of *Phleum* (μ/μ/min $\times$ 10^2); average length of epidermal cells ($\mu \times 10^{-2}$); estimated rate of formation of new transverse cell walls in a single row of epidermal cells (number of cells /μ/min $\times$ 10^3). Below the graph is a diagrammatic longitudinal section through the triarch root showing the levels at which the youngest vascular elements are differentiated. In the center is one of three rows of xylary cells (X). They may be recognized within approximately 100μ of the root apex, become vacuolate at 300μ, and show characteristic secondary thickenings at 970μ. Two of the three protophloem strands (P) are shown. (From Goodwin and Stepka, *Am. J. Bot.* **32**, 36–46, 1945.)

optical methods, Goodwin and Stepka (1945) located the point of maximum elongation rate along the root of *Phleum* (Fig. 1–27) and showed how very close to the tip of the root this occurs (0.4 mm).

Thus each organism, or organ, in question starts with a finite or, as it were, built-in capacity for growth which unfolds in an orderly way in time. When this capacity has run its course, growth may no longer respond even to favorable external conditions of environment or nutrition.

The growth of an individual and preferably unbranched root is often used to illustrate Sachs' Grand Period of Growth. However, this is in part a function of its organization for, by cutting off the root tip and implanting it in new nutrient media, growth may often be continued indefinitely, at least in the roots of some dicotyledonous plants. Moreover, individual tissues can be removed from plants and used to establish clones or cultures, which by the accepted methods of tissue culture can be kept in a continuous and apparently indefinite state of unorganized growth, especially if the explants are continually renewed by subculture. Thus, much of the limitation of the growth of the individual cells and tissues of the plant body is not inherent in their nature but is part of the price paid for the degree of organization in the plant body which a complex plant requires. In later chapters (4 and 10) it will be shown that by appropriate nurture the original capacity for growth of the zygote may be restored so that even some mature, differentiated cells will give rise again to whole plants and in so doing simulate the behavior of zygotes in normal embryogeny.

Summary

The plant body of flowering plants, highly organized into cells, tissues, and organs, with obvious forms and structures to fulfill special functions, presents the problems of growth and development, of differentiation and morphogenesis, in their most dramatic form in plants. Nevertheless, some lower plants achieve a surprising degree of complexity in a body which is seemingly less highly organized, which may exist as single cells or may be composed of filaments of similar cells, or which may even perform its functions in the non-cellular, or coenocytic, state. Therefore, the problems of growth and development can be presented in many different ways, with the aid of diverse concepts which have been outlined above in very general terms. In multicellular plants the inherent capacity for growth resides in special structures like spores and zygotes. As this innate or built-in capacity for growth unfolds, it may take different forms, for which different units or standards of measurement are appropriate. In some situations, size may be a proper criterion of growth and units of length or area, weight or volume, may each be suitable units of measurement. For other aspects of growth the increase in the number of cells, or the time taken to reach definitive stages in the life cycle, may be more to the point. The term development is here appropriate. Growth also creates order out of disorder as free molecules, statistically distributed, become part of organized structures. As an angiosperm plant body achieves greater size and complexity, the ability to grow is centered in special regions: the apices of shoot and root, the intercalary meristems, the adventitious or axillary buds, the vascular cambium causing increase in girth, cork cambium, and the meristems responsible for wound healing and regeneration. Thus the organization of the plant body places certain restrictions upon the continued growth of many of its cells and tissues, although these restrictions can be circumvented if cells grow free and in isolation from the plant body. As the facts of vegetative propagation of shoots, and of continued culture of root tips, show, the integrity of the organized growing regions of shoot and root may be maintained indefinitely. Nevertheless the behavior of the plant body, particularly in shoots, responds to a variety of external environmental stimuli. Evident contrasts occur in the organization of those flowering plants which are dicotyledons or monocotyledons. These contrasts are traceable to the organization of their respective plant bodies. The incidence of secondary growth by vascular cambia in the dicotyledons contrasts with its absence—though there is marked intercalary growth at the bases of leaves—in monocotyledons. This leads to such obvious but marked contrasts as that between the tree habit of dicotyledons and the predominantly herbaceous habit of grasses and even massive monocotyledons. But the unit which can grow, whether a spore, a zygote, a seed, or a cell or cell population, characteristically traces out a sigmoid curve of growth in time. In this sequence, growth is at first exponential, for every unit grows to its fullest capacity. It is later limited to approximately equal amounts of growth in equal intervals of time and, still later, growth slows down as the system merely maintains itself. A period of maximum growth rate, termed by Sachs a Grand Period of Growth, is found by plotting the first derivative of the curve of growth against time; it occurs conspicuously in the roots very close to the tip.

It is now appropriate to look at the process of growth in terms of nutrition, the accretion of substance, and the methods by which the organism acquires material from its environment and builds it into its own plant body. Still later these aspects of growth, more properly termed development, differentiation, and morphogenesis, will need to be examined in terms of the causal agents by which the behavior of cells and growing regions is regulated.

chapter two

GROWTH AND NUTRITION:
INORGANIC NUTRITION

So long as true equilibrium obtains, and free energy approaches its minimum, and molecules obey statistical laws of chance distribution, organization is not in question—nor is life! Therefore, biology is essentially concerned with organization above the molecular; this permits one part of the system to do work on another; i.e., free energy is increased so that work can be done, and the organism can function as a molecular machine. Thus structures and arrangements are necessary to preserve the identity of the several parts of the biologically working machine, to provide for the "division of labor" which is involved, and to maintain the essential continuity of the system. Organisms do not merely run down; in order to exist they must replace their substance and produce facsimiles of themselves and their parts, using the materials in the environment in which they are to live.

Nutrition furnishes the materials which create this distinctively organized living state during growth, and maintains it, and permits it to be perpetuated. Hence life makes demands for material substance from the environment; it is the means of making these substances available to the organism that constitutes its nutrition.

It is convenient to distinguish between, on the one hand, those nutritive processes (organic nutrition) which are concerned with the production in bulk of the compounds of carbon, as well as those built up from the six lighter nonmetallic elements C, H, O, N, P, and S which constitute so much of the organism's substance in the form of dry matter, and, on the other hand, those processes concerned with the equally important mineral elements which comprise the ash content (inorganic nutrition) of the organism. The distinction between inorganic and organic nutrition is, however, more convenient than valid.

While there are functions of the mineral elements which are discharged in the free ionic state, they all (with the possible exception of potassium) owe their essentiality, in part, to their ability to exist in highly specific molecular configurations. Examples are magnesium in chlorophyll, calcium in wall substances, iron in cytochromes and hemeproteins, copper in oxidases, and molybdenum in the enzyme protein of nitrate reductase and nitrogen fixation. Although potassium fulfills its functions in the ionic state, it nevertheless affects, ultimately, virtually all vital functions. Consistent with this role are the many observations that enzymes have an optimum potassium concentration for their activity (Nason and McElroy, 1963; Evans, 1963). Potassium is, however, especially prominent in plant growing regions (Penston, 1931) where protein synthesis is prevalent and is now being implicated even in *in vitro* studies of RNA-mediated protein synthesis (Lubin and Ennis, 1964; Spyrides, 1964). One could, therefore, begin the study of nutrition and growth with the events of organic nutrition of heterotrophic organisms or cells. Most plants do not rely on their mineral or ash content for any very obvious part of their skeletal structure, but they do depend on their mineral elements for the means to make their organization work in a controlled and distinctive way. Diatoms with their siliceous skeletons and some other plants that include silica in their walls, as well as some plants with calcareous skeletons (cf. Fig. 1–1), are obvious exceptions. The important effects of the principal mineral nutrients are mediated through the organic system which is already composed of the six essential non-metallic elements.

It is a tenable hypothesis that the requirements for essential and mineral elements may have become progressively more specific during evolution to meet the increasing demands of morphogenetic and physiological specialization. Nevertheless it is a time-honored custom to begin the relations of growth to nutrition with the consideration of the mineral or inorganic nutrients, i.e., elements, other than those derivable from carbon dioxide and water, which may in turn be in combination with the other non-metallic elements nitrogen, phosphorus, and sulphur. This is done in this chapter; the events of organic nutrition will be dealt with in Chapter 3, even though there may be good reasons why one might appropriately reverse this order.

The ability to grow—that innate or built-in capacity for growth which is characteristic of the zygote or embryo in a sexually reproduced organism, or of spores in asexual growth—presupposes the process of nutrition. But whereas growth is the consequence of nutrition, the reverse is, paradoxically, also true. Nutrients are required to support growth, but without the inherent ability to grow the organism would neither incorporate nutrients from its environment nor build them into its own body. Thus a mere supply of, or access to, nutrients is often not enough. Plants and cells have to absorb to grow; it is equally true that to absorb nutrient substances they often also need to grow, to develop or become more complex. The use of potassium or molybdenum by a growing organized cell or organism is not to be likened to the mere accretion of molecules by a crystal. Whereas the latter process leads to a state of matter which is more probable, has lower free energy, and represents an approach to an equilibrium state, the former events lead to a more highly organized but less probable system in which free energy is increased and entropy is reduced. Nutrition and growth, which go hand in hand, are therefore dual features of systems which are already organized and which are destined to work out a prescribed history in time and space.

What then is a nutrient? Nutrients provide the substances of which organisms are made; they are necessary to the life of the organism and are supplied by the environment. Water is by far the most conspicuous of these substances and, in this sense, should properly be regarded as a nutrient.

Water

It is as difficult to conceive of organized nature without the peculiar and unique properties of water, as it would be to regard life without the particular properties of the element carbon or even phosphorus or nitrogen. Although the most common and familiar fluid, water would nevertheless be regarded as a most unusual chemical substance if it could suddenly be rediscovered. Being composed of light elements, it packs a great many atoms into a relatively small space. It has many physical properties such as high surface tension, high specific and latent heat, and a high dielectric constant, which are unique amongst fluids at ordinary temperatures. Many of these properties flow from the stereochemistry of water, for the individual molecule is not symmetrical, since the hydrogen atoms are linked to oxygen by bonds which diverge at angles of approximately 105° (Fig. 2–1). Consequently, each water molecule has a more positive region and a more negative region and, by the property known as hydrogen bonding, hydrogen atoms may be shared between different oxygen atoms. Water tends to form open lattice-like structures such as those which occur in ice (Fig. 2–2). These hydrogen bonds, which are less stable than chemical linkages, nevertheless prove to be of great importance in maintaining the structure of the molecular films and sheets of fibrils formed by many complex organic substances. For these reasons water is important in the so-called "molecular architecture" of cells and organisms.

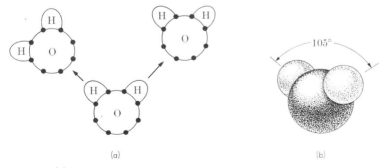

(a)   (b)

FIG. 2–1. (a) Hydrogen bond. The hydrogen bond arises from the attraction of the hydrogen in one molecule to an oxygen of adjacent molecules. (b) Three-dimensional sketch of water molecule. Note the bond angles.

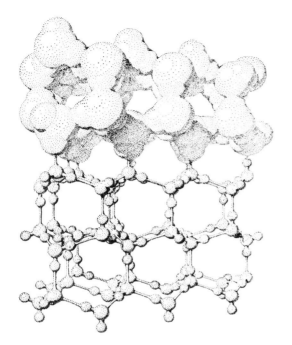

FIG. 2–2.   Crystal structure of ice is based upon the geometry of the water molecule. The molecules at the top are shown with their atoms and interatomic distances in the correct proportion. The atoms at the bottom have been reduced in size to clarify the structure of the crystal. (From *General Chemistry*, Second Edition, by Linus Pauling. W. H. Freeman and Company, San Francisco. Copyright © 1953.)

The extremely high water content of many organisms is generally recognized. In plants, particularly, the high water content of many of the most actively growing systems is so apparent that to restate this now amounts to quoting an aphorism. A vivid example of the importance of water in organisms was originally presented by the biochemist R. A. Gortner. A large jellyfish (*Aurelia* sp.) was placed on a sheet of newsprint which was photographed through the transparent body of the animal, with hardly any visible distortion. The organism, when dried upon the paper, produced a barely perceptible smudge and an almost negligible increase in the dry weight of the paper. Thus the weight of the delicate machinery which represented the organism consisted almost entirely of water. Yet the relatively minute amount of dry matter, superimposed upon the properties of water, made the *Aurelia* recognizable as a beautifully integrated, highly organized, living, growing animal, and thus something fundamentally different from the aqueous medium in which it grew, i.e., the sea.

Spores and resting air-dried seeds may have low water content, but a general parallelism often exists between their relative water content and their metabolic activity and growth. It is, moreover, no accident that horticulturalists have come to regard "hardening off," or the production of a less succulent type of growth, as an essential part of the preparation for rest and dormancy. Plant

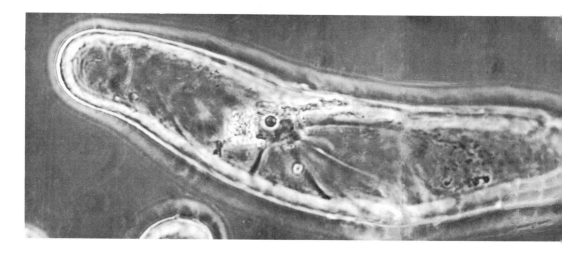

FIG. 2–3. Large, freely suspended cultured carrot cell as seen under the phase contrast microscope. Note especially the nucleus, nucleolus, cytoplasmic strands, and large vacuoles.

tissue cultures which are stimulated to grow rapidly, commonly have a very high water content, whereas the resting tissue from which they were derived may have had a lower water content. An example is the case of carrot tissue which when freshly explanted from the root contains about 80 percent water and when vigorously growing in culture has 90 to 93 percent.

The growing cells of carrot, when cultured in liquid media, may have an average weight of about 0.10 to 0.15 μg per cell (Fig. 2–3). Considerably less than $\frac{1}{10}$ of this weight is dry matter. The weight of an individual water molecule can be calculated by the use of Avogadro's number. Hence, the number of individual water molecules per cell may be estimated to be of the order of 3×10^{15}—this vast number of water molecules being consistent with the presence of aqueous vacuoles in plant cells. From the known protein nitrogen content per unit fresh weight, one can also calculate the number of protein molecules, estimating their molecular weight; if this is about 64,000, the number would be of the order of 10^9. For every protein molecule in a plant cell there may be about 10^6 water molecules and, if the estimated size of the protein molecules was too low, then the ratio of water molecules to protein molecules would be even higher. Nevertheless, a minute amount of special organic matter, chiefly proteinaceous, endows the cells, which consist so largely of water, with their intrinsic properties.

The Role of Dry Matter: Autotrophic and Heterotrophic Nutrition

To regard water as the principal growth substance obtained from the environment would, of course, leave out the essential role of the dry matter. This, in fact, was Van Helmont's dilemma when, in the early 17th century, he believed that all the substance of which plants were made came from water. When considering the acquisition of dry matter, there are two contrasting modes of nutrition: namely, the autotrophic and the heterotrophic. In the former, the organism is able to exist in a completely inorganic world, for it utilizes carbon from carbon dioxide, combining it with the elements of water to build up complex carbohydrates. An autotrophic organism thus derives its nutrition from inorganic sources and its nitrogen principally from nitrate, or ammonia, or less frequently, even from the nitrogen of the air. Perhaps the most completely autotrophic organisms now known are certain blue-green algae (e.g., species of *Anabena*), which utilize carbon dioxide and water and may derive their nitrogen by direct fixation from the air. Thus blue-green algae are often conspicuous as the first colonists of naked surfaces such as the laval slopes of volcanos or salt marsh flats. At the other extreme are some plants which show varying degrees of heterotrophy, even for nitrogen, and these, like animals, will not grow without a variety of complex nitrogenous organic molecules. Many microorganisms which are properly plants, and more particularly those which have developed, by mutation, a dependence on an external supply of particular amino acids, may to this extent resemble higher animals more than higher plants. For example, the wild type of *Neurospora* grows on a minimal medium which contains only inorganic nitrogen, but there are mutant strains that require exogenous supplies of specific nitrogenous compounds (see Srb, Owen, and Edgar, 1965). Nevertheless there is a fundamental distinction in the nutrition of plants and animals which needs to be stressed, for the former are distinguished by their ability to use simple nitrogen compounds, the latter by their extreme dependence on already synthesized organic nitrogen, particularly in the form of the essential amino acids which they need for growth and protein synthesis.

Perhaps even more fundamental, in terms of the respective organization of higher plants and animals, is the ability of plants to reuse their nitrogenous waste and breakdown products, while animals must excrete and eliminate them.

Concepts of Inorganic Nutrition of Plants and their Origins

A consideration of the nutritional requirements for plant growth therefore begins with the inorganic nutrients, assuming that water and carbon dioxide are incorporated in the photosynthesis of green plants and that they are readily available from air (CO_2) and soil (H_2O), respectively. The primitive idea of "mother earth" emphasized the long held, tacit assumption that the essential stuff of which plants were made was derived from the soil. The classical experiment of Van Helmont (published posthumously about 1648), which was conceptually anticipated by Nicholas de Cusa* in the 15th century, focused attention upon water as the principal ingredient of the plant body. Van Helmont grew a willow twig for five years and observed an increase of approximately 164 lb in the twig, whereas the tub of soil lost but a few ounces. Had Van Helmont added to his experiment (which was surprisingly well designed for that time) the comparison of the dry weight of the starting willow twig with the dry weight of the end product, he might have shown that, during growth, dry substance was also acquired from sources other than the water or the soil, i.e., from the air.

TABLE 2–1
Woodward's experiments (1699)

Sources of Water	Weight of Plants, Grains		Gain in 77 days
	When put in	When taken out	
Rainwater	$28\frac{1}{4}$	$45\frac{3}{4}$	$17\frac{1}{2}$
River Thames	28	54	26
Hyde Park conduit	110	249	139
Hyde Park conduit + $1\frac{1}{2}$ oz garden mold	92	376	284

Although Van Helmont drew attention primarily to the nutrient role of water, he is usually credited, though with a somewhat generous disregard of experimental error, with the first observation suggesting that small amounts of ash substances are absorbed from the soil. The significance of the observation, however, passed unnoticed for many years. Perhaps the later work of the Cambridge geologist Woodward, who grew mint cuttings in rainwater, Thames river water, Hyde Park conduit water, and in such waters nourished by an infusion of garden loam, first directed attention to the need for soluble substances in the nutrient solution (see Table 2–1). Our modern views on the inorganic requirements for the growth of plants emerged from the work of the great pioneers in the study of plant nutrition in the 19th century and from the advances made by Sachs and Pfeffer in the techniques of water and sand culture.

---

* Krikorian and Steward (1965) were able to consult the complete and original works of Nicholas de Cusa. Translations of the relevant passages (*Idiota, De Staticis Experimentis*, 1450), written in the dialogue style of that day, leave no doubt that Nicholas de Cusa was familiar with the type of experiment which Van Helmont performed later. Since no actual data are given, one cannot tell whether Nicholas de Cusa actually performed such an experiment, nor can it be proved that Van Helmont did in fact derive his idea, upon which his experiment was planned, directly from Nicholas de Cusa. There is, however, every reason to believe that both Van Helmont and Boyle, who later performed essentially the same experiment (1661), were indebted to Cusa. Another, and independent, study traces the same theme to even further antiquity (Howe, 1965).

FIG. 2–4. One of Gilbert's charts drawn for his American lectures (1893), showing the effect of phosphates on root development. Top row, unmanured; middle row, superphosphate and potash; bottom row, superphosphate, phosphate, and nitrogen.

It was no historical accident that the great developments in this field came in Europe in the 19th century. The Napoleonic wars had left Europe prostrate. Rising populations and the demands of the industrial revolution, which was gathering momentum in western Europe, necessitated greater efficiency in agriculture. This prompted the work of Boussingault in France, Liebig in Germany, and Lawes and Gilbert in England. The careful nutrient balance sheets of Boussingault (about 1834) cleared the way for the realization of the role of nitrogen and of the value of legumes in crop rotations. This realization was enhanced by the work done in England by Lawes and Gilbert in the years after 1843. The balanced agricultural economy, which had developed through the centuries in the vicinity of London, was destined to become imbalanced by the rising population and this, in turn, led Lawes and Gilbert to seek new ways of regaining the fertility of the soil. In the established economy, sheep had furnished meat for the city; the sheep were fed, especially in winter, on root crops (turnips, etc.) which were in turn fertilized by stable manure, which was hauled from the city to the farms in the carts which had been emptied of their farm produce. As this system fell into imbalance, Lawes and Gilbert presided over the birth of the artificial fertilizer industry by converting rock phosphate to an available form (superphosphate) with acid (cf. Russell, 1950). In this development Lawes and Gilbert followed an earlier but an unsuccessful trial by Liebig to increase growth and fertility by the use of phosphates. By the end of the century, however, the importance of nitrogen, phosphorus, and potassium (that is, of N-P-K) in agricultural practice was well established. It is, nevertheless, surprising that as late in the 19th century as 1893, Gilbert needed to make a lecture tour in the United States primarily to advocate the use of these now familiar fertilizers, especially for the growth of root crops (Fig. 2–4).

TABLE 2–2

Contents of a liter of nutrient solution. This solution had a high iron level as sparingly soluble ferrous phosphate and was relatively concentrated. Modern molecular formulae are used instead of those in the original.

Magnesium sulfate ($MgSO_4$)	$\frac{1}{100}$ molar equivalent
Calcium nitrate ($Ca(NO_3)_2$)	$\frac{2}{100}$ molar equivalent
Potassium dihydrogen phosphate (KH_2PO_4)	$\frac{1}{100}$ molar equivalent
Ferrous phosphate ($Fe_3(PO_4)_2$)	$\frac{1}{1000}$ molar equivalent

After Birner and Lucanus, 1866

The Essential Elements

Prior to the turn of the 20th century it was recognized that almost any inorganic element may be found in plants, if the search is careful enough; it was also well known that most of these elements are in fact dispensable. The minimum requirements for "satisfactory" growth of most plants had been reduced to a list of ten "essential elements" which were deemed necessary in relative bulk and which could be supplied by a minimum number of salts, as in the so-called three-salt culture solutions. The essential elements in question were carbon, hydrogen, oxygen, nitrogen, phosphorus, sulphur, potassium, calcium, magnesium, and (in a relatively minute amount) iron. It was found that these minimum requirements could be furnished to a green plant by carbon dioxide, water, and solutions which contained potassium dihydrogen phosphate, calcium nitrate, and magnesium sulfate, with a small amount of a suitable salt of iron. Although the three-salt culture solutions were not to come into widespread use until long afterwards, an early record of such a culture solution is attributed (Russell, 1950) to Birner and Lucanus in 1866. Their nutrient solution is recapitulated, using modern formulae, in Table 2–2. Iron was first added to a nutrient solu-

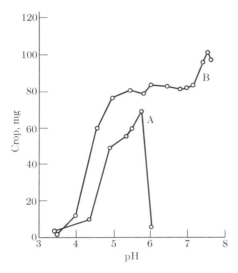

FIG. 2–5. Growth of *Chlorella* as influenced by pH. A. Growth-pH curve with normal culture solution from which the iron was lost by precipitation and adsorption at the higher pH values. B. Growth-pH curve with culture solution in which calcium was replaced by ammonium and soluble iron citrate was present. (From Hopkins and Wann, 1925.)

tion by means of an inorganic iron salt such as ferric chloride or sulphate, or preferably a substance like iron tartrate, or iron citrate, which will retain the iron more readily in solution, especially at reactions which approach neutrality. This was shown clearly by the significant work of E. F. Hopkins, who demonstrated that the growth of *Chlorella* as affected by pH is a function of the availability of iron (Fig. 2–5). In even more recent times the so-called iron chelates have been found to be even more effective in furnishing iron in a readily available form.

Following the first recognition that plants could be grown in water which contained salts, the composition of the solutions was simplified in various ways that are irrelevant here. A typical modern inorganic culture solution is that associated with the name of Hoagland (Table 2–3). The elements furnished in small amounts (B, Mn, Cu, Zn, and Mo) constitute the so-called trace elements, and knowledge of these emerged as follows. There were many early signs that the elements of the so-called three-salt culture solution were really not enough, even if they contained iron as a supplement. Manganese had been recognized at an earlier date as a stimulant to plant growth, and the element zinc had long been known to stimulate the growth of fungi. This was well known in the late 19th century. It was also well known that some plants, such as grasses and diatoms, contained silicon in their cell walls, or skeletons. However, it was the French physiologist Mazé who stated categorically, just prior to World War I, that adequate growth of plants would not occur in the culture solutions of the day if the salts, water, and containers were rigorously purified and if the plants were protected from dust. Though plant physiologists were at first incredulous, they later came to recognize the truth of these claims and, in due course, other elements were recognized as normal requirements for the growth of angiosperms.

TABLE 2–3
A modern nutrient solution, based on proportions of macronutrients absorbed by tomato—an efficient solution for sand and water cultures, especially for high light intensities

	gm/liter	molar		mg/liter
KNO_3	1.02	0.010	H_3BO_3	2.86
$Ca(NO_3)_2$	0.492	0.003	$MnCl_2.4H_2O$	1.81
$NH_4H_2PO_4$	0.230	0.002	$CuSO_4.5H_2O$	0.08
$MgSO_4.7H_2O$	0.490	0.002	$ZnSO_4.7H_2O$	0.22
			$H_2MoO_4.H_2O$	0.09

$FeSO_4$	0.5%	
Tartaric acid	0.4%	0.6 ml/liter three times weekly

After Hoagland and Arnon, 1938

The Trace Elements

It was eventually established (Brenchley and Warington, 1927) that the improbable element boron was required in the nutrient solution, in amounts of between 5 and 50 ppm (parts per million). This was shown first for certain legumes and later for many other angiosperms, and boron is now presumed to be a general requirement of flowering plants. Manganese, copper, zinc, and more recently molybdenum (the latter in incredibly small amounts) represent (with boron) the five prominent trace elements, the absence of any one of which severely limits growth. However, the list may not yet be complete. Other elements have been or are being considered. Notable among these are chlorine (as chloride), long known to stimulate growth of buckwheat; sodium, in the nutrition of such halophytes as *Atriplex*; and the elements vanadium and even gallium, though the case for the latter is not strong. Cobalt is required by ruminant animals, and it is certainly elaborated into such molecules as vitamin B_{12} by certain fungi. Since cobalt also occurs in certain enzymes, notably peptidases, it would be surprising it it were completely dispensable but, so far, a requirement for it in plants has not been generally accepted. As surprising as some of the essential elements first proved to be (notably copper and zinc), there are still certain conspicuous absentees from the general list. For most land plants, sodium is dispensable except in the most infinitesimal amounts, though its most closely related chemical element, potassium, is among the most essential of those required in quantity by all organisms. It is true that sodium supply seems to stimulate certain plants, as for example the beet root or sugar beet (*Beta vulgaris*). Since sodium-free seawater is a physical impossibility, one could in this respect regard sodium as required for all marine plants. However, even many marine plants have an uncanny faculty for accumulating potassium from its very dilute solution in the sea, while they tend to reject sodium, which is present in about 10 times the concentration of potassium. Also, as has been said, the almost ubiquitous element silicon, a prime constituent of clays and of the

TABLE 2–4
Raw materials used by plants as shown by the estimated requirements
to grow 100 bushels of corn

Substance	Symbol	Pounds	Approximate Equivalent
Water	H_2O	4,300,000 to 5,500,000	19 to 24 in. of rain
Oxygen	O_2	6800	Air is 20% oxygen
Carbon	C	5200 carbon or 19,000 carbon dioxide	Amount of carbon contained in 4 tons of coal
Nitrogen	N	160	Eight 100-lb bags of a 20% nitrogen fertilizer
Potassium	K	125	Three 100-lb bags of muriate of potash
Phosphorus	P	40	Four 100-lb bags of 20% super phosphate
Sulfur	S	75	78 lb of yellow sulfur
Magnesium	Mg	50	170 lb of epsom salt
Calcium	Ca	50	80 lb of limestone
Iron	Fe	2	2 lb of nails
Manganese	Mn	0.3	1 lb of potassium permanganate
Boron	B	0.06	A quarter pound of common borax
Zinc	Zn	Trace	The shell of one dry cell battery
Copper	Cu	Trace	25 ft of No. 9 copper wire
Molybdenum	Mo	Trace	A small saltspoonful of ammonium molybdate

Adapted from *Hunger Signs in Crops*, National Fertilizer Association, 1949

earth's crust, is not essential for the growth of most plants, although it may
be used in the skeletal structure of some.

Inorganic Requirements for Growth

A general table (Table 2–4) of some years ago shows the mineral requirements
for the annual growth of a common plant, namely corn (i.e., *Zea mays*). The
periodic table of the chemical elements (Table 2–5) shows that the 15 elements
(cf. Table 2–4), which are generally recognized to be essential for angiosperms,
represent a small and very restricted part of the classification of the elements.
Therefore, to elaborate the full complexity of the organization and life of plants,
nature has used the properties of comparatively few of the chemical elements.

But are these inorganic requirements for growth equally essential for all
organisms? That this is obviously not so was appreciated early in the last century. Pasteur grew yeast in a nutrient solution which at first consisted of the
redissolved ash from yeast, plus sugar as a source of carbon and ammonium
tartrate as a source of nitrogen (Table 2–6). It was soon realized that the inorganic requirements necessary to sustain the growth of certain microorganisms
differed from those for higher plants. Calcium can either be omitted entirely
from the culture solutions of bacteria, fungi, and certain algae or be included

TABLE 2-5 The periodic table

IA	IIA	IIIA	IVA	VA	VIA	VIIA	VIII	VIII	VIII	IB	IIB	IIIB	IVB	VB	VIB	VIIB	0
1 H 1.00797																	2 He 4.0026
3 Li 6.939	4 Be 9.012											5 B 10.811	6 C 12.011	7 N 14.007	8 O 15.9994	9 F 18.998	10 Ne 20.183
11 Na 22.990	12 Mg 24.312											13 Al 26.98	14 Si 28.086	15 P 30.97	16 S 32.064	17 Cl 35.453	18 Ar 39.95
19 K 39.102	20 Ca 40.08	21 Sc 44.96	22 Ti 47.90	23 V 50.94	24 Cr 52.00	25 Mn 54.94	26 Fe 55.85	27 Co 58.93	28 Ni 58.71	29 Cu 63.54	30 Zn 65.37	31 Ga 69.72	32 Ge 72.59	33 As 74.92	34 Se 78.96	35 Br 79.91	36 Kr 83.80
37 Rb 85.47	38 Sr 87.62	39 Y 88.91	40 Zr 91.22	41 Nb 92.91	42 Mo 95.94	43 Tc 99	44 Ru 101.07	45 Rh 102.91	46 Pd 106.4	47 Ag 107.87	48 Cd 112.40	49 In 114.82	50 Sn 118.69	51 Sb 121.75	52 Te 127.60	53 I 126.90	54 Xe 131.30
55 Cs 132.90	56 Ba 137.34	57–71 La series*	72 Hf 178.49	73 Ta 180.95	74 W 183.85	75 Re 186.2	76 Os 190.2	77 Ir 192.2	78 Pt 195.1	79 Au 196.97	80 Hg 200.59	81 Tl 204.37	82 Pb 207.19	83 Bi 208.98	84 Po 210	85 At 210	86 Rn 222
87 Fr 223	88 Ra 226	89– Ac series†															

*Lanthanide series	57 La 138.91	58 Ce 140.12	59 Pr 140.91	60 Nd 144.24	61 Pm 147	62 Sm 150.35	63 Eu 151.96	64 Gd 157.25	65 Tb 158.92	66 Dy 162.50	67 Ho 164.93	68 Er 167.26	69 Tm 168.93	70 Yb 173.04	71 Lu 174.97
†Actinide series	89 Ac 227	90 Th 232.04	91 Pa 231	92 U 238.03	93 Np 237	94 Pu 239	95 Am 241	96 Cm 242	97 Bk 249	98 Cf 252	99 Es 254	100 Fm 253	101 Md	102 No	103 Lw

In the periodic table, all known elements are arranged into groups which show similar chemical characteristics. These groups are represented by the vertical columns of elements. For example, all of the elements in the column under hydrogen have one valence electron and display certain common properties. All elements listed under beryllium (Be) have two outermost (valence) electrons and show certain specific characteristics in common. For each element, the atomic number is given above the symbol for the element, while the atomic weight is given below. The two rows of elements shown separately below the others are two series, the first of which fits between barium and hafnium, and the second of which follows radium. Elements in these series have special electron distributions which give them certain common properties. Hence, they best fit into the periodic table as separate groups. (From J. J. W. Baker and G. E. Allen, *Matter, Energy, and Life.* Addison-Wesley Publishing Co., Inc., Menlo Park, California, 1965.)

TABLE 2-6
Pasteur's nutrient solutions for yeast

Pasteur's Solution, 1860	A Later Pasteur's Solution
Ammonium tartrate, 0.1 gm	Ammonium tartrate, 1.0 gm
Ash of 1 gm of yeast	Tribasic calcium phosphate, 1.02 gm
Cane sugar, 10 gm	Potassium dihydrogen phosphate, 1.2 gm
Water, 100 gm	Magnesium sulfate, 0.04 gm
	Sucrose, 15 gm
	Water, to 100 gm

TABLE 2-7
Nutrient solution (used primarily for *Aspergillus niger*)

Water	1500 gm
Cane sugar	70 gm
Tartaric acid	4 gm
Ammonium nitrate	4 gm
Ammonium phosphate	0.60 gm
Potassium carbonate	0.60 gm
Magnesium carbonate	0.40 gm
Ammonium sulfate	0.25 gm
Zinc sulfate	0.07 gm
Iron sulfate	0.07 gm
Potassium silicate	0.07 gm

After Raulin, 1869. *Note:* There is no calcium in this solution for fungi; certain algae also tolerate reduced, or even no calcium.

in only very minute amounts. Though the stimulus caused by zinc in the growth of the fungi was known (cf. the culture solution of Raulin, 1869, as shown in Table 2–7) long before its role in higher plants was recognized and proved, there seems to be, even today, no absolute requirement for boron in the fungi. The lack of a requirement for boron and calcium by fungi, although both elements are essential for higher plants, has suggested that they are needed for the formation of intercellular or cell wall material. Such requirements, probably involving the galacturonic acids of the pectins, may be lacking in the microorganisms mentioned.

Nutrition in Relation to Development

A common device in the study of plant nutrition is to evade the problems of development in higher plants by the study of unicellular microorganisms like *Chlorella*. By this means one can easily deplete, or even ignore, the prior content of nutrients in the cell inoculum and, since the entire organism is unicellular, its dependence upon a preceding generation, as in the seeds of angiosperms, is not in question.

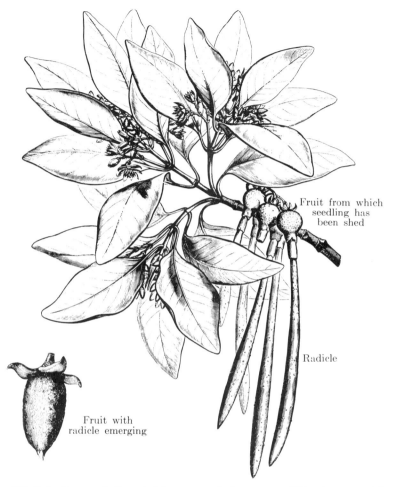

Fruit from which
seedling has
been shed

Radicle

Fruit with
radicle emerging

FIG. 2–6. Flowers, fruit, and viviparous seed of mangrove (*Rhizophora* Mangle). (From Kerner von Marilaun; Oliver's translation of 1894).

Most experiments on the mineral nutrition of crop plants begin with a seed or a fruit (e.g., the caryopsis of cereal grains). But a seed has already passed through critical stages of its development in the environment of the ovule and, while there, it has been nourished by both organic and inorganic substances from the parent sporophyte. In some cases, of which the mangrove (*Rhizophora Mangle*) is an outstanding example, the seed germinates while the fruit is on the parent plant and, in this case, bursts through the ovary wall to be shed as a relatively massive structure with much food material stored in the radicle (Fig. 2–6). The small embryo in a mature grain of wheat, barley, rice, or corn

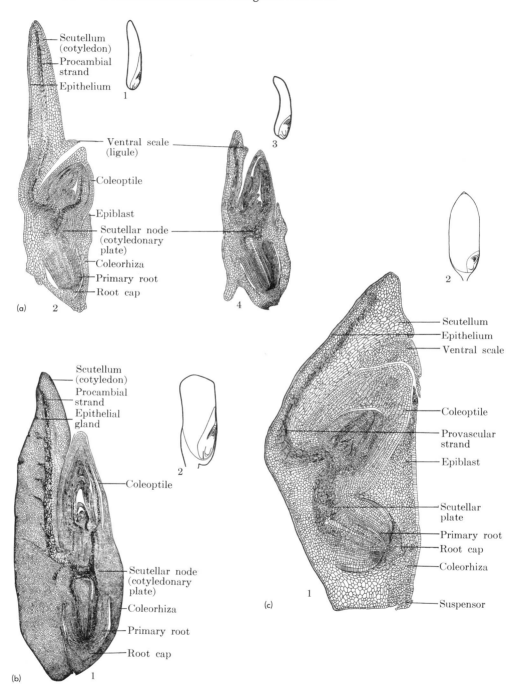

(a) 1 Scutellum (cotyledon), Procambial strand, Epithelium

2 Ventral scale (ligule), Coleoptile, Epiblast, Scutellar node (cotyledonary plate), Coleorhiza, Primary root, Root cap

3

4

(b) 1 Scutellum (cotyledon), Procambial strand, Epithelial gland, Coleoptile, Scutellar node (cotyledonary plate), Coleorhiza, Primary root, Root cap

2

(c) 1 Scutellum, Epithelium, Ventral scale, Coleoptile, Provascular strand, Epiblast, Scutellar plate, Primary root, Root cap, Coleorhiza, Suspensor

2

◀FIG. 2–7. Caryopses of some cereal grains showing the advanced development of their embryos. (a) 1–2, *Avena sativa:* 1, diagram of a median longitudinal section of caryopsis, showing location of embryo; 2, median longitudinal section of embryo; 3–4, *Triticum vulgare:* 3, diagram of a median longitudinal section of caryopsis, showing location of embryo; 4, median longitudinal section of embryo. (From Avery, *Botan. Gaz.* **89**, 1–39, 1930.) (b) *Zea mays:* 1. median longitudinal section of embryo; 2, diagram of median longitudinal section of caryopsis, showing location of embryo. (From Avery, *Botan. Gaz.* **89**, 1–39, 1930.) (c) *Oryza sativa:* 1, median longitudinal section of embryo; 2, diagram of median longitudinal section of caryopsis, showing location of embryo. (From Yung, *Botan. Gaz.* **99**, 786–802, 1938.)

is already highly developed (Fig. 2–7). The embryonic axis contains all the essential tissues of the plant body. The root system is represented in the grain, not only by a well-formed primary root tip, but also by a number of seminal roots already preformed and ready to emerge. The plumule, or seedling shoot, has a number of leaf primordia, some of which are in a relatively advanced stage of their development. Moreover there are cells in the embryo of the grain which are already destined to give rise, in their lineal cell descendants, even to such organs as the parts of the flower. When Randolph exposed corn grains to radiation damage in atomic test explosions, he found that there were discrete sectors of abnormal development in the tassels of plants developed from the treated grains; this showed that affected areas, even in the tassels of the plants developed from these grains, could have been identified with particular cells in the embryos of the ungerminated grain (cf. Chapter 8).

The prior deposition of organic food reserves in the endosperm or in cotyledons is conspicuous and has been referred to earlier (cf. Fig. 1–12). But the embryo also acquires its initial endowment of mineral nutrients from the parent sporophytic plant; this suffices for the extensive development of the embryo in the seed and also to carry it through the stages of germination. The transfer of organic and inorganic matter from the cotyledons into the plumule of etiolated peas may easily be measured; by actual observation it is found to be of the order of 0.10 gm of organic dry matter per 100 embryos per 10 to 12 hours and, simultaneously, approximately 0.006 gm of minerals appeared in the ash of the same plumules.

Ideally, then, one should begin the study of the mineral nutrition of an angiosperm with the zygote as it occurs in the embryo sac (Fig. 2–8). To do this one should be able to remove the zygote from the ovule, culture it in isolation, or otherwise determine what is the required input of mineral as well as organic nutrients into the developing embryo over the period and stages of development during which the embryo is normally within the ovule of the ovary.

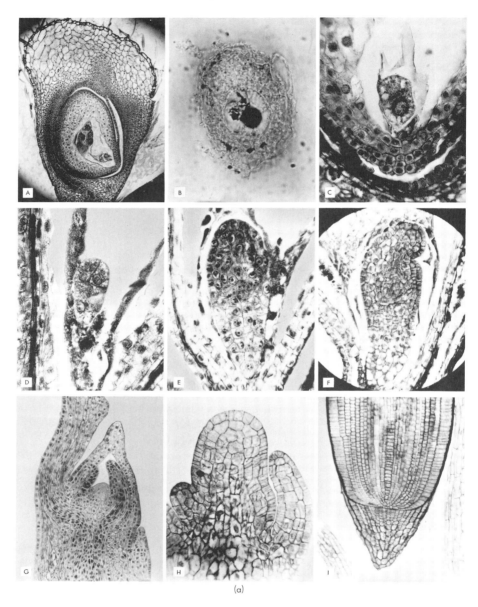

(a)

FIG. 2–8. The zygote and developing embryos in oats (*Avena sativa*). (a) Photographs. (b) Interpretive drawings. [A. Dorsiventral section through a pistil, showing the ovary wall (*ow*), the ovule (*ov*), and the nucellus (*nu*), with the inner integument (*int*) and the embryo sac (*es*) and included cells (×90 in the original). B. Egg with the male nucleus within the nuclear membrane (*nm*). Early pro-phase chromosomes are indicated (×1350 in the original). C. Longitudinal section of a pro-embryo at the two-celled stage (*n*, nucleus) (×450 in the original). D. Longitudinal

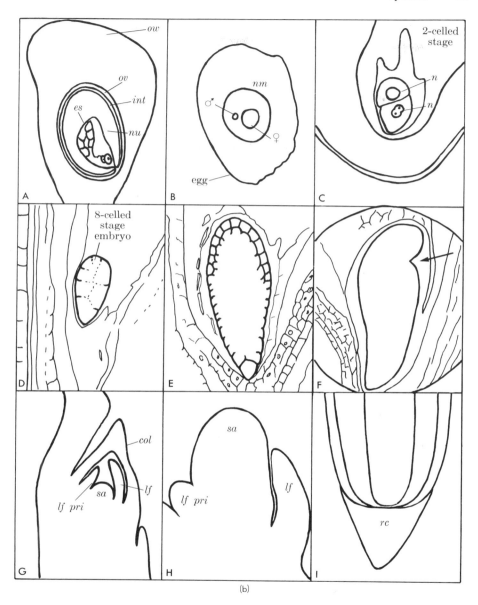

(b)

section of a pro-embryo at about the 8-celled stage (×450 in original). E. Longitudinal section of a pro-embryo prior to organ formation (×400 in original). F. Early stage of embryo development showing the first notch, indicated by the arrow (×225 in original). G. Shoot apex (*sa*) with leaf (*lf*) and leaf primordia (*lf pri*; *col*, coleoptile) (×150 in original.) H. Apex of the main shoot in the vegetative stage (×360 in original). I. Radicle showing root cap (*rc*) and zonation in the root apex (×150 in original).] (From Bonnet, 1961.)

FIG. 2–9. *Monotropa* sp. growing in the field. This plant is completely devoid of chlorophyll and therefore is saprophytic. It also has very simple seeds with reduced embryos. Inset A. Diagram of an ovule, with its embryo (em), reduced endosperm (en) and micropyle (m) (after Eames, 1961, from Koch, 1882). B. Photograph of an ovule, one of many hundreds borne centrally in a five-loculed capsule, with its embryo. Calibration I represents 0.5 mm.

Since the culture of isolated zygotes is very difficult, for young embryos prior to the heart or torpedo stages usually fail to grow when explanted, this problem has been evaded. Many completely or partially saprophytic angiosperms (e.g., *Orobanche* or *Monotropa*, Fig. 2–9) have, however, curiously underdeveloped embryos in their seeds. Among the best known examples are the orchids, in which embryos are undifferentiated and seeds are virtually devoid of endosperm. Knudson perfected aseptic culture methods for growing orchid embryos (Fig. 2–10) and devised suitable nutrient solutions (Table 2–8). From their reduced embryos, many orchids develop a massive storage organ, known as a protocorm, upon which the true shoots develop. In these orchids, the embryo accumulates, from its environment during its early independent growth, a mass of nutritive substances which nourish its later development. The nutritive role of the protocorm, with respect to the later development of the orchid plant, can be likened to the nutrition which most seed plants receive from their parent sporophytes (cf. Fig. 2–10B). This is particularly true in the case of oats, where the pro-embryo becomes rather large before it organizes.

TABLE 2–8
Knudson solution C

$Ca(NO_3)_2.4H_2O$	1.000 gm	When this solution was devised the importance of the trace elements B, Mn, Cu, Zn, and Mo was not known and they entered the solution as contaminants. They can, however, now be added separately as in the Hoagland-Arnon nutrient solution (Table 2–3), or as an A–Z solution containing many such substances in small amounts. The solubility of iron was maintained by a pH of the order of 5.0 and an effective source of sugar was 2 percent sucrose.
$(NH_4)_2SO_4$	0.500 gm	
$MgSO_4.7H_2O$	0.250 gm	
KH_2PO_4	0.250 gm	
$FeSO_4.7H_2O$	0.025 gm	
$MnSO_4.4H_2O$	0.0075 gm	
Sucrose	20.00 gm	
Agar	15.00 gm	
Distilled water	1000.00 ml	

(From Knudson, 1951)

The effect of the early environment of the angiosperm embryo on its nutrition and development may be illustrated by reference to hybrid vigor. It is beyond dispute that part of the explanation of hybrid vigor is genetic; i.e., there are more favorable combinations of genes in the hybrid than in either parent. This is not the whole story, as Ashby (1949) showed, for by continuous selfing the vigor of the hybrid strain declines. The common practice with corn is to use the first hybrid grains which have developed in the environment of the ovule of the female parent. In his analysis of hybrid vigor in corn, Ashby shows that there are two possibilities: either the "initial capital" available for growth in the hybrid grain is greater or its rate of increase, after germination, is greater. In cases cited, the relative growth rates, after germination, of hybrid and parental strains were compared by plotting their weights "on a logarithmic scale of weight so that their slopes represent relative growth rates" (i.e., rates of interest, cf. Chapter 9). Ashby states that this leads "to the unequivocal

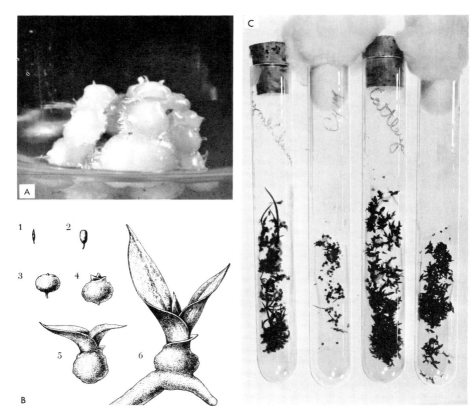

FIG. 2–10. The development of orchids. A. Close-up of developing *Cymbidium* protocorms grown aseptically. Note the pointed vegetative apices that are just beginning to develop (×4.). (From work of Mapes and Steward.) B. Stages in the germination of *Cattleya:* 1, swelling of the embryo inside the seed coat; 2, embryo growing after it has burst out of the seed coat; 3, embryo forming a protocorm with a vegetative apex; 4, the protocorm becoming disc-like and showing leaflets; 5, the protocorm forming a plantlet with two spreading leaves; 6, the plantlet forming larger leaves and the start of a root system. (From J. Arditti, "Orchids." Copyright © 1966 by Scientific American, Inc. All rights reserved.) C. Developing young plants of *Cymbidium* and *Cattleya* from protocorms. (Unpublished photo by the late Prof. L. Knudson, Cornell University.)

conclusion that the hybrid, although so much larger than its parents, is growing at exactly the same relative rate as one of them. To put it another way, the relative advantage in weight at the end of the experiment was already present at the beginning of the experiment. It is as though the 'initial capital' in the hybrid were greater, but the rate of interest was no greater." In other words, the advantage of the hybrid was determined during the development that occurred in the environment of the ovule, and it was not the sole consequence of the genetic constitution of the embryo. Thus, in the maternal environment of the ovule, the greater potentiality of the hybrid is expressed and its consequences are already evident and determined when the grain is mature. This being so, the nutritional role of the parent sporophyte has undisputed significance.

Qualitatively there seems to be no mineral nutrient requirements that are peculiar to zygotes or to young embryos. Salt solutions which are complete for any autotrophic green cell like *Chlorella,* or for an organized system like an excised root, should suffice also for an embryo. However, it is equally clear that all these requirements for both macronutrients and trace elements commonly need to be mobilized in the nucellus and embryo sac for the embryo's use. If there are nutrient requirements, or stimuli, that are peculiar to embryos, it seems much more probable that these would be organic than inorganic and that these requirements would disappear when the young embryo becomes green, develops a root, and enters upon a fully autotrophic existence. It is, in fact, in situations in which the development of embryos is arrested (e.g., the coconut *Cocos,* or the Maidenhair tree *Ginkgo*) that special *organic* provision is made in either the liquid endosperm (*Cocos*) or the female gametophyte (*Ginkgo*) for its later development. As shown in a later chapter (Chapter 4), these situations have provided the evidence for special non-nutrient organic substances which stimulate growth by cell division.

It does, however, seem to be feasible that during differentiation and morphogenesis when cells use only a part of their genetic complement of information, they also may use only a part of an otherwise full complement of nutrient elements. Thus the full range of inorganic nutrients may not be needed for every type of cell in every type of tissue or organ. Quantitatively, however, the requirements of a given essential element may be accentuated by the need to support either a particular kind of metabolism or a particular enzyme formation which characterizes the differentiated cells, tissues, or organs.

Are there data, then, to show what mineral nutrients are absorbed throughout the life cycle of a typical crop plant? The literature of crop science is replete with data on the responses of plants (usually recorded in terms of fresh and dry weight as the percentage composition with respect to this or that constituent) to externally applied nutrients. What one would like to know, however, is the progressive absorption and retention of the different mineral elements throughout a life cycle, i.e., from one fertilization to the next. Before considering the nutritional data that may, or may not, be available to cover this life span of an angiosperm, one may at least make the following point.

The peak period of requirement for the mineral nutrients of plants is early in their development. This is so because some nutrient ions are readily mobile. As potassium or phosphorus move into the young leaves of a shoot, even into the growing primordia, they will contribute to the growth of that leaf; the same is true of roots and root tips. Later, however, when the growth and

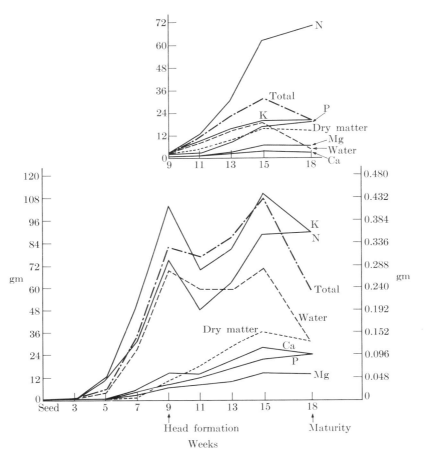

FIG. 2–11. The relation of the growth of a barley plant (roots excepted) to its total acquisition of water, dry matter, and minerals. The scale of ordinates to the left in the larger figure relates to the increment of total weight (gm), total water, and total dry matter. The scale of ordinates to the right refers to the increment of mineral matter (K, Ca, Mg, N, P). The smaller figure gives on the same scales the time course in the development of the flowering spikes. (From data of J. S. Burd, 1919.)

metabolic activity of that organ subsides, the more mobile mineral nutrients may be withdrawn and move to more active centers of growth and development. Therefore, some nutrients are, as it were, used over and over again, while others (such as iron, or other heavy metals, or even calcium) may be wholly or partially immobilized and become unavailable, so that a constant new intake of these nutrient elements is needed. Having appreciated these points here, we defer further consideration until Chapter 6, which is more concerned with translocation and redistribution of nutrients within the plant body. However, one

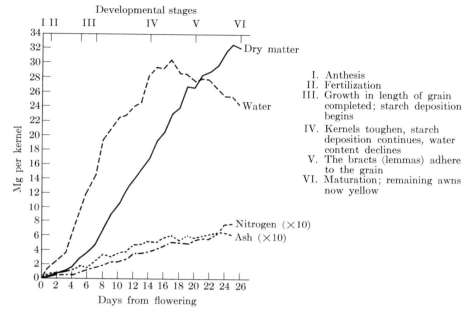

Developmental stages

I. Anthesis
II. Fertilization
III. Growth in length of grain completed; starch deposition begins
IV. Kernels toughen, starch deposition continues, water content declines
V. The bracts (lemmas) adhere to the grain
VI. Maturation; remaining awns now yellow

FIG. 2–12. Graph showing the development, the dry matter, nitrogen, water, and ash content at daily intervals from flowering to maturity in single barley grains. (Adapted from data of Harlan, 1920.) This figure has a modern counterpart in the work of Jennings and Morton (1963) in which the time courses of increase in dry weight and protein in the endosperm, testa, and embryo are recorded. The mature grains weighed about 33 mg dry, of which 27 mg (4 mg protein, the rest mainly starch) was in the endosperm, whereas their embryos represented less than a gram of dry weight.

may show here that the organs of the plant body may be interconnected by vascular strands, as revealed by brief treatment with radioactive Cs^{137}, for this shows how the different organs are interconnected to form interdependent nutritional units. By these means it may be seen that, as ions move preferentially to the younger, actively growing parts of an angiosperm shoot (Fig. 6–26), they may also be accumulated in the growing cells of the cambium and its derivatives along the vascular strands in which the nutrients also move. There are, then, problems of internal nutrition within the plant body, as well as the nutritive problems which relate to the ability of the external environment to supply that which is needed during growth.

The total acquisition of water and dry matter, organic and inorganic, during the development of barley grains and barley plants is shown in Fig. 2–11. From these admittedly old data, and in the literature of plant nutrition as a whole, there is remarkably little to be found about the detailed nutrition of the fertilized egg (i.e., the zygote) as it develops in its ovule, or fruit (caryopsis or one-seeded fruit), in the manner shown in Fig. 2–8. Figure 2–11 shows only the time course in the accretion of water and of organic and inorganic material as barley grains grow into barley plants. Ripening and maturity of the grain, at about 15 weeks from germination, are associated with some "drying out," or a relative decline in the increase of water while dry matter continues to increase, notably in the endosperm. When growth is resumed, at germination, one should ideally begin with the already highly organized embryo itself (cf. Fig. 2–8) and trace, first, the movement of stored material from the endosperm across the scutellum into the embryo as it grows. (The magnitude of movement from the cotyledons in an exalbuminous seed into the plumule has already been indicated). Secondly, one should be able to trace the increment of water, organic material, and ash, and of particular substances, as the embryo develops and is nourished by external sources. Just as there is a paucity of data on the early nutrition of zygotes, there is also a lack of it with respect to the early nutrition of embryos following the germination of seeds. One can, however, put Figs. 2–11 and 2–12 together and, for barley, cover the range from one germinating grain to the next to show the increment of total substance with time.

The data of Fig. 2–12 subsequent to the germination of the grains refer only to shoots; they also lack reference to the relative size of endosperm and embryo in a whole barley grain. One may, however, pardonably interpret them in the following way.

The size of barley grains and their parts can, however, be estimated from data of Brenchley (1912) or from actual observations. Whereas a whole grain of barley should have weighed approximately 40 mg (38.5 mg in an actual test), the embryo should have weighed about 0.5 mg (0.52 mg by actual test). The total weight of a barley shoot, in Fig. 2–12, at three weeks was 763 mg, and its dry matter was 76.3 mg. Thus the embryo shoot increased in dry matter in three weeks from something less than 0.5 mg to 76.3 mg (much of this weight came from the endosperm*) and, in a similar period, it increased in water from about 0.05 mg to some 686 mg, the water content of the shoot. Therefore, the relative increase in *water* in the plantlet was of the order of $\times$ 10,000 whereas the relative increase in dry matter was of the order of $\times$ 150. In other words, in the first three weeks after germination the embryo increases in total water many times more rapidly than in dry matter; this is only another way of saying that the embryo in the grain has, preformed, a great deal of the organization to carry it far through its subsequent growth.

The subsequent increase of water and dry matter from three to nine weeks is smooth and exponential as organs already formed in the embryo (cf. Fig. 2–8) grow and new ones develop (Fig. 2–11). The increment of organic

---

* The increase of dry matter in this period by attached barley embryos that draw upon their endosperm is much greater than the increase derived from an appropriate nutrient solution by the isolated embryo. This emphasizes the efficient role of the scutellum as an absorbing organ (cf. Joy and Folkes, 1965, Fig. 1, p. 654).

matter here outstrips the increment of inorganic substance, for mobile inorganic nutrients (e.g., K) are recirculated and re-used. With the onset of flowering (at about nine weeks), and until the fruits and heads of grain develop, the net increase of inorganic substance in the shoot is arrested, so that it may actually be depleted by recirculation to the root, but thereafter, as the fruits develop and mature (up to about 15 weeks), the net gains in the shoots resume. The inset in Fig. 2–11 shows the time course in the accretion of substances, following flowering, in the development of the flowering spikes, and Fig. 2–12 shows the similar data per grain, or kernel.

The growth and intake of substance by the developing leaves of wheat, prior to their emergence, has been subjected to a more modern study by Williams and Rijven (1965). The relative growth rate of each leaf primordium rises to a maximum prior to its emergence, and then it declines. For a brief period, each leaf plays a dominant role in the growth of the apex as a whole. Williams and Rijven have traced the intake of dry weight, cellulose, protein, and nucleic acid phosphorus into these primordia as they grow, and they have estimated the doubling time for each component. As might be anticipated, the dry weight of the young leaf (up to 5 mm) is heavily determined by protein and nucleic acid; thereafter, the importance of these constituents declines as cellulose increases more than protein.

Therefore, the overall requirements to nourish a barley plant, i.e., to provide its substance as it develops from the zygote throughout the complete life cycle to the next fertilization, are even today not easy to specify. There is an important gap, since one cannot, from the available data, distinguish between the developing whole grain, with its stored materials, and the embryos they contain; that is, one cannot estimate the full extent of the nutritional contribution of the parent sporophyte to the early development of the embryos it supports. In fact, the full nutritional requirements (organic and inorganic) of the developing zygote in this all-important phase of its growth preceding the development of the mature grain will not be known until this phase of growth is accomplished in isolation, or is recapitulated using free cells that grow like embryos (cf. Chapter 10). Even thereafter, when the plantlets are autotrophic, their growth does not require a smoothly continuing total increment of water, dry matter, and particular nutrients *pari passu* with their growth, for the relative composition of the plant and its parts is subject to change as its development proceeds and as redistribution of previously absorbed materials occurs.

Consequently, one should also ask whether all the essential elements are equally necessary for the cells of all organs or tissues of the plant body, or are equally required at all developmental stages. There is no obvious reason why this should be so. It is true that cultures of excised roots, growing as organized structures, seem to have all the nutrient requirements of the whole plant. However, secondary phloem from the storage root of carrot, in the presence of coconut milk freed of calcium, seems able to proliferate and to grow well, but in an unorganized way, in a solution with a concentration of calcium that would not support the growth of whole plants. And if carrot cells grow heterotrophically for nitrogen using exogenously supplied amino acids in the form of casein hydrolysate or even ammonium ion, it is more difficult to demonstrate their requirement for molybdenum which is, however, demonstrable when the only source of nitrogen is nitrate.

A very much neglected question is the relation to genetics of the requirement for trace elements. Characteristically, the trace element requirements of plants have been investigated with economically important plants, usually plants with a long history of selective breeding directed toward specific objectives. Many examples have occurred in which the growth of a crop plant has been limited in the field by factors later diagnosed as lack of a trace element (e.g., zinc in the case of prunes and apricots in California), whereas the native plants (in this case deciduous trees) in the same area had long flourished without any additional supplies of this element. Also, many of the cases of trace element deficiency have been observed when varieties, developed and adapted to one set of conditions, were grown under very different ones. Since breeding and selection of commercial varieties are always occurring, a watch needs to be kept so that, unawares, biochemical variants are not produced which will show abnormalities that can only be relieved by the use of still other trace elements. The fact that Pope and Munger (1953a, 1953b) have disclosed cases in which the level of requirement for a given nutrient element is regulated by a single gene difference, gives point to this view. A comprehensive study that would check whether native species in their habitat require any different, i.e., fewer, trace elements than the cultivars developed from them would be profitable. If this were so, it could be concluded that ever more demanding nutritional requirements are part of the price that is paid for greater specialization and adaptation of the organism in question. In these terms one ought to visualize the most primordial forms of life as those which required the fewest chemical elements upon which to base their organization and growth.

Concentration Levels: Accumulation of Ions and Nutrients

A striking difference between the nutrient media for saprophytic microorganisms and angiosperms is immediately apparent: the former tolerate their nutrients in much higher concentrations than is commonly necessary for higher plants. While most plants tolerate only extremely dilute external solutions, they need to concentrate certain ions during their growth by fostering "up-hill movement" against diffusion gradients; this is especially true for potassium. By contrast, the bacteria and the fungi often grow in relatively strong solutions of certain organic and inorganic materials. Indeed some organisms will inhabit brine from which salt is being crystallized and will even grow in solutions strong enough to act as preservatives for food.

FIG. 2–13. Coenocytic plants. A. *Valonia macrophysa*. B. *Valonia ventricosa*. (From Steward and Martin, 1937.) C. *Nitella flexilis*. (From Hoagland, 1944.)

It is, therefore, a salient property of many plant cells that they "accumulate" in true solution many of the ions they receive from the very dilute solution with which they are in contact. This process has been studied in many plant materials, notably in large coenocytic vesicles of plants such as *Valonia* or *Nitella* (Fig. 2–13); in thin slices cut from massive storage organs like potato tuber,

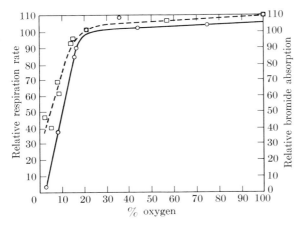

FIG. 2–14.   Relative bromide absorption (solid line with circles) and relative respiration rate (broken line with squares) of thin discs of potato tuber plotted against percent oxygen in the gas aerating the system. (From Steward, 1933.)

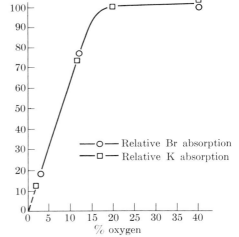

FIG. 2–15. Uptake of potassium and bromide ions by Jerusalem artichoke tuber tissues. (From Steward, Berry, and Broyer, 1936.) ▶

carrot root, artichoke tuber, etc.; and in roots excised from seedling plants such as barley. The effect of light on the intake of ions by certain green cells (e.g., *Nitella*) first led to the recognition that the process is an active one which is dependent on the use of metabolites, and that it ultimately requires light for their production. Early work on *Nitella* by Hoagland *et al.* (1926) showed that the accumulation of the bromide ion was a function of the intensity of light, occurred little if at all in the dark, and was affected by the duration and intensity of light during the daily period of illumination. Work on thin discs cut from plant storage organs (potato and artichoke tubers) drew attention to the role of oxygen pressure in this active absorption process, and thus to the importance of aerobic metabolism in the process of ion intake (see Figs. 2–14 and 2–15). Absorption of ions by excised roots from barley and potato was soon found to

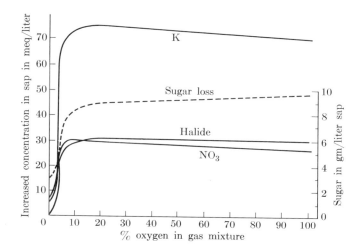

FIG. 2–16. Influence of oxygen concentration of the flowing gas stream to the accumulation of potassium and halide in cell sap of barley root systems. The effect of varying oxygen supply on sugar utilized in respiration is also indicated. (From Hoagland and Broyer, 1936.)

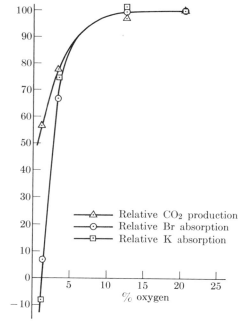

FIG. 2–17. Curve showing that both anion and cation (bromide and potassium) absorption is limited by oxygen in potato roots. (From Steward, Berry, and Broyer, 1936.) ▶

present similar features (Figs. 2–16 and 2–17). But the behavior of cells at the surface of a thin disc of tissue (as they progress toward the condition shown in Fig. 1–17), or near the apex of a root (Prevot and Steward, 1936; Steward, Prevot, and Harrison, 1942), or in young developing leaves, is particularly relevant to this discussion. In each of these active regions, salt accumulation occurs alongside, and somewhat parallel to, the ability of cells to grow and to perform those metabolic functions that are characteristic of growing cells. Thus this process of active ion accumulation, which is an integral part of inorganic plant nutrition, normally occurs during growth, characteristically involves energy which is released to the cells in usable form by their aerobic respiration, and thus depends upon oxygen tension (Figs. 2–14 through 2–17). This being so, one can see how even the content of inorganic nutrients in cells may be dependent upon aspects of the very organization for which they are in turn so necessary. The source of the metabolic power of heterotrophic cells, i.e., the organelle which releases energy by respiration (oxidative phosphorylation) in usable form (ATP or other phosphorylated compounds) is the mitochondrion. Hence when ions, e.g., potassium ions, are moved in free solution from the low concentrations at which they commonly occur in the ambient fluids that bathe cells externally, to the high concentrations that obtain within, one may assume that the functioning of this energy-releasing organelle is brought into play.

New developments in the study of photosynthesis have also shown that the chloroplasts of green cells may fix light energy directly (photosynthetic phosphorylation) in the form of energy-rich compounds (e.g., ATP). It was previously thought that these compounds could only arise from respiration (oxidative phosphorylation). This discovery may, therefore, go far toward explaining the success of green cells in the light (quite apart from their content of carbohydrate) with respect to their general ability to grow and their specific ability to accumulate their solutes. One has, therefore, only to look at the structure of mitochondria (cf. Fig. 5–2) and of chloroplasts (cf. Fig. 3–11) to see the arrangements that furnish the usable energy that may drive the "pumps" which cause ions to accumulate in cells during their growth. These arrangements are obviously not simple. Essentially, however, the process of ion accumulation in cells has to be seen as a feature of organized cells working as active machines in which, by virtue of their metabolism and organization, they are capable of expending energy to do physicochemical work and to create and maintain a nonequilibrium condition with respect to their aquatic environment.

The organelle which is primarily responsible for the release of energy as oxygen is absorbed and as electrons flow over the electron transport chain, and as ATP is generated, is the mitochondrion. In the words of Lehninger (1964, p. 159), "mitochondria may therefore contribute to active transport of ions (cf. K^+) by virtue of their role as an ATP generating system and as a respiration-dependent ion-sequestering system." Since Lehninger's recent work and experience (1966) is on animal cells, he naturally sees it against the old problem of the means by which K^+ is maintained as the principal ion in muscle cells or erythrocytes, even though the bathing fluids are richer in Na^+. The examination of isolated mitochondria with respect to their content of ions presents an even simpler system than intact cells—perhaps deceptively so, because it locates within one organelle the ion content and the energy expenditure for the ion transport. In vacuolated plant cells, the main repository for the accumulated ions is the vacuole, whereas the main source of usable metabolic energy to bring the process about is the mitochondrion. Nevertheless, one can see in the animal mitochondria a system that illustrates the point that even such an apparently direct question as the uptake of a potassium ion by an organelle cannot be answered without reference to its structure and organization and in the full recognition that this structure provides for the juxtaposition and orderly arrangement of all the enzymes and coenzymes which enable its respiratory system to work smoothly.

TABLE 2–9
Metal-ion content of freshly isolated
rat liver mitochondria

Ion	mμmoles/mg protein
K^+	130.0
Na^+	6.3
Mg^{++}	42.0
Ca^{++}	5.6
Zn^{++}	1.9
$Fe^{++}(Fe^{+++})$	7.5
Mn^{++}	0.4

From Lehninger, 1964, p. 159

Table 2–9 shows the metal-ion content of rat liver mitochondria in relation to their protein content. On any reasonable estimate of the molecular weight of this protein, the number of ions in the mitochondrion would far exceed the number of protein molecules. Hence, this is not mere binding to protein sites. It is estimated, however (Lehninger, 1964), that there is a "distinct relationship between the ratio of atoms of Ca^{++} accumulated, to atoms of oxygen taken up" and "approximately 1.7 molecules of Ca^{++} may be accumulated by the mitochondria from the medium as a pair of electrons traverses each phosphorylation site in the respiratory chain." The isolated rat liver mitochondrion turns out to be an active system for the accumulation of Ca^{++} and inorganic phosphate from a medium which contains both respiratory substrate and ATP (cf. Fig. 2–18), and these absorption activities are "integral with and driven by the energy-conserving sites in the respiratory chain." Thus even such a minute organelle as a mitochondrion creates the impression of an elaborately structured body with its external and internal membranes along which are disposed all the complexities of the respiratory system. These membranes, via oxygen uptake, may negotiate the flow of electrons and produce the ATP, and this may drive the machinery which absorbs and accumulates the inorganic ions into the mitochondrion. Moreover, despite some variation from organ to organ, mitochondria from diverse sources (rat liver, kidney, brain, heart, skeletal muscle, maize and bean seedlings, *Neurospora*, and yeast) show essentially the same ability to accumulate calcium ions, as well as other cations. Therefore, work on isolated animal mitochondria, as also the earlier work on intact plant cells, recognizes that these ion absorption phenomena are integral parts of inorganic nutrition. Hence the problems of inorganic nutrition should be understood in terms of the cellular and the sub-cellular organization of the system of which the absorbed ions form a part and of the ways in which this organization controls the ionic movements.

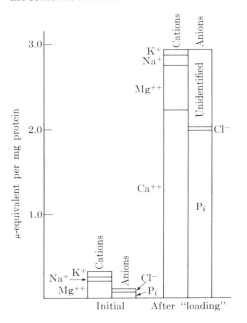

◄FIG. 2–18. Cation and anion content of rat liver mitochondria before and after respiration-linked "loading" with Ca^{++} and P_i. (From A. L. Lehninger, *The Mitochondrion.* W. A. Benjamin, Inc., New York, 1964. Used by permission of the publisher.)

FIG. 2–19. Development of the vacuome. A. *Dactylis glomerata:* vacuoles developing as swellings on filaments. B, C. *Anthoxanthum odoratum:* detail of vacuoles developing as swellings on filaments. [*v*, vacuole; *r*, endoplasmic reticulum which may connect with the nuclear membrane (*nm*); *f*, section of elongated filaments resembling reticulum, which open into vacuoles; *pl*, plasmalemma; *t*, tonoplast; *m*, mitochondrion; *n*, nucleus.] (After Poux, 1962). ►

Figures 2–11 and 2–12 imperfectly describe the increment of substance in an organism during its life cycle; this summarizes its nutrition. However, one should also recognize the interplay of organic nutrition (Chapter 3) upon inorganic nutrition and that the very processes of growth which the nutrition supports also invoke the complex mechanisms in cells by which their nutrients are absorbed and become available. This point will recur in Chapter 6, which is concerned with the ways in which physiological functions are correlated with growth.

The ultimate fate of non-metabolized but accumulated solutes in plants is to be internally secreted into the vacuoles of parenchyma cells. An interpretation of the sequential events that occur during ontogeny suggests that in any given cell there is first a phase in which salts or solutes may be absorbed because sites, or organelles, which they can occupy are being multiplied. This has been described (cf. Chapter 6) as phase I of the overall process. So long as the absorption of solutes is dominated by cells in this state, the relations between internal and external concentrations are simple and linear and they suggest a form of stoichiometrical binding. But when self-duplication of the sites subsides and cells grow mainly in volume and largely by increase of the vacuole, a second step (phase II) supervenes. Salts or solutes previously bound may be

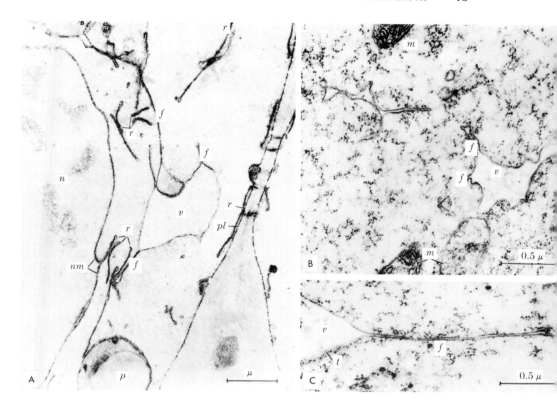

removed and secreted into the developing vacuoles and, as they are removed, they can be replaced from without. It is in this type of system that the accumulation process works with greater efficiency at greater dilution of the solute in the external solution, so that the relationship of internal to external concentration becomes logarithmic. The relations between salts accumulated and the growth of organs is to be considered later (Chapter 6), but it may be said here that the accumulatory mechanism is at its height in the cells that are rapidly growing, such as cells just behind the root tip or in leaf primordia during Sachs' Grand Period of Growth. All this has suggested that the developing vacuome in cells, as it forms from the often thread-like, deeply staining inclusions which take basic dyes as vital stains and which swell and coalesce, is the type of internal inclusion in which the solutes accumulate *de novo*. The genesis of vacuoles as organelles is still not wholly clear. It is, however, very suggestive that work with the electron microscope traces the development of vacuoles to vesicular swellings of filaments which either resemble, or are identical with, the endoplasmic reticulum as shown in Fig. 2–19. This being so, it is plausible to see the initial binding sites as the granular, ribosomal bodies which occur in cytoplasm and are attached to the reticulum. When these sites no longer multiply, and vacuoles form by vesiculation, ions must vacate their sites to be secreted into the vacuole before further absorption can take place. In some such way the processes of ion intake need to be interwoven with the way cells grow, since the energy for the secretory process is made available from the metabolism of cells which can also grow.

The Role of Essential Elements

The interpretation of growth in terms of nutrition involves the functions or general role of the inorganic ions and nutrients. Reference may be made here to an entire volume on the subject of the inorganic nutrition of plants (Steward, 1963). The following comments are, therefore, only of a very general nature. Relatively few of the elements of the periodic table as it is known today are used to support growth and to nourish plants. Of course, none of the heavier and unstable elements, which are known only by radioactive synthesis and which bring the number of chemical elements currently to 103, are used. The most complex structures of organisms are built from the lighter elements: hydrogen, carbon, nitrogen, oxygen, phosphorus, and sulfur—all non-metallic elements. It is unnecessary to dwell upon the great range of chemical compounds which these elements may form in combination. Suffice it to say that what used to be called "organic chemistry," because it dealt with the chemistry of those substances that seemed to be characteristic of organized nature, is now a synonym for the chemistry of carbon compounds. Thus the non-metallic elements comprise the main structural framework of the compounds which contribute to the architecture of cells. But what of the metallic elements?

It is a challenge and a paradox that the need for potassium, the most easily demonstrable essential element for growth, still defies explanation. We can say much about the requirement for potassium, which extends to almost every vital activity, but the true reason why potassium is not dispensable and fully replaceable by sodium or rubidium cannot yet be easily stated. Specific and direct uses for calcium and magnesium are well known. Magnesium is required for chlorophyll formation in green plants, but it is equally necessary for all protoplasm, whether green or not; its role as a cofactor in many enzyme systems is here important. Calcium has functions in the middle lamellae. Iron is an important catalyst in many heme-catalyzed oxidation systems, and the essential role of iron as a carrier of oxygen in the hemoglobin of blood in the animal body is obvious. But iron is also a ubiquitous requirement for all protoplasm, so far as is known, and its unique ability to transfer electrons in the oxidation systems which are involved in respiration applies here.

For boron, no clearly proven explanation exists, although the ability of boric acid to combine with substances which have two cis-hydroxyl groups (i.e., on the same side of the molecule) has often been thought to have biological significance. Where minute amounts of inorganic elements, such as manganese, copper, zinc, or molybdenum are involved, the expectation now is that these represent the metallic component of some enzyme system which plays an essential role in the

TABLE 2–10

Trace elements as components of some metallo-enzymes

Enzyme	Reaction	Metal
Carbonic anhydrase	$CO_2 + H_2O \rightleftarrows H_2CO_3$	Zn
Inorganic pyrophosphatase	Pyrophosphate $+ H_2O \rightarrow PO_4$	Mg
Catalase	$2H_2O_2 \rightarrow 2H_2O + O_2$	Fe
Cytochromes	Electron transport (cf. Fig. 6–11)	Fe
Tyrosinase	Tyrosine $+ \frac{1}{2}O_2 \rightarrow$ hallochrome	Cu
Laccase	Phenols $\rightarrow$ ortho- and para-quinones	Cu
Ascorbic acid oxidase	Ascorbic acid $\rightarrow$ dehydroascorbic acid	Cu
Prolidase	Glycylproline $\rightarrow$ proline	Mn
Carboxypeptidase	Chloroacetyl-tyrosine $\rightarrow$ tyrosine	Mg
Glycylglycine dipeptidase	Glycylglycine $\rightarrow$ glycine	Zn
Carboxypeptidase	Carbobenzoxyglycyl-L-phenylalanine $\rightarrow$ phenyl-alanine	Zn
Alcohol dehydrogenase	Ethanol $+$ DPN $\rightleftarrows$ acetaldehyde $+$ DPNH	Zn
Glutamic dehydrogenase	Glutamate $+$ DPN $\rightleftarrows$ ketoglutarate $+$ DNPH $+ NH_3$	Zn
Lactic dehydrogenase	Lactate $+$ DPN $\rightleftarrows$ pyruvate $+$ DPNH	Zn
Inorganic pyrophosphatase	Pyrophosphate $+ H_2O \rightarrow$ 2-orthophosphate	Mg
Succinic dehydrogenase	Succinic acid $\rightarrow$ fumaric acid $+ 2H$	Fe
Peroxidase	H_2O_2 oxidation of aromatic amines and other compounds	Fe
DPNH-cytochrome-c reductase	DNPH $+$ cytochrome c $(Fe^{+++}) \rightarrow$ DPN $+$ cytochrome c (Fe^{++})	Fe
Uricase	Uric acid $+ O_2 \rightleftarrows$ allantoin $+ H_2O_2 + CO_2$	Cu
Nitrate reductase	$NO_3 +$ TPNH $+ H^+ \rightarrow NO_2 +$ TPN$^+ + H_2O$	Mo
Xanthine oxidase	Xanthine $+ O_2 \rightarrow H_2O_2 +$ uric acid	Mo
Aldehyde oxidase	Acetaldehyde $+ O_2 \rightarrow$ acetate $+ H_2O$	Mo

metabolism involved in growth. For most of these elements clear cases exist where this could be so (cf. Table 2–10); in fact, so firmly entrenched is this idea that the discovery of a new metallic trace element would immediately lead to the search for an enzyme system in which it might participate. But for potassium no single and unique role that accounts for its essentiality can yet be stipulated.

Interactions between Nutrients and Factors in the Environment

The main nutrient requirements for the growth of plants became known inasmuch as they were each investigated separately. It was and is important to know that there are functions of potassium which cannot be replaced by sodium, or of iron which cannot be replaced by manganese, etc. However, when one considers the impact of the nutrients and essential elements upon growth, their interactions with each other and with factors in the environment also become important. In other words, nutritional requirements are not absolute: they are to a considerable extent a function of the conditions under which plants grow.

Well-known examples of these interactions, which are reflected in growth, occur between iron and manganese; between the level of nitrogen supplied, the prime nutritional factor which pushes growth of crop plants to its maximum, and the requirements for other elements, especially trace elements; between the use of nitrogen by plants and the conditions of illumination as well as the access of the plants to potassium and/or calcium; between the intensity of illumination and the symptoms due to lack of zinc. To document all these and other inter-actions here is neither possible nor appropriate. There is, however, a general lesson to be drawn. The unit that can grow, whether it is a zygote, an embryo, a seed or a spore, a cell, an organ or an organism, has some inherent genetically determined potentiality for growth. Some factors, nutritional and environmental, are of such overriding importance that their lack will completely dislocate the expression of this capacity to grow. However, once conditions compatible with growth are established, its magnitudes are not fixed absolutely, for a great many factors, nutritional and environmental, may intervene to control or modulate the growth which occurs. In fact, there is here both a difficulty and a challenge.

So many factors of the environment (long days, short days, high night tem-peratures, low night temperatures) interact with the nutritional variables that it now becomes a major problem to design experiments effectively and to interpret their results so that the effect of all the different parameters that affect growth can be both detected and evaluated. This was the theme of a recent contribution to a symposium on the effects of environment upon growth (Steward, 1963). Work on the mint plant (Steward *et al.*, 1962) has already shown that both the nutrition and metabolism, as well as the morphology, of this plant are greatly affected by, and interact with, the conditions that determine its growth.

Therefore, plants not only need nutrients to grow (i.e., to make the stuff of the plant body) but the growth and metabolism of which they are capable in any given situation becomes a function of *both* the innate or built-in, genetic, capacity to grow with which they are initially endowed, and those nutritional and environmental parameters by which its expression may be modulated. The investigation of growth cannot, therefore, be pursued without close regard to the environment in which it occurs and to the substances by which it is nourished. It is the recognition of these principles which has prompted the design and con-struction of growth chambers or large installations for the control of all the environmental or climatic factors that control the growth of plants. These in-stallations are equally necessary for the interpretation of their nutrition, for it is now known that nutritional levels and consequent metabolism of plants are modified by, and interact with, the environment in which they are grown.

Summary

In the molecular arrangements of the inanimate world, which are governed by equilibrium criteria, by free energy which tends toward its minimum, and by molecules which obey statistical laws of chance distribution, there is no parallel for biological growth and nutrition. In the organized living state growth and nutrition proceed concomitantly. Only autotrophic (usually green) plants can live in an inorganic world, and for these the nutrient requirements may be satisfied by those molecules that comprise the essential minimum of chemical elements that will support life. The composition of an organism is thus set off from the composition of its environment. Hence, a plant builds into its body during growth the substances or compounds which are essential for the metabolism by which it operates and for its structure and organization as a working machine; it may also accumulate many dispensable substances, merely because they are there, and store these in vacuoles. The environment must, therefore, furnish these substances, and thus nourish the organism. The chemical elements so required range from those which are involved in large quantity to those involved only in the most minute traces. For growth to proceed, unlimited by external events, the environment must be able to furnish these nutrients in balanced amounts. The typical angiosperm passes through critical formative stages of its growth in the ovule and is there nourished by the parent sporophyte. To obtain many of their nutrients from the dilute solutions in which they occur, cells and organisms must be able to concentrate them, and plants display this activity to a surprising degree, although this property is not reserved for substances for which the organism has obvious need. While it is true that nutrients are required to nourish the organism, it is equally true that many of these nutrients are concentrated by organisms and removed from the environment only as an inherent part of their growth. The absorption of the solutes is, therefore, also subject to the driving force which the growth itself imparts. Special organelles (the mitochondrion in respiration and the chloroplast in photosynthesis) furnish energy in usable form (ATP by oxidative phosphorylation and by photosynthetic phosphorylation) to concentrate ions in the developing vacuoles of cells and to make them grow. Furthermore, the growth of higher plants is now seen as the result of many complex interactions. Though essentially dependent upon certain innate, or built-in, genetically determined capacities, it is nevertheless controlled and modulated by a great many nutritional and environmental factors which interact with each other. It becomes, therefore, a major task to define these various parameters and to demonstrate and interpret their effects, singly and in combination, upon plants. It is to these ends that modern growth chambers or climatic control installations, which have been devised as essential facilities for the control of the variables that affect the growth of plants, should now be used, i.e., to determine the interactions between the nutrition, metabolism, and development of plants.

chapter three

GROWTH AND ORGANIC NUTRITION:
THE BUILDING OF COMPLEX MOLECULES

This chapter, which covers a very wide field, is presented in three parts. The first part is essentially introductory; the second makes special reference to the carbohydrates that are important in growth and metabolism; and the third refers mainly to the nitrogen compounds and the accessory substances that are involved in growth with its concomitant protein synthesis. Throughout the chapter growth is seen as the building of complex molecules in already organized systems, even though many, or all, of the individual chemical reactions can be made to go on in cell-free systems.

Autotrophy and Heterotrophy: Organic and Inorganic Nutrition

An essential distinction between autotrophic cells, organs, and organisms and heterotrophic systems is that the former can obtain their nutrition from an inorganic world, while the latter are wholly or partially dependent upon more complex materials already elaborated by organisms or by synthetic processes.

Organic nutrition furnishes to the organism all the carbon compounds which build its structure, as well as the molecules that negotiate its vital processes. Ultimately all these organic substances are derived from the products of photosynthesis. In photosynthesis, carbon dioxide, the fully oxidized carbon compound present in the atmosphere, is reduced in the formation of carbon chains and rings of varying degrees of size and complexity with the utilization and storage of energy. For all practical purposes this source of energy is sunlight made available through the photosynthesis of green plants. Green plants decompose water by the aid of visible light, and hydrogen is transferred to acceptors from which it is eventually passed to carbon dioxide, the molecule ultimately reduced. Other organisms also use light energy on the same general principle, notably the pigmented sulfur bacteria which substitute hydrogen sulfide for water. However, there are other ways by which carbon dioxide is reduced by organisms; these mechanisms utilize chemical, rather than photochemical, sources of energy, and therefore they result in a net loss of energy content rather than a gain. Indeed, it was an outstanding achievement that led to the recognition that carbon dioxide fixation and its conversion into molecules of higher molecular weight, forming new carbon-carbon bonds, is not the sole prerogative of photosynthetic cells for, in varying degree, virtually all living cells are able to do this. This so-called "dark" fixation, which requires the expenditure of metabolic energy, contributes to the organic nutrition of cells in a quite different way from the reduction of carbon dioxide that is brought about by photosynthesis. Dark fixation of carbon dioxide in heterotrophic cells is a means by which they perform certain essential, intermediate, chemical steps of metabolism rather than a way of organic nutrition. The consideration of this subject here would be a digression but, it may be noted, the chemical compounds called α-keto acids may pick up carbon dioxide to form other acids with additional carbon atoms; an example is the conversion of the 3-carbon keto-acid, pyruvic acid, to α-ketoglutaric acid, as shown:

$$
\begin{array}{ccc}
CH_3 & & {}^*COOH \\
| & +{}^*CO_2 & | \\
C{=}O & \xrightarrow[(NADPH)]{TPNH} & CH_2 \\
| & & | \\
COOH & & C{=}O \\
& & | \\
& & COOH \\
\text{Pyruvic} & & \text{Oxaloacetic} \\
\text{acid} & & \text{acid}
\end{array}
$$

By the repetition of this process it is even possible to pass from molecules with a relatively low molecular weight, with only 2 or 3 carbon atoms, to acids with 6 carbon atoms which are, therefore, of the general order of complexity of hexose sugars. But to do all this, energy is necessary, energy which can only arise in these cells from the degradation of preformed organic compounds of a similar degree of complexity. One may also note that this apparently simple chemical reaction—the addition of a molecule of carbon dioxide—can only be brought about by the aid of an elaborate system consisting of an enzyme (carboxylase) composed of its protein and coenzyme (thiamine pyrophosphate) moieties. In other words this reaction can only be brought about *in vitro* by the use of molecules which not only mediate the transfer of energy but also provide the setting in which the reaction can occur. This setting is a product of biological organization. Therefore, when this, or any other enzyme-mediated reaction, is carried out *in vitro* it does not evade, but in fact, utilizes, an essential product of biological organization, namely the enzyme itself.

Chapter 2 suggests that the organic and the inorganic processes of nutrition should not be regarded as separate and distinct, even though they are often conveniently discussed separately. For example, the essentiality of potassium for growth is very evident and its role is apparent in practically all metabolic processes; one should, therefore, conceive of the organic and the inorganic nutrition of plants as two faces of the same coin. Similarly, there are in most angiosperms green areas of the shoot which can be regarded as autotrophic and other areas or organs of the plant, such as the root, which are as clearly heterotrophic, at least for carbon. There is apparent reciprocity and "division of labor" within a single plant body. A single green algal cell is not commonly regarded as embodying both autotrophic and heterotrophic centers, but no doubt this is strictly true in that one type of metabolism may be located in certain organelles (e.g., the chloroplast) and other kinds of metabolism elsewhere in the cytoplasm and in other cell inclusions (e.g., mitochondria). Parenthetically it may be noted that Oparin (1961) regards the anaerobic and heterotrophic kinds of metabolism as most nearly like the metabolism of primitive forms of life which originated when the earth's atmosphere was a reducing one and contained ammonia and hydrocarbons.

With these reservations, it is convenient to consider what seem to be the essential *organic* requirements for growth, i.e., sugars in carbon-heterotrophic cells and, later, nitrogen compounds where cells use sources of nitrogen other than nitrate or ammonia.

Sources of carbon for heterotrophic cells. Sugars are the most obvious and the most important sources from which heterotrophic cells, organs, or organisms meet their requirements for carbon. Nevertheless, it was known by the turn of the 20th century that a very wide variety of compounds could furnish the carbon requirements of bacteria and fungi. In Volume I of Pfeffer's three-volume treatise (1899), the following series purported to show, in descending order, the readiness with which a variety of compounds could furnish carbon to *Penicillium glaucum* and to *Aspergillus niger*: sugar, peptone, albumen, quinic acid, tartaric acid, citric acid, asparagine, acetic acid, butyric acid, ethyl alcohol, benzoic, propylamine, methylamine, phenol, and formic acid. Pfeffer did state that "the order is, however, different with other organisms. . . ." Today one could add the idea that with modern knowledge of biochemical genetics it is possible to produce mutant cells or strains of organisms, which may utilize, or require, almost any external carbon source that is not actually toxic to protoplasm. Nevertheless, sugars are normally the main source from which most organisms meet their requirement for carbon in order that they may grow. Some general considerations apply at this point.

The Molecular Architecture of Carbon Compounds:
Biosynthesis and Organization

The ability of carbon to form regularly repeating patterns in space is fundamental to the understanding of its role in nature. This follows from the ability of carbon to combine with itself, from the arrangement of its bonds in space, their divergence at angles of 120°, and the possibilities of stereoisomerism to which these properties lead. The importance of "molecular architecture," or the arrangement of atoms in space, may be seen from the contrasted structure and properties of graphite (Fig. 3–1) and of diamond (Fig. 3–2). Whereas the

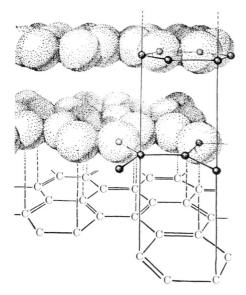

FIG. 3–1.   Structure of graphite.   (From *General Chemistry*, Second Edition, by Linus Pauling.   W. H. Freeman and Company, San Francisco. Copyright © 1953.)

FIG. 3–2.   Structure of diamond.   (From *General Chemistry*, Second Edition, by Linus Pauling.   W. H. Freeman and Company, San Francisco. Copyright © 1953.)

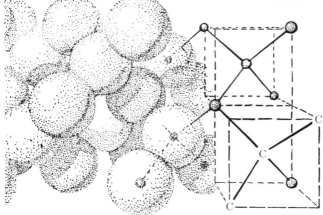

close-packed structure of carbon atoms in diamond leads to one of the hardest substances known, graphite is a soft substance. The presence in graphite of lamellar sheets of atoms, arranged in hexagonal rings, enables the atoms to slip past each other. This graphite is soft and can even be used as a lubricant. Also, molecules which contain carbon attached to four different groups can exist in many possible isomeric forms, the number of such forms depending on the number of such asymmetric carbon atoms present in the molecule. The number of isomeric forms is 2^N where N is the number of asymmetric centers.

In an aldehyde-hexose sugar molecule, like glucose, there are four immediately obvious asymmetric centers and, in consequence, a minimum of 16 theoretically possible aldohexoses. These possibilities are compatible with the somewhat old-fashioned way of writing the formula for an aldehyde sugar which resulted from the classical work of Emil Fischer. In this method of designating the sugar (glucose), two possibilities exist: in the first, the hydroxyl group attached to the so-called carbinol carbon, at the lower extremity of the formula, is shown as written on the right-hand side of the carbon backbone (formula I);

I	II	III	IV	V
H	H	H	H	
C=O	C=O	C=O	C=O	CH₂OH
HCOH	HOCH	HCOH	HOCH	C=O
HOCH	HCOH	CH₂OH	CH₂OH	CH₂OH
HCOH	HOCH	d-glyceraldehyde	l-glyceraldehyde	Dihydroxyacetone
HCOH	HOCH			
CH₂OH	CH₂OH			
D-glucose	L-glucose			

$$\begin{array}{ccccc} \text{I} & \text{II} & \text{III} & \text{IV} & \text{V} \\ \text{H} & \text{H} & \text{H} & \text{H} & \\ \text{C=O} & \text{C=O} & \text{C=O} & \text{C=O} & \text{CH}_2\text{OH} \\ \text{HCOH} & \text{HOCH} & \text{HCOH} & \text{HOCH} & \text{C=O} \\ \text{HOCH} & \text{HCOH} & \text{CH}_2\text{OH} & \text{CH}_2\text{OH} & \text{CH}_2\text{OH} \\ \text{HCOH} & \text{HOCH} & & & \\ \text{HCOH} & \text{HOCH} & & & \\ \text{CH}_2\text{OH} & \text{CH}_2\text{OH} & & & \end{array}$$

d-glyceraldehyde   l-glyceraldehyde   Dihydroxyacetone

D-glucose   L-glucose

Fischer formulae

I	VI	VII	VIII
H		H	H
$\overset{1}{C}$=O	$\overset{1}{C}H_2OH$	$\overset{1}{C}$=O	$\overset{1}{C}$=O
H$\overset{2}{C}$OH	$\overset{2}{C}$=O	HO$\overset{2}{C}$H	H$\overset{2}{C}$OH
HO$\overset{3}{C}$H	HO$\overset{3}{C}$H	HO$\overset{3}{C}$H	HO$\overset{3}{C}$H
H$\overset{4}{C}$OH	H$\overset{4}{C}$OH	H$\overset{4}{C}$OH	HO$\overset{4}{C}$H
H$\overset{5}{C}$OH	H$\overset{5}{C}$OH	H$\overset{5}{C}$OH	H$\overset{5}{C}$OH
$\overset{6}{C}H_2OH$	$\overset{6}{C}H_2OH$	$\overset{6}{C}H_2OH$	$\overset{6}{C}H_2OH$
D(d)-glucose	D(l)-fructose	D(d)-mannose	D(d)-galactose

the other formula (formula II) is represented as the mirror image of formula I. The first formula corresponds to the D-sugar, not necessarily because it may rotate the plane of polarization to the right, but rather because it can be degraded to, or built up from, the simplest molecule which represents an aldo-sugar, namely, the triose glyceraldehyde. At this point an arbitrary choice was made, namely, that the glyceraldehyde (represented by formulae III and IV) which rotates the plane of polarization to the right has its hydroxyl on the carbon atom next to the carbinol carbon written as though it were on the right-hand side of the molecules (formula III). Thus the dextrorotatory glyceraldehyde became the prototype of a family of D-sugars all of which can be derived from, or degraded to, D(d)-glyceraldehyde. Thus the arrangement of the groups around the carbon next to the carbinol group distinguishes a sugar as belonging either to the D or L family of sugars.

For all practical purposes the important carbohydrates of plants belong to only one of the two great families of sugars—that is, they are D-sugars in the generic sense—and their effect on the plane of polarized light, i.e., their optical rotation, can then be designated by using the lower case d or l (or + and −). Thus, at the outset, it is recognized that nature has elaborated its carbon compounds by utilizing approximately half of the various chemical possibilities that exist.* But there are also some other simplifications.

Under formulae of the type shown in formula I above, there are a minimum of 16 aldehyde-hexose sugars, but for all practical purposes plants utilize and elaborate upon only three of these; namely, glucose (formula I), mannose (formula VII), and galactose (formula VIII). Another class of sugars, of which the parent substance is not glyceraldehyde but dihydroxyacetone (formula V), are the keto-sugars, in which the reducing group is a keto group, at the second carbon in the chain.

The most familiar keto-sugar is fructose or levulose (formula VI) (so-called because of its ability to rotate the plane of polarization to the left). Despite this strong levorotatory character it is, in the generic sense, a D-sugar in that it may be related to D-glyceraldehyde on the one hand and to D-glucose and mannose, with which it is interconvertible, on the other. Thus, out of all the possible aldo- and keto-hexoses, plants mainly elaborate upon four: D-glucose, fructose, mannose, and galactose. Of these four sugars, three are closely related in that they differ only in the configuration around the two carbon atoms, numbered 1 and 2 in the chain.

Similarity of chemical structure is also shown by similarity of biological function, for the three most closely related and naturally occurring sugars (D-glucose, fructose, and mannose) are those which are most readily fermented by wild yeasts.

Before considering further the molecular structure of carbohydrates one may relate it to problems of asymmetry in amino acids.

Molecular configuration of nitrogenous compounds. As the concepts of molecular asymmetry and chemical configuration are applied to the interpretation of the amino acids and proteins, many more possibilities arise. In proteins there is not merely a single, repeated building unit, like a hexose molecule as in starch or cellulose, but approximately 20 or more chemically different amino

---

* There are, however, some notable exceptions; ascorbic acid is classified as an L-sugar derivative, and L-arabinose also occurs. These are, however, somewhat special cases, for these 5-carbon L-sugar derivatives can be shown to originate from 6-carbon compounds which belong to the D family.

acids, each of which, like alanine (represented below), may exist in its D and L, or enantiomorphous, forms:

H   H

|

C — NH₂   C—CH₃

H₃C   COOH   H₂N   COOH

When these formulae are represented in space with correct atomic diameters and bond angles, the atoms appear more "close-packed" and the asymmetry of these molecules is emphasized (see Fig. 3–3).

How may the D and L configurations of the sugars be related to the conventions used for the enantiomorphous forms of the amino acids? If there is a preferential selection in nature for carbohydrates that belong to the D family, how is this structurally related to the equally pronounced preference for amino acids which have come to be labeled L? This relationship is purely one of nomenclature, because, preparatory to the union with nitrogen, the asymmetry of the α-carbon as it existed in the sugar is lost in the formation of a keto-acid (pyruvic acid in the case of alanine) which is the actual acceptor of the nitrogenous group. (Keto-acids constitute the "ports of entry for nitrogen" into organic combination.) Thus the preference for the D or L configuration of the amino acid may be ultimately determined by the same feature of organizational asymmetry in the living systems that also determines the preference for D- rather

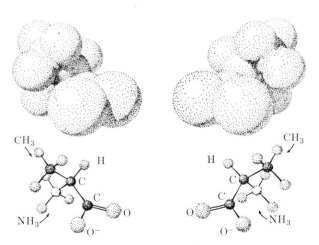

FIG. 3–3. The two molecular mirror images (or stereoisomers) of alanine: D-alanine (left) and L-alanine (right). Only amino acids of the L configuration are found in proteins. (From *General Chemistry*, Second Edition, by Linus Pauling. W. H. Freeman and Company, San Francisco. Copyright © 1953.)

than L-hexoses; But this consequence is not *direct* in the sense that the amino acid is being made from a D- rather than an L-sugar, the asymmetry of which is preserved in the configuration of the amino acid to which it gives rise. This may be illustrated in the case of the natural or L-alanine in the following series of formulae IX to XIII:

IX	X	XI	XII	XIII
COOH $\vert$ H_2N—C—H $\vert$ R	H $\vert$ C=O $\vert$ H—C—OH $\vert$ CH_2OH	COOH $\vert$ H—C—OH $\vert$ CH_3	COOH $\vert$ HO—C—H $\vert$ CH_3	COOH $\vert$ H_2N—C—H $\vert$ CH_3
Generalized formula for α-amino acid (α = carbon atom next to carboxyl)	D(+)-glycer-aldehyde	D(−)-lactic acid	L(+)-lactic acid	L-alanine

These show that the levorotatory form of lactic acid was found to correspond to D(+)-glyceraldehyde and it was therefore designated D(−), whereas it is the L(+)-lactic acid that stands in a direct relation to the naturally occurring alanine which, in this convention, becomes L-alanine.

It is true that nature has utilized mainly the amino acids of one family (L) to build proteins, for where D-amino acids occur infrequently in combination, the compounds often have unusual physiological properties like those of certain antibiotics (e.g., bacitracin, polymyxins, tyrocidins, subtilin, gramicidins, and certain penicillins). Even when amino acids are recognized in the peptides of certain structural constituents of bacterial walls, this need not detract from the generalization that proteins are built out of L-amino acids.

Asymmetric synthesis. The important general concept of asymmetric synthesis can be extended indefinitely as one proceeds from the simpler molecules like sugars and amino acids to more and more complicated molecules such as those of cellulose, starch, and protein, in which the ultimate carbon framework is nevertheless derived from sugar.

Apparently organic nature abhors symmetry, for all the important structures and molecules, and indeed even many organs and organisms, are asymmetric. Left-handedness and right-handedness are characteristics of the constituent molecules as of many of the structures they produce. In the chemical processes of unorganized systems there is equal tendency, statistically, to form both left- and right-handed members of an asymmetric pair. In plants or animals, these chemical reactions are directed to the formation, or utilization, of one asymmetric molecule to the virtual exclusion of the other. The requirement of statistical probability, which is more characteristic of chemical reactions in an inorganic world, is defeated in organisms because their organic nutrition occurs in a milieu which is already asymmetric.

Protoplasm is made up of proteins which are themselves highly asymmetric molecules since every α-amino acid has at least one asymmetric carbon. The proteins of cytoplasm and hence the enzymes (which are also proteins) furnish highly directed and asymmetric milieus for the chemical processes of life.

This fascinating train of thought should, however, be postponed. Nevertheless one may here note that Pasteur recognized the asymmetry of the crystals of the D- and L-tartaric acids, and this led to the first physical separation of such isomers by their crystalline form. It was the recognition of the nutritional dependence of organisms on one or other of the enantiomorphous forms that later led to methods for their separation which utilized the preference of a microorganism for one or the other of a pair of optical enantiomorphs.

Stereoisomerism and molecular architecture of the sugars and polysaccharides.   Other considerations dictate that the structure of hexose sugars is far more complicated even than is indicated by the formulae already shown (i.e., formulae I, VI, VII, VIII).

First, instead of four asymmetric centers in an aldohexose there must in fact be five, because there are more forms of glucose than are compatible with the formulae indicated above. This is explained by the formation of a ring including one oxygen atom, so creating a new asymmetric center at carbon 1 with the possibility of α- and β-forms of glucose, which exist as their stable compounds or glucosides (formulae XIV and XV). The phenomenon of muta-

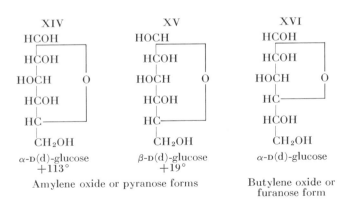

XIV
HCOH
HCOH
HOCH   O
HCOH
HC
CH₂OH
α-D(d)-glucose
+113°

XV
HOCH
HCOH
HOCH   O
HCOH
HC
CH₂OH
β-D(d)-glucose
+19°

XVI
HCOH
HCOH
HOCH   O
HC
HCOH
CH₂OH
α-D(d)-glucose

Amylene oxide or pyranose forms   Butylene oxide or furanose form

rotation shows that D-glucose can exist in the α-form with a specific rotation of +110° and in the β-form with a rotation of +19°; and their equilibrium mixture has a rotation of +52.5°. The convention is that α-glucose has the hydroxyls at carbons 1 and 2 on the same side of the molecule, whereas the β-compound has them on opposite sides. This increases the possible number of stereoisomeric aldohexoses to 32, but again we see that nature has utilized only a few of these possibilities; only a few of the possible molecules are compatible with biological organization. Certain enzymes selectively hydrolyze α-glucosides (e.g., the enzyme maltase), whereas others (e.g., emulsin) hydrolyze the β-glucosides.

But even these structural possibilities do not exhaust the stereoisomerism of sugar molecules with 6 carbon atoms. The recognition that there were even further isomeric possibilities arose when compounds of glucose were hydrolyzed and yielded forms of glucose which had unusual chemical properties. These forms were first called γ-sugars and their structure was explained in terms of rings of different size. The stable configuration of glucose is the form which includes 6 atoms in the ring, 5 carbons and 1 oxygen. (This was first called an amylene oxide ring, but is now more usually called a pyranose ring.) But glucose can also exist, though not in a form which is stable in the free state, in a form which contains a 5-atom ring, 4 carbons and 1 oxygen (see formula XVI). (This was first called a butylene oxide ring, but is now termed a furanose ring.)

By this device (i.e., the formation of both pyranose and furanose rings) the number of possible compounds is again increased by an additional factor of 2, but it is to be noted that again only a few of the possible compounds have been used in organisms.

To visualize the form of the sugar molecules, they are represented in their ring configurations, by analogy with the "parent" substances pyran and furan respectively, in such a way that the C—O rings are shown as if lying in a horizontal plane; the substituent groups are disposed above and below the plane of the ring. It is necessary here to identify the front, or forward edge, of the "lozenge-shaped" ring (represented by heavy lines) and to adopt a convention regarding the position of the oxygen in the ring.

Here the convention is to write the oxygen to the fore, although it is now often written to the rear.*

To transpose formula XIV to the Haworth pyranose-type formula, one may proceed as follows:

a) Number the carbon atoms in the ring 1 to 5 and represent these in the same orientation as formula XVII for pyran.

b) Imagine a person lying along the axis of the molecule from the head at 1 to the feet at 5, facing the oxygen atoms, so that the part then above the plane of the ring represents the right-hand side of the molecule (as in IX) and the part below the plane of the ring represents the left side of the molecule.

---

* In all these formulations the convention used is to represent the oxygen in the ring as though it is in the forefront of the molecule. (This was Haworth's original convention.) Many more recent authors and texts place the oxygen to the rear. Either convention is correct for the sugar molecule can, in effect, be rotated about its horizontal axis from carbon 1 to 6 without change.

c) The position of the carbinol (i.e., terminal CH_2OH) group is best represented as opposed (i.e., on the left) to the oxygen of the ring in formula XIV.

This then leads naturally to the formula for α-D(d)-glucopyranose which is
written as in formula XIX. The hydroxyls on carbons 2 and 3 must be represented above the ring, to correspond with formula XIV for D-glucose, and this
fixes the position of that on carbon 1 for the α-sugar, as shown in formula XIX.
Formula XX, which differs only in the orientation around carbon 1, now represents the β-form. Proceeding in a similar way one may write the formulae for
the α- and β-forms of D-glycofuranose.

To write the corresponding formulae for the α- and β-forms of fructose in
its pyranose and furanose states, one needs to remember that glucose and
fructose are interconvertible and that the orientation of the OH's at carbon 2
and other carbons in the ring may be written in the same way for fructose as
glucose: this leads to the formulae XXIV to XXVII for the four forms of
fructose.

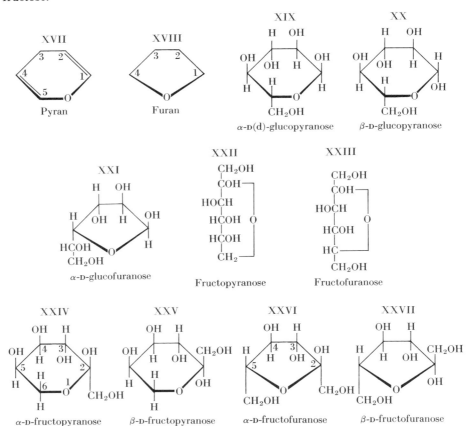

One may well ask why it should be necessary to dwell on what may seem to be the minutiae of the structure of these organic compounds; there is a reason, however. It is precisely these minute differences of molecular structure which identify key compounds within the architecture of the cell. Thus, an essential part of the understanding of growth is an appreciation of the construction of these and even more complicated molecular structures.

One very familiar substance (perhaps the most important ultimate carbon substrate) for the nutrition of a variety of heterotrophic cells is the compound sucrose, or cane sugar. On hydrolysis this yields glucose and fructose. Both of these are D-sugars, in the family or generic sense, although one (glucose) is strongly dextrorotatory and the other (fructose) is strongly levorotatory. The important distinction is that the glucose in sucrose is in the α-pyranose form, whereas the fructose in sucrose is in the β-furanose form. Since the conversion of the pyranose to the furanose form of sugars requires energy, and the reconversion of the furanose to the pyranose form releases energy, it becomes very apparent that sucrose does not merely furnish a stated number of carbon atoms but it furnishes those carbon atoms in configurations which have very special properties. Perhaps the great importance of sucrose lies in its ability to yield fructose, or, more important still, fructofuranose in the form of its 1,6-diphosphate. The molecular structure of cane sugar (sucrose) may be represented by the formulae XXVIII and XXIX.

XXVIII

Glucose   Fructose

XXIX

α-D-glucopyranose β-D-fructofuranose

It follows from the structure of carbohydrates that apparently very small differences of chemical configuration produce profound differences in the behavior of the substances in nature. Both starch and cellulose, on complete chemical hydrolysis, yield D-glucose; but the fundamental differences between these two complex polysaccharides are illustrated by the two formulae XXX and XXXI (given below) which show the arrangement of the atoms in space. The inertness of cellulose, as a structural component of plants, may be contrasted with the ease with which starch (composed of amylose and amylopectin) may be reincorporated into metabolism, after its temporary role as a storage product. Even so, the profound differences between the behavior of starch (e.g., amylose made up of α-D-glucopyranose units linked in 1,4 combination) and cellulose (β-D-glucopyranose units linked in 1,4 combination) seem due to relatively slight rearrangements of these molecules in space.

XXX

1,4-α-D-glucopyranoside (starch)

XXXI

1,4-β-D-glucopyranoside (cellulose)

A full understanding of starch as it occurs in plants is not conveyed even by the considerations outlined above. The molecular weight, the existence of branched chains (involving 1,4-glucose linkages), the forces that hold the parallel chains of glucose residues together, the presence of other substances in the lamellar configuration of the grain, are all part of this complex problem. Moreover there are factors still to be considered which determine the form of starch grains.

Although the essential building unit of cellulose is represented by formula XXXI, cellulose as it occurs in nature has properties which require still other considerations for their interpretation. The almost indefinitely long individual molecules of cellulose are held togther by firm chemical bonds, but they lie alongside other chains to which they adhere by forces that are less strong. The closer the parallelism of the fibrils, the more crystalline the cellulose, and in highly crystalline parts of the cell wall the minimum-sized cube which encloses enough to comprise all the properties of cellulose (the crystal lattice) is known—and has the dimensions 10.3 A $\times$ 8.3 A $\times$ 7.9 A. Strands of cellulose, 2 glucose residues long, run along the length of each edge of the cube; one other strand, which runs in the reverse direction, is at the intersection of the diagonals (Fig. 3–4). The picture is that glucose moieties are added enzymatically and indefinitely to the ends of these reversed cellulose chains (cf. Frey-Wyssling and Mühlethaler, 1965, p. 36). The discovery of the nucleoside diphosphate sugars (uridine diphosphate-D-glucose, i.e., UDP, and its analog guanidine diphosphate-D-glucose, i.e., GDP), stemming from the work of Leloir, provided evidence of the carrier molecules which mediate the enzyme incorporation of glucose into many complex carbohydrates. A bacterium (*Acetobacter xylinum*) utilizes UDP in the synthesis of a bacterial cellulose and in higher plants GDP is credited with this role. The complex of reactions which link hexoses from photosynthesis with the structurally important polysaccharides and pectins is shown in Table 3–1 from Gibbs (1966). But still other considerations are involved before one can fully interpret a cellulose cell wall.

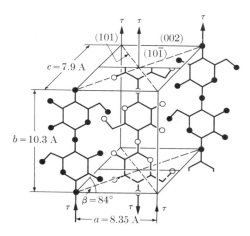

FIG. 3–4. Crystal lattice of native cellulose [*a*, unit cell (From Meyer and Misch, 1937); *τ*, two-fold helical axis (After A. Frey-Wyssling and K. Mühlethaler, *Ultrastructural Plant Cytology*, Elsevier, Amsterdam, pp. 325 and 228, 1965.)]

Biologists have long recognized the relationship between biological forms and their function, and chemists have long sought relationships between specific physiological actions and the chemical constitution of the active molecules. But there is now a deeper application of form at the molecular level, for what is often called submicroscopic morphology is now recognized even at the molecular level. The building of what may be called the architecture of each characteristic molecule, which organisms synthesize, and often also degrade, must comprise the unit steps by which biological growth occurs. It is, of course, a fundamental principle of science that each of these steps is chemically determined and explicable. Indeed, it may seem simple and adequate to say that sugar, glucose or sucrose, is a nutrient from which heterotrophic cells meet their requirements for carbon and carry out their growth. On chemical grounds such a statement does not do full justice to the orderly and prescribed and even beautiful way in which in nature carbon atoms are assembled in chains and rings, with hydrogens and hydroxyls disposed in a very precise manner, to form units which, as in starch or cellulose, are almost indefinitely repeated in space. While each unit event is to be comprehended solely in chemical terms, the overall sequence requires an organization, or milieu, in which to occur and a pattern by which

TABLE 3–1

Reactions connecting intermediates of the photosynthetic carbon cycle with carbohydrate synthesis in higher plants. Reactions designated "?" have not been established.

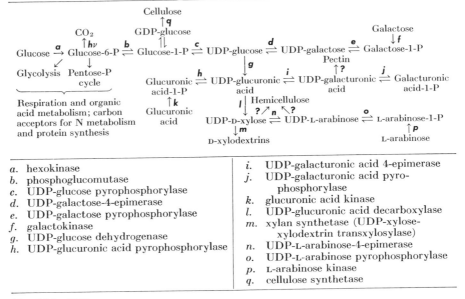

a. hexokinase	*i.* UDP-galacturonic acid 4-epimerase
b. phosphoglucomutase	*j.* UDP-galacturonic acid pyro-
c. UDP-glucose pyrophosphorylase	phosphorylase
d. UDP-galactose-4-epimerase	*k.* glucuronic acid kinase
e. UDP-galactose pyrophosphorylase	*l.* UDP-glucuronic acid decarboxylase
f. galactokinase	*m.* xylan synthetase (UDP-xylose-
g. UDP-glucose dehydrogenase	xylodextrin transxylosylase)
h. UDP-glucuronic acid pyrophosphorylase	*n.* UDP-L-arabinose-4-epimerase
	o. UDP-L-arabinose pyrophosphorylase
	p. L-arabinose kinase
	q. cellulose synthetase

After Gibbs, 1966

the design is prescribed. This may be represented by the small amount of starch which Hanes supplied to act as a template upon which glucose-1-phosphate could condense and the enzyme phosphorylase by which the reaction was brought about. The surface of the preformed starch and the structure of the enzyme represent the point of contact between the *in vitro* synthesis of this complex molecule and the features of the *in vivo* system in which that synthesis normally occurs. But a completely *de novo* synthesis of starch, with claims to be chemically self-sufficient should surely be able to dispense with enzymes for they, as proteins, are the prime examples of the way in which biological organization furnishes the milieu in which chemical syntheses occur according to a plan. It is the compounds which include nitrogen, therefore, that illustrate most dramatically the role which molecular architecture plays. One should visualize growth as the building of complex, often inherently improbable, structures, whose form prescribes their function, out of simple, randomly distributed substances.

Organizational aspects of photosynthesis: implications for carbohydrate metabolism. A full discussion of carbohydrates and their metabolism in plants is beyond the scope of this book (references may be made to a

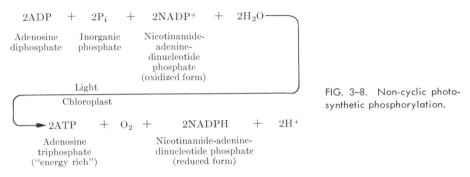

FIG. 3-7. Role of pyridine nucleotides in photosynthesis.

$$2ADP \quad + \quad 2P_i \quad + \quad 2NADP^+ \quad + \quad 2H_2O$$

| Adenosine diphosphate | Inorganic phosphate | Nicotinamide-adenine-dinucleotide phosphate (oxidized form) |

Light

Chloroplast

FIG. 3-8. Non-cyclic photosynthetic phosphorylation.

$$2ATP \quad + \quad O_2 \quad + \quad 2NADPH \quad + \quad 2H^+$$

Adenosine triphosphate ("energy rich")   Nicotinamide-adenine-dinucleotide phosphate (reduced form)

the work done with C^{14}-labeled substrates (Fig. 3–5). The involvement in photosynthesis, as in respiration, of phosphorylated compounds, by which the reactions are mediated, is well known. The use made in photosynthesis of many of the enzyme systems that function in respiration, both to pass the reduced carbon along its route to sugar and also to regenerate essential carrier molecules, is also now familiar (Fig. 3–6). The knowledge that photosynthesis develops reducing power by utilizing the versatility of the pyridine nucleotides which, with the appropriate enzymes, can either accept hydrogen from, or donate it to, other molecules, links light to an array of oxidation-reduction steps (Fig. 3–7). The fact that leaves contain and utilize an even more strongly reduced hydrogen transport system in the form of the heme compound ferredoxin has been more recently disclosed. A powerful concept emerged when it was seen that green leaves in the light can mobilize energy directly into a chemically usable form (as ATP) by photosynthetic phosphorylation (Fig. 3–8); therefore, green cells are not exclusively dependent on oxidative phosphorylation to harness energy after carbohydrate breakdown in respiration. Both cyclic and non-cyclic photosynthetic phosphorylation are known (Fig. 3–9).

The question arises whether the mechanisms of all these light-mediated steps are physically identical. Current views (Kok, 1965; Clayton, 1965) seem to accept two distinct light systems, which are designated Systems I and II. System II utilizes the shorter wavelengths and accomplishes the photolysis of water, as in the Hill reaction. System I, on the other hand, utilizes the longer wavelengths and, mediated by chlorophyll *a*, is concerned with the production of the reducing power (TPNH) that is needed to reduce carbon dioxide. It is in the coupling of Systems II and I in electron transfer (probably involving

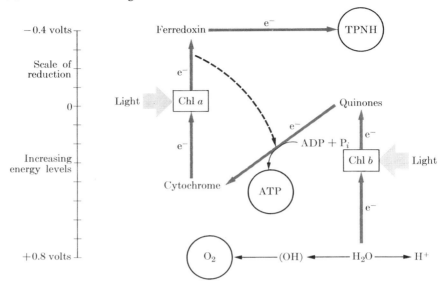

FIG. 3–9. Photosynthetic phosphorylation. Light expels electrons from chlorophyll *b* which are transferred to quinones. (The OH ions from water furnish electrons to replace those lost from the chlorophyll.) The electrons then flow to cytochrome, generating high-energy ATP. In a second light step, electrons are expelled from chlorophyll *a* and picked up by the carrier molecule ferredoxin which passes them on to TPN. The TPN then combines with a proton to yield TPNH. The electron pathway shown in the figure by the heavy arrow is involved in "non-cyclic phosphorylation." An alternative electron pathway, shown by the dotted arrow, denotes a "cyclic phosphorylation" without TPNH formation, as can be demonstrated *in vitro* with added artificial electron carriers. (After Arnon.)

the cytochrome *f* of leaves) that energy in the form of ATP is generated by photosynthetic phosphorylation. But the prime purpose of photosynthesis may still be seen as the conversion of light energy to chemical reducing power, as TPNH, and to usable energy, in the form of ATP. For every molecule of carbon dioxide reduced 2 TPNH and 3 ATP are required. However, the problem now is to localize all these diverse catalytic events in the organization of a chloroplast, for this is the organelle that permits them all to work together as a harmonious and integrated whole.

While estimates vary and controversy has raged around the normal and/or maximum energetic efficiency of the use of light, several safe comments may be made.

It is still true that a green leaf uses but a small part of its incident energy *directly* in photosynthesis; much is dissipated in other ways. Under steady state conditions in which photosynthesis is the prominent feature of the leaves in question, they seem consistently to require more than the reasonable minimum of the four mole quanta per mole of carbon dioxide reduced. In part, this is due to the fact that the system does not work in all its parts with 100 percent efficiency; of necessity, internal losses and frictions occur. In part this may be due to the fact that energy barriers and compartments need to be set up so that the successive steps work, as it were, independently and so that the products of a forward reaction are not immediately consumed in a backward degradative one. In so complicated a system there is room for divided opinions and even polemic controversy. But, in the final analysis, the polemics may have arisen as much from different ideas of the nature of the process whose efficiency is to be measured, as from disagreement on the value set upon that efficiency when calculated. Light clearly impinges upon the photosynthetic process at several points (Fig. 3–10) (it also affects cells in many other ways), and slower and dark reactions supervene to convert the light-activated products. It may, therefore, seem artificial to isolate and measure the efficiency of a single light-mediated photosynthetic step. Nevertheless, Warburg would have it that this can be done and he would assign a virtually 100 percent *maximum* efficiency to this one quantum-requiring step, recognizing that for every quantum so fixed it is necessary that the equivalent of three-quarters of the photosynthetic product needs to be chemically and oxidatively consumed to complete the reduction of the remnant to the oxidation-reduction level of sugar (CH_2O). Thus in four turns of such a cycle one molecule of carbon dioxide would be reduced. Although it may seem unrealistic to believe that one could so detach a single light-mediated step from all the other light reactions in the leaf, or to believe that any conditions that seem to do this have significance for photosynthesis in the field, nevertheless Warburg has declaimed that "in a perfect nature, photosynthesis is perfect too."

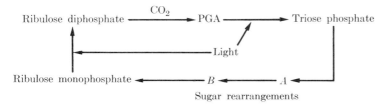

FIG. 3–10. Intervention of light in the carbon cycle. (After Gaffron, 1960; from Calvin.)

But what is lacking? Obviously the most important fact of all, namely, how to reconstruct a system which vies with green cells, or green leaves, in carrying out the process upon which the whole balance of nature depends. It is, indeed, one thing to explain a complicated process by a series of feasible integrated steps; it is quite another to reconstruct the system which carries them out in a controlled way. For this we are still essentially dependent upon green cells with chloroplasts, which exist as living, self-duplicating organelles in a complex cytoplasm, with an elaboration of structure and organization that can only be related incompletely to the processes they carry out (Figs. 3–4 through 3–10, Table 3–1). The best we can say is that it works *in vivo*. Although ever more optimistic estimates are being made of the efficiency of isolated chloroplasts to carry out photosynthesis, the fact remains that they only maintain their initial high rates for short periods of time. This is in marked contrast to their behavior in the leaf cells. Nor should it be forgotten that photosynthesis does not occur in a green cell in the light in physiological isolation, for the same cells at the same time may be, and usually are, engaged in protein synthesis and they may also, as they grow, participate by furnishing energy in such active events as water uptake and the internal secretion of salts and solutes into vacuoles.

Therefore, as one sees that more and more of the details of the formation of carbohydrates by photosynthesis become feasible, the more imperative is the need to define the organization within which the process occurs and how it functions *in vivo*. And the best way to obtain or recapitulate that organization is to permit it to grow!

Considering that the functions of chloroplasts can be reduced essentially to a few biochemical steps, their structure and ontogeny seem surprisingly complicated to achieve these ends, and remarkably little is known about the way their structure and function are related. Long known to be rich in lipid and protein, in addition to leaf pigments (chlorophyll *a* and *b*; the yellow pigments like carotenes and carotenoids), and to contain reducing systems capable of reducing silver nitrate, the chloroplasts still seemed remarkably homogeneous and free from internal structure so long as the light microscope was the preferred and sole means of investigation. The presence of subunits (grana) within a more continuous stroma became evident when the biochemical properties of isolated chloroplasts were tested on disrupted plastids. But the early speculations on the laminated ultrastructure of chloroplasts, with their layers of protein on which molecules of phospholipid are absorbed and between which chlorophyll and carotenoids are interspersed, hardly anticipated the wealth of form which the electron microscope now reveals.

Chloroplasts have a double boundary membrane and they are distinguished by an internal system of flattened sack-like vesicles (now termed thylakoids). Where the thylakoids are stacked compactly they constitute grana; where they traverse the stroma for the length of the chloroplast they represent stroma lamellae. In either event, each thylakoid has two boundary surfaces (of the order of 20 A) with a minute space (of the order of 35 A) between; within this hollow tube or sac is a larger clear space. By the use of appropriate staining techniques as applied to the chloroplasts which develop in totipotent cells from carrot root, it is possible to show the central cavity of the thylakoid either as electron dense (Fig. 3–11A) with the boundary surface transparent or, conversely, as transparent with the surfaces of the thylakoids electron dense

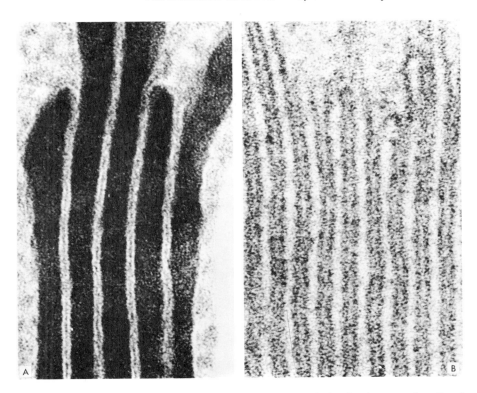

FIG. 3–11. Developing chloroplast in totipotent carrot cells in light, showing central cavity of thylakoid as electron dense (A), and as electron transparent with surfaces electron dense (B). (From Israel and Steward, *Ann. Botany* N. S. 31, 1–18, 1967.)

(Fig. 3–11B). From work on moss cells which regenerate into plants, Bell and Mühlethaler, supported by Frey-Wyssling, believe that chloroplasts originate from minute organelles called proplastids which are "budded off" from the outer surface of the nucleus (cf. Frey-Wyssling and Mühlethaler, 1965). The proplastid has a double outer membrane and encloses within itself some nuclear "groundplasm," presumably including enough DNA and RNA to provide for its own duplication. The inner membrane of the proplastid, corresponding to the inner surface of the nuclear envelope, is then held to invaginate and by progressive tangential development to build up the system of thylakoids as now seen in so many illustrations of mature chloroplasts. This origin of plastids from proplastids is held to be in sharp contrast to any supposed change of well-differentiated chromoplasts, as they might develop in the dark, into green chloroplasts. Nevertheless an ontogenetic study of chloroplasts in cultured carrot cells does show that pre-formed, dark-grown plastids transform themselves in the light into functional chloroplasts and, in so doing, they "spin out" their

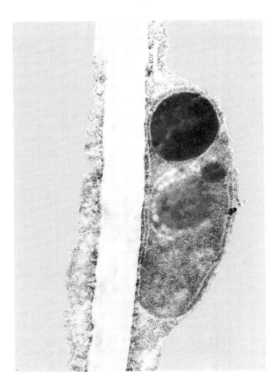

FIG. 3–12. A fully developed, dark-grown plastid in a cultured, totipotent carrot cell. This contains an electron dense, membrane-bounded *prethyla-koidal* body and a *globular center,* ringed by lipid droplets. (From Israel and Steward, *Ann. Botany* N. S. 31, 1–18, 1967.)

thylakoids from a large, dense, membrane-bound body which can be seen in the plastids before the grana and stroma lamellae appear (Figs. 3–12 and 3–13). This origin of thylakoids from a large "prethylakoidal" body is quite distinct from the supposed invagination of a surface originally continuous with the inner nuclear envelope. These two views are mentioned, however, not to press the one at the expense of the other, for the systems are quite different, but to emphasize the extent of morphogenetic development which produces a functional chloroplast within a cell. Nor is this all. The internal lamellar surfaces of chloroplastids are no longer regarded as smooth, but are supposed to consist of minute granules (100 to 200 A) in orderly array. These granules are called quantasomes and they have been thought to consist of four subunits. From the dimensions of the subunits it has been estimated that each could contain almost 8 protein molecules. Hence, if each quantasome were to have its maximum enzymic diversity and so to be capable of the maximum contribution to the known reactions of photosynthesis, one might postulate 32 distinct enzyme proteins per quantasome.*

* Later discussions of this concept questions both the size of the quantasomes and their function as the ultimate photosynthetic units, cf. *Brookhaven Symposia in Biology* No. 19, 1967.

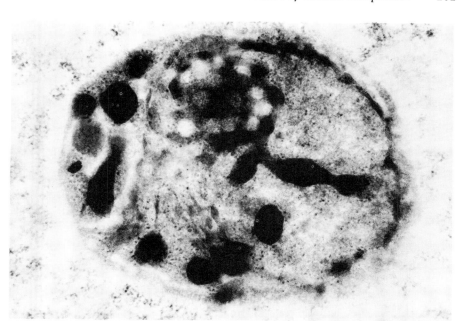

FIG. 3–13. Formation of thylakoids in light by spinning out the membranous material from the prethylakoidal body, as seen in dark-grown cultured carrot cells (cf. Fig. 3–12). (From Israel and Steward, *Ann. Botany* N. S. 31, 1–18, 1967.)

Enough has been said to emphasize that the mechanism of photosynthesis is only known in the sense that biochemically feasible unit reactions are known. Their relationship to the organization which alone permits the whole sequence to work in a controlled way can only be surmised. While the biochemical schemata (Figs. 3–5 through 3–9) may say how the process might occur, we cannot say how it does occur until we understand why it is so dependent upon the organization, the fine structure and the molecular architecture, that is only imperfectly described in Figs. 3–11 through 3–13. For these essential requisites we are still dependent upon the living chloroplast in the cytoplasm in which it is maintained and upon the cell in which it can grow and develop.

Organization and growth of a plant cell wall. All cellulose may be aptly represented chemically and for all practical purposes by the formula (XXXI) that has been indicated but, in organisms, cellulose exists in the form of long chains or fibrils, probably of indefinite length, held together along their length by the stable carbon-oxygen-carbon bonds. The units that are recognized as cellulose consist of bundles of these fibrils arranged in space in a characteristic, often parallel fashion. The strands or bundles of cellulose fibrils are held together, not by chemical bonds, but by physical forces and by the looser chemical linkages which are due to the asymmetry of the oxygen atoms and their ability to share hydrogen atoms with other molecules—that is, the well-known property of hydrogen bonding. Thus the ultimate unit of cellulose structure is a large one. Nägeli, the great 19th century botanist, recognized it as a micelle long before the true significance of this concept became clear.

There is, however, another essential point. In producing cellulose from sugar the cell builds not only the elaborate framework which is recognizable at the level of the light microscope, but it achieves these ends by events at the sub-microscopic level which are only now being understood. This may be illustrated in the formation of a cellulose wall at a naked protoplasmic surface such as an artificially induced sporeling of the marine coenocytic alga, *Valonia*, a member of the Siphonales. The following sequence of events can be traced.

The first-formed wall, or what might be called the primary wall, is secreted at the surface of a naked spherical protoplasmic globule; the protoplast utilizes sugar from the cytoplasm and builds it into long threads of cellulose which first appear at the surface in a tangled, felt-like mass. The expectation is that the sugar from which cellulose is made is donated in the form of uridine diphosphate glucose, commonly written UDPG, for this is the form in which glucose is rendered compatible in plants with many compounds with which it is to combine:

Uridine diphosphate glucose

The similar compound guanidine disphosphate glucose may play a similar role. A recent authoritative study of the enzymic synthesis of polysaccharides by preparations from cotton bolls is briefly reported by Barker and Hassid (1965). These authors started with the foreknowledge that C^{14} could be incorporated into cellulose by an enzyme system from mung beans if the donor of the C^{14}-glycosyl moiety was guanidine diphosphate-D-glucose. Curiously, the extent of this incorporation was increased in the presence of GDP-D-mannose, an effect attributed to the formation of another polysaccharide in these preparations. Since the cotton boll makes virtually pure cellulose, it is somewhat surprising that the same effect of GDP-mannose uniquely donates the glycosyl moiety to cellulose in a synthesis catalyzed by an enzyme system from cotton bolls. However, the problem does not end with the enzymic production of glucose-glucose links in cellulose. The most baffling problem remains in the formation of an organized cell wall.

The minimum strand of cellulose (the "elementary fibril" of Frey-Wyssling and Mühlethaler) which can be seen under the electron microscope is of the order of 30 to 35 A and this may comprise some 32 parallel cellulose chains. Commonly, however, cellulose is seen as fibrils (microfibrils) which are much coarser than this and are of the order of 100 A thick. Whenever cellulose appears at a first-formed (primary) cell wall the cellulose fibrils are arranged at random in a felt-like mass embedded in an amorphous matrix. The mystery is that, during the growth of the cell wall, this random arrangement gives way rapidly to an increasing degree of organization. Strands rearrange and show an increasing degree of parallelism, until sheets of cellulose fibrils are laid down in the form of strands which run parallel over most of their length. There is also an increasing degree of compact organization in the mature, or secondary, cell wall (Fig. 3–14 A, B, C, D). An almost identical situation has been described, with appropriate photographs, for the wall of the laticiferous system in *Euphorbia splendens* by Moor (1959). However, a further problem remains. Before a simple, almost spherical, sporeling of *Valonia ventricosa* (Fig. 3–15) can grow, it must become attached to the substratum and it then acquires polarity—that is, contrasted organization or growth along its axis. At the point of contact with the substratum, rhizoidal cells appear and, at its other extremity, the vesicle remains rounded and unbranched. For some reason yet to be explained, the cellulose layers which are now laid down as the wall thickens are produced in such a way that they wind around the cells spirally; periodically the spirals shift their direction through angles of approximately 120°. After three such shifts the original fibril direction may be, approximately, regained. These events are illustrated in a few selected pictures showing the development of the wall of *Valonia* (Fig. 3–14 D, E, F).

A very remarkable example that requires forces to direct the arrangement of microfibrils of cellulose in a developing cell wall is provided by the formation of bordered pits in conifer wood. These structures, precisely opposite in adjacent wood elements, possess a thickened torus that forms on each side of the middle lamella that separates the adjacent elements. Whereas the torus is more compact and less permeable, the periphery of the pit membrane is more open and permeable. The first formation of the bordered pit membrane (visible under the electron microscope) is on the radial longitudinal walls of the wood elements. As seen under the electron microscope it consists of arrangements of the cellulose fibrils in a ring to form the torus and in a more open radial arrangement to form the pores of the pit membrane (Fig. 3–16). This is a clear example of the way in which a morphogenetic stimulus provided by the juxtaposition of the developing wood elements mysteriously intervenes to determine the arrangement of cellulose fibrils in a wall. Less dramatically, the formation

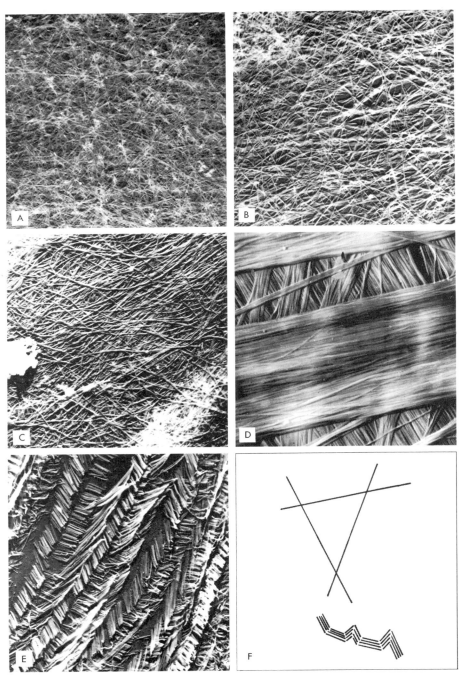

FIG. 3–14. The wall structure of *Valonia ventricosa*. A, B, C. The wall of the aplanospore, showing increasing degrees of order of parallelism (all ×12,000). D. The wall of a mature vesicle seen in surface view; note the three lamellae with directions at approximately 120° [cf. F] (×18,000). E. The wall of a mature vesicle seen in cross section (×9000). F. Diagram of the three lamellae visible in D. (From Steward and Mühlethaler, *Ann. Botany* N. S. 17, 295-325, 1953.)

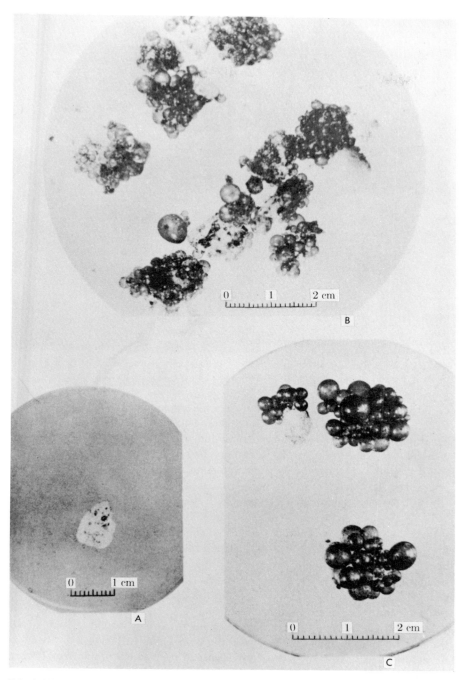

FIG. 3–15. Growth of plants from aplanospores. *Valonia ventricosa* growing on marble blocks. A. Sporelings at about six weeks from "sowing." B. Sporelings at about six months from "sowing." C. Sporelings at about 10 months from "sowing." (From Steward, 1939.)

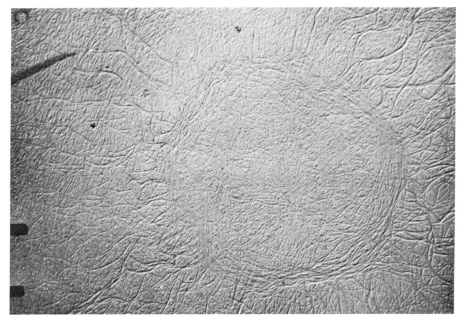

FIG. 3–16. Arrangement of cellulose fibrils in a developing bordered pit of *Pinus sylvestris.* (From A. Frey-Wyssling, *Die pflanzliche Zellwand.* Springer-Verlag, Berlin, 1959.)

of opposite simple pit fields, permitting plasmodesmata to connect adjacent living cells, determines the contrasting arrangement of cellulose fibrils near the simple pits (Fig. 3–17) and its more random arrangement over the rest of the cell wall. However, simple pit fields only form when cells develop in organic contact which is maintained by plasmodesmata, as may be shown by the culture of free cells and by contrasting the new inner transverse walls of cultivated cells which have plasmodesmata and pits with the external walls which do not (Fig. 3–17). (Also see Israel and Steward, 1966.) The shift from a random net-like arrangement of cellulose fibrils to the more parallel, and later spiral, arrangements as the cells grow still baffles explanation. This is even more true of the localized but highly oriented arrangements of cellulose fibrils which occur in the vicinity of bordered pits in wood or of simple pit fields in paren-chyma. The events of wall formation and the causal factors that impinge upon it during the growth of cells need, therefore, to be more accurately known. As yet, neither the attempts at mathematical interpretation of the growth of cell walls (Probine and Barber, 1965) nor the many observations on the structure of mature walls in relation to their physical and mechanical properties (Probine and Preston, 1962) convey a clear picture of how the development of the plant cell wall is biologically controlled.

Celluloses and also starches, as they exist in different organisms, differ, not so much in their chemical structure (as shown by their glucose-glucose

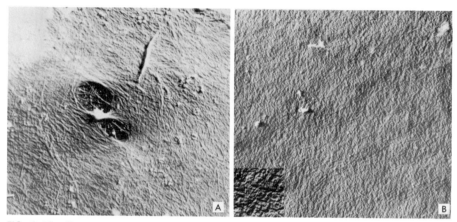

FIG. 3–17. Electron micrographs of cell walls of carrot in (A) explants of secondary phloem (×30,000) and (B) freely suspended cells (×20,400). Note pit fields with oriented cellulose fibrils in A and extremely uniform wall structure in B. (Inset: ×64,000.) (From work of Newman and Steward.)

linkages) as in their architectural configuration, which is determined by the way in which the fibrils or threads are laid down. Subtle differences can arise because the glucopyranose ring can be strained in different ways, giving "chair" or "boat" configurations to the molecule. When such forms combine to create fibrils they superimpose upon the strand other modifications which may be responsible for the characteristic properties of polysaccharides in different plants.

Thus organic nutrition supplies and utilizes the food to build the molecules that organisms need in all the subtleties of molecular architecture on which the properties of biologically important compounds depend. But organic nutrition should also be conceived as the conversion of sugar (from the reduction of carbon dioxide in photosynthesis) and of acceptable forms of nitrogen (from the reduction of nitrate) into biological form as cells and as organisms. This leads to morphological, as well as molecular, complexity (Chapter 5) and involves forces of different kinds and organization at different levels. Some organization depends upon the formation of firm chemical bonds; large aggregates may also be held together by van der Waal's forces, which operate over distances that obtain in thin films and in closely adjoining sheets of molecules. But there may be still other directing forces, whose nature is ill-understood, which permit relatively large units to be repeated in space in the growing organism, to be duplicated, and to be arranged in ways that can only be understood at present by the recognition that the organism and its cells are able to re-create pre-existing supra-molecular patterns. Though the nature of all this self-duplicating process is still one of the essential mysteries of life, it seems to be mediated by nucleic acid in the nucleus (i.e., DNA) or in any other self-duplicating organelle.

The constitution of proteins.   A protein molecule, formed by peptide linkages between its 20 or so constituent α-amino acids, possesses a far greater degree of inherent complexity at the level of its primary chemical configuration than exists in starch or cellulose.

Hydrolysis of proteins by acids may yield a mixture of the amino acids shown in Table 3–2. The molecular formulae, however, hardly convey the impression of the asymmetric form of these molecules which is seen in molecular models (cf. Snell *et al.*, 1965 pp. 64–68). In plant proteins, hydroxyproline has a more restricted distribution than in animals, where it is very prominent in structural proteins like collagen. The two sulfur amino acids cysteine and cystine may be regarded as interconvertible forms of one substance, and methionine exists in hydrolysates as its sulfoxide and sulfone. Thus there are 18 to 20 chemically different units which are united in protein by the firm peptide bonds between the amino groups of one molecule and the carboxyl of another:

$$\begin{array}{ccccc}
 & O & R_1 & H & \\
 & \| & | & | & \\
H & C & CH & N & H \\
\diagdown \, | \diagup & & \diagdown & \diagup \diagdown \, | \diagup & \\
C & & N & C & C \\
| & & | & \| & | \\
R & & H & O & R_2
\end{array}$$

Here R, R_1, and R_2 represent the residues of the constituent amino acids. Where these residues contain free carboxyl groups (as in aspartic and glutamic acid), the acids may also exist in the form of their amides, i.e., as combined asparagine and glutamine, the semi-amides of these dicarboxylic acids. Where the combined amino acids also contain free basic groups, as in lysine and arginine, these groups may combine with acidic substances. Where the amino acids also contain hydroxyl groups, as in serine and threonine, these groups may be esterified, as in combinations with phosphate. But the long central backbone of peptide-linked amino acids is only one feature of a protein molecule which may consist of parallel strands held together by crosslinks between the chains; alternatively, it may consist of a looped or contorted strand with a shape that is determined by cross-links between adjacent groups of the same chain. Disulfide bonds, formed when free SH groups are converted by oxidation to S—S links, are the prominent cross-linkages between protein chains (as in keratin), though phosphate bridges and hydrogen bonds also occur. However, the configuration of a protein is understood from the standpoint of its biological role only when one knows (a) the primary structure, in terms of the nature and arrangement of the amino acids that constitute the backbone of the molecule, and (b) the manner in which the protein chains so constituted are folded, contorted, or arranged, close-packed, in a configuration which constitutes the secondary or tertiary structure of the protein.

TABLE 3–2
The amino acids of proteins. The dicarboxylic acids, aspartic and glutamic, may also exist in proteins as their semi-amides.

Name	Symbol	R-group	Model
Glycine	Gly		
Alanine	Ala		
Valine	Val		
Leucine	Leu		
Isoleucine	Ileu		

From Snell, Shulman, Spencer, and Moos, 1965.

TABLE 3–2 (*continued*)

Name	Symbol	R-group	Model
Serine	Ser		
Threonine	Thr		
Phenylalanine	Phe		
Tyrosine	Tyr		
Tryptophan	Try		

TABLE 3–2 (*continued*)

Name	Symbol	R-group	Model
Cystine	(CyS)$_2$		
Cysteine	CySH		
Methionine	Met		
Proline	Pro		
Hydroxyproline	Hypro		

TABLE 3-2 (*continued*)

Name	Symbol	R-group	Model
Aspartic Acid	Asp		
Glutamic Acid	Glu		
Asparagine	Asp-NH$_2$		
Glutamine	Glu-NH$_2$		
Histidine	His		

Aspartic Acid (Asp):

$$\begin{array}{c} O \\ \parallel \\ {}^{-}O{-}C{-}CH_2{-}\overset{\displaystyle H}{\underset{\displaystyle \underset{+}{NH_3}}{C}}{-}\overset{\displaystyle O}{\underset{\displaystyle O^{-}}{C}} \end{array}$$

Glutamic Acid (Glu):

$$\begin{array}{c} O \\ \parallel \\ {}^{-}O{-}C{-}CH_2{-}CH_2{-}\overset{\displaystyle H}{\underset{\displaystyle \underset{+}{NH_3}}{C}}{-}\overset{\displaystyle O}{\underset{\displaystyle O^{-}}{C}} \end{array}$$

Asparagine (Asp-NH$_2$):

$$H_2N{-}\overset{\displaystyle}{\underset{\displaystyle O}{C}}{-}CH_2{-}\overset{\displaystyle H}{\underset{\displaystyle \underset{+}{NH_3}}{C}}{-}\overset{\displaystyle O}{\underset{\displaystyle O^{-}}{C}}$$

Glutamine (Glu-NH$_2$):

$$H_2N{-}\overset{\displaystyle}{\underset{\displaystyle O}{C}}{-}CH_2{-}CH_2{-}\overset{\displaystyle H}{\underset{\displaystyle \underset{+}{NH_3}}{C}}{-}\overset{\displaystyle O}{\underset{\displaystyle O^{-}}{C}}$$

Histidine (His):

$$\begin{array}{c} HC{=}C{-}CH_2{-}\overset{\displaystyle H}{\underset{\displaystyle \underset{+}{NH_3}}{C}}{-}\overset{\displaystyle O}{\underset{\displaystyle O^{-}}{C}} \\ | \quad\quad | \\ N \quad\ NH \\ {\diagdown}\ /\ \\ C \\ | \\ H \end{array}$$

TABLE 3–2 (concluded)

Name	Symbol	R-group	Model
Arginine	Arg		
Lysine	Lys		

For Arginine:

$$H_2N\!-\!\overset{\displaystyle H_2N}{\underset{+}{C}}\!-\!NH\!-\!CH_2\!-\!CH_2\!-\!CH_2\!-\!\overset{H}{\underset{\underset{+}{NH_3}}{C}}\!-\!\overset{O}{\underset{O^-}{C}}$$

For Lysine:

$$H_3\overset{+}{N}\!-\!CH_2\!-\!CH_2\!-\!CH_2\!-\!CH_2\!-\!\overset{H}{\underset{\underset{+}{NH_3}}{C}}\!-\!\overset{O}{\underset{O^-}{C}}$$

When a protein is distributed as a surface film, floating as it were on water at a water-air interface, its "backbone"

$$\overset{NH}{\underset{CO}{}}\underset{CH}{\overset{}{}}\overset{CO}{\underset{CH}{}}\underset{NH}{\overset{}{}}\overset{CH}{\underset{CO}{}}$$

lies in, or on, the surface. When protein spreads to its maximum area, it occupies approximately 1 m^2 per mg. In this condition the thickness of the film corresponds to the known dimensions of the "backbone" (9.8 A). The film, however, may be held together by cross-linkages between the protein chains, which are weaker than firm chemical bonds. This is protein in a so-called β-configuration. However, when a protein comes off such a surface, its configuration may change. Its long chains do not remain straight, but may become more or less coiled, or wrinkled. A stable, or α-configuration, is widely found to be the protein chain wound around an axis in helical form and, since spirals have left-handedness and right-handedness, the right-handed α-helix is found to be a common state of affairs, as described by Low and Edsall (1956). Thus the nitrogen compounds, and proteins in particular, like the natural carbohydrates, are characterized by a degree of order, structure, and asymmetry which both contribute to, and are the consequence of, the biological environment in which they are formed.

The nucleic acids.   In relation to the nucleic acids the importance of molecular architecture and asymmetric synthesis is very apparent, for, to quote a now familar phrase by Crick (1957), "if the proteins are the principal stuff of life, the nucleic acids are its blueprints." The nucleic acids appear to possess (in the case of DNA) the key to their own self-duplication and to the production of a characteristic pattern of RNA and/or protein molecules. In DNA along a backbone chain composed of sugar (deoxy-D-ribose)-oxygen-phosphate-oxygen-sugar-oxygen-phosphate groups four nitrogen bases, two purines (adenine and guanine), and two pyrimidines (thymine and cytosine) are distributed by attachment to the sugar residue. The number of possible arrangements of such bases along strands that may comprise some 200 nucleotide residues is obviously very large indeed.

It has also been found that the nucleic acid of the nucleus (DNA) is a highly asymmetric structure, for it is conceived to be in the form of a double spiral in which the sequence of bases along one thread, or coil, is matched by a complementary sequence along the other thread of the pair. Hydrogen bonds link complementary points of these spirals, i.e., adenine to thymine, guanine to cytosine (Watson and Crick, 1953). It was also visualized that the two chains of DNA "fit together as a hand fits into a glove" and, when separated, "the hand then acts as a mold for the formation of a new glove, while the glove acts as a mold for a new hand." We have here a supreme example of the fact that, in nature, syntheses occur in an asymmetric environment determined by the "molecular architecture" of the substances which, by their catalytic power, direct the course of synthesis.

Thus the important molecules which form the more structural compounds of organisms, which used to be regarded as non-crystalline or colloidal in nature, are now recognized to have the internal molecular, orderly structure which was previously regarded as the essential characteristic of the crystalline state. This underlying orderliness of structure was first recognized by the technique of X-ray diffraction. At an even higher level of organization, order may now also be recognized with the electron microscope and, at this level, one may see that even the best chemical descriptions of large molecules (e.g., cellulose) are still not adequate to describe such substances fully so that one may appreciate what is involved both in their formation and in their function *in vivo*. Before discussing these points, however, a still more detailed knowledge is needed of the chemical configuration of the molecules in question.

Organic Nutrition for Growth: The Nitrogenous Compounds, the Accessory Growth Substances, and the Organized Milieu

Nitrogen compounds in nutrition: proteins and protein synthesis.
The carbohydrates and their use in nutrition have been cited to show the range of problems to be faced when considering even the use of carbon compounds in

growth. For most plant cells the carbon requirements of metabolism and growth are satisfied by direct access to the hexose sugars glucose or fructose, or by indirect access to them in the form of their sugar phosphates, which may be derived from sucrose or starch as available, energy-rich, storage carbohydrates. But what are the requirements for nitrogenous compounds?

By contrast with animals, plant cells are able to utilize inorganic nitrogen sources (namely nitrate or ammonia), though if furnished exogenously with organic forms of nitrogen these can often be used. Many saprophytic and parasitic organisms, which are obviously plants, do this habitually or even preferentially. The reduction of nitrate (mediated by enzymes that utilize molybdenum in their structure), or the conversion of ammonia to organic forms of nitrogen (which may be independent of molybdenum though requiring manganese), may occur preferentially in certain regions of the plant body. These events occur often in roots and commonly in green leaves. The entry of nitrogen into organic combination is negotiated via the carbon compounds known as α-keto acids, of which three have long been recognized, namely, pyruvic acid, oxaloacetic acid, and α-ketoglutaric acid. Whether these keto acids combine with ammonia, or with some other reduced form of nitrogen, such as hydroxylamine, to form

$$R.C{=}N.OH$$
$$|$$
$$COOH$$

oximes which can also be reduced, amino acids readily arise. From the three keto acids mentioned, functioning as "ports of entry" for nitrogen, the amino acids alanine (from pyruvic acid), aspartic acid (from oxaloacetic acid), and glutamic acid (from α-ketoglutaric acid) are formed. However, it is now known that many other keto acids occur in plants (e.g., glyoxylic and oxalosuccinic acids) and many corresponding amino acids, some of which never appear in protein, also exist (cf. a recent summary by Steward and Durzan, 1965).

From the first-formed amino acids (aspartic acid, glutamic acid, and alanine) others arise by the group transfer reactions known as transaminations, by which an amino group is enzymically transferred from an α-amino acid (like glutamic acid) to a keto acid. Thenceforward, a great array of metabolic reactions occur and these culminate in the eventual synthesis of protein. Although most plant cells readily utilize nitrate or ammonia, together with carbon compounds derived from sugar, to manufacture protein and protoplasm they can, and commonly do, utilize certain "nitrogen-rich" storage and translocatory forms of nitrogen as the source from which protein is made. Among these latter substances, the commonly occurring soluble nitrogen compounds of plants are important.

While the range of known soluble, non-protein, nitrogen compounds in plants has been greatly extended since the use of paper chromatography, the substances recognized by Pfeffer, Schulze, and Prianischnikov during the late

19th century are still important. Among these were the amides asparagine and glutamine, the basic guanido-compound arginine, and some free amino acids. When supplied to cells exogenously, these substances can often replace the requirement for nitrate and ammonia; in fact, a common device in the aseptic culture of heterotrophic cells, or organisms, is to furnish organic nitrogen in the form of a protein hydrolysate such as casein hydrolysate.

Knowledge about proteins and their synthesis developed slowly, but has gathered momentum in recent years. The 1902 polypeptide hypothesis of Emil Fischer led to the view that amino acids could form protein by elimination of water to make a succession of peptide bonds between the α-amino group of one acid and the carboxyl group of another. In this way synthesis was regarded as the reverse of hydrolysis. As in the case of the carbohydrates, however, the hydrolysis is essentially irreversible and our knowledge of protein synthesis had to await knowledge of the role of the phosphorus compounds. Phosphorylated compounds convey respiratory energy to a given site and incorporate it into a given molecule or reaction. The compounds in question exist in the form of certain energy-rich phosphoric anhydrides, which are more stable in the cell than anhydrides would otherwise be expected to be, because they exist as complexes (e.g., adenosine triphosphate, ATP; guanidine triphosphate, GTP; uridine phosphates, UTP, etc.). These substances have been aptly termed the "energy currency" through which energy-requiring transactions may be negotiated.

Thus any viable, non-senescent plant cells may synthesize protein. To do this they need access, either exogenously or endogenously, to suitable carbon compounds (derived from sugars) and to acceptable forms of nitrogen (derived from inorganic sources or furnished as nitrogen-rich compounds in which reduced nitrogen is present in substances like the amides.) To synthesize protein, however, more organization is needed. Certain organelles (e.g., ribosomes) provide the surfaces upon which the protein synthesis occurs; the nature of the template surface which acts like a mold for the synthesis of the protein is prescribed by the kind of transient ribonucleic acid, designated as mRNA, which it receives; the amino acids, when fabricated from the organic and inorganic nutrients mentioned, need to be mobilized at the template surface in an acceptable form, and the energy to form the peptide bonds that link the amino acids together is donated by the phosphorylated compounds (ATP) that are produced by respiratory breakdown of sugar. Granted all this, the current concepts of proteins and their synthesis may now be summarized.

Each protein has its own characteristic linear arrangement of amino acids along the polypeptide chain. Some specialized and well-purified proteins, such as hemoglobin, insulin, myoglobin, and certain enzymes (ribonuclease), have yielded to special study and have provided the basis for this knowledge (Fig. 3–18).* So far, plant proteins have not been studied intensively enough in this

---

* The configuration of the active site of ribonuclease, a very important enzyme, is now yielding to further investigation (Kartha *et al.*, 1967).

TABLE 3–3

The Genetic-Code Dictionary lists the code words that correspond to each of the 20 common amino acids, assuming that all the words are triplets. Although many of the amino acids have more than one code word, it is believed that each triplet codes especially for a particular amino acid. However, it is now admitted that there is considerable "degeneracy" of the code, by which the "language" is "blurred." For a recent treatment of this subject see Cold Spring Harbor Symposia for Experimental Biology, Vol. XXVIII, *Synthesis and Structure of Macromolecules*, 1963. Also see Nirenberg, 1963.

Amino Acid	RNA Code Words				
Alanine	GCC	GCU	GCA	GCG	
Arginine	CGC	CGA	CGU	CGG	AGG
Asparagine	AAC	AAU			
Aspartic acid	GAU	GAC			
Cysteine	GUU				
Glutamic acid	GAA	GAG			
Glutamine	CAA	CAG			
Glycine	GGU	GGC	GGA	GGG	
Histidine	CAU	CAC			
Isoleucine	AUU	AUC	AUA		
Leucine	CUA	CUU	UUA	CUC	CUG
Lysine	AAA	AAG			
Methionine	AUG				
Phenylalanine	UUU	UUC			
Proline	CCC	CCU	CCA	CCG	
Serine	UCU	UCC	UCG	UCA	
Threonine	ACC	ACA	ACU	ACG	
Tryptophan	UGG				
Tyrosine	UAU	UAC			
Valine	GUU	GUC	GUA	GUG	

bonds. And again, having done so, how and why do they vacate the template surface to allow it to be reoccupied as a new molecule is made? The so-called genetic code (or the languages of the genes) specifies the number (3) and sequence of nitrogen bases which make each sRNA complex specific for each amino acid. This "code" is summarized in Table 3–3, and concepts of the overall scheme are summarized diagrammatically in the accompanying chart (Fig. 3–20).

Progress in the rapidly moving field of study concerned with the elucidation of the genetic code, i.e., the relationships between the structure of polypeptides and of the ribonucleic acids by which their synthesis is mediated, can best be seen by the third article on this subject published in *Scientific American* (Crick, 1966). The three-base combination on the messenger RNA that corresponds to a given amino acid is called a "codon," and the corresponding sequence on the sRNA by which it is recognized is an "anticodon." Incidentally, the structure of specific sNRA's, e.g., the one for alanine (Holley, 1966) elucidates the three bases by which the alanine specificity is determined. The distinctive four-letter alphabet of the mRNA language comprises letters (i.e., bases) which correspond to others in the language of the DNA: A (adenine), G (guanine), T (thymine),

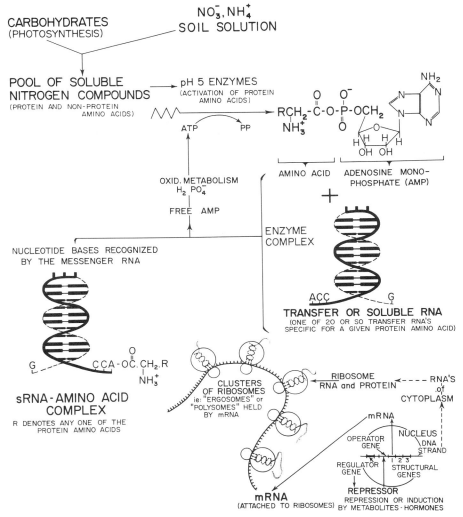

FIG. 3–20. A schematic representation of current views on protein synthesis as visualized in molecular terms and utilizing ideas drawn from the study of bacteria and of cell-free systems. It comprises a synthesis of the views on (1) amino acid activation and recognition by specific enzymes, (2) the transfer of amino acids by sRNA and their location at specified points on a ribosome template surface, (3) the genetic (DNA) control over the nature of the template surface via mRNA, and (4) the carrying by mRNA, by a linear sequence of bases in triplets (each specific for an amino acid), of the information to arrange the protein amino acids in the linear order in which they are bound. Attention should be focused on the broad principles involved rather than upon the detail of the individual schematic diagram (e.g., of the nature of sRNA or the precise relations of mRNA to the ribosome and to the genetic apparatus), for these may well be subject to change in this rapidly moving field. (From F. C. Steward and D. Durzan, in Steward (ed.), *Plant Physiology, A Treatise*, Vol. IVA. Academic Press, New York, 1965.)

C(cytosine) in DNA correspond to, and give rise to, U (uracil), C (cytosine), A(adenine), and G (guanine) in the RNA. As shown in Table 3–3, it was concluded that each amino acid messenger word, which sufficed to locate a given amino acid in a protein, was composed of three letters ("the triplet code"). Knowing that four letters arranged there at a time will compose 64 sequences, the recent work attempts to be more precise concerning the role of each of the 64 possible base combinations. The progress described by Crick (1966) has only been possible by confining attention to microorganisms and by substituting for the evidence of true protein synthesis that which is derived from studying the binding of amino acids from sRNA-AA complexes on columns which contain ribosomes. The 64 combinations fall into 16 groups of 4, each of which has the same two first letters: e.g., CCU, CCC, CCA, CCG (all of which code for proline); or ACU, ACC, ACA, ACG (all of which code for threonine). In seven of the 16 cases the relationship between the first *two* bases of the triplet and the amino acid for which they code is absolute and unambiguous. In these cases all combinations of bases, which include the first two, code for the single specifiable amino acid—this accounts unequivocally for 28 out of 64 possible "codons." Leucine, proverbially good for protein-labeling studies, exhibits a relationship to two types of "codon," with initial letters which may be either UU or CU. Other amino acids share their relationship to the first two bases of their codons but are specific for the third: e.g., GAU, GAC = aspartic acid; GAA, GAG = glutamic acid, though their respective amides differ more widely; AAU, AAC = asparagine N; CAA, CAG = glutamine N.

Thus there is mounting evidence, much of it indirect, concerning the way chemical information may be mobilized to direct the unit reaction steps that are involved in protein synthesis. Nevertheless, cells are still necessary to make proteins in bulk, and there is much still to be learned about the way the ribosomes work and how the physiological control, as distinct from the genetic control, of protein synthesis is achieved.

The nature of a protein molecule and the features which determine its biological activity or role, also involve some other properties. The amino acid sequence represents the primary structure, but the folds and coils in the chain, and the unrolled or globular nature of the protein, represent the secondary and tertiary structures. Cross-linkages between amino acids such as the sulfur amino acids (held together by S—S bonds) and linkages maintained by hydrogen bonds may give to the protein a complex geometrical form. The specific role of a protein, whether it acts as an enzyme or in some other way, may depend upon some very subtle combination of groups in space that will be determined as much by the folding and coiling of the molecule as by the linear arrangement itself. The well-known example of myoglobin is a case in point (Fig. 3–21).

Thus the long journey of plant nutrition, insofar as it concerns nitrogen, supplied initially as nitrate or ammonia, culminates in the making of protein molecules which have a highly specific amino acid sequence and a highly ordered

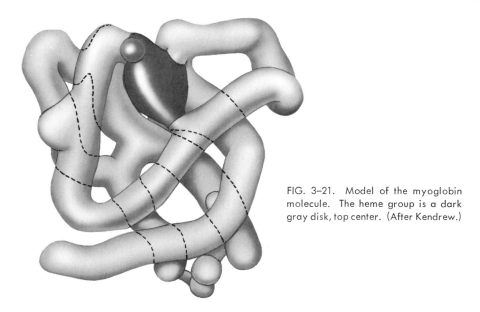

FIG. 3–21. Model of the myoglobin molecule. The heme group is a dark gray disk, top center. (After Kendrew.)

geometry. Every cell which grows can do all this, and it is a requirement of its nitrogen autotrophic or heterotrophic nutrition to furnish both the necessary raw materials, the enzymes, energy source, and the highly asymmetric directing milieu in which these innumerable but complex syntheses can take place. When one contemplates the vast number of protein molecules within a single cell (of the order of 10^9) and the great complexity of any one molecule, one begins to appreciate the tremendous problem of chemical logistics which growth presents. In fact one is led to pose the question why such elaborate protein molecules had to be made to act as the enzymes that catalyze what often seems to be such relatively simple acts—such acts, in fact, as the addition or removal of H, the addition or removal of water or phosphate, or the transfer of small groups from one site to another. These acts are indeed the very basis of cellular metabolism. Though the acts so performed may in themselves be relatively simple, their catalysis by such elaborated, highly specific, and seemingly improbable structures enables these essential reactions of living cells to be made to go, or not to go, in a rigorously controlled and highly directed manner. The essential conservatism of the cell's biochemistry is, in fact, linked to the specialized catalysts that make the reactions go. In this context, F. F. Blackman's description (1905) of the cell as a "congeries of enzymes, a honeycomb of catalytic agents, as many in number as there are cell functions, and each capable of being isolated . . ." takes on a new meaning in terms of the molecular structure of proteins and enzymes.

Although much has rightly been made of the structure of the DNA in the determination of all these events, it is not *of itself* the whole story. Apart from the environment of the living cell, pure DNA is merely a long fibrous molecule which is no more "alive" than a thread of nylon. It is no more capable of replicating itself, or yielding RNA, or determining protein synthesis than is a tape recording of a symphony capable of a replay without the sound-producing mechanism. It is true that virus protein is made by a specific nucleic acid, but for all practical purposes this occurs *only in the environment of the cell.* Therefore, the course of organic nutrition is not merely determined by the sources furnished, for it is intimately a function of the organized system which is nourished and which can grow. In fact, while paying due tribute to the achievements of what is often called molecular biology, one should recognize that all its essential steps and reactions are enzyme-catalyzed. Therefore, when one starts with an enzyme, preformed, one is already presupposing a substance which is itself the product of a highly organized, asymmetric system which as yet cannot be created *de novo.* Molecular biology has not yet escaped from the mystery of biological organization; it has consciously or unconsciously exploited it, while describing the events of growth in molecular terms.

Accessory substances: vitamins and hormones.   Sources of inorganic salts, carbon, and nitrogenous "building blocks" are, however, not always enough. In the entire organism certain cells, such as those of the green leaf exposed to light and those of growing apices, elaborate substances other than those that are needed in bulk, but which play an essential part in nutrition. These are the accessory substances which fall into two obvious categories; namely, the vitamins and the hormones. In fact, for some growth-regulating substances neither of these categories is wholly appropriate.

The terms "vitamin" and "hormone" were both derived from animal physiology. The vitamins, discovered in this century, were the accessory growth substances without which an ostensibly complete nutrient medium consisting of carbohydrate, fat, essential amino acids, and salts would not suffice for the growth of higher animals. After the discovery of such substances, like the vitamin A now known to be formed from carotene, many others have been found.

Essentially, however, a vitamin is a substance not elaborated by the organism itself and which is necessarily furnished exogenously in a diet of nutrient medium. A vitamin is not required in bulk, but only in catalytic amounts, for it plays a regulatory role rather than that of a nutrient in bulk. Many such vitamins are now known, as for example: vitamin B_1 (thiamine), vitamin B_2 (riboflavin), vitamin B_6 (pyridoxine), vitamin C (ascorbic acid), etc. These substances, especially when water soluble, are now known to be organic molecules which often act as cofactors, or coenzymes, in essential enzyme systems, and, though the organism may build up the protein moiety of the enzyme, it may be quite unable to manufacture the coenzyme without which the enzyme system cannot function.

The hormones are, however, in a different category of accessory substance, for they are essentially molecules manufactured by the organism but at strictly localized sites—often in the ductless glands of the animal body. When the hormones are secreted into the blood stream, "action at a distance," as it were, results. However, hormones produce effects on the overall growth and nutrition of the organism far out of proportion to the small number of catalytically active molecules which are involved. The term "hormone," proposed by Bayliss and Starling in 1904, is often said to mean a chemical messenger—a sort of "chemical Paul Revere." The true derivation, however, is even more suggestive, for the word "hormone" is derived from the Greek word *hormao* which strictly means "I arouse or incite into activity." In other words, in Starling's usage the emphasis was not strictly on the *messenger* but rather on the nature and outcome of the *message*. Moreover, the particular Greek verb in question was used in contexts such that it often denoted the kind of activity that was aroused at a port when the instruction came to a ship to set sail and embark upon a voyage. Familiar examples of hormones in the animal body are the following: thyroxine from the thyroid gland, adrenaline from the adrenals, testosterone from the testes, estrogen from the ovaries, etc.

Characteristically, then, vitamins and hormones, each of which produces profound effects on the growth and nutrition of the organism, each of which is active in minute and catalytic amounts, have essential points of difference. The vitamins are exogenous and are required in the diet of the higher animal, while its hormones are produced internally. Whereas the vitamins often have effects of a more general nature, usually diagnosed by overall effects on the morphology of the organism and its overall growth, the hormones are much more specific in their action and tend to promote one particular reaction, often at a particular or target site. In plants, with their very different organization, there are reasonable equivalents for both vitamins and hormones and, perhaps unfortunately, both terms have been applied in the terminology of plant nutrition and growth.

Many roots, excised from the plant body, are unable to grow continuously in what would seem to be complete nutrient media without the addition of yeast extract. The active agent in the yeast extract is now known to be vitamin B_1, or thiamine. Thiamine is no doubt manufactured in the intact plant, although not in the roots—at least, the root requires essentials derived from the shoot. Thiamine is well known to be an active component of certain enzyme systems, particularly the enzymes that catalyze carboxylation and decarboxylation. So far as the isolated root system is concerned, therefore, the requirement for thiamine is of an obvious vitamin-like nature; although, as far as the entire plant body is concerned, thiamine formed in one place may act at another in a manner similar to that of a hormone. Nevertheless, thiamine is commonly recognized as a vitamin in plants. Among the bacteria and fungi a great variety of nutrient requirements of this general kind are known. In fact, fungi and bacteria with natural, or artificially induced, requirements for vitamins are among the most favored organisms used for the laboratory assay of known vitamins, and for the detection of new ones.

The catalytic substances that stimulate the responses of phototropism and geotropism act through cell enlargement at a distance from their point of formation. Then the substances known as auxins, of which indoleacetic acid is the prime example, have been recognized as the botanical equivalent of the hormones. Although some suggestions have been made, there is no unequivocal example in which indoleacetic acid plays a part in an enzyme in the manner known for most vitamins. Indeed, in retrospect, certain features of the role of such auxins as indoleacetic acid imply differences in the way the hormone concept should apply to plants and to animals.

As noted above, the effects of most hormones in the animal body are extremely specific; this is perhaps a natural consequence of the early differentiation of the animal body into organs with highly specialized functions. In higher plants, the attributes of the entire organism persist to a much greater extent throughout the living cells of the plant body, as shown by the facts of regeneration and of vegetative propagation; thus extreme specificity of the so-called plant hormones is less obvious. The action of indoleacetic acid, which may be primarily upon cell enlargement, extends through a wider range of physiological and biochemical consequences than is commonly attributed to a hormone of the animal body. These effects include the plastic extension of the cell wall, the uptake of water, effects on the osmotic concentration of solutes in the vacuole, even a general stimulation of cellular activity which may culminate in growth by cell division. Auxins are also known to stimulate rooting where roots would not otherwise readily occur. All these effects (which are discussed in Chapter 4) imply a more generalized stimulation of biological activity than the classical concept of an animal hormone at first usually conveyed. In this sense facile comparisons between plant hormone systems and endocrinology in animals seem to be overdrawn.

With these reservations the terms vitamin and hormone will remain in the terminology of growth and plant nutrition, and we will recognize requirements of plants for organic substances which are not nutrients, in the sense that their carbon is not built into the structure of the cell, but, instead, play a catalytic role.

Still other categories of such catalytic substances may exist, for a variety of agents which promote cell growth are now being revealed. The activities of these substances seem to be focused more upon cell division than upon cell enlargement and more upon the kinds of syntheses, protein synthesis particularly, which the dividing cell requires. Indeed Went, one of the pioneers in work on the auxins, would extend his original concept to include a variety of the so-called caulines, which are endowed with organ-forming abilities: caulines for leaf formation, root formation, etc. The validity of this latter concept remains to be generally accepted. However, it is clear that we are now at a stage where it is necessary to recognize a number of highly active molecules in a special category of substances regulating growth or cell division. Some of these growth substances obviously occur naturally and act in the intact plant body, or organs (such as roots), which may be cultivated by the methods of tissue culture.

Nutrient requirements of cell, tissue, and organ cultures.   With great foresight, Haberlandt (1902) recognized the advantages that would acrue from the ability to cultivate single cells, small groups of cells, or even tissues and organs outside the intact plant body. Erwin F. Smith (cf. Whetzel, 1918) also realized the great consequences to plant pathology of such a method of approach. Early attempts to grow such isolated cell or tissue systems met with some limited success, but principally they encountered obstacles. In this century, however, success was first achieved in experiments to cultivate excised root tips, when the nutrient medium which contained salts, nitrogen sources, and sugars was supplemented with such catalytically active materials as yeast extract; its effective component, as mentioned above, quickly proved to be thiamine. This led to the idea that it should be possible to determine specifically the requirements for the cultivation of many cells, organs, and tissues, by utilizing known synthetic substances.

The methods of plant tissue culture have been applied by White (cf. White, 1943, for an account of earlier work) and Gautheret (1942) with success to certain tissues and organs. Both White and Gautheret, by the use of rather empirical media, have always advocated reliance upon synthetic substances in media that could be completely specified. This is laudable provided all the requirements for that growth are known. However, such a classical example of a tissue from the higher plant body, which could be separately cultured, as carrot root tissue has now been shown to grow at a very much greater pace if it is furnished with substances which are present in more complex fluids of natural origin, notably the liquid endosperm of the coconut (i.e., coconut milk or coconut water). To some, the inclusion of fluids of this sort, i.e., coconut milk, immature corn extract, etc., or even casein hydrolysate, in the media for the culture of tissues has seemed a retrograde step. However, it is only by the inclusion of such materials that the requirements for *maximum* growth and development of these cells and tissues can be revealed. This aspect of the requirements of rapidly growing cells will be discussed in a later chapter.

Organic nutrition and organization.   Properly, one should now take a closer look at the system that is nourished. Organic nutrition is not an end in itself, it is the means by which cells grow, function, and survive. In the preceding discussion the emphasis has been upon the need to build chemical complexity in a system that can grow; it has also stressed that the molecules built in the preferred and directed way are formed in a system which prescribes their pattern and also precludes many of the possibilities that could arise in a symmetrical environment which operated according to the statistical laws of chance. This is only another way of saying that the system that grows and is nourished is also organized, so that the chemical events of organic nutrition are those which selectively maintain it and contribute to its growth. A living system that can grow and survive must furnish the milieu within which the reactions of metabolism and nutrition can proceed in their appointed way. A balanced view of nutrition and metabolism requires that eventually one should be able to localize all these events and their interrelationships in cells, and to comprehend how the cell does what it does using the cytological machinery (i.e., its organization) which has emerged for that purpose and which is able to keep the metabolic wheels turning and maintained by the events of organic and inorganic nutrition which have been crudely outlined in Chapters 2 and 3. It would be quite appropriate, therefore, to describe the organization now in terms of the fine structure of protoplasm as revealed by the electron microscope, and in terms of the nature and structure of its organelles. However, such a discussion of morphological complexity of cells falls more properly within the scope of Chapter 5, which is to be concerned with cells, cell growth, and cell division. However, the consequences of the organization within which the reactions of organic nutrition proceed are to be seen, chemically, in the asymmetric way in which molecules are built as a consequence of the asymmetric environment in which their synthesis occurs. One may then fittingly conclude with some further reference to the problem of asymmetry and life.

Asymmetric synthesis and life.   In organic nature the asymmetry of molecules is utilized and asymmetric synthesis is a universal feature of life as we know it on this planet. Molecules, such as carbohydrates, amino acids, nucleic acids, protein, etc., have right-handedness and left-handedness, but nature distinguishes between these and usually utilizes only one member of any theoretically possible pair. Of all the known organisms and carbohydrates, it is almost a universal fact that it is the D family of sugars and the L-amino acids upon which nature elaborates. And in a variety of ways that have been described the structural asymmetry in the architecture of complex molecules is a feature of, and is utilized by, living organisms to endow them with the specificity they need.

In the non-living world, from the standpoint of chemical properties, energy, and thermodynamic relations, the two groups (D and L) of asymmetric molecules are normally completely equivalent and indistinguishable. This means that organisms might have been constructed equally well upon the model of the L family of sugars and the D-amino acids. Had this occurred, there is no reason to suppose that such organisms could not have functioned: but the significant thing is that it has *not* occurred (or at least it has not survived) on this planet, nor have mutations yet caused, or are they likely to cause, this shift. However, if life based on a carbon and nitrogen type of "organic" chemistry exists elsewhere in space, this might conceivably occur. There is then room for a wealth of speculation, but no proof, to guide our thoughts upon "biopoesis," i.e., the origin of animate from inanimate matter, and upon the means by which, or the reasons why, the existing patterns of organization have emerged and been pre- served. One conclusion is self-evident, namely, that the existing pattern, based on asymmetric synthesis as a characteristic of life, exists because it works and is successful.

In the rarefied world of modern physics, different concepts have prevailed. Professor Morrison, then at Cornell University, in a lecture reported in the *New York Times* for February 2, 1959, spoke as follows:

According to the law of parity, nature did not distinguish right and left so that an exact mirror counterpart was possible for every event. Each event in nature was thus subject to a universal symmetry between an object and its mirror image, the looking glass world functioning exactly as the actual world. . . . To illustrate, the elusive particle the neutron spins counter-clockwise when moving away from an observer, whereas the particle known as an antineutron spins in a clockwise direction.

To physicists it came, therefore, as a matter of surprise, as indicated by the award of a Nobel prize for the discovery, that the law of conservation of parity does not hold universally, and in this respect the symmetry in the cosmos is not complete. Nevertheless physicists do recognize an underlying symmetrical pat- tern in the properties of the unitary particles that comprise the structure of matter, and this principle—the principle of unitary symmetry—is invoked both to discover new particles (e.g., omega minus) and to understand their arrange- ment. This principle is of such general significance that it is even noted in the public press (cf. *Manchester Guardian*, February 27, 1964).

But in that earthly part of the universe which is occupied by organisms, the symmetry which is held to be so important at the level of the ultimate par- ticles clearly does *not* obtain at the molecular level or at the level of biological organization. It is a fundamental characteristic of life that symmetry does not obtain, for one configuration is accepted and the other is rejected. Organisms *do* distinguish between D and L forms of carbohydrate. In fact, life itself might be described in terms of this ability to utilize one asymmetric molecular object and not its mirror image.

Physicists may speculate that hydrogen, which is composed of one proton and one electron, may be contrasted with an "anti-hydrogen" which is postulated to contain an "anti-proton" and the positive analogue of the electron. But or- ganic nature, as yet necessarily confined to this planet, is of one general con- stitution and plan and no others have yet been seen. In short, the environment or organization within which chemical molecules have come to perform the func- tions we recognize as life, is itself *not* symmetrical. Even though, from the standpoint of the properties of matter and the laws of energy, it would seem that protoplasm should be able to exist in "enantiomorphous" opposites (related as object and mirror image), this does not occur on earth. Indeed, wherever the reflection of a biologically active molecule can be inserted into the living organism, it may not be assimilated or, if it is, it may often prove to be antagonistic to its enantiomorph. Thus if one could conceive of organisms built from asymmetric molecules which were right-handed in one case and left-handed in the other, then the metabolites of one might be the poison of the other, for their organizations would be related as life and "anti-life" respectively!

Asymmetric synthesis is, therefore, a prime characteristic of life on this planet. Although it is stretching credibility very far, there are those who would say that the universality of the D-sugars and the L-amino acids in nature merely indicates that life once started off this way and having so started, as it were, by an initial accident, all the rest has followed historically in genetical continuity from this primeval pattern. One may here paraphrase some famous words uttered in another context with the remark "Some accident, some history!" Others then will see the consistency in these facts of stereoisomerism and biology not only as evidence of "historical accident" but as the expression of order in nature which requires some explanation and is itself the antithesis of chance. Oparin (1961) quotes J. D. Bernal for the suggestion that asymmetric organic substances might have arisen on earth prior to the origin of life, because they might have been synthesized on the surfaces of crystals of quartz which exist in right- and left-handed forms. This suggestion, however, still leaves entirely unexplained the question why one form only was utilized throughout living organisms.

If life had several entirely chance origins, however, it might seem that the accident which selected a right-handed configuration at one start should have been counterbalanced by a left-handed start at another, and each such occasion would have had a chance to lead to a system of biology on earth. Had this occurred, each such system could have been internally consistent, although the two types would have been incompatible. A "right-handed" water flea would have had to feed on "right-handed," not "left-handed," algae, and so on. One may choose to regard the universality of but one such system as an indication that it has succeeded by virtue of its priority and by the abundance of the compatible asymmetric compounds it produced. On the other hand, from the purity of the entire range of organisms with respect to the families of asymmetric compounds they employ, we know that life as we see it does not depend now upon a slavish adherence to all chemical or statistical possibilities. On the contrary, biological organization intervenes to select one of the chemical possibilities whenever there is a choice between a chemical molecule and its mirror image.

In the allegorical account in the First Chapter of Genesis, symmetry and probability may have governed the outcome of the first days, but on the third, when "God said let the earth bring forth grass," the distinction between "the quick and the dead" came in an environment, or milieu, in which order and organization was to prevail; molecular asymmetry could be distinguished and perpetuated by that asymmetric synthesis which is a cardinal feature of all life as we know it today. Whether the choice to build biology upon D-sugars and L-amino acids was essentially accidental or part of a more purposive plan (that is, determined by some unrecognized property of our World or Universe, i.e., the Cosmos) is largely a philosophical question that can hardly be tested by experiment—at least, so long as biology is a terrestrial science, and until it appears that the reverse choices have been made successfully in other worlds. Till then it is to be regarded as part of an overall orderly system which operates in *Chlorella* or in man. There are those who will regard the very order in this plan as evidence of underlying purpose—a purpose which reaches its culmination when man's own substance, however beautifully it is made, is still not the end but serves as the "temple of the human spirit."

Summary

This chapter begins with carbon dioxide as the ultimate source of carbon through photosynthesis, and with nitrate or ammonia as the ultimate source of nitrogen in plant nutrition. It passes, through the consideration of the molecular architecture of the substances of which cells are composed, to the recognition that the events of organic and inorganic nutrition not only nourish the growth of cells but also maintain them in all the complexity of their sub-cellular structure as finely balanced working machines. Organic nutrition is, therefore, seen to be vastly more intricate and challenging than the mere chemical conversion of simple food molecules like sugar into energy and metabolites. It involves a range of stereochemical arrangements and biological controls which are necessary to erect the molecular architecture which underlies biological form and function. This is illustrated by reference to both the carbohydrates and proteins of cells. In the conversion of carbon compounds to the ultimate structural and metabolic components of the cell, synthesis occurs in an asymmetric environment (i.e., one which is already organized); relatively few of the total chemical possibilities are realized and, by asymmetric synthesis, certain stereochemical configurations are selectively fostered. Then enzymes by which this is brought about are themselves the products of and the agents of a synthetic system which is organized and asymmetric. The supreme act of synthesis in growing cells is the manufacture of the great diversity of proteins that are needed by cells and their organelles. Granted the "information" which resides in the DNA of the nucleus, the cell can elaborate the RNA of the cytoplasm according to current concepts, which are derived more from the study of bacteria than of angiosperms. The RNA characteristically may exist in three forms. These are the RNA of ribosomes which exists in bulk in cells in the form of granules, some free in the cytoplasm and some attached to membranes; the transient "messenger RNA" which transmits from nucleus to ribosome the message that determines the precise nature of the protein-synthesizing surface; and, finally, the "transfer" or "soluble" RNA which can transport an amino acid for which it is specific and locate it upon the appropriate part of the protein-synthesizing template surface. In this way proteins which have a highly specific linear arrangement of their amino acids can be formed. In doing all this, some nutrient substances are needed in bulk; some are needed only in catalytic amounts; and the plant equivalents of the vitamins and hormones of the animal body may be recognized. But it is now also necessary to recognize an as yet ill-defined and ill-understood group of substances that intervene to determine whether cells, even when furnished with otherwise complete nutrient media can, in fact, divide and grow. To achieve maximum rates of cell division, such empirical culture media as those devised by White and Gautheret may need to be supplemented. The effective supplements are, first, such biological fluids as those which nourish immature embryos, whether obtained in the form of coconut milk, extracts of immature corn grains, or the liquid endosperms from various dicotyledons. However, when the chemistry of the effective agents is ultimately known, they will (like thiamine) be available for introduction as such and they will then replace the more empirical addition of the complex fluids which have been named. The next chapter will consider these factors somewhat more closely and ask: What are the factors or conditions which ultimately determine or induce the maximum capacity of cells to grow?

Reference is also made to the essentially unsolved riddle by which the organization that is recognized as life so infallibly selects, by asymmetric synthesis, the molecules that are needed from all of those that are theoretically possible. The synthesis and use of D-sugars and L-amino acids in nature is essentially a mystery which is described, but not explained, by the interdependence of asymmetric synthesis and life. To explain this present evidence of order in nature one may even need to know how life began.

chapter four

THE NON-NUTRIENT REQUIREMENTS
AND STIMULI FOR GROWTH:
GROWTH-REGULATORY SUBSTANCES

Responses to Growth Regulators and Sites of their Action

Growth of cells: division and enlargement. For convenience, growth of cells may be visualized in two stages, although these are neither sharply nor irrevocably separated.

First, growth may be considered in terms of cell division or the multiplication of all self-duplicating units. Among such units, nuclei and plastids are obvious but other organelles, such as mitochondria Golgi bodies and ribosomes, must also multiply; even the membranes of the cell may be replicated. Also, the synthesis of cell protein, which must accompany this phase of growth, may occur by a process of replication at a template surface. It is in this context that the role of genes in regulating synthesis and growth is currently considered (cf. Fig. 3–20).

The second phase of cell growth is much more one of cell enlargement than of cell division, but a certain amount of "chemical differentiation" also occurs, even though this is not accompanied by marked morphological differentiation. It is true that cells of the angiosperm plant body often remain capable of cell division after enlargement and differentiation have occurred, but it is also clear that the conspicuous phase of growth by enlargement occurs with a minimum of simultaneous cell division. In this case existing sub-cellular structures are regarded as having been formed before enlargement began; the principal events in this stage of growth include intake of water, expansion of the vacuole, accumulation of salts, extension of the cell wall (if not its actual synthesis), and much of the increase of cell substance (e.g., protein) which growth entails.

It is during the phase of growth by cell enlargement that the main, total increment of solutes in vacuoles occurs. Hugo de Vries thought that absorption into vacuoles was due to the secretory action of the tonoplast (the inner plasma membrane or the "wall of the vacuole") which he regarded as an autonomous organelle of the cell. The secretion of solutes into vacuoles is now conceived to be due to the harnessing of metabolic activity to furnish the energy which is necessary for the movement of the solutes into the vacuole (cf. Chapter 2). In this movement of solutes into the vacuole, aeration and the oxidative metabolism which it regulates are important. The osmotic concentration of the solutes in the vacuole contributes directly to the absorption of water, and thus to growth by cell enlargement, by furnishing the "diffusion pressure deficit," or "suction pressure" as it was first called, of the cells. This being so, indole-acetic acid and other auxins, which contribute to the enlargement of the cell by "auxin-induced intake of water" (Bonner *et al.*, 1956), may also intervene at the site (presumably the tonoplast) at which the internal secretion of water and solutes occurs.

As mentioned in Chapter 1, the criteria of growth adopted depend upon the way the problem is to be approached. This is true of the relative importance which is attached to growth by cell division and to growth by cell enlargement. Some would even go so far as to confine the term growth virtually to that phase in which size is increased and "growth" thus becomes synonymous with "enlargement" of cells. One can conceive of growth as cell enlargement in a structure which has already accomplished its cell division and has lost the capacity for further division. This occurs commonly in fruits (e.g., the apple) shortly after fertilization (i.e., after about three weeks). It is impossible, however, to visualize growth of a multicellular plant such as an angiosperm completely independent of cell division. Both phases are obviously essential and it is their occurrence in sequence which is important in the growth of cells and of the organism. One phase of growth merges into the other but each phase has distinct controlling mechanisms. Although the bulk of both solutes and water may be taken in during cell enlargement, the ion and water intake which occurs earlier, while cells can still divide, are also important, even though they contribute only a small part of the total water and salts present in the mature cell. Indeed the method of salt intake in dividing and enlarging cells may be quite different in kind. Because of their intimate involvement with the growth of cells the absorption of water and ions merits some separate comment at this point.

Absorption of water and ions during growth of cells.   In meristematic cells the vacuole is inconspicuous, although the vacuome (a term first used by the French school of cytologists) is represented by minute, conspicuously non-aqueous, highly colloidal, deeply staining, cytological inclusions. Recognizing this, one hardly expects cells in the dividing state to absorb ions by the same mechanism as in the cells which possess large vacuoles and do not divide. In fact, meristematic cells of angiosperms, actively growing cells of tissue cultures, and probably bacteria and other non-vacuolated systems, seem to absorb ions, particularly cations, by a process of stoichiometrical binding at specific sites which are created during the course of growth. The ion-binding sites are themselves self-duplicating. Metabolism is concerned in this type of ion absorption because it is necessary for the formation and multiplication of the sites which are to be occupied. But different relations to metabolism apply when the ions leave the binding sites and pass into the aqueous vacuole where they eventually occur in true solution and at relatively high concentrations.

It has been possible to distinguish two steps, or stages, in ion uptake. Both are parts of the overall process, but in dividing cells the one (stage 1) is especially emphasized, and in the ensuing phase of cell enlargement the other (stage 2) is the more conspicuous. The examples of ion absorption investigated in the 1920's and early 1930's in the laboratories of Hoagland and of Steward using the large cells of *Nitella*, cut slices of storage organs, and later excised roots, all involved that part of the overall process which is characteristic of cells which, though they grow, can do so in part by cell enlargement and the absorption of water. Nevertheless, for the indefinite continuation of the absorption of ions, the ability to grow by cell division (or multiplication of protoplasts in a coenocyte) obviously has to be retained.

It is now known that the growing cells of the root apex, i.e., cells nearest the apical meristem of the shoot, and cells which are retained in the permanently dividing state in tissue cultures by the use of special growth factors, may not achieve as high *total concentrations* of ions in their total water as more fully vacuolated cells. Nevertheless, they absorb salts by methods that are characteristic of cells that are growing by cell multiplication. The absorption of ions by these dividing cells is related much more directly to the *first power* of the external concentration of the ion in the solution than is the case when the cells grow predominantly by cell enlargement. In the latter state, cells accumulate their salts in aqueous vacuoles and their chief characteristic is their ability to counteract the effects of great external dilution by what has been termed the mechanism of salt accumulation. In this mechanism the accumulation ratio (internal concentration of an ion divided by its external concentration) actually *increases* as the external concentration is reduced. This "secretory activity," which was first attributed by de Vries to the tonoplast, is now known to be due to mechanisms by which growing cells utilize their own metabolism to do work; this activity is most intense in cells which are at the height of that phase of their growth which occurs predominantly by cell enlargement. But the accumulation of ions in the phase of cell elargement occurs so rapidly after the absorption that occurs in the phase of cell division that it is difficult to separate the two stages. (Information on which the above is based may be found in the general account by Steward and Sutcliffe, 1959, and in references there cited.)

Stimuli to cell division.   It has been stated (cf. Chapter 2) that the mere external supply of nutrients, essential as they may be, is not enough to induce cell growth. At fertilization some essential stimulus occurs, and whereas the gametes alone do not grow, the zygote does. Early in this century much interest was aroused in artificially induced parthenogenesis, particularly in sea urchin eggs, when it was discovered that the stimulus of fertilization could be replaced by chemical means. In certain cases in plants it is also well known that the need for gamete formation and nuclear fusion (as the prerequisite to embryo formation in higher plants) may be, in a sense, evaded by the apomictic

FIG. 4–1. Crown gall tumor (or teratoma) on *Kalanchoe*.

development of embryos from diploid cells of the plant body. Even though the nature of the stimulus that produces this effect may be unknown, it is obviously important. Polyploid species of *Taraxacum* provide classical examples of apomixis; despite an elaborate floral organization, embryos are formed not as the result of nuclear fusion of two gametes but by the development of an unreduced egg cell. Embryo development from cells other than the fertilized egg, e.g., formation of the nucellar embryos of *Citrus*, is known also in many other genera.

It has long been known that stimuli to the division of the fertilized egg emanate from the juxtaposition of pollen tubes and the style; in fact, one of the first cases of growth-promoting stimuli was that observed in 1909 by Fitting in orchids. In these plants a great deal of the development of the pistil follows from the stimulus of contact with the pollen tube. Similarly the development of ovary walls and false fruits, which is stimulated by the presence of embryos, is now familiar. The chemical basis for these morphological events presents a challenging problem.

Stimuli to cell division were discerned long ago in the responses of host plants to the crown gall organism, which used to be called *Phytomonas* and is now classified as *Agrobacterium*. The significance of this phenomenon was appreciated by the plant pathologist Erwin F. Smith (1920; also see Smith *et al.*, 1912). A natural "tissue culture" results from the interaction of the crown gall organism with the cells of the host, e.g., *Bryophyllum* (or *Kalanchoe*), which then embark upon renewed growth. The cells of the crown gall may continue to divide and produce a large overgrowth (Fig. 4–1). The cells so affected by the bacterium become permanently changed, for they will continue to divide long after the original stimulus of the bacterium has been removed and the tumorlike overgrowth (teratoma) is rendered bacteria free. Other naturally occurring stimuli to cell division may be seen in such familiar examples as the formation of root nodules on legumes by the bacterium *Rhizobium* and in the formation of insect-stimulated galls. The normal stimulus from the presence of an embryo which causes adjacent somatic cells to grow and to divide (although in a more orderly fashion than do cells of nodules, galls, or tumors), as in the formation of pomes or of false fruits, has also been noted above. It is obvious, therefore, that in all these situations there must be a chemical basis for the observed cell division stimulus. Substances which produce these effects on plant cells exogenously have been called kinins, cytokinins, or phytokinins, although, as will become clear, the effect may involve, not single, but combinations of, substances.

Stimuli to cell enlargement. The evidence for the existence and role of these stimuli emerged from very well-known investigations on tropisms in higher plants. A tropism, or movement produced by growth due to an external stimulus such as light or gravity, is a response in an organ which is capable of growth by elongation. Classical examples are the hypocotyl of the sunflower, the coleoptile of grasses, or the elongating region of roots. Such systems, therefore, produced the evidence for growth-regulatory substances which act primarily by their effect upon cell elongation.

The natural auxins. An extensive digression would be needed to trace in detail the fascinating but now well-known story of the discovery, isolation, and eventual identification of the well-established natural auxin, indoleacetic acid. This occurred after Darwin's work on canary grass (*Phalaris*) and the observations which established the material nature of the stimulus that emanates from the shoot tip but acts upon the elongating region. These events, which are conveniently summarized in a historical chart (Fig. 4–2), required the contributions of many workers and culminated in the work of F. W. Went. All this led to the eventual isolation and chemical identification of the principal natural auxin as indoleacetic acid—in this work Thimann and Kögl played key roles. It is also known that the principal site where auxin is formed is in the tip of the shoot. Characteristically, auxin moves basipetally and promotes growth in the elongating region of the shoot; in fact it is the imbalance in auxin distribution, which occurs in asymmetrically stimulated organs, that leads to tropistic responses by the greater extension of the cells on one side of the organ than on the other. Many paradoxes still exist, such as the strangely different response of roots and shoots to auxins, for auxin is inhibitory to the growth of roots at concentration levels which are stimulatory to the growth of shoots. Also, there is now some question that auxin may have been regarded as the *direct* cause for a too varied range of responses. For example, the stimulus for cambial activity in the spring which emanates from buds is commonly ascribed to auxin (i.e., indoleacetic acid), although the nature of this response is primarily one that involves cell division.

For many years indoleacetic acid (IAA) was the one critically identified example, and came to be thought of as *the* auxin. The other representatives, the substances designated by Kögl as auxins *A* and *B*, had been described by highly complicated but entirely unconfirmed chemical structures. These substances, auxins *A* and *B*, are for the present best forgotten because, despite the passage of time, they have not been re-isolated and their structures have not been confirmed. On the other hand, the use of paper partition chromatography has produced abundant evidence that there are other substances in plants which show similar ability to stimulate growth by cell enlargement in a coleoptile assay system for auxins. Some of these substances are obviously related to indoleacetic acid, and, in the opinion of many, they represent alternative sources for indoleacetic acid as the substance that produces the ultimate response. The best example here is the neutral substance indoleacetic acid nitrile, which was isolated by Jones and his group (1952) from large amounts of *Brassica* leaves. An indoleacetic acid ester was reported to occur in corn grains though it was later regarded as an artifact of alcohol extraction. From immature corn (*Zea*) grains a growth substance, which is active in promoting cell division, has been isolated in this laboratory and it has been shown to yield on hydrolysis one molecule each of indoleacetic acid and a sugar (arabinose). Since peptides of indoleacetic acid and amino acids are now known to occur naturally, the probability is that there are many other indole compounds still to be isolated and tested for their growth-promoting activity. A symposium held at Gif, in France, the proceedings of which were edited by Nitsch (1964), and an account by Shantz (1966), contain recent information on this subject.

Gibberellins. However, it is clear that the ability to promote growth by cell enlargement is not the sole prerogative of indole compounds; a striking example of a substance, or group of substances, which offsets this view is that of gibberellic acid, or the class of gibberellins. The knowledge of these substances emerged years after certain observations made on rice. A fungus (*Gibberella fujikuroi*) causes symptoms in the rice plant which suggest that it acts by promoting growth by enlargement, one of the symptoms being the formation of long and narrow leaves. Rice plants so affected were called "foolish seedlings,"

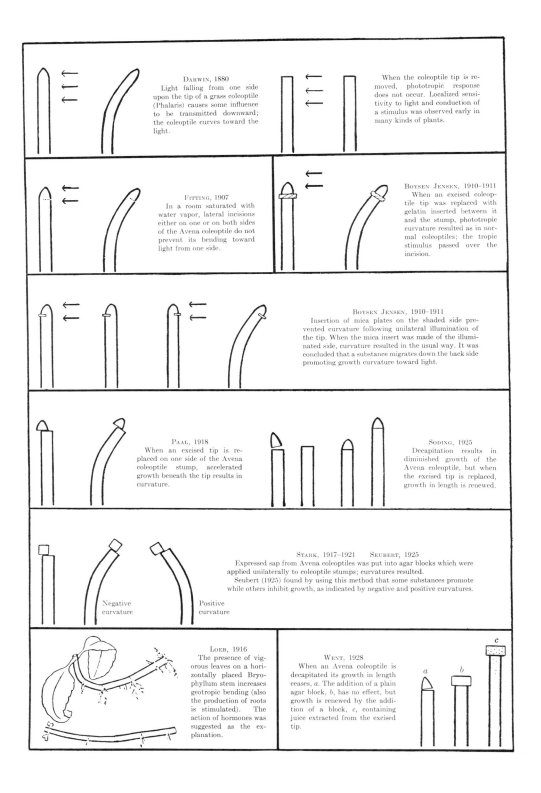

DARWIN, 1880
Light falling from one side upon the tip of a grass coleoptile (Phalaris) causes some influence to be transmitted downward; the coleoptile curves toward the light.

When the coleoptile tip is removed, phototropic response does not occur. Localized sensitivity to light and conduction of a stimulus was observed early in many kinds of plants.

FITTING, 1907
In a room saturated with water vapor, lateral incisions either on one or on both sides of the Avena coleoptile do not prevent its bending toward light from one side.

BOYSEN JENSEN, 1910–1911
When an excised coleoptile tip was replaced with gelatin inserted between it and the stump, phototropic curvature resulted as in normal coleoptiles; the tropic stimulus passed over the incision.

BOYSEN JENSEN, 1910–1911
Insertion of mica plates on the shaded side prevented curvature following unilateral illumination of the tip. When the mica insert was made of the illuminated side, curvature resulted in the usual way. It was concluded that a substance migrates down the back side promoting growth curvature toward light.

PAAL, 1918
When an excised tip is replaced on one side of the Avena coleoptile stump, accelerated growth beneath the tip results in curvature.

SÖDING, 1925
Decapitation results in diminished growth of the Avena coleoptile, but when the excised tip is replaced, growth in length is renewed.

STARK, 1917–1921   SEUBERT, 1925
Expressed sap from Avena coleoptiles was put into agar blocks which were applied unilaterally to coleoptile stumps; curvatures resulted.
Seubert (1925) found by using this method that some substances promote while others inhibit growth, as indicated by negative and positive curvatures.

Negative curvature

Positive curvature

LOEB, 1916
The presence of vigorous leaves on a horizontally placed Bryophyllum stem increases geotropic bending (also the production of roots is stimulated). The action of hormones was suggested as the explanation.

WENT, 1928
When an Avena coleoptile is decapitated its growth in length ceases, a. The addition of a plain agar block, b, has no effect, but growth is renewed by the addition of a block, c, containing juice extracted from the excised tip.

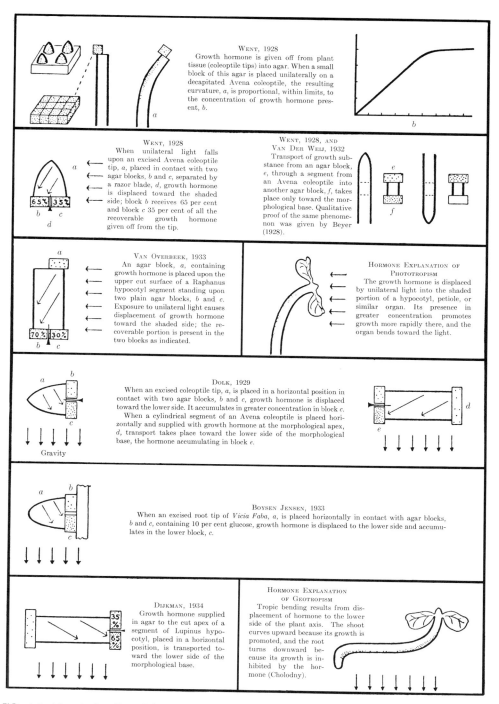

WENT, 1928
Growth hormone is given off from plant tissue (coleoptile tips) into agar. When a small block of this agar is placed unilaterally on a decapitated Avena coleoptile, the resulting curvature, *a*, is proportional, within limits, to the concentration of growth hormone present, *b*.

WENT, 1928
When unilateral light falls upon an excised Avena coleoptile tip, *a*, placed in contact with two agar blocks, *b* and *c*, separated by a razor blade, *d*, growth hormone is displaced toward the shaded side; block *b* receives 65 per cent and block *c* 35 per cent of all the recoverable growth hormone given off from the tip.

WENT, 1928, AND VAN DER WEIJ, 1932
Transport of growth substance from an agar block, *e*, through a segment from an Avena coleoptile into another agar block, *f*, takes place only toward the morphological base. Qualitative proof of the same phenomenon was given by Beyer (1928).

VAN OVERBEEK, 1933
An agar block, *a*, containing growth hormone is placed upon the upper cut surface of a Raphanus hypocotyl segment standing upon two plain agar blocks, *b* and *c*. Exposure to unilateral light causes displacement of growth hormone toward the shaded side; the recoverable portion is present in the two blocks as indicated.

HORMONE EXPLANATION OF PHOTOTROPISM
The growth hormone is displaced by unilateral light into the shaded portion of a hypocotyl, petiole, or similar organ. Its presence in greater concentration promotes growth more rapidly there, and the organ bends toward the light.

DOLK, 1929
When an excised coleoptile tip, *a*, is placed in a horizontal position in contact with two agar blocks, *b* and *c*, growth hormone is displaced toward the lower side. It accumulates in greater concentration in block *c*.
When a cylindrical segment of an Avena coleoptile is placed horizontally and supplied with growth hormone at the morphological apex, *d*, transport takes place toward the lower side of the morphological base, the hormone accumulating in block *e*.

Gravity

BOYSEN JENSEN, 1933
When an excised root tip of *Vicia Faba*, *a*, is placed horizontally in contact with agar blocks, *b* and *c*, containing 10 per cent glucose, growth hormone is displaced to the lower side and accumulates in the lower block, *c*.

DIJKMAN, 1934
Growth hormone supplied in agar to the cut apex of a segment of Lupinus hypocotyl, placed in a horizontal position, is transported toward the lower side of the morphological base.

HORMONE EXPLANATION OF GEOTROPISM
Tropic bending results from displacement of hormone to the lower side of the plant axis. The shoot curves upward because its growth is promoted, and the root turns downward because its growth is inhibited by the hormone (Cholodny).

FIG. 4–2. Historical outline of the early discoveries concerning plant growth hormones. (From Boysen Jensen, translated by Avery and Burkholder, *Growth Hormones in Plants*. Copyright © 1936, McGraw-Hill Book Co., Inc.)

because of their abnormal elongation. Purified products were eventually obtained, by growing the fungus in liquid media, and it was soon found that the substances (many of which are now known) were able to convert otherwise dwarf plants (e.g., peas or corn) to tall plants. Their principal effect, however, is to stimulate growth of internodes, laminae, etc., that is, phases of growth that occur by cell enlargement rather than by cell division, although they are now being implicated in other morphogenetic responses such as flowering (see Chapter 8). It is now clear that this relatively recent and dramatic example of naturally occurring growth regulators, which have some auxin-like activity but which are not indoleacetic acid, is but one example of many that still await discovery and isolation. Cucurbitaceous seeds, particularly immature seeds, are also sources of similar gibberellin-like activity; no doubt, other examples occur. (For a general account of the gibberellins see Phinney and West, 1960; Paleg, 1965.)

One should, therefore, now recognize numerous chemical stimuli which promote growth by cell enlargement. The cell which is receptive to such stimuli retains all the essential self-duplicating structures; but the stimuli in question intervene in some as yet unexplained manner to promote all the remaining phases of growth, namely, expansion of the cell wall (and perhaps actual synthesis of cell wall material), intake of water, uptake of salts and solutes into the vacuole, and that synthesis of protein which occurs even in elongating, nondividing cells. The fact that these substances, whether generically termed auxins or gibberellins, act in such minute catalytic amounts mean that they are not nutrients *per se* but growth-regulating substances. Suitable assay systems which demonstrate these effects are available, notably the use of the *Avena* coleoptile in various ways (the straight growth test, or the bending test, or the growth of cut coleoptile segments). The mesocotyl of grasses, as used by Nitsch and Nitsch (1956) is an alternative auxin-sensitive organ to the coleoptile. Other tests which depend upon the use of cut segments of pea stems or hypocotyls of sunflower, are merely referred to here because they are well known and their use has been well illustrated by Wain and Wightman (1956), by Went and Thimann (1937), and by Skoog (1951). For the substances known as gibberellins there are now standard assays which are based upon the release of the limitations to growth in otherwise dwarf plants, such as mutant strains of corn (*Zea*) or pea (*Pisum*) as described by Phinney (1956) or Brian and Hemming (1955).

Synthetic auxins. Based upon the naturally occurring auxins, whole families of synthetic growth-regulatory compounds have been prepared to duplicate or extend the action of their natural counterparts. At first the main emphasis was placed upon indoleacetic acid as the model substance and, by analogy with its structure as a substituted acetic acid, the various phenoxyacetic acids, which have now come into such prevalent use, appeared in the course of time. The first effect of these phenoxyacetic acids is frequently a greatly accentuated growth by cell extension, although this may eventually lead to enough imbalanced growth to cause death; this has been widely exploited in herbicidal practices (e.g., by the use of 2,4-D and similar substances).

One can, however, visualize many other chemical configurations as prototypes from which growth-regulatory substances of this sort may be developed. Indeed, the rules which relate chemical configuration to auxin-like activity, as they were originally conceived by Thimann (1951) have been greatly modified, for such activity now can be seen in a baffling array of dissimilar chemical compounds (cf. Wain and Fawcett, in press). As other naturally occurring auxins are isolated and identified (Bentley, 1961), such as those that are now recognizable only by areas on paper chromatograms, and as the significance of such complex substances as the gibberellins is more fully understood, it is predictable that there will be an increasing range and variety of chemical substances able to affect growth by acting first on cell enlargement.

One should now turn, however, to that area of growth regulation which emphasizes cell division rather than cell enlargement. It is true that applications of indoleacetic acid, and many model compounds based upon it, have also been found to stimulate cell division. Indeed, imbalance in the naturally poised hormonal regulation of cells and organs, which is produced by many different means, may lead to many indirect results, including cell division. Nevertheless, it is clear that the *primary* effect of such auxins as indoleacetic acid, and perhaps also of the gibberellins, is to promote cell enlargement; indeed their effect may often end there if the test system itself emphasizes growth by extension.

Cell division factors. *Tissue cultures as assay systems.* The technique of tissue culture provides a convenient system for the detection and assay of substances that stimulate cell division. The pioneers of plant tissue culture, P. R. White in the U.S.A. and Gautheret in France, refrained from complicating their media unduly by the addition of substances that could not be chemically characterized. However, a major advance was made when it was found that the addition of coconut milk or coconut water, as it is often called (the liquid endosperm of the coconut), to tissue cultures of carrot root phloem, already a standard material for plant tissue culture work, caused an intensity of growth

TABLE 4–1
Analysis of growth curve of carrot tissue cultures in terms of cell numbers

Time, days	Cells per culture, $\times 10^3$	Milligrams per culture
0	28.0	2.60
2	30.6	2.60
3	36.1	3.11
5	86.4	4.95
6	118.3	6.73
7	213.1	8.96
8	355.0	16.4
9	488.8	18.0
10	658.1	—
13	1037.0	41.0

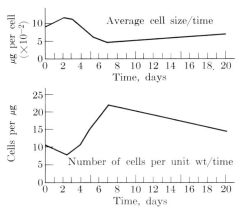
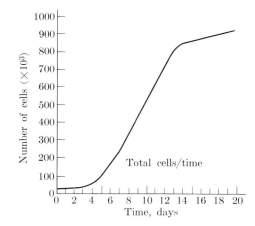

FIG. 4–3. Growth of carrot explants in a medium containing coconut milk. (From work of Caplin and Steward.)

that could not be duplicated in any other way (Caplin and Steward, 1949). The amounts of growth thus induced in small tissue explants (initially of the order of 2 mg) clearly indicated that the effect was not merely one of cell expansion, but was primarily a stimulation of growth by cell division (growth increments of the order of 80- to 100-fold in about 20 days were achieved). This is shown in Table 4–1 in which growth was traced in terms of both the weight of the individual tissue explant and of the number of cells it contained as it grew under the standard conditions devised to study the effect of coconut milk upon otherwise mature cells of the carrot root.

When these data are plotted against time, as shown in the accompanying figure (Fig. 4–3), one can see clearly that the typical sigmoid growth curve can be dissected into the following phases:

1. A preliminary lag phase, in which outward signs of growth develop only slowly. This period lasts approximately 4 days, and it is distinguished by an increment of growth due largely to stimulated cell expansion.

2. A succeeding exponential phase in which there is an increasing tendency for cell division, which gathers momentum with time, so that the cells, dividing rapidly, remain small. In this period, in which cell division has the ascendancy over cell expansion, cell multiplication proceeds very rapidly, so that after about 10 to 14 days an explant which originally had about 25,000 cells will have well over a million, and in some 20 to 21 days may have two and a half to three and a half million.

3. As the explant becomes larger, its surface-volume relations change and, probably for a variety of reasons, the early exponential growth increase tends to decline (Fig. 4–3). In this respect the curve follows the typical sigmoid curves of growth.

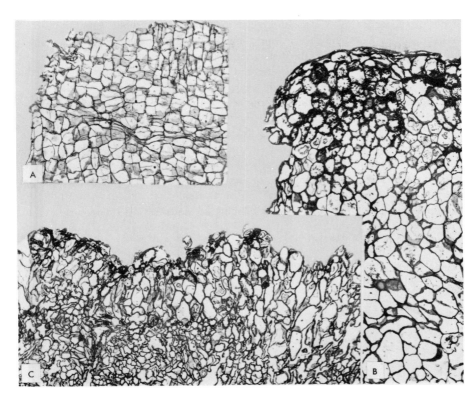

FIG. 4–4. Structure of carrot tissues grown in different media. A. A portion of the surface of the original explant. Note the many cells in which divisions had occurred in the carrot root, but the daughter cells had not fully expanded. B. A portion of the surface of an explant which had grown for 21 days in basal medium. Note that the average cell size is larger than in A. In the central portion, the original cells have enlarged in a disorderly manner, but there is little evidence of cell divisions having occurred throughout the tissue mass. This growth in basal medium, which is a variable function of the individual carrot root, depends mainly on preformed cells which can expand. C. A portion of the surface of an explant which had grown for 21 days in basal medium plus casein hydrolysate plus coconut milk. Note the abundance of small cells, the air spaces, and some larger cells toward the periphery of the culture. (From Steward and Caplin, *Année Biologique* **30**, 385–394, 1954.)

Cell division factors in the ontogeny of cells. Cells cut off from the cambium of the carrot root rapidly differentiate and, at a distance of one to two milli-meters from the cambium, cambial derivatives no longer divide, nor do they return to the rapid cell division intrinsic to cells of the cambium in the normal course of development of the carrot root. In this state the tissue has the appear-ance shown in the section (Fig. 4–4A) which was cut from such an explant as it was removed from a carrot root. If furnished with a variety of nitrogenous materials, such as casein hydrolysate, and no doubt when also stimulated by endogenous indoleacetic acid, these cells can enlarge; in this way weight increments of the order of $\times 2$ or more can be achieved, without appreciable cell division. Such cells, however, would normally divide very slowly, if at all, and they would persist in the tissue culture largely in the mature, expanded state. In this condition they respire and metabolize but, for some reason, the cells do not harness their metabolic energy to growth by *rapid* cell multiplication. It is as though the metabolic engine is running to waste, like a motor car engine out of gear. Fuel is consumed, heat is produced, wastes are excreted, but the essential motive power is not engaged by the clutch. What the coconut milk apparently does is to furnish such a metabolic "clutch," which now puts the cellular engine into gear so that its metabolism becomes directed along channels in which energy can be supplied to all those essential processes that lead to growth by cell division. It is significant that the growth-promoting substances that act in this way, which can be detected by the use of tissue-cultured carrot explants, are principally to be found in fluids which nourish immature embryos.

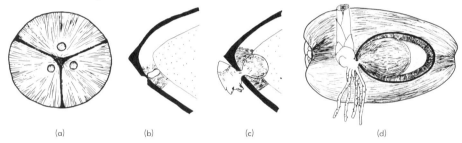

(a)   (b)   (c)   (d)

FIG. 4–5. Development of the coconut embryo. (a) An end view of the coconut, without its husk, showing the three carpels and the "eyes." The fertile carpel is the one included in the largest angle. (b) Longitudinal section of fruit of *Cocos nucifera*, showing the embryo embedded in the solid endosperm (under the micropyle). The shell is indicated by the heavy outline. (c) In a later stage in the development of the embryo, the incipient stem and roots are to be seen. The cotyledon has enlarged within and without the shell. (d) A longitudinal section through the whole nut somewhat to the side of the median line, showing the nut imbedded in its fibrous husk. The conditions found after germination had gone on for about five months. The absorbing organ has filled about two-thirds of the cavity of the nut but has absorbed comparatively little of the solid endosperm. The stem has proceeded upward through the husk, the roots downward through the husk into the soil. (After Kirkwood and Gies, 1902.)

Natural occurrence of cell division factors. In the coconut this type of nutrient fluid constitutes the liquid endosperm which develops in advance of the growth of the embryo. The development of the coconut embryo is delayed; it is immature even when the nut has reached its full size (Fig. 4–5). The embryo sends into the fluid-filled central cavity an organ—a part of the cotyledon—which absorbs the content of that liquid (i.e., the endosperm) and furnishes it to the growing embryo. Thus, coconut milk is the natural culture medium in which the coconut cotyledon grows. Coconut milk is remarkable, however, in that it can also incite division in cells and tissues drawn from quite unrelated plants. It is noteworthy that the potency of the growth-promoting substances present in the coconut milk, i.e., obtained from a monocotyledon, was first recognized by stimulating growth in cells of *dicotyledons*, namely of the carrot (*Daucus carota* L.) and the Jerusalem artichoke (*Helianthus tuberosus*). Therefore, the physiologically active substances in question must have a range of activity far wider than the plants in which they occur. For example, coconut milk will stimulate cell growth in many other plants—even in *Ginkgo* pollen, i.e., in the cells of a gymnosperm (Tulecke, 1957).

Two outstanding problems immediately present themselves:

1. What other sources of similar growth-promoting substances which induce quiescent cells to divide exist in the plant kingdom?

2. If the substances which induce cells to divide are obtained from different sources, are they also active on cells of widely different origins, i.e., from different tissues and organs of the same plant or from different parts of the plant kingdom?

These questions have received attention and alternatives to coconut milk are now known. The first alternative source came, not unnaturally, from another monocotyledonous plant (Steward and Caplin, 1952a). It was found that extracts from immature corn grains (*Zea*), lyophilized at the stage when the embryos were immature, yielded aqueous extracts fully as potent as coconut milk (Fig. 4–6). Thus, the environment of the immature embryo, whether of corn or coconut, furnished extracts capable of inducing cell division in otherwise quiescent cells of carrot root explants.

However, the search for similar activity in dicotyledonous plants was at first without avail. Many dicotyledons pass through a brief stage in which the endosperm is liquid, and exists even in a free nuclear state. In the case of exalbuminous seeds, however, the development of cotyledons occurs rapidly and at the expense of the endosperm. Therefore, many attempts to obtain cell-division-promoting extracts from sources such as pea and other exalbuminous dicotyledons failed. Attention was then turned to albuminous seeds, in which the storage of nutrient for the embryo persists in the endosperm, rather than in cotyledons, so that it is not completely absorbed until the embryo germinates. Tests upon the mature or developing endosperms of *Ricinus* and *Fagopyrum*, after their embryos had organized, also proved of no avail.

Extremely potent sources of growth-promoting activity equivalent to that of coconut milk were, however, eventually found in dicotyledonous plants. In the cultivated walnut, *Juglans nigra*, the fluid endosperm accumulates early in the development of the fruit and it may persist until relatively late in the season, since the cotyledons grow somewhat slowly. When this fluid was extracted from immature walnut fruits it was found to be very effective in stimulating the growth of carrot explants (Steward and Caplin, 1952a). This observation was

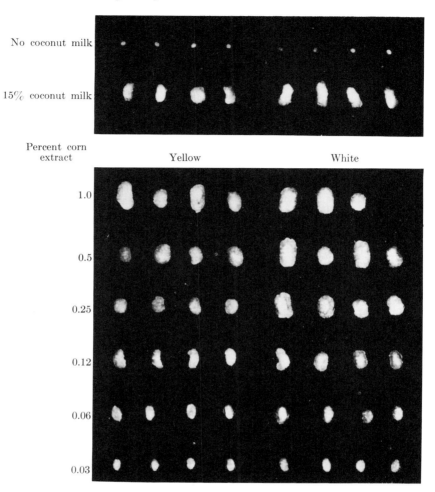

No coconut milk

15% coconut milk

Percent corn extract

Yellow

White

1.0

0.5

0.25

0.12

0.06

0.03

FIG. 4–6. The activity of extracts from immature corn grains (a yellow and a white variety) upon the growth of carrot explants, compared with that of coconut milk. (From work of Caplin and Steward.)

followed by the use of an even more potent fluid which can be more conveniently extracted from the spineless, immature fruits of a species of horse chestnut (*Aesculus woerlitzensis*). The effectiveness of *Aesculus* and similar sources again lies, therefore, in the fact that the liquid storage reserve develops precociously and accumulates while the development of the embryo, which it will eventually nourish through the cotyledons, proceeds more slowly. Evidence of the activity of this source, alternative to coconut milk, and some details of the extraction method, are shown in Figs. 4–7 and 4–8, and the development of the vesiculate embryo sac of *Aesculus*, which contains the growth-promoting substances, has been described in detail by List and Steward (1965).

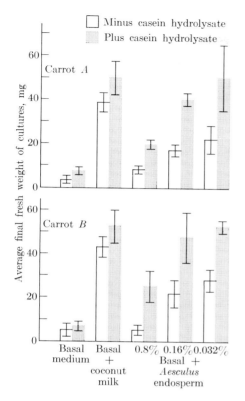

☐ Minus casein hydrolysate
▨ Plus casein hydrolysate

Carrot *A*

Carrot *B*

Average final fresh weight of cultures, mg

Basal medium | Basal + coconut milk | 0.8% | 0.16% | 0.032% Basal + *Aesculus* endosperm

◀FIG. 4–7. Effect of liquid endosperm from immature fruits of *Aesculus woerlitzensis* on the growth of carrot phloem explants, compared with growth in basal medium and in basal medium plus 10% coconut milk. (From work of Shantz and Steward.)

FIG. 4–8. The occurrence in and extraction from *Aesculus* fruits of a growth-promoting liquid for carrot explants. A. Immature smooth fruits of *Aesculus woerlitzensis* showing ovules containing sap. (From List and Steward, *Ann. Botany* N. S. 29, 1–15, 1965.) B. Extraction of liquid from the vesiculate embryo sac of *Aesculus woerlitzensis*. (From work of Shantz and Steward.) ▼

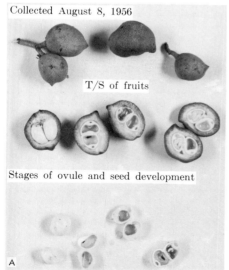

Collected August 8, 1956

T/S of fruits

Stages of ovule and seed development

A

B

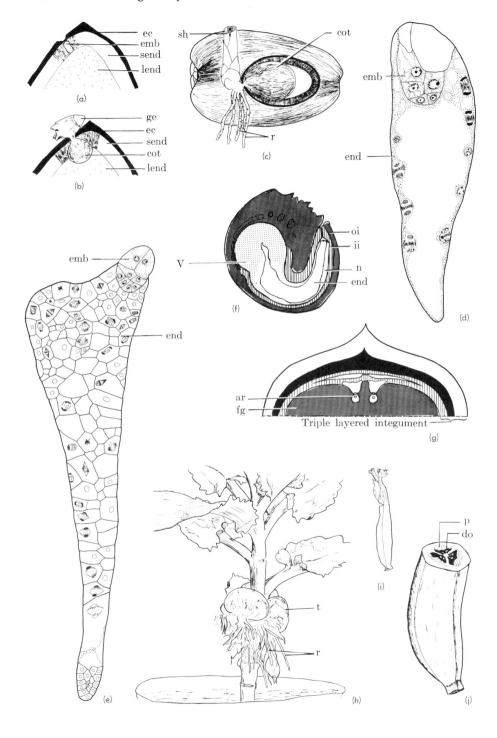

◀FIG. 4–9. The sources of growth factors and their morphology. (a) Longitudinal section of fruit of *Cocos nucifera;* note the embryo embedded in solid endosperm. (After Kirkwood and Gies, 1902.) (b, c) Same section, showing different stages of seed germination. (After Kirkwood and Gies, 1902.) (d) Free nuclear endosperm in *Zea mays.* (After Randolph, 1936.) (e) Cellular endosperm in *Zea mays.* (After Randolph, 1936.) (f) Longitudinal section of ovule of *Aesculus,* showing free nuclear endosperm and vesicle at the chalazal end. (Reproduced from Steward and Shantz, *Ann. Rev. Plant Physiol.* 10, 379–404, 1959; originally drawn by A. List.) (g) Longitudinal section of ovule of *Ginkgo.* (Redrawn from Coulter and Chamberlain, 1917.) (h) Crown gall tumor on the stem of *Kalanchoe.* (i) The flower of banana (*Musa* sp.) at the time of shooting. (j) Parthenocarpic fruit of the same, cut to illustrate the inner layers of pericarp which develop into pulp. (*ar*, archegonium; *cot*, cotyledon; *do*, degenerated ovule; *ec*, endocarp; *emb*, embryo; *end*, endosperm; *fg*, female gametophyte; *ge*, germinating embryo; *ii*, inner integument; *lend*, liquid endosperm; *n*, nucellus; *oi*, outer integument; *p*, pulp; *r*, roots; *send*, solid endosperm; *sh*, shoot; *t*, crown gall tumor; *V*, vesicle.) (Entire figure from Steward and Mohan Ram, *Advances in Morphogenesis,* Vol. I, Academic Press, New York, 1961.)

The general idea is now quite clear. Following fertilization, the angiosperm egg forms the zygote. In the embryo sac and the surrounding tissue of the nucellus, during the development of the endosperm (which is also stimulated by the fertilization process), there accumulates a mass of reserve material which furnishes to the developing embryo a kind of nutrient that is never again duplicated during that life cycle. If this material develops in advance and in excess of the embryo's needs, it may constitute a rich reservoir of powerful growth-promoting substances; substances that have the ability to induce many otherwise quiescent cells to divide, even though they had already reached a stage of development in which they would not normally do so again. In other situations comparable nutritional relationships exist, such as that between the female gametophyte of *Ginkgo*, which nourishes the archegonia and embryos; here also, similar growth-promoting stimuli can be demonstrated (Steward and Caplin, 1952a). There can, therefore, be little doubt that many more examples of such activity remain to be found. In fact, the parthenocarpically developed banana fruit furnished such an example.

The fleshy tissue of the Gros Michel banana (*Musa acuminata*) fruit has a somewhat complex origin (Mohan Ram *et al.*, 1962) but it grows without requiring the stimulus of either an embryo or pollination. The inner layer which bounds the loculi (i.e., the wall of the loculus) of the ovary and which also involves the septa that subdivide the ovary is the site of the growth-promoting activity. It is interesting that an extract of this formative layer will also stimulate carrot explants to grow (Steward and Simmonds, 1954)! Here the stimulus to growth induction resides in the inner pericarp and in the septa which subdivide the ovary, and not in a liquid endosperm. In *Aesculus* some similar activity can also be demonstrated in the fleshy portions of the fruit which are absorbed as the embryo matures. The morphological situations from which extracts have been obtained and which have induced growth in carrot cultures are illustrated in Fig. 4–9. It will be noted that they are as diverse as the nucellus, the contents of embryo sacs, liquid and cellular endosperms, fleshy integuments of seeds, the fleshy pericaps of certain fruits, and the female gametophyte of a gymnosperm. Since the above observations were made some other examples have been noted of the cell division stimulus in young developing fruits like plum (Letham, 1963) and apple (cf. Zwar *et al.*, 1964).

If, however, the growing system or embryo is furnished with all available nutrients, flooded as it were with the growth-promoting stimuli which direct its growth predominantly toward cell division, one wonders why it does not form a large, indefinitely proliferating, tumorous mass. Indeed, with *Datura* embryos treated with autoclaved coconut milk this did occur (Van Overbeek *et al.*, 1941).

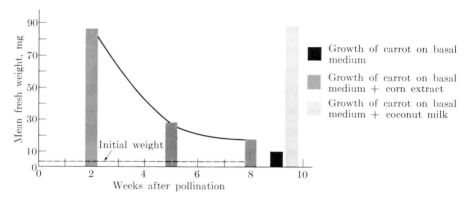

FIG. 4–10. Changes in the growth-promoting activity of extracts of immature grains of *Zea* as affected by their development. (From Steward and Caplin, *Ann. Botany* N. S. 16, 477–489, 1952.)

Differentiation, however, presupposes control over cell division, so that it may proceed in a coordinated manner. In part, this control may be exercised by the restricted physical space for the embryo's development, but the more probable control is that which may be due to the action of antagonists, or inhibitors, of the substances that at first stimulate cell division. Indeed, these inhibitory or controlling substances or mechanisms seem to gain ascendancy as differentiation proceeds. Thus the effects of the growth-promoting substances for cell division have virtually disappeared from a mature corn grain (Fig. 4–10); that is true of most seeds when their storage organs, whether cotyledons or endosperm, are fully formed and are filled with stored food.

Inhibitors and the regulatory control of growth. Many situations in plants yield growth-inhibitory substances that are capable of counteracting the cell-division-promoting effects attributable to coconut milk or to extracts with similar properties. The same tissue culture system that is used to detect and assay the growth-promoting substances may also be used to detect the inhibitory substances or mechanisms. Somewhat unexpectedly, such inhibitors were found in the tissue of the dormant potato tuber (Fig. 4–11). This organ contains plentiful supplies of inorganic and organic nutrients and is commonly used in media for the growth of saprophytic microorganisms, but it will completely counteract the effect of coconut milk on carrot tissue explants even when it is added in relatively small amount to an otherwise competent culture medium. This effect has been attributed to the presence in the mature, non-growing potato cells of inhibitors for such cell division factors as those óf coconut milk. Similar inhibitory substances or mechanisms exist in the bud scales of the onion bulb (Fig. 4–12).

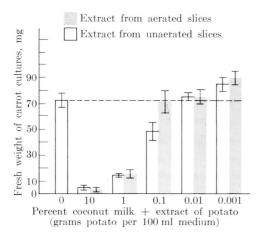

FIG. 4–11. Antagonistic effect of potato tuber extract on growth of phloem explants of carrot root as stimulated by coconut milk. (From Steward and Caplin, *Ann. Botany* N. S. 16, 491–504, 1952.)

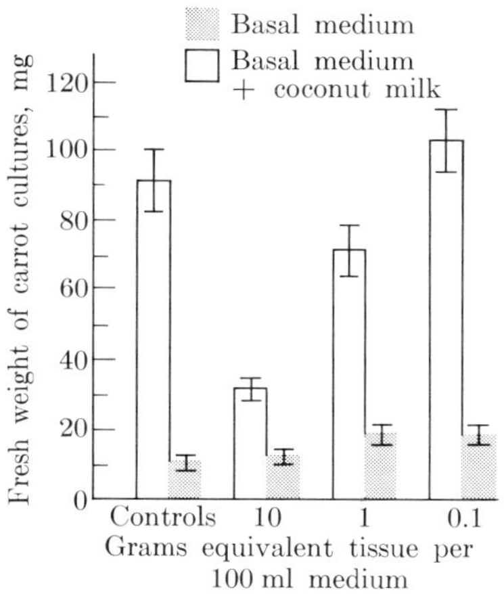

FIG. 4–12. Effect of extract of onion bulb on the growth of explants from carrot root. (From Steward and Caplin, *Ann. Botany* N. S. 16, 491–504, 1952.)

The resting buds of a maple tree present an interesting situation. While dormant in late summer and early autumn, the buds of maple seem to contain an inhibitor of cell division, but, after dormancy is broken by exposure to cold, this inhibitor disappears or is reduced in concentration until it is ineffective in neutralizing the effect of coconut milk on carrot explants (Steward and Caplin, 1952b).

The occurrence of natural inhibitors of growth has recently been stressed by the isolation and identification of several specific compounds. A compound which was first recognized in cotton and is implicated in abscission (and therefore termed by Addicott *et al.*, 1964, as abscisin II) was later shown to be involved in dormancy of sycamore buds (*Acer pseudoplatanus*) and designated by Eagles and Wareing as dormin (a representative of a larger class of "dormins" which endogenously induce dormancy). The same substance was synthesized by Cornforth *et al.* (1965), who named it terpolinic acid, on the basis of its chemical structure. The preferred name is now, however, abscisic acid.

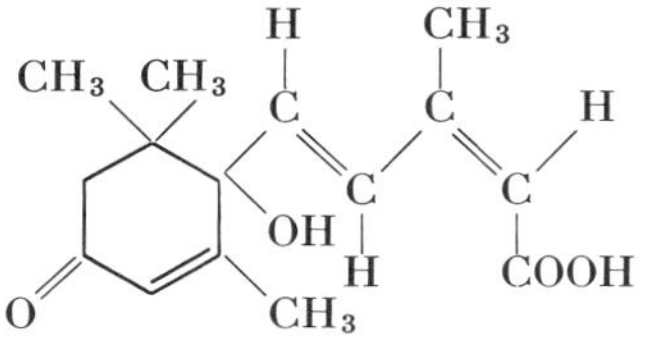

CH₃ structure — Abscisin II

Abscisin II

Present indications are that this substance is widely distributed in mature plant organs; it certainly antagonizes the cell division activity of coconut milk in the carrot assay system and it has been shown to inhibit the action of gibberellic acid (GA_3) in an assay system depending upon the activity of that substance in the formation and release of α-amylase by the aleurone layer of cereal grains (Varner and Ram Chandra, 1964; Chrispiels and Varner, 1967); but it also tends to inhibit auxins in the coleoptile and mesocotyl tests. A compound isolated by Rothwell and Wain (1964) from yellow lupin is also now known to be terpolinic acid. Thus abscisic or terpolinic acid may turn out to be a widely occurring and selective natural inhibitor of growth and growth-promoting substances.

Similarly, Japanese workers (Tagawa *et al.* at the University of Hokkaido) have isolated a solanidine glycoside from potato tubers and believe that this is implicated in the dormancy of that organ.

Solanidine glycoside

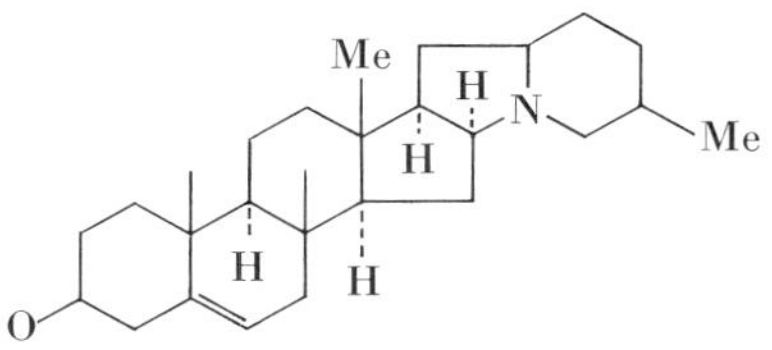

Solanidine

Dirhamnose-glucose ------ O

It has been shown that this substance is also effective, but at rather high concentrations, in counteracting the growth-stimulating role of coconut milk upon carrot explants. Another substance, heliangine, from *Helianthus* is now regarded as the substance that is responsible for the light-induced inhibition of growth in internodes (Shibaoka, 1961; Yamaki *et al.*, 1966).

Heliangine

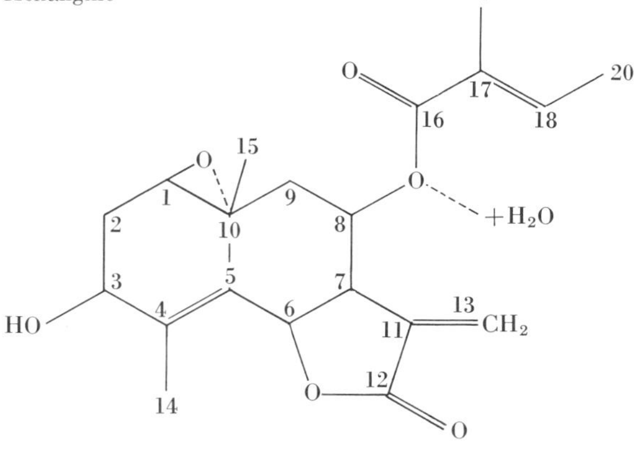

Tiglic acid

$+H_2O$

HO

Helianginol

These observations all mean that the ability of plant cells to grow is conditioned in the following ways:

1.   First, there are needed supplies of essential nutrients—water, salts, trace elements, suitable sources (whether endogenous or exogenous) of carbon and nitrogen compounds.

2.   Secondly, there are various vitamins which are essential to ensure that the nutrients needed in large amount by the cells can be utilized in the array of chemical reactions that are involved in their growth. Often, if not always, the vitamin functions as a coenzyme in some essential enzyme system.

3.   But, over and above the nutrients and the vitamins, certain accessory stimuli or growth-regulating compounds are also needed, and these are of two main types: (a) those, like the coconut milk factors, which act primarily to promote cell division, and (b) those, like the auxins and gibberellins, which seem to act primarily upon cell enlargement.

To some extent cell division and cell enlargement may thus appear to be in opposition. However, both division and enlargement must occur in sequence and in balance whenever cells grow continuously. The seeming antithesis between the stimuli that lead to enlargement and to division arises because one event (cell enlargement) occurs and is best measured under conditions where the other (cell division) is at a minimum.

There is, however, an evident balance between the overall mechanisms that promote growth and those which tend to suppress it, and this balance is subject to chemical regulatory control. Factors that stimulate cell division, or cell enlargement, have their counterparts in inhibitors, and when the balance between these is disturbed, anomalous effects result. Thus a tumor or an overgrowth, or a rapidly proliferating tissue culture, may be due to an imbalanced, often exogenous, supply of the cell division growth-promoting substances; if there is continued endogenous formation of these growth-promoting substances, a cancerous-like growth may appear. Such cancerous-like growth in plants may be a response to the activity of the crown gall organism, or to the tumor-producing viruses (cf. Black, 1949). Essentially, however, each such stimulating agent operates through an effect upon the otherwise delicately poised balance between the cell-division-promoting mechanisms and those which hold them in check. The observations (Steward, Caplin, and Shantz, 1955) that an extract of *Kalanchoe* (*Bryophyllum*) crown gall tumor had an excess of growth-promoting materials that would stimulate carrot cells to grow, whereas tissue from the normal host would not do this, confirmed the same general idea. Moreover, tumor-forming hybrids of tobacco (*Nicotiana glacua* × *Nicotiana langsdorfii*) have the balance between cell-division-promoting agents and their inhibitors disturbed, for their tissues, unlike those of the more normal parents, yield aqueous extracts which will induce growth in carrot explants.

Therefore, the investigation of the nature, chemical configuration, and mode of action of the naturally occurring growth-regulatory substances is one of the most challenging current problems in the understanding of the physiology of growth. A knowledge of the chemical nature of these stimuli and of how they act could lead to a new degree of control over the growth of plants.

Periodicity in growth and its determination.   Periodicity in the incidence of growth and development is a striking natural phenomenon. In perennial plants rest and dormancy are conspicuous in temperate latitudes and are determined by seasonal cycles. Even in tropical climates, less obvious cycles exist, with their probable basis in rainfall rather than in cycles of temperature or of daylight. It is, however, a paradox that the buds of trees in temperate climates prepare for, and enter, dormancy under the very conditions in which it seems that their growth should be at a maximum. Maple buds may be laid down in the current year of growth, and enter upon dormancy in the summer when all the conditions of nutrients, temperature, etc., seem optimal. It is well known that the dormancy of resting buds is subsequently broken by a period of exposure to cold, though by various chemical treatments the effects of cold may be replaced. Here, then, is an area in which the onset of rest and dormancy, and its subsequent breaking by exposure to cold, must be regulated by some chemical stimuli which control the contrasted metabolism of the growing and the resting cells.

Recognition of the photoperiodic determination of the onset of flowering and of the formation of such organs of perennation as tubers, bulbs, corms, etc., is one of the outstanding developments of this century. It followed the pioneer work of Garner and Allard (1920, 1923) in the United States. More recently, however, recognition has been given to another rhythmic phenomenon, namely, the alternation of high and low temperature in successive periods of day and night; it is now known that many profound events flow from the way in which thermoperiod and photoperiod interact diurnally (Went, 1957). One may illustrate this by reference again to the mint plant.

Mint is markedly photoperiodic; it forms flowers under long days and stolons under short days, and the whole habit of the plant is different when it is grown under long- and short-day conditions (cf. Figs. 1–16A and B). Later it will be shown that these growth habits are also associated with characteristic metabolic states that have been recognized by chromatographic examination of the soluble compounds in the leaves, stems, etc. But, although the mint plant behaves as a long-day plant, it is still subject to the even more overriding control of thermoperiod. When mint is grown under long days, but low night temperatures, *the effect of night temperature overrides the effect of day length.* In fact the most powerful external stimulus which controls the composition and metabolism of the leaves of the mint plant now appears to be the night temperature; so great is the effect of this stimulus that the metabolic consequences of exposure to a few cool nights, or even to one such period at low temperature, can be detected even when it is superimposed upon the composition which has been predetermined during growth (cf. Steward *et al.*, 1962).

Therefore, one sees in these photoperiodic and thermoperiodic stimuli the consequences of some as yet unknown chemical entity through which the effects of the environmental conditions are mediated and which ultimately regulate the behavior of the growing regions. The well-known effects of vernalization, by which ungerminated cereal grains are exposed at minimum water content to relatively low temperature, is another example of temperature regulation of flowering, for it effectively converts a normally biennial plant into an annual.

Vernalization works because it permits sufficient development to proceed within the environment of the grain, so that a certain amount of organ formation and cellular activity occurs before the embryo bursts through the testa. The exposure to cold thus converts what would otherwise be a biennial rye grass into an annual rye grass in the sense that it grows, flowers, fruits, and sets seed in one season. Similar events, however, are also known to flow from the stimulus of low temperature upon many seedlings in their early stages of growth after germination. Such normally biennial plants as celery, onion, beet, etc., can be caused to "bolt" by brief periods of exposure to low temperature in the early stages of seedling development. Once caused, these effects are irreversible. Again it seems quite clear that there must be some chemical basis for these observed responses, and while they may be of a more specific nature, one can visualize that they also operate through local control of cell division and cell enlargement of the kind that has been referred to above. Harada and Nitsch (1964) have recently claimed to have isolated, or at least concentrated, a "bolting factor" which affects some flowering plants in this way.

In the phenomena of tuberization and the formation of storage organs, where these are subject to temperature and photoperiodic control, one can readily see that mobilization of the storage food material to the organ could cause cells to multiply and to expand, so that the stimulus to this end must also flow from the environmental variables which ultimately control this kind of growth.

All the above examples have one feature in common. They concern situations in which chemical substances exogenous to cells, or environmental or developmental factors that induce effects no doubt mediated by such chemical substances, intervene to control the behavior of organized cells. Intrinsically each living cell, whether it be at rest, or dividing, or enlarging, whether it is metabolizing at a high or a low rate, possesses within its organization the innate abilities for all these types of activity. But in the determination of what shall occur these innate, genetically determined features of the organization are subject to extrinsic chemical and physical controls.

Terminology and classification of growth substances.   Plant physiologists have tacitly adopted conventions by which the physiologically active substances they recognize are grouped and classified by the often very general responses they elicit. Thus, auxins, assayed by one of the various tests (e.g., the coleoptile straight growth test) are so grouped together, even though there may be marked differences between the substances in question and they may even elicit their responses by different means. Similarly, the so-called gibberellins are recognized by their effect on the growth of genetically dwarfed plants. Despite the fact that a baffling array of substances, single or in some synergistic combination, affect cell division, the activity in question is often held to be that of a kinin (or, as it is now termed, a cytokinin).

There are two features which distinguish the accessory growth-regulating substances of plants from the classical concept of the accessory physiologically active substances, i.e., the vitamins and hormones in the animal body. The first difference is in the generality of the responses which are elicited by the plant regulators; this is itself a consequence of the greater totipotency of living plant cells and the lesser degree of their ultimate specialization of function. The second point of difference is in the number of substances, not always closely related, which may elicit a given response. One does not expect to find several or many vitamins A or B_1 or several different thyroxins or adrenalins which elicit the same ultimate response. Therefore, if one were to start over again and to adopt a distinctively plant terminology for the accessory growth-regulating substances, preferably with foreknowledge of how they act, it might be done very differently and with fewer ambiguities. Indeed, one wonders whether it would then be found as necessary to place what are now termed auxins and gibberellins in such rigidly distinctive categories as is now done.

The Nature and the Action of Growth-Regulating Substances

What constitutes an auxin?   Speculations on the mode of action of auxins were dominated by references to indoleacetic acid after its discovery as the principal, if not the sole, natural auxin. With the discovery of other auxin-like naturally occurring substances, this position has entirely changed. Substances (e.g., indoleacetonitrile, IAN) which are closely related to indoleacetic acid may cause a physiological response by similar means to indoleacetic acid itself; there is still room, however, for the view that indoleacetic acid is not necessarily, nor always, the only effective molecule. However, the activity of the gibberellins, which is due to molecules that have little or nothing in common with indoleacetic acid, raises entirely different problems; although some would attribute to the gibberellins a secondary role of protecting indoleacetic acid from destruction. If there are many still unidentified auxin-like substances it is unwise to formulate theories of auxin activity which are too closely identified with the structure and precise role of indoleacetic acid.

The proceedings of a conference on growth substances held at Wye College, England (Wain and Wightman, 1956) reveal the range and complexity of synthetic substances then known to have auxin or growth-regulating activity when they are applied to plants. Two later conferences (their proceedings edited by

Klein, 1961, and by Nitsch, 1964), one held in 1959 and one in 1963, have been concerned with both synthetic and natural growth-regulating substances. Thus the original rules that prescribed the chemical structure of an auxin are now difficult to maintain. The discovery, first made in Holland and extended in England, that such straight chain compounds as thiocarbarmates have growth-promoting and auxin-like properties, undermined the treasured idea that such physiological activity requires the presence of a ring in the molecule; this idea was already difficult to maintain because even ethylene displays certain auxin-like properties!* Though it is still difficult to stipulate the chemical configuration that will exclusively endow a substance with the growth-promoting properties of an auxin, nevertheless, certain conclusions may be drawn from the behavior of a family of *similar* compounds which display auxin-like activity. This is comparable to a situation in genetics where it is possible to manipulate and recognize factors for different kinds and breeds of cats without in the least knowing what it is that determines "catness."

In a series of phenoxy acids with side chains that vary in length, auxin activity was found by Wain and Wightman (1953) to occur only if the side chain is broken down by β-oxidation in which the two terminal carbon atoms are removed at each oxidative step. When the side chains have an even number of carbon atoms the phenoxy acids are physiologically active; when they have an odd number of carbon atoms they are inactive. For a phenoxy acid with a long side chain to be effective as a growth regulator, the plant to which it is applied should possess the enzyme system which will first degrade the side chain, as well as the enzyme systems which allow the substituted acetic acid to function. In some plants both systems occur—in others this is not so. Different chemical configurations in the aromatic ring of the phenoxy acids influence the compatibility of the molecules with the enzymes that degrade the side chain, as well as the final activity of the resulting phenoxyacetic acid. By working on these lines it has been possible to devise situations in which a given synthetic herbicide is more markedly toxic to one species of plant than to others (Wain, 1955a). This principle has been elaborated ingeniously to obtain selectivity in the application of these growth-regulating substances. For example, ω-(2-methyl-4-chlorophenoxy)-butyric acid (MCPB) is toxic to a number of common weeds but not to the clovers with which they often occur (cf. Wain and Fawcett, 1967).

The consideration of synthetic growth-regulating substances that have asymmetric carbon atoms in the molecule leads to another generalization. The specificity of these substances is so great that one enantiomorph is usually active and the other is usually inactive and may even be inhibitory to the active form (cf. Fig. 4–40). This was found by Wain (1955b) in some α-substituted propionic acids which were prepared in their optically active forms. Thus, at

---

* There are, however, very recent ideas that link auxin action causally to the metabolism and role of ethylene in plants (Burg and Burg, 1965, 1966a and b, 1967; Burg and Clagett, 1967).

the site of activity the molecule must show a very close degree of geometrical fit, so close in fact that even the mirror image of the active molecule may not suffice!

It is not possible here to discuss all the suggestions upon the mode of action of the known auxin-like substances in relation to their structure but reference can be made to Section II of the volume edited by Wain and Wightman (1956) and a chapter by Wain and Fawcett in a forthcoming volume of the treatise on plant physiology being edited by Steward. A few salient ideas follow.

The ability of a substance to function as an auxin is conceived to be a sensitive function of its molecular structure. In this respect the overall shape and size of the molecule are important as well as the functional groups it contains. The auxin is conceived to act at some receptor site in the cell, probably a protein, and a highly specific relationship between auxin and receptor is generally considered to be essential; this relationship may even involve actual chemical combination. (More recently it has become the vogue to invoke relationships, even actual combination, between auxin and the nucleic acids of cells.) To account for the sensitivity to changes in the molecular configuration of active molecules, it has been proposed that the auxin and the receptor site may need to engage correctly at two, or even multiple, points of contact. Therefore, very minute differences of structure might distinguish an active auxin from an inhibitor which could preempt a given site. Thus, to understand the possible role of different substances it is not enough to examine their molecular formulae; the substances should also be seen to scale in three-dimensional models.

The striking fact is that so little is known about what growth-regulating substances actually do. This is so despite the large amount of synthetic work that has preceded the choice of substances to be manufactured as growth regulators and the large amount of empirical testing that has been undertaken to demonstrate their usefulness. The range of applications of growth-regulating compounds now extends from the chemical control of weeds by selective herbicidal action through the controlled defoliation of plants, the prevention of abscission of fruit, the promotion of parthenocarpic development of fruits, and attempts to control the onset and breaking of dormancy—and even in certain substances, controls that operate through the water balance of plants in their aerial environment (Waggoner and Zelitch, 1965; Waggoner, 1966).

The main ideas concerning the mode of action of the auxin-like growth-regulating substances that have been suggested, or held, can now be listed. All, or most, of these, directly or indirectly, invoke the ability of the molecules in question to affect water absorption and cell enlargement in the tissues concerned.

Possible mechanisms of auxin action.   Many papers (Bonner *et al.*, 1956; Ordin *et al.*, 1956) are concerned with what is described as auxin-induced water uptake. The concept is that the auxin, usually indoleacetic acid, causes cells which exist in a given osmotic environment to take in more water than they otherwise would; this could occur in different ways.

The resistance to further enlargement by water intake of an expanded cell is usually ascribed to the back pressure of the elastic cell wall. An early idea of auxin action dates back to papers by Heyn (1931) and postulates that auxin affects the plasticity of the cell wall and so enables it to be deformed by plastic flow, in contrast to elastic extension. Such effects are attributable to the action of the auxin on the pectin or non-crystalline moiety of the cell wall, since it is difficult to visualize how the indoleacetic acid could affect the elastic extension of the already formed cellulose fibrils. A difficulty exists in the interpretation of the cell wall as a completely enveloping, elastic sheet. This is especially so in certain situations in which cells elongate rapidly. The first-formed wall does not usually contain the parallel, rope-like strands of cellulose which are obviously well fitted to restrict further expansion. On the contrary it often consists of a random net of cellulose fibrils which are embedded in amorphous material. This type of wall is not constituted to resist stretching but it is adapted to enlargement since the random threads can be pulled apart. Since this type of wall in the tips of fibers, root hairs, and possibly other situations does not restrict further intake of water, it may even be suggested that water relations in these areas must be under metabolic control, since the cells would otherwise burst at their growing tips.

Also, if auxin is to operate during cell extension by virtue of its effects in the cell wall, then the kind of system to be affected is illustrated in Fig. 4–13.

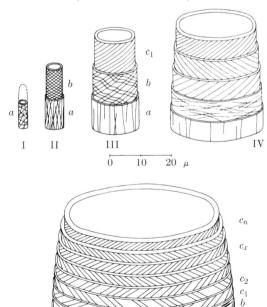

FIG. 4–13. Development of the cell wall in a laticiferous element showing lamellations and the texture of the cellulose. The lines in each layer in the diagram reflect the density of the fibrils as they occur naturally; the secondary wall of stages IV and V can only be shown in part. (a, primary wall; b, transition cell lamella; c, lamellae; in c_x, the x designates the numbered lamella in question; the total may amount to 60–70.) (From Moor, *J. Ultrastruct. Res.* **2**, 393–422, 1959.)

These diagrams relate to the orientation of cellulose fibrils in the first-formed wall and in the subsequent layers of secondary wall of latex tubes. The general idea is applicable, however, to other cells in which wall substance is laid down during elongation in successive layers.

It has also been suggested that auxin, directly or indirectly, stimulates salt accumulation in the cells and so builds up an osmotic concentration in the vacuole; consequently, a greater suction pressure, or diffusion pressure deficit, is established, which, in turn, causes the cells to enlarge.

More indirect views of auxin action invoke its effect on respiration; this was first assumed by Thimann and Bonner (1950) and Ordin *et al.* (1956) to arise from some effect of auxin upon the respiration that passes over the organic acid or Krebs' cycle. On this view, indoleacetic acid should have some coenzyme function, in one or another of the enzymes involved in the respiratory process, although one should add that neither at the time this idea was enunciated, nor at the present, is there any clear-cut evidence that indoleacetic acid is a coenzyme for any enzyme that seems to be responsible for an essential step in respiratory metabolism.

Two different approaches to the problem of IAA action have concentrated on its supposed effects on the properties of the cell wall. Bennet-Clark (1956) suggested that methylation of compounds in cell walls tends to affect their rigidity, that choline is a methylating agent and that IAA may exert its effect by intervening in metabolic cycles in which lecithin, a substance long supposed to be present in the protoplasmic surface and to penetrate the cell wall, may be split to yield choline. There is some evidence that IAA can act as an inhibitor of choline esterase, an enzyme that splits choline from combinations with acidic substances such as glycerophosphoric acid. This observation led Bennet-Clark to implicate IAA in the methylation of cell wall substances by controlling the availability of free choline.

A somewhat similar approach was followed by Ordin *et al.* (1955, 1957), who substituted methionine for choline as the methylating agent and believed

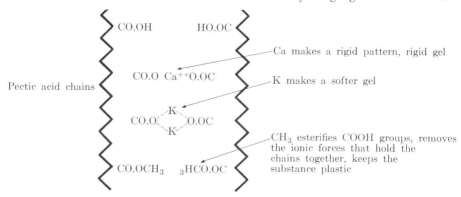

FIG. 4–14. Diagrammatic representation of the effect of K, Ca, and CH₃ on rigidity of a pectic acid gel.

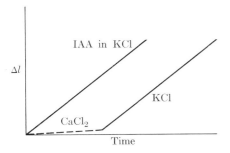

FIG. 4–15. Diagram to show effects of potassium (KCl) and calcium (CaCl$_2$) on the extension of the cell walls of *Avena* coleoptiles as this is promoted by indoleacetic acid (IAA).

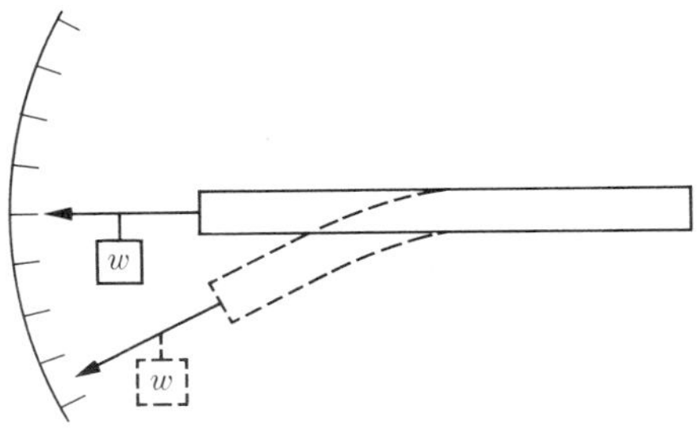

FIG. 4–16. Deformation of an *Avena* coleoptile by a weight (w).

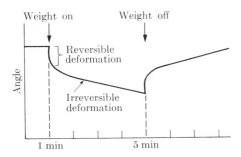

FIG. 4–17. Diagram to illustrate reversible and irreversible deformation of an *Avena* coleoptile.

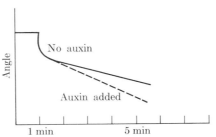

FIG. 4–18. The effect of auxin (IAA) on the plastic flow of the cell wall.

that the CH$_3$ groups of methionine can be donated to the galacturonic acid of the pectic substances of the cell wall (cf. Fig. 4–14). Bonner (1960), following the older work of Heyn (1931), analyzed coleoptile sections as an engineer would a metal bar under test for its ability to withstand a bending strain. From the manipulation of coleoptiles in this way, the following general kinds of observations have been made:

1. IAA causes extension of coleoptile segments.
2. KCl will permit wall extension, CaCl$_2$ will not (cf. Fig. 4–15).
3. When a coleoptile segment is deformed by a weight (cf. Fig. 4–16), it undergoes
   a) Elastic, or reversible, deformation.
   b) Plastic, or irreversible, deformation.
   c) Therefore, IAA does not change the osmotic pressure or alter the metabolic formation of substance, but it affects the ability of the cell to absorb water by increasing the effective "Diffusion Pressure Deficit" (DPD) by decreasing the effective "wall pressure" of the cell. Thus, auxin-treated coleoptiles behave in ways which are attributed to the plastic flow of the wall (cf. Figs. 4–17 and 4–18).

d) Pretreating the coleoptiles with Ca makes them more stiff, whereas K makes them more deformable.

e) The pectin content of coleoptiles is high; some two-thirds of the wall is pectic material which has a high binding capacity for cations. Therefore, the pectin may be the material on which the IAA acts.

CH_3 of C^{14}-methionine donates methyl groups to galacturonic acid. C^{14}-labeled galactose labels pectin but IAA does not have a large effect on the total pectin formation. Apparently the CH_3 groups in pectin are constantly being turned over by the activity of pectin methyl esterase. Treating radioactive CH_3 pectin in the presence of C^{12}-methionine permits CH_3 to enter the methionine. Moreover, if coleoptiles are put in labeled methionine and IAA is added, the amount of radioactivity which enters the methylated pectins is increased by an additional two-thirds, i.e., the IAA promotes the turnover of pectins (Fig. 4–19).

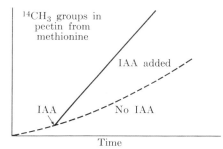

FIG. 4–19. The effect of auxin (IAA) on the turnover of pectins, as shown by the incorporation of C^{14} methyl groups. (Figs. 4.15 through 4.19 drawn to illustrate the general views of Bonner *et al.*, circa 1956.)

f) The incorporation of CH_3 groups into the coleoptile pectins is:
i) inhibited by ethionine, which inhibits transmethylation by substituting C_2H_5 for CH_3 groups.
ii) inhibited by an auxin antagonist such as 2,4,6-trichlorophenoxyacetic acid.
iii) behaves like auxin-induced growth to other variables.

But if this is all true why should not IAA exert its effect on almost any cell wall which contains pectin as, for example, the walls of algae? Moreover, why should IAA have this unlikely effect of promoting pectin turnover? On this view there is still need to explain and locate the effect of IAA in the methylation enzyme system in order to account for its effects upon cell walls.

[With reference to the suggested effect of IAA upon cellulose walls, it is of interest that griseofulvin, a naturally occurring substance which has fungicidal activity (as discovered by Brian *et al.*, 1946) acts upon those fungi which have chitinous walls and causes the filaments to elongate, to form spirals, and to swell.]

The precise mode of action of auxins is still unknown. For many years ethylene has been known to cause hormone-like effects in stimulating roothair formation, epinasty, intumescences (as on apple cuttings) and also physiological effects by inducing ripening, as at the onset of a climacteric in several fruits. Ethylene has therefore been cited as a very simple molecule with hormonal (often auxin-like) properties. As such it has often seemed to confound the supposed relation between the structure of a hormone and its physiological action. Curiously, however, the respective roles of ethylene and auxin now seem to be linked. Auxin stimulates the formation of ethylene from the C_3-C_4 carbons of methionine, and many of the properties hitherto attributable to auxins can now be visualized as though mediated by ethylene. These effects range from the swelling of cells which underlies root geotropism and perhaps other tropisms commonly attributed to IAA or the flowering inducible in pineapple by NAA. The way in which the ethylene so formed acts still remains to be determined, although high carbon dioxide and low oxygen now impair the binding of ethylene to a metal containing receptor site upon which its action is supposed to depend. Relevant literature will be found in the early work of Crocker *et al.* (1935) and in the later works of Burg and Burg (1965–67) and of Lieberman *et al.* (1966).

Recently, a great deal of attention has been focused on the regulatory action of genes, located in the DNA of the nucleus, and their ability to transmit to soluble RNA some specific instructions which will be impressed upon the protein-synthesizing surfaces, where specific enzyme proteins may be made. The organelle where protein is made is the ribosome, which is composed of ribosomal ribonucleic acid, but the precise nature of the template where a given synthesis occurs will be determined by a transient or messenger RNA. Against this background it is not unnatural that attempts should be made to involve relationships between auxins and RNA. This Galston and his associates have done (Meundt and Galston, 1962; Kefford *et al.*, 1963) in the belief that actual compounds between RNA and IAA exist. At this point, however, the evidence to support this approach still seems tenuous, for it is very difficult to interpret the significance *in vivo* of the supposed, but very indeterminate, combinations between RNA and IAA that have been studied *in vitro*. If auxins were to exert their effect through the now conventionally visualized scheme of protein synthesis it would seem as though they should intervene by affecting the role of the DNA and either activate or suppress the RNA at its formation. So far there is no conclusive evidence that this is so, although these ideas have motivated the recent works of Key (cf. Key and Shannon, 1964) and Cherry (cf. Carpenter and Cherry, 1966).

Some cell division factors from the environment of embryos. The main problem in relation to those growth-regulatory substances which primarily affect cell division, rather than cell enlargement, is to specify the types of molecules which are effective. Here we are still embarrassed by the incomplete state of our knowledge. Attempts to isolate the active principles from growth-promoting fluids, such as coconut milk, which are obtained from the environment of embryos but which, nevertheless, stimulate cell division in cultures of mature tissues, have not yet been completed because the systems are far more complicated than was at first expected.

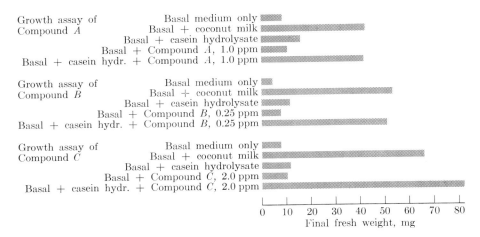

FIG. 4–20. Activity of Compounds A, B, and C from coconut milk in the induction of growth of carrot root phloem explants. Each bar represents the average weight of four carrot phloem explants after a 14-day test period. Original weight of each explant was 2.6 mg. These tests were not done concurrently and therefore each of the three groups depicts the growth of explants from a different carrot root. (From Shantz and Steward, *J. Am. Chem. Soc.* **77,** 6351–6353, 1955.)

Coconut milk itself, by means of various complicated separations which started with heavy metal precipitation (using mercuric acetate or nitrate) and extensive fractionation of the precipitate, originally yielded three substances which were designated as Compounds *A*, *B*, and *C*. These compounds were obtained in a crystalline state and were sufficiently characterized to ensure their recognition. Compounds *A*, *B*, and *C* were shown to be separately active and, in presence of appropriate amounts of casein hydrolysate and with the particular strains of carrots used, they could reproduce almost completely the full activity of whole coconut milk (Fig. 4–20). Only one of these substances has been completely characterized and this (Compound *A*) turned out to be symmetrical 1,3-diphenylurea (Fig. 4–21). The isolated Compound *A* was active in the presence of casein hydrolysate on explants from most carrots (Fig. 4–22). For some reason, however, the synthetic compound was less active than the isolated substance when it was later tested upon most strains of carrot; in spite of this discrepancy the chemical identity of the isolated substance was demonstrated beyond any doubt. This was shown by comparing the infrared absorption spectra of the two substances, as shown in Fig. 4–23. While the ability of

1,3-diphenylurea   FIG. 4–21. Formula of isolated Compound A from coconut milk.

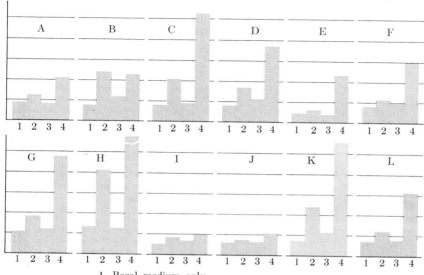

1. Basal medium only
2. Basal + casein hydrolysate, 500 ppm
3. Basal + Compound *A*, 1.0 ppm
4. Basal + casein hydrolysate + Compound *A*.

FIG. 4–22. Growth assays of Compound A with explants from 12 different carrot roots, showing lack of response to Compound A in absence of casein hydrolysate (treatment 3), and differences in response of explants from different roots to Compound A plus casein hydrolysate (treatment 4). (From work of Shantz and Steward.)

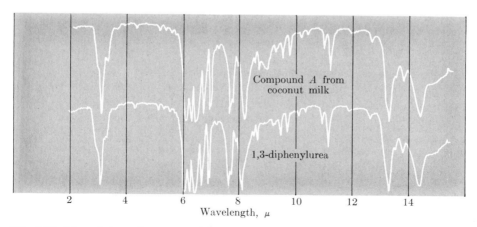

FIG. 4–23. Infrared absorption spectra of Compound A from coconut milk and 1, 3-diphenylurea (synthetic Compound A). (From Steward and Shantz, in Wain and Wightman, eds., *The Chemistry and Mode of Action of Plant Growth Substances*, Academic Press, New York, 1956.)

TABLE 4–2
Effect of 1,3-diphenylurea (DPU) on growth of plant tissue cultures

Treatment	a) Carrot Tissue (Grown 17 Days at 24°C)					
	Fresh weight, mg		Cell number, $\times 10^3$		Cells per μg	
	B	C	B	C	B	C
Basal medium	7.2	4.6	45.2	28.8	6.3	6.4
Basal medium + DPU, 2.0 ppm	9.4	7.5	50.2	49.0	5.4	6.5
Basal medium + casein hydrolysate	29.4	64.8	201.4	536.1	6.8	8.8
Basal medium + casein hydrolysate + DPU, 2.0 ppm	56.8	108.5	508.6	1042.7	8.9	9.7
Basal medium + casein hydrolysate + coconut milk, 10%	294.4	323.1	2662.8	2692.5	9.1	8.3
	b) Artichoke Tissue (Grown 29 Days at 24°C)					
Basal medium + casein hydrolysate	6.0		10.7		1.9	
Basal medium + DPU, 0.08 ppm	12.0		63.2		4.8	

1,3-diphenylurea to promote cell division in carrot tissue has been fully established (Table 4–2), the activity of many synthetic carbanilides is much lower, although many synthetic ones with activity have been prepared (Kefford, personal communication). Compounds *B* and *C*, however, are still not completely identified.

In the attempt to isolate the active principles of coconut milk, use was made of methods which did not require heavy metal precipitation. Low-temperature evaporation, as used in the commercial concentration of orange juice, followed by liquid-liquid separations on an extensive scale using an automatic liquid-liquid separator, has yielded different substances which, unlike Compounds *A*, *B*, and *C*, are free from nitrogen. Without giving the supporting evidence here, it turns out that in coconut milk, as well as in the more solid tissue (integument) from the immature fruit of *Aesculus*, there are active growth-promoting molecules which belong to the general class of substances known as leucoanthocyanins. The chemical properties of the isolated substances, which are very difficult to purify and characterize, and which have hitherto defied synthesis, are consistent with the structures shown in Fig. 4–24. It is now known, beyond any doubt,

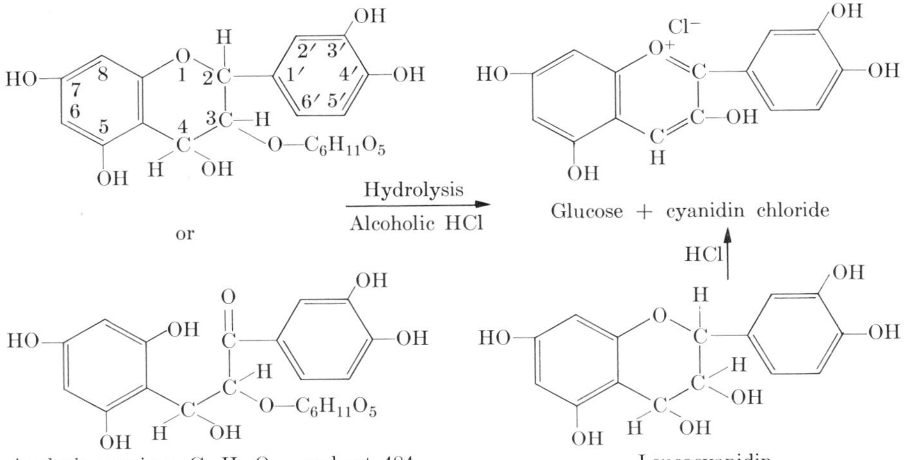

Analysis requires: $C_{21}H_{24}O_{13}$, mol wt 484

Found: $C_{21}H_{28}O_{13}$, mol wt 474

FIG. 4–24. Possible structure of leucoanthocyanin glucoside isolated from *Aesculus*. (From Steward and Shantz, in Wain and Wightman, eds., *The Chemistry and Mode of Action of Plant Growth Substances*, Academic Press, New York, 1956.)

that molecules of this general type can stimulate growth and cell division in isolated carrot explants (Fig. 4–25 and Table 4–3). The unexpected association of growth-regulating activity by the control of cell division with the leucoanthocyanin structure raises a number of interesting possibilities.

Chemical conversion of the leucoanthocyanin either to the colored anthocyanin, or to cyanidin, seems to render these molecules inactive; this suggests that the colored compounds are the inactivated products of others which had the growth-promoting activity. If it is recognized that leucoanthocyanins, the natural precursors of the anthocyanins, may have growth-promoting properties, a number of observations become suggestive.

In many plants the appendages first laid down by the shoot growing points are colorless or creamy yellow for a time and they may remain so during the period in which cell divisions are prominent but, thereafter, colored stages intervene before chlorophyll causes the shoot tissue to turn green. This may be seen in certain subtropical legumes, such as *Brownea* and *Amherstia*, in which the primordia of the compound leaf develop to their full size while they are rolled in the bud; in this condition the leaf is almost free from pigment. Subsequently, variegated portions arise, especially in the epidermis, which are red because of the presence of cyanin; only after this first pigmentation has become somewhat general is it masked by the formation of chlorophyll. This association between the growing leaf in the bud and the precursors of anthocyanin present while the leaf primordia are in the meristematic state, is suggestive, to

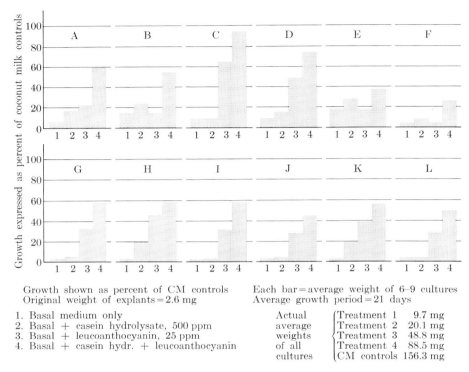

Growth shown as percent of CM controls
Original weight of explants = 2.6 mg

Each bar = average weight of 6–9 cultures
Average growth period = 21 days

1. Basal medium only
2. Basal + casein hydrolysate, 500 ppm
3. Basal + leucoanthocyanin, 25 ppm
4. Basal + casein hydr. + leucoanthocyanin

Actual
average
weights
of all
cultures

Treatment 1   9.7 mg
Treatment 2   20.1 mg
Treatment 3   48.8 mg
Treatment 4   88.5 mg
CM controls 156.3 mg

FIG. 4–25. Growth induced by purified leucoanthocyanin from *Aesculus* in explants from 12 different carrot roots, with and without added casein hydrolysate. (From work of Shantz and Steward.)

say the least. Similarly in *Eucalyptus* it has been found (Hillis, 1955) that leucoanthocyanins occur in the leaf while it is in its formative stages, and the Australian workers also suggest that leucoanthocyanins are prominent in the cambial tissue of *Eucalyptus* at the time when the spring flush of growth occurs. Some saprophytic angiosperms, like the Indian pipe (*Monotropa*), which are virtually colorless, become deeply colored when killed, again suggesting the presence of large reserves of leuco-compounds in the living tissue. Thus it would be extremely important if a physiological function could be found for the leuco-compounds which give rise to such substances as anthocyanins. The general class of flavonoids has so often been regarded as one of mere metabolic waste products that some direct physiological function for them would be illuminating.*

* A recent isolation was made of about 10 mg of a product from *Aesculus* by Shantz in the author's laboratory. This substance is active in the carrot growth assay. It yields one molecule of IAA attached to a residue of $C_{12}H_{24}O_{12}$ which contains a sugar moiety, consisting of both glucose and rhamnose.

TABLE 4-3

Tests on compounds and preparations related to the leucoanthocyanins, received from various sources. Growth response for each experiment is expressed as percentage increase of fresh weight and cell number over corresponding control cultures grown in basal medium plus casein hydrolysate.

Supplement	Percent Increase over Controls by Fresh Weight	Percent Increase over Controls by Cell Number
Leucoanthocyanin from *Pinus*	54	159
	35	24
	144	197
	75	179
	33	56
Leucoanthocyanin from cocoa	25	86
	21	27
	111	106
	88	163
Crude leucoanthocyanin (Persimmon)	65	69
Crude grape pigment	156	214
Pelargonidin chloride	39	81
Pelargonidin-3-monoglucoside	240	428
l-epicatechin	29	78
	22	−3
	122	129
	98	179
d-catechin	43	20
	54	94
	29	8
	67	62
	102	352
	27	24
Catechin monohydrate	42	23
	31	69
Dihydroquercitin	28	32
	50	131
	27	40
	33	50
Quercitin	53	25
Phloridzin	21	45
	4	36
Crude chrysanthemin	39	123
	20	0
Chrysanthemin chloride	40	47
Idaein chloride	28	4
Cyanin chloride	−6	−11
Protocatechuic acid	8	47
	52	78

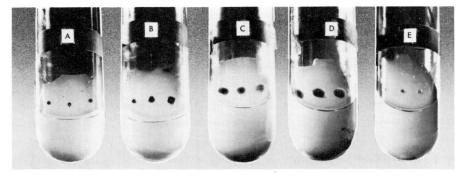

A. Basal medium + casein hydrolysate, 0.05%

B. Basal medium + casein hydr. + coconut milk, 10%

C. Basal medium + casein hydr. + BTOA, 10.0 ppm

D. Basal medium + casein hydr. + BTOA, 2.0 ppm

E. Basal medium + casein hydr. + BTOA, 0.4 ppm

Mean original explants: 3.2 mg; 10.0×10^3 cells;
3.2 cells per μg

	A	B	C	D	E
Weight per culture, mg	6.5	22.1	52.2	114.5	6.5
Cells $\times 10^3$ per culture	7.1	70.5	432.7	1084.1	16.2
Cells per μg	1.1	3.2	8.3	9.5	2.5

FIG. 4–26. Effects of 2-benzothiazolyloxyacetic acid (BTOA) on growth of explants from Jerusalem artichoke tuber. (From Steward and Shantz, in Wain and Wightman, eds., *The Chemistry and Mode of Action of Plant Growth Substances*, Academic Press, New York, 1956.)

However, the complex cyclical nitrogenous compounds, of which Compounds *A, B,* and *C* from coconut milk are examples, and another such compound which has been designated Compound *F,* and the nitrogen-free leucoanthocyanin-like molecules from coconut milk, and the more solid endosperm of *Aesculus,* by no means exhaust the possibilities inherent in the naturally occurring substances that promote cell division. The liquid endosperm of *Aesculus* has been examined, with particular reference to certain soluble fractions that have growth-promoting activity for carrot explants. This has led to the isolation of active substances which absorb in the ultraviolet and which seem to belong to the general class of nucleosides. Various bases, such as adenine, have been isolated from the liquid endosperm and have been obtained in the crystalline state, and positively identified. So far, however, the various purine and pyrimidine bases *alone* will not produce the cell division activity in question. It seems, moreover, that the active compounds of this general class are more apt to be active at the level of the nucleosides. Even so, however, there seems little chemically in common between substances of the sort designated Compounds *A, B,* and *C* from coconut milk, and the leucoanthocyanins or the nucleoside-like materials from *Aesculus.*

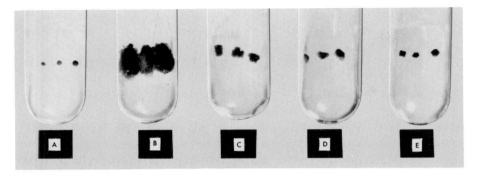

A. Basal medium + casein hydrolysate, 0.05%

B. Basal medium + casein hydr. + coconut milk, 10%

C. Basal medium + casein hydr. + BTOA, 10.0 ppm

D. Basal medium + casein hydr. + BTOA, 2.0 ppm

E. Basal medium + casein hydr. + BTOA, 0.4 ppm

Mean original explants: 3.3 mg; 34.74×10^3 cells;
10.5 cells per μg

	A	B	C	D	E
Weight per culture, mg	10.3	1046.3	81.1	59.1	19.5
Cells $\times 10^3$ per culture	33.2	4590.4	548.2	225.5	66.1
Cells per μg	3.2	4.4	6.8	3.8	3.4

FIG. 4–27. Effects of 2-benzothiazolyloxyacetic acid (BTOA) on growth of carrot root explants. (From Steward and Shantz, in Wain and Wightman, eds., *The Chemistry and Mode of Action of Plant Growth Substances*, Academic Press, New York, 1956.)

All this suggests that there is no single, overall, controlling substance that promotes and regulates cell division in flowering plants. On the contrary, the same ends may be achieved by the use of a baffling array of diverse chemical substances. This was aptly, but unexpectedly, demonstrated (Steward and Shantz, 1956) by the use of a synthetic compound called 2-benzothiazolyloxy-acetic acid, with the structure (a), but which may have been, according to Brookes and Leafe (1963), the substance (b), namely, 2-oxobenzothiazolin-3-ylacetic acid.

(a)

(b)

This substance is remarkably effective in the presence of casein hydrolysate in reproducing on artichoke tissue (Fig. 4–26) the kind of result previously obtained with coconut milk, and, beyond any doubt, it greatly stimulates cell division. With carrot tissue, on the other hand, its effect (Fig. 4–27), though real, is not so great in comparison with that of coconut milk. Again, it is difficult to see any very obvious connection between this molecular configuration and those others which have been mentioned above. Therefore, until we have more evidence concerning the chemical configuration of the various substances that will promote division in cells that otherwise would not divide, too much speculation is unprofitable.

Interactions between the components of fluids rich in naturally occurring cell division factors: a summary. The effect of fluids in contact with embryos, which promote cell division even in mature cells, is now known to be the result of the interaction between at least three parts of a complex system. First, there are the non-specific sources of reduced nitrogen—these may be any of a number of amino acids or even urea, or in some cases ammonia itself is effective (Shantz and Steward, 1959). Second, there are certain non-ionic substances (other than sugars) which although unable to induce cell division are nevertheless essential if this activity is to be evoked by the growth factors proper. Three substances in this category have been isolated from coconut milk and identified as hexitols, the inositol-like substance known as scyllitol (*scyllo*-inositol), *myo*-inositol, and sorbitol (cf. Fig. 4–28). The counterpart of the coconut milk neutral fraction has also been demonstrated in extracts of immature corn grains and *Aesculus* fruits. Third, there are the various cell division factors proper which, in the presence of the substances in the two former categories, can evoke the cell division. Even this category is heterogeneous, for it includes the various compounds (*A, B, C,* and others) from the early work on coconut milk, certain leucoanthocyanins, and some polyphenolic compounds among which even protocatechuic acid is weakly active, an indolearabinose compound of still incompletely known structure from corn, as well as an array of substances that still remain to be isolated and purified from the various natural

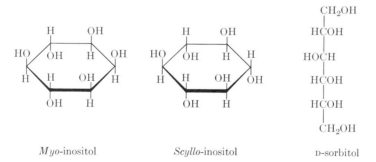

Myo-inositol   *Scyllo*-inositol   D-sorbitol

FIG. 4–28. Identified constituents of neutral fraction of coconut milk. Mannitol has also been isolated from coconut milk found in the Philippines, whereas that from Central America gave more sorbitol. (From Pollard, Shantz, and Steward, *Plant Physiol.* **36**, 492–501, 1961.)

sources of the activity which promotes cell division. Moreover the naturally occurring substances, in the environment of embryos, which promote cell division have their synthetic counterparts in such substances as 2-benzothiazolyloxyacetic acid and many others of which the substituted 6-furfurylamino purines are the conspicuous examples. The evidence for the different parts of complex, naturally occurring growth-promoting systems and the way they interact must now be considered.

The large-scale fractionation of coconut milk, the fluid from the vesicular embryo sac of *Aesculus*, and extracts of immature corn. It is not possible to present here the full biochemical procedures by which these naturally occurring fluids or extracts have been fractionated and their component parts tested by the carrot assay method, nor all the evidence for the nature of the substances so obtained. This work has extended over many years and it is conveniently summarized in three charts (Figs. 4–29, 4–30, and 4–31).* The evidence of Figs. 4–32, 4–33, and 4–34 substantiates the view that each of these natural nutritional fluids for immature embryos exhibits cell-division-promoting properties by virtue of complex interactions between different component parts of the entire system, each of which may contain several substances. The parts in question are those already mentioned, namely, (i) the source of reduced nitrogen (replaceable by casein hydrolysate, CH), (ii) the neutral fraction (NF replaceable, largely if not wholly, by *myo*-inositol), (iii) the active fraction (AF, which specifically promotes cell division), and (iv) an exogenous auxin (IAA or NAA), which may be dispensable if the entire system is complete. A very good example of the way these different component parts interact to promote the growth of carrot explants is represented in Fig. 4–35; this shows that the best growth was obtained when an otherwise complete basal medium was supplemented by all of the four components already named (i.e., CH, NF, AF, IAA). The four types of supplement were separately ineffective. When the supplements were combined two at a time they only caused substantial increments of growth over that in the basal medium when *both* the neutral (NF) and active (AF) fractions were present. The most dramatic effect upon the carrot tissue was obtained in response to the mutual interaction of these two supplements (NF and AF) with the others (CH and IAA). This is shown in Fig. 4–35. This feature of the overall problem, i.e., multiple interactions of different growth regulations, presents a serious complication in the isolation and identification of the active principles of such fluids as coconut milk, corn extract, and *Aesculus* extract, for each substance needs to be tested, during its isolation, in a medium which contains the proper balance of the other synergistically

---

* From Shantz and Steward, in J. P. Nitsch (ed.), *Régulateurs Naturels de la Croissance Végétale*, Centre National de la Recherche Scientifique, Paris, 1964.

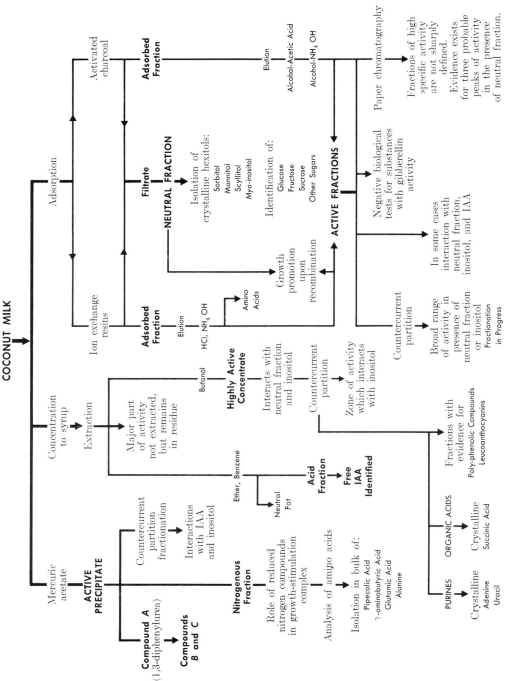

FIG. 4–29. Summary scheme for the large-scale fractionation of coconut milk.

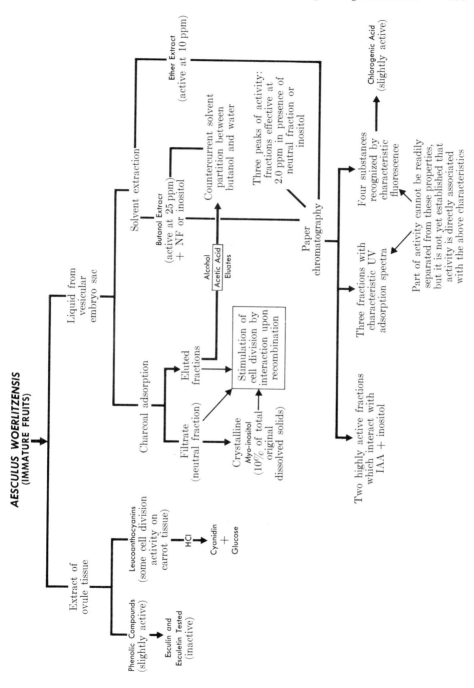

FIG. 4–30. Summary scheme for the large-scale fractionation of the liquid endosperm of *Aesculus woerlitzensis*.

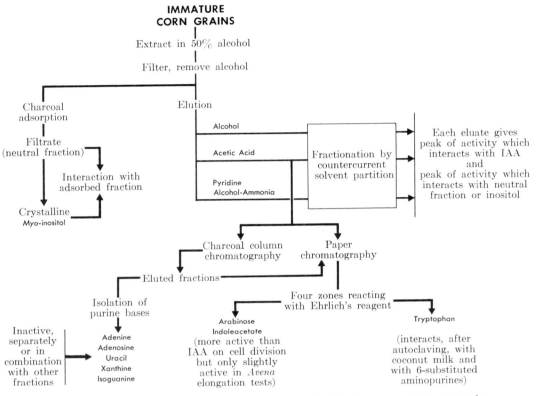

FIG. 4–31. Summary scheme for the large-scale fractionation of immature corn grains.

effective component parts of the entire system. On the other hand, an appreciation of the importance of these synergistic interactions is essential to a proper
understanding of the growth induction which is caused by coconut milk, etc.;
moreover, it discourages exaggerated claims for any particular substance or
component part of the entire system. Indeed it now appears that some active
cell division factors are more strongly linked to IAA and others to inositol and
that individual carrot roots may display different degrees of responsiveness to
the one or the other combination. Finally, it has to be recognized that combinations of substances which are even more effective for the growth of carrot
cells may yet be found; perhaps these might emerge if the substances to which
immature carrot embryos are exposed in their ovules could be obtained in quantities sufficient for their fractionation and identification. Or again, one could
fractionate the material which actively growing carrot explants supply to maintain the very rapid growth of their surface cells and which they even release
to activate free cells in their immediate vicinity (Steward and Mapes, 1963;
Blakely and Steward, 1964).

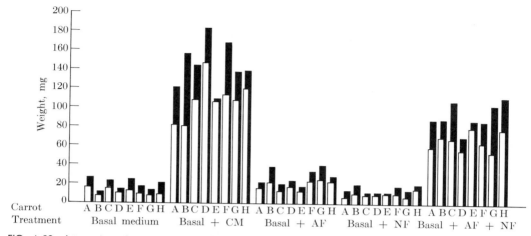

FIG. 4–32. Interaction of neutral fraction (NF) and active fraction (AF) isolated from coconut water in the growth of carrot explants. The interaction was tested in the presence (black bars) or the absence (open bars) of casein hydrolysate. (From Shantz and Steward, in J. P. Nitsch, ed., *Régulateurs Naturels de la Croissance Végétale,* Centre National de la Recherche Scientifique, Paris, 1964; cf. Steward et al., 1961.)

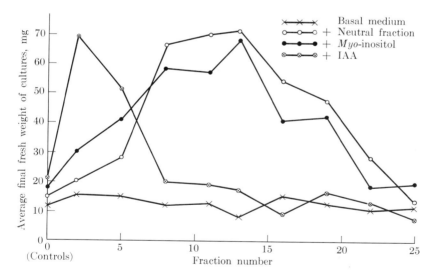

Fractions were tested at 5.0 ppm in basal medium alone and in combination with corn neutral fraction at 250 ppm, *myo*-inositol at 25 ppm, and indoleacetic acid at 0.5 ppm. Original weight of explants = 3.0 mg   Growth period = 18 days

FIG. 4–33. Growth-promoting effects on carrot root phloem explants of fractions obtained from the acetic acid eluate of charcoal-adsorbed corn extract by countercurrent partition between butanol and water. (From Shantz and Steward, in J. P. Nitsch, ed., *Régulateurs Naturels de la Croissance Végétale,* Centre Nationale de la Recherche Scientifique, Paris, 1964.)

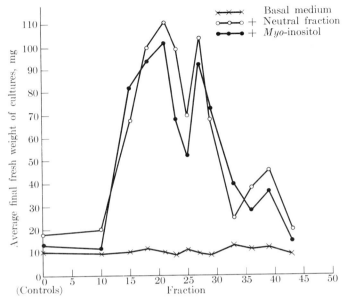

Fractions were tested at 2.0 ppm in basal medium alone and in basal medium plus 50.0 ppm of *Aesculus* neutral fraction or plus 25.0 ppm of *myo*-inositol. Original weight of explants = 3.0 mg   Growth period = 18 days

FIG. 4–34

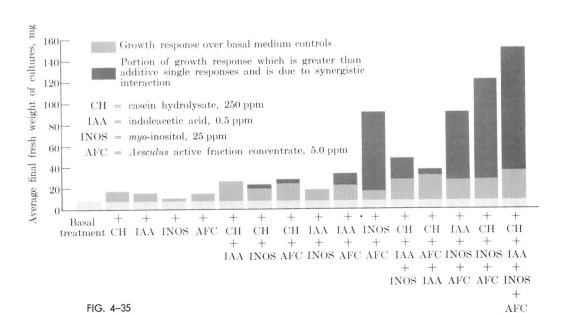

FIG. 4–35

◀FIG. 4–34. Growth-promoting effects of fractions obtained by countercurrent partition between butanol and water of the active fraction from *Aesculus* liquid eluted after adsorption on activated charcoal. (From Shantz and Steward, in J. P. Nitsch, ed., *Régulateurs Naturels de la Croissance Végétale*, Centre National de la Recherche Scientifique, Paris, 1964.)

Kinetin and related compounds.   Reference should now be made to another system and type of molecule which has been tested. Miller *et al.* (1955) recognized that aged specimens of nucleic acid were able to cause internal cell divisions in the very large hypertrophied cells of proliferated tobacco callus tissue. The effect of aging could be replaced by treatment of large amounts of nucleic acid in the autoclave. From this material a substance was isolated which was both identified and synthesized and which proved to be 6-furfurylaminopurine. This substance is apparently a modification, by rearrangement, of the more familiar natural substance, adenosine, and the trivial name kinetin has been given to the synthetic substance.

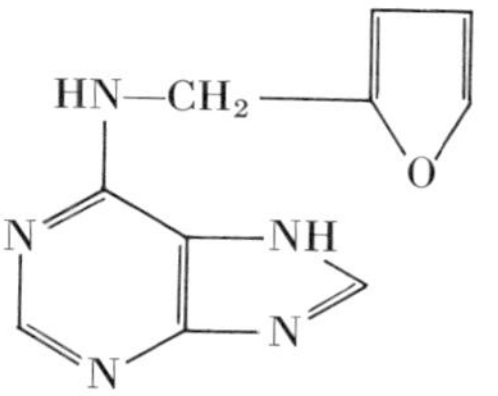

Kinetin: 6-furfurylaminopurine

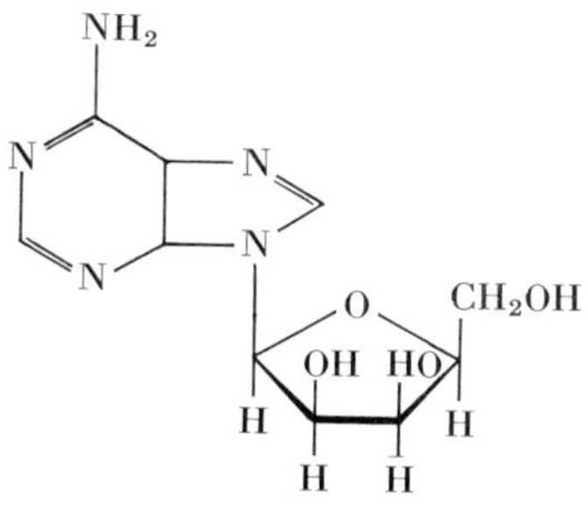

Adenosine: adenylribofuranose

Again, it is beyond all doubt that this substance promotes cell division in the enlarged cells of the tobacco callus, although the presence of IAA is a prerequisite for this action.

Kinetin has been tested in the carrot tissue culture system by using it in lieu of coconut milk, and it has been shown to possess the ability to promote cell division, *but again only in the presence of indoleacetic acid.* However, the extent of the cell division that can be evoked in carrot tissue by kinetin does not,

◀FIG. 4–35. Growth-promoting effects and interactions of casein hydrolysate, indoleacetic acid, *myo*-inositol, and *Aesculus* active fraction concentrate on carrot phloem explants. (From Shantz and Steward, in J. P. Nitsch, ed., *Régulateurs Naturels de la Croissance Végétale*, Centre National de la Recherche Scientifique, Paris, 1964.)

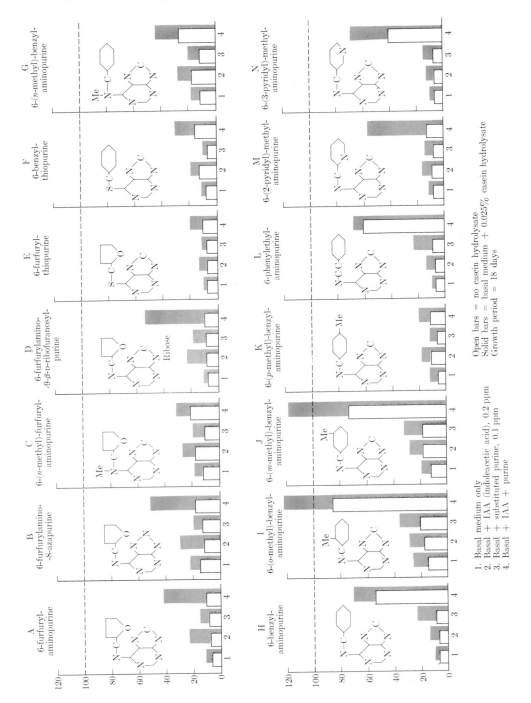

Open bars = no casein hydrolysate
Solid bars = basal medium + 0.025% casein hydrolysate
Growth period = 18 days

1. Basal medium only
2. Basal + IAA (indoleacetic acid), 0.2 ppm
3. Basal + substituted purine, 0.1 ppm
4. Basal + IAA + purine

A
6-furfuryl-
aminopurine

B
6-furfurylamino-
-8-azapurine

C
6-(n-methyl)-furfuryl-
aminopurine

D
6-furfurylamino-
-9-β-D-ribofuranosyl-
purine

E
6-furfuryl-
thiopurine

F
6-benzyl-
thiopurine

G
6-(n-methyl)-benzyl-
aminopurine

H
6-benzyl-
aminopurine

I
6-(o-methyl)-benzyl-
aminopurine

J
6-(m-methyl)-benzyl-
aminopurine

K
6-(p-methyl)-benzyl-
aminopurine

L
6-phenylethyl-
aminopurine

M
6-(2-pyridyl)-methyl-
aminopurine

N
6-(3-pyridyl)-methyl-
aminopurine

TABLE 4–4
Effect of kinetin on growth of carrot and artichoke explants

Treatment	Carrot Explants (18 Days at 24.5°C)			Artichoke Explants (19 Days at 24.5°C)		
	Weight, mg	Cell number, $\times 10^3$	Cell size, μg/cell	Weight, mg	Cell number, $\times 10^3$	Cell size, μg/cell
Basal medium	8.2	33.1	0.25	4.2	11.7	0.36
Basal medium + coconut milk	89.6	973	0.09	53.6	290	0.19
Basal medium + IAA + kinetin*	12.5	222	0.06	8.0	32.4	0.24

*Indoleacetic acid and kinetin applied separately do not give this characteristic effect

by any means, approach that which is elicited by the use of whole coconut milk (Table 4–4). Nevertheless, the substance is unquestionably active. Differences between this substance and coconut milk are also seen in their effects on other tissues. Whereas whole coconut milk induces growth in Jerusalem artichoke tuber tissue about as well as in carrot root tissue, kinetin, even in the presence of indoleacetic acid, has virtually no activity on artichoke tissue explants.

As another type of molecule that possesses cell-division-promoting properties, kinetin and its analogues have great interest, and its isolation, identification, and synthesis are distinguished achievements. However, it has yet to be shown that kinetin itself exists free in the higher plant body, for the particular compound in question seems to arise as a chemical artifact by autoclaving (or aging) of nucleic acid. Again, it should be noted how the other interacting substances mentioned also promote growth by cell division in these tissue explants. Many kinetin analogs have now been synthesized and tested. In some cases (Shantz, Mears, and Steward, 1958), the resultant molecules have even greater activity than kinetin in the presence of IAA upon carrot tissue, whereas in others, the substances are either inactive or even toxic. Within this family of substituted aminopurines it is again clear that the relations between chemical structure and physiological action are quite subtle (cf. Fig. 4–36, which shows the growth-promoting effect and formulae of many of these substances).

◄FIG. 4–36. Effects of various 6-substituted purines, indoleacetic acid, and casein hydrolysate on the growth of tissue cultures from 3 mg explants of carrot root phloem. Each bar represents the final fresh weight of nine replicate cultures, calculated relative to a value of 100 for cultures grown in basal medium containing 10% whole coconut milk. (Data reported by Dr. E. M. Shantz of this laboratory at the Fourth International Conference on Plant Growth Regulation, Yonkers, N. Y., 1959.)

The concept of kinins.* From the kinetin molecule as a starting point a whole family of synthetic substances emerges; in greater or lesser degree these promote division in plant cells. The name kinetin, however, was ascribed to a particular substance (6-furfurylaminopurine) even before it had been synthesized. The derivation of the trivial name suggests that the substance in question (kinetin) was hopefully to be regarded as *the* substance that promotes division, or "karyokinesis" and "cytokinesis," in plant cells. Any such interpretation should certainly be avoided and indeed there are some obvious difficulties in the concept that single substances may be specifically regarded as "kinins" when they act to promote cell division, in contrast to the "auxins" which act predominantly upon cell enlargement. It will become apparent that unless one knows the complete milieu in which a given molecule acts one may easily attribute to it one or the other type of activity when, in point of fact, it may be only a part of a more complex system in which substances interact synergistically, while by themselves they may produce quite different effects.

The kinin concept has recently been extended by the isolation and identification and synthesis of zeatin, 6-(4-hydroxy-3-methylbut-2-enyl)-aminopurine, a growth-stimulatory compound recognized in plum fruits but isolated from corn grains by Letham, and later synthesized by Shaw (for references see Shantz, 1966).

Zeatin

Zeatin, like kinetin, stimulates cell division, and like kinetin, it does so in the carrot assay system in synergistic response to indoleacetic acid (Shantz, Sugii, and Steward, 1967). It now seems clear that the compounds termed kinins by Skoog and Miller and later designated cytokinins, and which are adenyl compounds, usually owe their activity to interactions with auxin (i.e., IAA). There are, however, the other growth-stimulatory compounds in fluids like coconut milk, *Aesculus* fluid, and extracts of immature corn which interact with hexitols (e.g., *myo*-inositol), and these are not adenine compounds. The respective roles of these two types of system (singly or in their sequential action) for growth and morphogenesis will be considered later (Chapter 10).

Some synergistic interactions of coconut milk and other growth regulators. These considerations, and indeed many comparisons between chemical structure and physiological activity, can be investigated by the use of

---

* The term cytokinins has now been suggested (Skoog *et al.*, 1965).

a tissue culture system in which one of a variety of chemical substances must interact with the whole coconut milk to produce growth, although the main stimulus to growth induction is the coconut milk. This assay system developed from the original observation that tissue explanted from the potato tuber could not be converted to a continuously growing tissue culture with coconut milk alone.

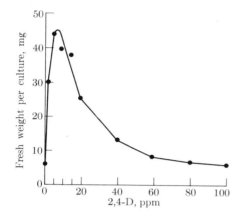

FIG. 4–37. Increase in fresh weight of potato cylinders in 26 days on media with different concentrations of 2,4-D. (From work of Caplin and Steward.)

It had been observed, however, that at low, and highly specific, concentrations of 2,4-D (2,4-dichlorophenoxyacetic acid) the potato tissue showed at least some increment of fresh weight (Fig. 4–37), but this apparent inception of growth was not maintained. Carrot tissue, on the other hand, required no exogenous substance other than coconut milk to cause it to grow and, having so started, it continued to grow indefinitely in its presence. It was then deduced that one might *start* a growing tissue culture from potato tuber using 2,4-D and *maintain* it with coconut milk. The resulting experiment was successful, as shown in the accompanying figure (Fig. 4–38), and it is now known that cultures of potato tuber tissue may be grown if coconut milk and 2,4-D are in the medium simultaneously. This result has been repeated many, many times in the intervening years and it has become the basis for a study of the chemical configuration of a large number of substances which can interact with coconut milk to promote the growth of potato tissue. Both the coconut milk and the 2,4-D-like substance are needed *continuously* because, if either is withdrawn, growth subsides promptly (Fig. 4–39). A plausible idea that gibberellic acid might stimulate such cultures by causing cells to enlarge was not fulfilled, for its effect, if any, was on cell division.

Using this tissue system it has been possible to show that α-substituted propionic acids can replace 2,4-D, but only one enantiomorph (D) is active whereas the other (L) is not only inactive, but is competitively antagonistic to its enantiomorph. Thus a sufficient addition of the inactive (L) enantiomorph

TABLE 4–5
Relative effects of gibberellic acid and 2,4-D on growth of potato tissue cultures with and without coconut milk

	No Coconut Milk					
	Potato A (46 days growth)			Potato B (45 days growth)		
Treatment	Fresh weight per culture, mg	Cell number per culture, thousands	Micrograms per culture	Fresh weight per culture, mg	Cell number per culture, thousands	Micrograms per culture
Basal medium	3.18	2.9	1.11	2.89	1.1	2.50
Basal medium + 2,4-D, 1 ppm	22.3	14.3	1.67	12.9	19.7	0.67
Basal medium + gibberellic acid, 5 ppm	3.02	1.8	1.67	2.33	0.9	2.50
With 10% Coconut Milk						
Basal medium	4.47	3.4	1.25	7.33	11.1	0.67
Basal medium + 2,4-D, 5 ppm	23.4	52.7	0.44	45.9	46.2	1.00
Basal medium + gibberellic acid, 1 ppm	5.67	10.1	0.56	6.26	8.4	0.77

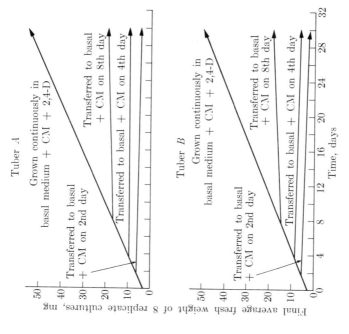

FIG. 4-39. Growth of potato tuber tissue explants started in basal medium with coconut milk and 2,4-D, followed by transfers at varying time intervals to medium without 2,4-D. (From Steward and Shantz, in Wain and Wightman, eds., *The Chemistry and Mode of Action of Plant Growth Substances*, Academic Press, New York, 1956.)

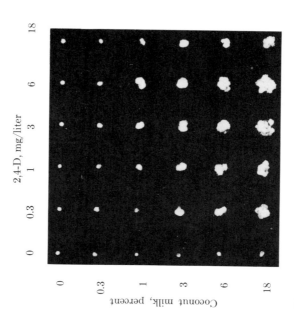

FIG. 4-38. Effect of coconut milk and 2,4-D on the growth of explants from potato tuber. (From Steward and Caplin, *Science* 113, 518–520, 1951.)

Concentration of (+)-form, ppm

Concentration of (−)-form, ppm	0	4	8	12	16		0	4	8	12	16
0	11.0	72.3	68.8	60.1	64.9	0	5.5	63.8	70.9	46.3	56.0
4	5.1	64.5	66.3	70.6		4	7.4	47.5	59.3	55.7	
8	6.6	52.6	67.1			8	4.6	43.5	49.7		
12	5.9	47.0				12	4.3	40.9			
16	4.5					16	3.8				

FIG. 4–40. Test for competitive inhibition between enantiomorphs of α-(2-naphthoxy)-propionic acid when used as a synergist with coconut milk in promoting the growth of potato tuber tissue explants. Each figure shows the average final weight in milligrams of five replicate cultures after 25 days of growth. Original explants, 3.0 mg. (From Shantz, Steward, Smith, and Wain, *Ann. Botany* N. S. 19, 49–58, 1955.)

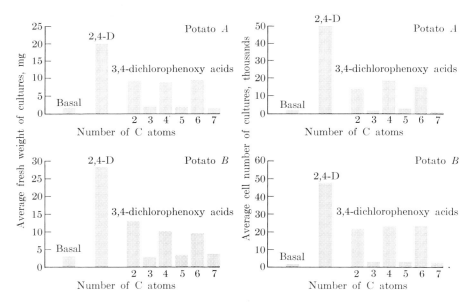

FIG. 4–41. Effects of side-chain length in the 3,4–dichlorophenoxy alkyl acids on the growth of potato tuber tissue cultures in basal medium containing 10% coconut milk, compared with effect of 2,4–D. Concentration of phenoxy acids, 1.0 ppm. (From work of Shantz and Steward in collaboration with R. L. Wain *et al.*)

to the system will actually counteract the active (D) enantiomorph. This result emphasizes the extreme specificity required of the molecule which is needed, together with the coconut milk growth factors, to promote cell division in the tissue from the potato tuber. Only one of a pair of molecules, related as object and mirror image, can fit on the site that results in growth promotion; the presence of the inactive enantiomorph blocks the site and prevents participation by the active enantiomorph (cf. Fig. 4–40).

By the aid of this tissue system the effect of side chain length has been investigated, using molecules like 2,4-D (in this case the 3,4-dichlorophenoxy acids) and, as Fig. 4–41 shows, a striking confirmation of a previous generalization by Wain and Wightman (1953) has been obtained. All the molecules with an even number of carbon atoms in the side chain are active; all the substances with side chains having an odd number of carbon atoms are less active or inactive. This result is consistent with β-oxidation of the side chain (according to the views of Wain) to degrade it by two carbon atoms at a time until the active molecule (in this case the 3,4-substituted phenoxyacetic acid) is obtained. The potato tuber tissue, therefore, must contain *both* the mechanism for degrading the side chain and the mechanism that can respond to the substituted phenoxyacetic acid.

These studies, however, have gained greater precision and interest by a device which determines the combined effect of coconut milk and the growth-regulating substance on the number of cells in the tissue explant and on the average cell size. The number of cells in the explant is determined by counting the cells after they have been separated by a maceration technique (using chromic acid and hydrochloric acid as the macerating agent); the cell size is determined by dividing the weight of the tissue in milligrams or micrograms by the number of cells in the tissue explant. Since the medium supplemented by coconut milk alone does not cause the cell number to increase appreciably, one can determine the relative effect on growth by cell multiplication of the addition of a variety of substances supplied at known concentration; one can also determine the relative effect of these substances on the average cell size in the resultant tissue culture.

Using the phenoxyacetic acids, it was found that substitution in the aromatic nucleus (by chlorine or methyl) had a marked effect upon the ability of that molecule to supplement the effect of coconut milk and to cause cell enlargement or cell multiplication in the potato tuber explants (Fig. 4–42). Substitution at the 2 or "ortho" position seemed to promote cell enlargement selectively; while substitution at the 4 or "para" position seemed required to promote the cell division. Thus in 2,4-D a happy combination exists, because the substitution at the 2-position and the 4-position combines a balanced ability to promote *both* cell division *and* cell enlargement in potato tissue. This result may explain the efficiency of 2,4-D in the establishment of a continuously growing tissue culture of potato tissue in the presence of basal medium supplemented with coconut

Treatment 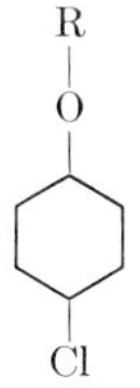 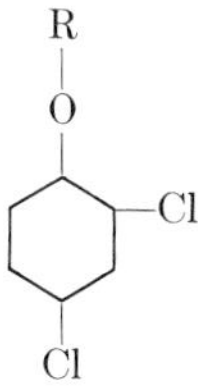 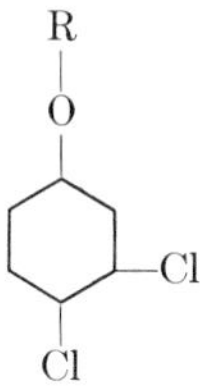 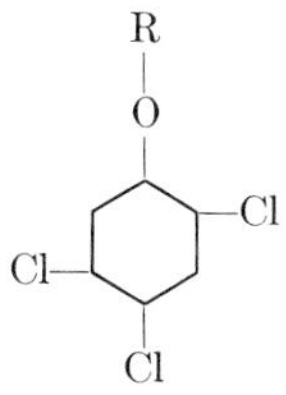 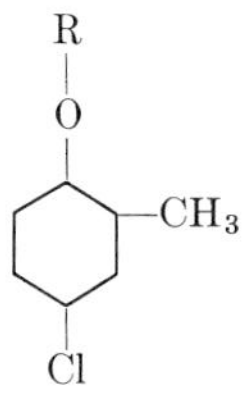 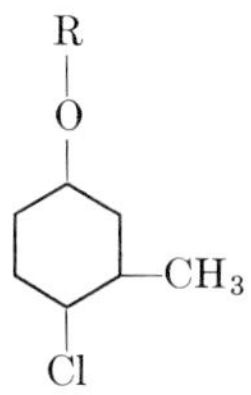 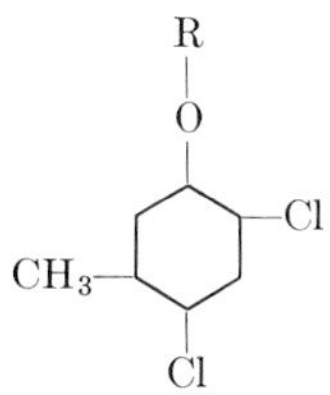 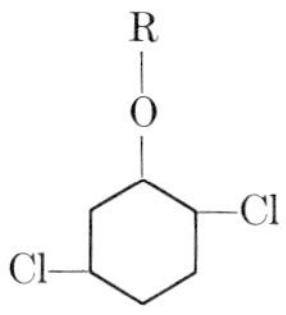							
Relative increase in fresh weight	× 6.9	10.2	5.0	12.0	14.2	4.4	11.4	4.4
Relative increase in cell number	× 2.9	2.8	1.8	2.0	2.9	1.8	1.6	0.8
Relative increase in cell size	× 2.3	3.8	2.7	6.0	4.6	2.5	6.7	5.5

Controls	Weight per culture	Cell number per culture	Cell size	
			Cells per μg	μg per cell
Basal medium	2.7 mg	1.9×10^3	0.70	1.4
Basal medium + coconut milk	5.7 mg	34.6×10^3	6.1	0.16

Relative increase in:

Fresh weight = weight of cultures under treatment divided by weight of coconut milk controls
Cell number = cell number of cultures under treatment divided by cell number of coconut milk controls
Cell size = cell size of cultures under treatment divided by cell size of coconut milk controls

FIG. 4-42 The effects of various phenoxyacetic acids on growth of potato tuber tissue in media containing coconut milk. (From work of Shantz and Steward on compounds furnished by Dr. R. C. Brian.)

milk. One may also note that 2,4-D exerts its herbicidal effect by an over-stimulus to growth in dicotyledonous plants and the site of its action seems to be the cambial region in which cells can grow spontaneously and which, therefore, do not need the added stimulus of the coconut milk or its equivalent. Mono-cotyledonous plants, however, lacking organized growing regions composed of cells with this "built-in capacity for growth," do not respond in this way to the 2,4-D. (Parenthetically, one may note that the first effective tissue cultures of a monocotyledonous plant were established by Morel and Wetmore, 1951, by the *combined* use of 2,4-D and coconut milk.)

Phenylacetic acids have come into prominence as growth-regulating sub-stances and, therefore, the analysis of growth induction in potato tuber tissue was extended to include the effects of the substituted phenylacetic acids (Fig. 4–43). The position of the substituent in the aromatic ring again leads to preferential stimulation of cell division or cell enlargement according to which positions are occupied. However, in this family of compounds, substitution at the 2 or 5 positions (the two ortho-positions) seems to be associated much more with cell division than cell enlargement, and substitution at the para or 4 position, which was of paramount importance to promote cell division in the case of substi-tuted phenoxy compounds, seems to be without effect in this series.

Very completely documented results of this sort emanate from Wain's laboratory at Wye College, England. These researches have documented the effects due to the exogenous application of whole series of similar synthetic compounds, such as the phenoxyacetic acids substituted with different groups in various positions of the aromatic nucleus; various substituted propionic acids; and trans- and cis-cinnamic acids. Wain stresses the importance of such struc-tural considerations as the presence of one hydrogen on the α-carbon to a COOH group; the critical size of substituents (F, Cl, Br, CH$_3$, etc.) adjacent to an active group which may need to rotate the larger substituents (e.g., Br) blocking this while the smallest (e.g., F) may allow it to occur. While the detailed con-clusions are not to be discussed here they are summarized by Wain and Fawcett in a forthcoming chapter in a work (*Plant Physiology: A Treatise*) edited by the author.

All these results emphasize the extreme specificity of these growth induc-tion effects and the fact that a wide range of growth-regulating compounds may have different results on different test materials.

These results also bear upon the "kinin" concept. Both coconut milk and a 2,4-D-like compound are continuously required to make potato tuber tissue grow indefinitely; cell division and enlargement are stimulated and the relative emphasis on division and enlargement may be modified by substitution in the aromatic nucleus. Coconut milk undoubtedly contains materials that stimulate cell division in carrot tissue, but coconut milk alone will not induce growth of potato tissue. Is 2,4-D therefore a "kinin" even though it may also promote cell extension and is usually thought of as a synthetic "auxin"? These difficulties

FW = average fresh weight of cultures, mg
Cell number = average number of cells per culture $\times 10^{-3}$
Initial explants: average FW = 3.6 mg, average cell number = 2000
Growth period = 23 days

		FW	Cell number			FW	Cell number			FW	Cell number
1.		86.4	72.3	7.		18.4	11.8	13.		6.1	2.2
2.		70.6	70.3	8.		13.6	6.9	14.	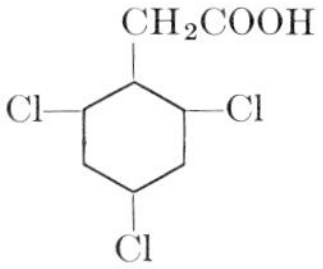	6.0	4.4
3.		67.3	44.4	9.		13.4	12.1	15.	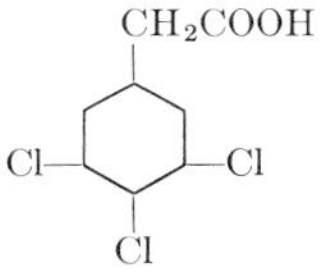	4.4	2.7
4.		33.2	15.6	10.		12.6	9.9	16.	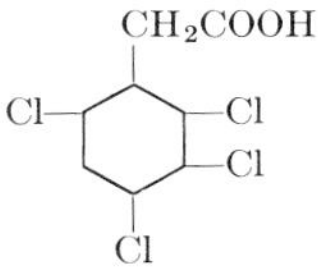	3.9	2.2
5.		32.6	32.2	11.		11.2	6.5	17.	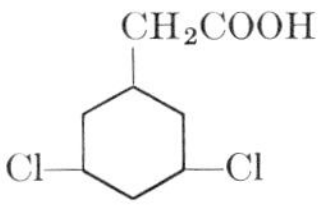	3.7	1.4
6.		25.2	27.4	12.		9.2	8.7	18.		29.3	18.4

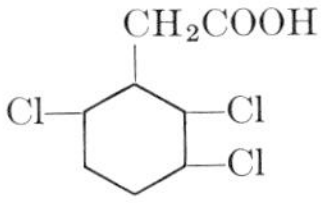

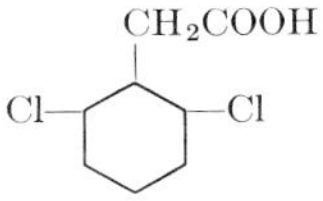

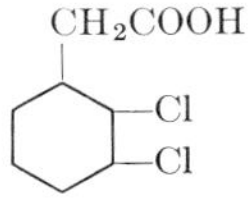

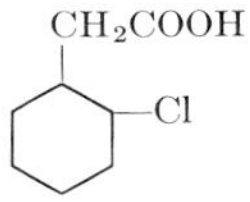

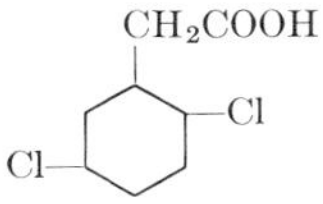

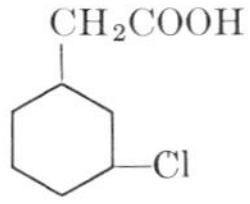

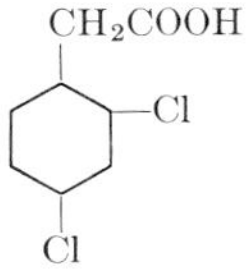

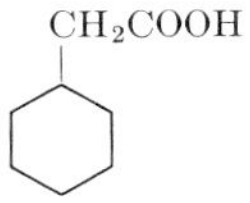

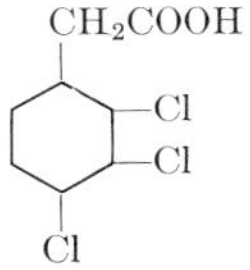

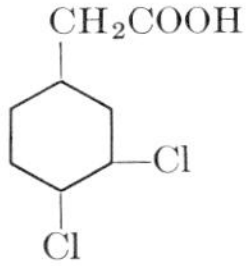

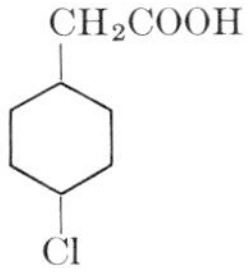

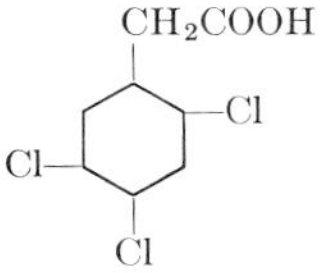

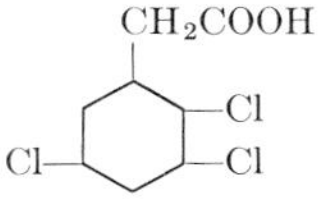

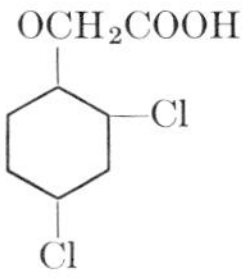

(2,4-D control)

Chloro-substitution positions favorable to growth:
  One or both ortho-positions (Nos. 1, 2, 3, 4, 5)
  Either, but not both, meta-positions (Nos. 1, 3, 5, 6)

Chloro-substitution positions unfavorable to growth:
  The para-position (Nos. 7, 9, 10, 11, 12, 14, 15, 16)
  Both meta-positions (Nos. 13, 15, 17)

FIG. 4–43. The effects of chloro-substituted phenylacetic acids on the growth of potato tuber tissue cultures in basal medium plus 10% coconut milk. (Compiled from data of Shantz and Steward.)

caution against the coining of names which relate to phenomena which are imperfectly understood. Moreover, inasmuch as the term "kinin" relates to substances that act by stimulating cell division, all such observed responses of cells or tissues may be attributed to the substances called "kinins." Used in this way the term kinin may have little chemical meaning in view of the great diversity of molecules that can produce these effects and the complex interacting mixtures of substances by which growth is so often induced.

Effects of gibberellins on cell division and enlargement. The gibberellins are complex compounds with interlocking rings in their molecules. At least 22 of these are now known and an interpretation of their representative structures, based on the work of P. W. Brian and his associates at Imperial Chemical Industries, England, is shown in Fig. 4–44. In this range of complicated ring compounds, their activity seems to depend upon the presence of the lactone ring, for allo-gibberellic acid is without physiological activity.

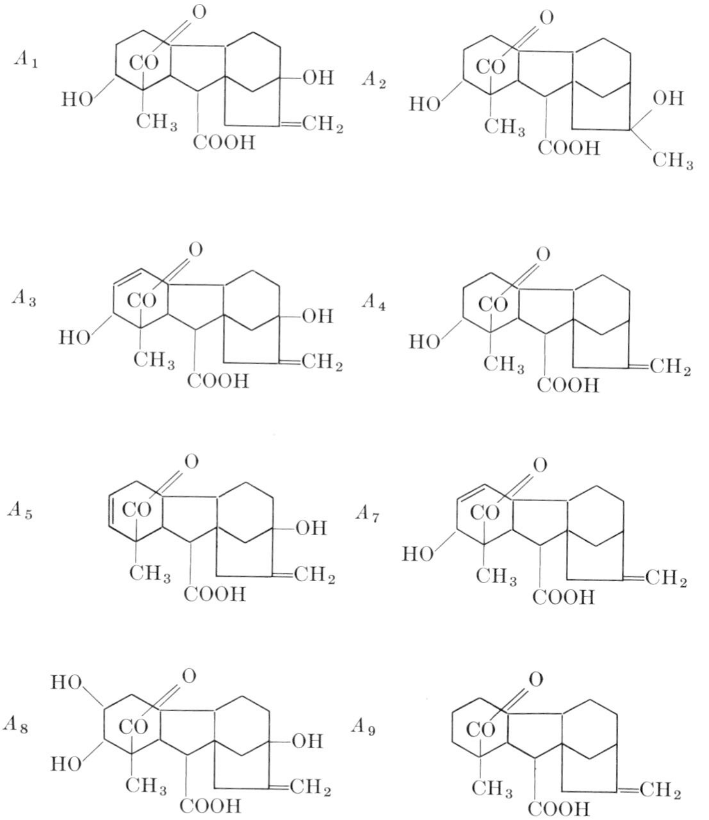

FIG. 4–44. Some representative gibberellins.

TABLE 4-6

Interactions of gibberellins with inositol, neutral fraction, and IAA on explants from Carrot A as seen by the number and size of cells in the treated explants. The numbers outside parentheses are total cells per culture in thousands; the following numbers in parentheses are average cell size in micrograms per cell.

Treatment	Basal Medium	$+ A_1$	$+ A_4$	$+ A_5$	$+ A_7$	$+ A_9$
Basal medium only	90.1 (0.111)	162.0 (0.078)	150.6 (0.076)	104.5 (0.112)	143.5 (0.080)	154.7 (0.094)
Basal medium + inositol	67.6 (0.180)	266.2 (0.092)	266.6 (0.092)	197.0 (0.085)	248.8 (0.097)	222.8 (0.099)
Basal medium + IAA	106.6 (0.119)	201.0 (0.079)	181.2 (0.083)	190.8 (0.076)	153.5 (0.079)	166.8 (0.089)
Basal medium + NF	132.3 (0.103)	281.3 (0.124)	140.4 (0.212)	95.2 (0.246)	215.8 (0.156)	222.1 (0.113)
Basal medium + inositol + IAA	130.0 (0.088)	248.1 (0.137)	192.2 (0.143)	280.8 (0.107)	196.3 (0.133)	212.5 (0.132)
Basal medium + NF + IAA	129.3 (0.131)	272.3 (0.108)	271.2 (0.122)	198.4 (0.132)	341.3 (0.132)	283.5 (0.104)

Summary. In most cases:

1. The gibberellins tested significantly increased cell division.
2. The gibberellin effect was significantly enhanced by interaction with inositol or neutral fraction.
3. Increases due to interactions with IAA were not significant.

Since the gibberellins are auxin-like in their effect, and since they are able to convert dwarf to tall plants, they might well have acted in the potato tissue culture assay system to replace the auxin-like substance 2,4-D. It was a possibility that the coconut milk would be able to supply the specific cell division factor for potato tuber explants, and the gibberellins might then complement it and meet the requirement otherwise satisfied by 2,4-D so that the divided cells could enlarge. Briefly, the first tests produced the entirely unexpected result that, in this milieu, the gibberellins had no pronounced effect on cell enlargement, although they did show some slight effect on cell division. (More recent results now suggest that the gibberellins, especially in combination with indoleacetic acid, may also be a contributory part of systems that control cell division; this is shown in Table 4-6 from the work of Shantz and Steward, 1964.)

Ring configuration in growth-regulatory compounds. The array of compounds which display physiological activity in the regulation of growth is now quite baffling. A frequent feature, however, is the presence of two or more rings in the molecule, often with hydroxyl as a substituent group.

Formula 1

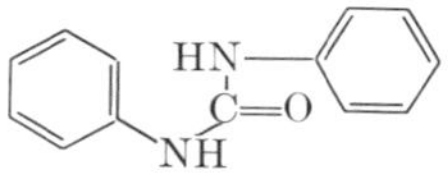

1,3-diphenylurea

Formula 2

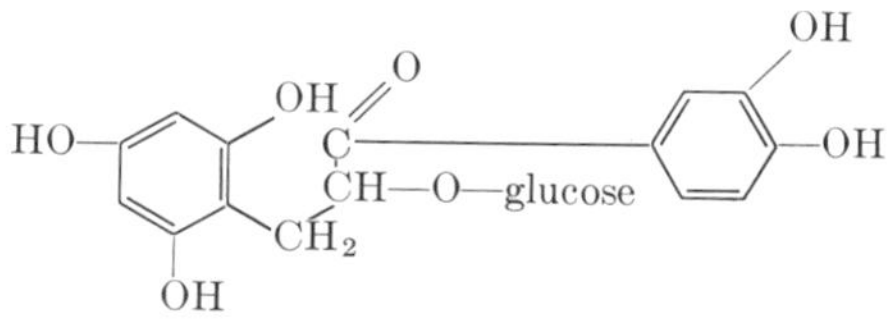

Leucoanthocyanin

Formula 3

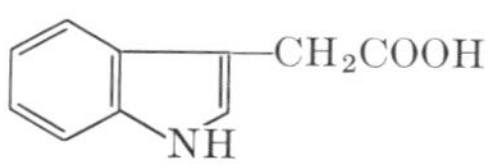

β-indolylacetic acid

FIG. 4–45. Structural similarities between 1,3–diphenylurea, leucoanthocyanin, and β-indolylacetic acid.

In diphenylurea (Formula 1, Fig. 4–45) there are two 6-atom rings with a 3-atom bridge between them; in leucoanthocyanins (Formula 2), two aromatic rings with hydroxyl substitution have a 3-atom link between them; the sugar (pyranose) moiety of leucoanthocyanins is also a 6-atom ring linked to two other rings by a short chain.

In β-indolylacetic acid (Formula 3) only one such ring is present and a short chain terminates not in a second ring but in a carboxyl group. In the indoleacetic acid-arabinose complex of Shantz and Steward (1957) it is possible that the physiological activity is again due to two rings linked by a short chain. The same is true of chlorogenic acid with its caffeic and quinic acid moieties. Kinetin again presents two rings linked by a short chain. The greatest complexity of interlocking units occurs in the gibberellins and it is significant that inositol, which is active, at least as a cofactor, also has a 6-atom ring.* One cannot press the point too far, but it does seem that many active substances owe their ability in part to the presence of these rings, for they confer a definite shape and molecular architecture upon the molecule as a whole. However, it must also be recognized that ethylene, a simple hydrocarbon with no rings, has long been known to be a very active substance which exerts a morphogenetic effect and may also cause the formation of "ethylene-induced intumescences."

Chemical regulatory control of growth by cell division and enlargement.   From the knowledge now available concerning the substances or systems that induce growth by cell division some conclusions may be drawn. A variety of substances, both natural and synthetic, have profound catalytic effects on growth and cell division. The relationships between the activating molecule and the conditions that prevail at the active site are extremely specific. Synergistic interactions exist which are highly sensitive to modifications in the structure of the synergists. This is compatible with the view that cell division may be conditioned, over and above the supply of essential nutrients and vitamins, by the growth promotion due to one type of molecule and growth inhibition by another; this forms the chemical basis of a delicately balanced, or poised, hormonal type of growth regulation. (Whereas protocatechuic acid had some stimulatory effect on carrot tissue, coumarin was inhibitory; cf. Table 4–7.) Such results lend support to the idea that growth responses now attributed to thermoperiod, photoperiod, or to certain pathological situations (such as crown gall and virus tumors) may eventually be explained on chemical grounds; they also indicate that work on plants has great interest for the general understanding of tumorous growth. But the main lesson to be learned from the multiplicity of interacting factors that seem to regulate growth is that they, in turn, reflect the fact that the cell division response occurs in a complex organization which must be chemically and simultaneously attuned at several salient points.

The tumor problem.   The plant tumors induced by the crown gall organism represent the classic example. From the work of Braun (see Braun and Stonier, 1958) of Rockefeller University, the following summary can be made.

---

* The recent discovery of IAA-inositol complexes now presents further interesting possibilities (Labarca, Nicholls and Bandurski, 1965).

TABLE 4-7

Growth-promoting activity of protocatechuic acid; growth inhibition of coumarin in the presence of casein hydrolysate on carrot tissue cultures

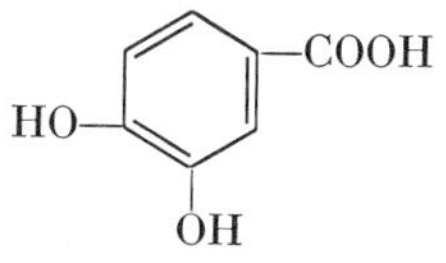

Protocatechuic Acid

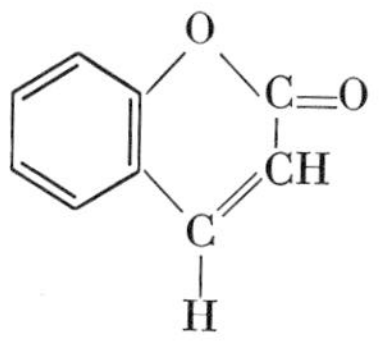

Coumarin

Treatment of Explants	No Casein Hydrolysate			With 0.20% Casein Hydrolysate		
	Fresh weight per culture, mg	Cell number per culture, thousands	Micrograms per culture	Fresh weight per culture, mg	Cell number per culture, thousands	Micrograms per culture
Basal medium	6.13	20.9	0.29	32.93	223.0	0.15
Basal medium + coconut milk, 10%	82.93	1090.2	0.08	117.13	1026.7	0.11
Basal medium + protocatechuic acid, 25 ppm	25.73	180.1	0.14	44.27	325.0	0.14
Basal medium + coumarin, 1 ppm	7.53	19.9	0.39	25.53	125.0	0.20

The transition from the normal to the tumorous state is accomplished by stages. The transition occurs most completely in cells that are returning to the growing state by wound healing, and Braun recognizes degrees in the capacity of cells for unorganized cell proliferation. For example, there are "fully altered cells" and "partially altered cells" which differ in their responses. Some of the characteristics of "fully altered cells" may be superimposed upon "partially altered cells" by appropriate manipulations of known growth-regulatory substances in the medium. Tobacco pith cells can be caused to grow in size by indoleacetic acid (IAA), forming cells 4 to 5 times the normal size; with coconut milk and an auxin they proliferate. This is an example of a two-fold stimulus required to cause the growth. A tumor extract plus naphthalene acetic acid (NAA) causes rapid growth in pith cells; therefore, to form a tumorous type of growth, a cell division factor (in the form of tumor extract or coconut milk) and an auxin (NAA) are needed. A tumor results when both the cell division factor and the auxin can be formed autonomously in greater than normal or imbalanced amounts in the cells. A later claim is that the cells, having been completely transformed to the tumorous state, may return to the normal condition. The environment which produces this change is achieved by transferring a culture grown from free cells of tumorous origin to the environment of a normal host by successive grafts (cf. Braun, 1959).

The final and unequivocal identification of the "tumor-inducing principle" would obviously shed much light on the causal factors involved in this type of cell division. However, the earlier claims of Klein (1953, 1954) that this principle could be identified as a deoxyribonucleic acid have now been abandoned (Klein and Braun, 1960) because the earlier effects could be attributed to bacterial contamination of the supposedly active extracts.

Mode and site of action of cell division factors.   The existence of substances that induce growth by cell division raises questions concerning the metabolic site in the cell at which they act. From results in the Cornell laboratory, which have only been published in summary form (Steward *et al.*, 1961), some suggestive ideas emerge.

It has been known for some time (Steward, Thompson, and Pollard, 1958) that one of the first detectable metabolic effects due to the coconut milk stimulus is a drastic effect upon the nitrogen metabolism of the tissue. The normal complement of alcohol-soluble nitrogen compounds, which is rich in amino acids and amides, particularly asparagine, and which is characteristic of both the resting carrot and potato tissue, rapidly gives place to a new complement characteristic of the growing and cultured tissue. The nitrogen compounds of the cultured tissue differ in several ways from those present in the tissue of the dormant organ from which it was explanted. The most important difference is that the growing tissue has its total nitrogen predominantly in the form of protein, with comparatively little in the form of soluble compounds existing free in the cells. Modern chromatographic methods permit the soluble compounds that exist in both types of tissue to be identified and quantitatively analyzed. Neither the dormant organ nor the actively growing cells contain amino acids of the kind and in the proportion necessary if they were to be converted by direct condensation into protein. Something very much more profound than this must occur, but it was recognized, almost at the outset, that the effect of the coconut milk is to stimulate protein synthesis in the cells. It is noteworthy, for example, that asparagine virtually disappears from the soluble fraction of the growing cells, though glutamine, commonly regarded as a nitrogen-rich substance which acts as a nitrogen donor for protein synthesis, remains conspicuous in the nitrogen of the cultured cells. Another curious observation is that the protein of the resting potato tuber contains proline, but little or no hydroxyproline. The protein of the tissue cultured on a medium which contains coconut milk and 2,4-D (or similar compounds) contains hydroxyproline in considerable amount. Also, the protein of tissue which is explanted from the resting carrot root may contain a very small amount of hydroxyproline, but the amount of this amino acid present in the protein of the cultured tissue is very much greater. This suggested that a protein moiety which is synthesized in these rapidly dividing cells may be different in chemical composition from that which is normally present in the resting tissue.

In other similar cases in which cells undergo rapid, unorganized, random proliferation, their protein was found to be unexpectedly rich in hydroxyproline, whereas the normal tissue, from which the culture was derived, contained either no hydroxyproline or only a very small amount (Steward, Thompson, and Pollard, 1958). This was found to be true of the tissue of tumors incited by crown gall on *Kalanchoe*; of the genetic tumors that arise on hybrid tobacco plants; and of carrot and potato tissue cultured on coconut milk. Other examples of hydroxyproline-rich protein in cultures stimulated by coconut milk have also been observed by others (Weinstein *et al.*, 1959; Lamporte and Northcote, 1960). Thus, some definite significance should be attached to a fraction which contains combined hydroxyproline, and which is especially rich in rapidly dividing cells. The significance of this effect remains to be determined. However, any agent that stops the formation of the new protein of the cells will also suppress the growth which is induced by coconut milk. The exogenous application of hydroxyproline and certain of its derivatives, which is not normally present free in the cells at any appreciable concentration, although it is readily absorbed by the cells, has this effect (cf. Steward, Pollard, Witkop, and Patchett, 1958). Apparently the cells which do not normally contain free hydroxyproline allow this substance to reach the sites of proline metabolism but, having occupied these, it cannot be embodied directly in the protein. Another substance which behaves in like manner is the unusual imino acid azetidine-2-carboxylic acid. Hydroxy-L-proline itself was the most effective inhibitor of the coconut-milk-induced growth out of some 64 hydroxyproline compounds which were tested by Steward *et al.* (1958). In fact, were the alternative explanation not known, hydroxy-L-proline could easily have been regarded as an "anti-coconut milk factor."

The relation between protein metabolism and the stimulus which is imparted by the coconut milk to carrot and other cells has been investigated in several ways. From other studies the idea emerged that plant cells may pass more of their carbon than is commonly supposed through protein prior to its use in respiration. Sugar and simple nitrogen compounds, or nitrogenous groups derived from a substance like glutamine, seem to move to some localized protein-synthesizing center in the cell and there form protein, without liberating the intermediate amino acids so that they can freely mingle with the stored amino acids of the cell. If, indeed, amino acids are formed at or near the protein-synthesizing site, as must surely be the case, they do not leave this site before they are bound into the protein of these growing angiosperm cells. [Modern knowledge of fine structure in the cytoplasm of plant cells provides obvious possibilities for the localization of one range of stored nitrogenous compounds in a given phase, or organelle, of the cells (e.g., in vacuoles), whereas protein synthesis and storage may occur in another (e.g., in ribosome granules which are either free or attached to endoplasmic reticulum).] Thereafter, the metabolically active protein moiety may break down, and its breakdown products (the amino acids) may be converted into nitrogen-rich storage products in which amides are conspicuous, a prominent condition in plant cells recognized since the time of Pfeffer and of Schulze. The protein breakdown products of plants, unlike those of animals, are not excreted but are re-utilized; this may occur in the following way.

By processes of deamination and deamidation, carbon frameworks of nitrogenous compounds are released largely in the form of keto acids which can be introduced into the respiratory cycle; the nitrogenous groups then pass again to the protein-synthesizing centers where, with new carbon derived from sugar, protein is reconstituted. Thus we now add to a respiratory cycle, in which carbon moves through the organic acid cycle from sugar to carbon dioxide, a further possibility that much of the carbon may move from sugar to protein, to protein breakdown products, to nitrogen-free residues, and then to carbon dioxide. This being so, the rate of exit of carbon dioxide over this route will be determined in part by the pace of protein synthesis and turnover. By the use of radioactively labeled sugar and radioactively labeled nitrogen compounds, like glutamine and γ-aminobutyric acid, it has been shown that a cell contains local compartments, inclusions, or organelles, in which the same molecular species may be subjected to quite different chemical reactions.

Thus protein synthesis may occur in one part of the cell, using a given substrate, while protein breakdown may release the same substance to another. By appropriate manipulations of the data for the specific activity of carbon in various metabolites, it can be shown that molecules which enter the cell from the outside may pass into the phase of the cell which enables sugar to contribute

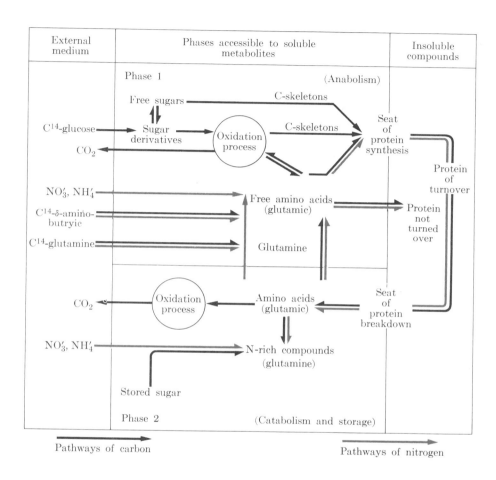

FIG. 4–46. Diagram to illustrate the main metabolic pathways in cultured carrot tissue explants. (From Steward, Bidwell, and Yemm, *Nature* **178**, 734–738, 789–792, 1956; for later work on these lines see Steward, Bidwell, and Yemm, 1958.)

carbon to protein synthesis, releasing glutamic acid by protein breakdown. It has also been shown that carbon may enter the protein molecule (as glutamic acid, for example) more readily and speedily from sugar than it does from the free, stored nitrogen compound in the cell. Work of this sort has led to a concept which is summarized by Fig. 4–46. It can also be shown that the effect of coconut milk is to stimulate both protein synthesis and the rate of *turnover of the metabolically active protein* as shown in the figure. This protein acquires its carbon more readily from sugar than from any other source, and the carbon of the amino acids which are found free in the cell may not be directly embodied into the protein when it is synthesized.

On the other hand, a *metabolically inactive moiety*, which does not turn over, does incorporate proline from the cell directly and there converts it, in part, to hydroxyproline.

In short, the main site of the effect of the cell division growth-promoting factors of coconut milk and similar fluids is at *the point at which protein is synthesized*, and moreover the presence of these factors seems to promote the formation of a particular kind of structural moiety, which embodies proline directly from the cell and thereafter converts it into combined hydroxyproline. In addition to the stimulus to protein synthesis, turnover of the metabolically active part of the protein seems to follow from the coconut milk stimulus; this occurs in such a way that the carbon that emerges from protein on breakdown contributes to the respiration of the cell. On this view a distinction may be drawn between the metabolism of actively dividing cells and the metabolism of resting cells. This distinction concerns, not merely the presence of distinctive molecules, but also the pace at which the cycle of protein synthesis and breakdown operates.

These ideas have been substantiated by studying the incorporation of exogenously supplied C^{14}-proline into the protein of carrot tissue cultures (Pollard and Steward, 1959); this incorporation occurs rapidly. In tissue cultures that are in their exponential phase of growth, C^{14}-proline commences to appear in the protein of the cell within 15 minutes after its addition to the outside solution and, thereafter, the content of C^{14}-proline and C^{14}-hydroxyproline in the cell protein increases markedly with time. It can also be shown that the protein that incorporates these two amino acids is not metabolized by the cells. These facts are well illustrated by Fig. 4–47. The fact that the metabolically inactive protein, or proteins, in these growing cells resembles collagen in its content of hydroxyproline and in its inert nature has also been noted, although the significance of this type of protein in this type of cell has yet to be determined.*

An obvious approach to the difference between the proliferating and the non-proliferating cells is to determine whether those which grow in the presence of coconut milk are more or less sensitive to enzyme inhibitors than the tissue from which they were derived; in this way the type of metabolism which is activated by the coconut milk may be ascertained. Early experiments indicated that the tissue which is growing in the presence of coconut milk is very sensitive to those inhibitors, like the nitrocresols, which uncouple phosphorylation, but it seemed to be much *less* sensitive to enzyme inhibitors, like cyanide, which inhibit cytochrome oxidase.

Further tests show that there are marked differences between the sensitivity of the dividing and the non-dividing cells to these enzyme inhibitors. The effect of cyanide has been repeated by methods which preclude the fixation of cyanide by keto acids to form cyanhydrins, with the consequent reduction in the

---

* For the present knowledge of the location of this protein in the cells see Chapter 6.

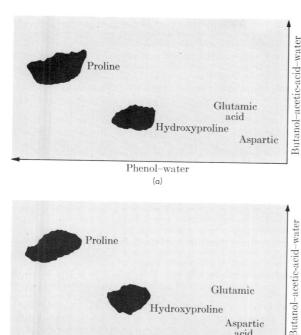

FIG. 4–47. Radioautographs of chromatograms of the hydrolyzed protein fraction of growing carrot explants showing that the C^{14}-proline and C^{14}-hydroxyproline in the protein are not metabolized further. (a) Tissue treated three days in labeled proline. Average weight per explants, 24 mg. (b) Tissue treated three days with C^{14}-proline and then grown eight more days in media free of C^{14}. Average weight per explant, 72 mg. (From Pollard and Steward, *J. Exp. Botany* 10, 17–32, 1959.)

effective concentration of the cyanide as applied. In these experiments a calcium cyanide buffer is maintained in the system continuously, and again it is found that the tissue is capable of at least some continued growth in the presence of cyanide concentrations $(10^{-3}$ and $10^{-4}\ M)$ which should inactivate the metal-catalyzed oxidative metabolism of the resting tissue.

The most striking effects are, however, obtained with carbon monoxide. This enzyme inhibitor affects cytochrome oxidase and its inhibition is characteristically reversed by light. The pressures of carbon monoxide required to do this are relatively high; therefore, one can best ensure the necessary partial pressure of carbon monoxide, without reducing the oxygen partial pressure to the point where the cells would suffer from oxygen lack, if the experiments are carried out at pressures above one atmosphere. This type of experiment was made possible by modifying a device of Schneiderman and Feder (1954) as used by Thimann, Yocum, and Hackett (1954) to study the effect of carbon monoxide upon potato tuber tissue. The experiments were carried out at two atmospheres pressure, and air was supplemented by either an atmosphere of carbon monoxide or an atmosphere of nitrogen. If this procedure is performed in the light and in the dark it can be shown that the growth induction due to coconut milk, i.e., the transfer of the tissue from the resting to the actively growing state, is completely inhibited by carbon monoxide; and this effect is definitely *not* light-reversible (cf. experiments carried out with Dr. H. Schneiderman as summarized by Steward *et al.*, 1961).

Therefore, when the coconut milk activates a resting cell and converts it to the growing state, it must do so at some site which is not primarily concerned with cytochrome oxidase or with the terminal oxidation processes that it can negotiate. However, when the tissue has already embarked upon its growth and is in its exponential phase, it is found that the effect of carbon monoxide is very much less and growth is not then completely inactivated by the carbon monoxide; however, the growth suppression which carbon monoxide causes *after growth induction has occurred* is in large measure light-reversible and may, therefore, refer to a cytochrome-mediated step.

These results re-emphasize the fact that the metabolism of cells in the growing, dividing state is quite different from that of mature cells in the resting, non-dividing, dormant state. The difference is especially noteworthy because so much of our knowledge of metabolism has been obtained from systems especially chosen to eliminate the "complications of growth and active metabolism." While this may simplify experimental procedures, it often robs the results of much of the biological significance that they might otherwise have. The attempt to understand living cells, wholly without reference to their behavior under the conditions in which they can grow, is like considering "Hamlet without the Prince of Denmark."

Another result shows the contrast between cells in the growing and the nongrowing condition. Radiation from a cobalt source can be applied to carrot explants in coconut milk media both *before* and *after* they have responded by growth induction. It is found that relatively low dosages of radiation (see Table 4–7 from Steward *et al.*, 1961) will completely inactivate the center at which the coconut milk acts, for such tissue, after irradiation, completely fails to respond by cell division to the growth-promoting stimuli although the cells could still expand. If, however, the carrot tissue has already embarked, in the presence of coconut milk, on active growth by cell division, and is in its exponential phase after seven days of such treatment, it *will withstand much higher dosages of radiation with comparatively little effect.* Therefore, there is in the effects of radiation another marked contrast between the cells in the resting and in the growing state, and the center at which the growth induction by coconut milk occurs appears to be vulnerable to the effects of radiation, as well as to inhibition by carbon monoxide and cyanide. It is now known, however, that the effects of Co^{60} radiation upon growth and growth induction of carrot explants may be mediated indirectly by the radiolysis products of sucrose in the culture medium (Holsten, Sugii, and Steward, 1965; Steward, Holsten, and Sugii 1967).

More recent studies have shown what happens in explanted pieces of carrot root in respect to their nucleic acid content. The RNA and DNA per cell in the resting carrot root is small. When an explant is removed and nourished by an otherwise complete solution (basal medium plus salts, sugars, and vitamins), the cells of the carrot synthesize nucleic acids, especially RNA, very readily. In fact, by about two days they have built up a complement of nucleic acids in the cells which may be as much as 15 to 20 times that of the resting cells. But this presumably ribosomal RNA is not enough to act as a protein-synthesizing surface. The apparatus for synthesis is there but the essential catalytic device to put the metabolic engines into gear and make the cells grow is lacking. This, however, is precisely what the coconut milk complex of growth factors accomplishes. As cells respond to coconut milk their nucleic acid content falls and levels off at a value still far above that of the resting storage root (Steward *et al.*, 1964).

It is now also clear that carrot tissue in the presence of coconut milk accumulates inorganic ions by a different method from the resting tissue which is not so conspicuously growing and dividing (Millar and Steward; cf. Steward and Sutcliffe, 1959). The non-dividing tissue takes in water, enlarges its vacuole, and accumulates its salt more effectively from dilute solution, and it achieves much higher concentrations in the tissue. In the presence of coconut milk the proliferating tissue absorbs cations, but to concentrations in the cells that are not as high as in cells which are more conspicuously vacuolated; moreover, the amount of the cation which is present in the proliferating cells seems to be directly proportional to the first power of the external concentration.

In the case of the dividing cells, the ions seem to be bound to cytoplasmic sites which are multiplied as the cell grows; in cells which are enlarging more than they are dividing, the ions are taken off these sites and secreted into the vacuole and, in so doing, the growing enlarging cell mobilizes metabolic energy to negotiate the transfer to the much higher concentrations which are built up in the vacuole (cf. Chapter 2).

These views are also compatible with the facts which were discovered by the application of a radioactive isotope, Cesium 137, to single roots of *Narcissus*. The point of highest concentration of Cs^{137} in the *Narcissus* root usually occurs just behind the apex, whereas the initiating cells of the root that are situated at the very tip exhibit a somewhat lower concentration of ions. Thus the study of cells in the contrasted states of metabolism represented by vacuolation and enlargement, on the one hand, and active cell division, on the other, has contributed to our knowledge of salt accumulation by revealing a step, or stage, of the process that might otherwise have passed unnoticed.

Work on the metabolism of tissue during the induction of growth shows that some endogenous metabolites exist in the cells in relatively inactive pools, remote from the main course of metabolism, whereas others, when supplied exogenously, bypass these pools and are directed to sites of protein synthesis. In some cases the growing cells pass the carbon of certain compounds, e.g., exogenous sugar, more directly than expected to protein rather than to respired carbon dioxide, whereas the carbon of others (e.g., asparagine or endogenous products of protein breakdown) is either stored in an inactive pool or respired away (Steward, Bidwell, and Yemm, 1956, 1958; Bidwell, Barr, and Steward, 1964; Steward and Bidwell, 1966, and references there cited). All this is also compatible with the drastic effects on the cellular organelles that may be seen under the electron microscope when resting cells respond to the stimuli that make them grow and divide (Israel and Steward 1966, 1967).

This chapter opened, hopefully, with the attempt to specify, singly and separately, the specific organic requirements of cells in order that their innate capacity to grow may be expressed by either cell expansion or by cell division. The evidence, however, reveals that each of these responses is controlled and regulated not by single, discrete, chemical substances but by a multiplicity of them. Neither growth by cell expansion nor growth by cell division can be treated as though it were a single event. On the contrary, the evidence shows that cells, with their manifold functions and multiplicity of parts, respond to a wide range of exogenous stimuli and, to ensure their smooth operation in growth, they require in balanced amounts an array of chemical stimuli that may affect cells at various salient points of their organization. To recognize this is not a retrograde step if it establishes the range of physiological functions that are mobilized by a growing cell during cell expansion and cell division, and if it stresses that there is room within the cells' organization for a multiplicity of exogenous factors that may act in very different ways to remove limitations to their growth and thus to control it. The intent, therefore, is not to oversimplify and seem to explain the complex phenomena of growth in simple, direct, and very discrete terms, but rather to understand how the variety of growth-regulatory substances intervene in the organization of cells to make them grow.

Summary

The conspicuous events in the growth of cells of angiosperms are marked by stages in which, first, cell division predominates, and then cell enlargement. These sequential steps, both of which are essential, are subject to different kinds of regulatory control. Moreover, they present contrasts in their relationships to the water and solute uptake without which growth cannot occur. Over and above the substances that are conventionally recognized as nutrients (organic and inorganic) or as vitamins, there are non-nutrient, catalytic requirements which selectively stimulate growth in the form of cell division and cell enlargement. Historically, the knowledge of the growth-regulatory substances which stimulate cell enlargement (auxins) came first, although more recently other classes of physiologically active substances (the gibberellins) which also affect cell enlargement have become known. The importance to be attached to stimuli which specifically act upon cell division, which tended to be overshadowed by the earlier emphasis upon the role of auxins, is now evident. The immediate environment of the young embryo is a potent source of these cell-division-promoting stimuli and they may often be demonstrated in liquid endosperms that normally nourish embryos of various plants. Other sources are also known. Aseptic cultures of explanted tissue of the carrot root furnish convenient assay systems both for the cell division factors and for their naturally occurring inhibitors. The cell division factors act like a sort of "metabolic clutch" which puts the idling metabolism of cells, which have stopped growing, back into gear and canalizes it in the direction of growth. By the interaction between cell division factors, their inhibitors, and their synergists, a balanced chemical regulatory control over growth is achieved. Along these lines interpretations may be sought to explain such phenomena as the incidence of plant galls and tumors, and of the growth effects which occur in response to such morphogenetic stimuli as diurnal periodicity in illumination and temperature, as well as the phenomena of vernalization. Although conventionally called hormones, by analogy with the substances that act in the animal body, the plant growth regulators by the very generality of their effects present important differences from the animal hormones.

The chemical substances which regulate growth, but which are not nutrients in the ordinary sense, are various. Some exert their effect predominantly through cell enlargement, some through cell division; the distinction is, however, not as sharp as current distinction between auxins and kinins implies. Many different kinds of molecules, natural and synthetic, accentuate growth by enlargement and thus qualify as auxins; many different substances converge upon and accentuate growth by their effects upon cell division. Because the so-called auxins are concerned with a relatively clear-cut, though terminal, phase of cell growth their chemical identification has been more direct and explicit, whereas the range of substances that control, or induce, growth by cell division, singly or in synergistic combinations, is only now being fully appreciated. Potent sources of the compounds which induce growth by cell division are found to be the morphological situations which nourish immature embryos or other comparable situations, and these yield an array of very different chemical compounds which are active in this respect. The outstanding conclusion is that the condition that leads to rapid and maintained growth requires different kinds of interacting substances. Potentially nitrogen-autotrophic cells, that can use nitrate or ammonia, nevertheless respond to casein hydrolysate (or even urea or other sources of reduced nitrogen), to neutral or non-ionic substances (of the class of inositols) that do not elicit cell division *per se* but are necessary for the growth induction, and also to cell division growth factors proper, that act at very low dilution if all other requirements are met. This group of cell division factors is chemically heterogeneous. Granted that cells are in a milieu in which they can grow by cell division and by cell enlargement, these processes are subject to intimate chemical control in which subtle changes in the chemical configuration of synergistically active components has a profound effect upon the quantity and the nature of the growth which occurs.

Of all the possible metabolic sites where the growth factors may operate, two have been most often considered. The effects of auxins have been most implicated in the plastic extension of the cell wall substance—especially through the rigidity or fluidity of pectins. The effects of cell-division-promoting substances or extracts seem to be mediated through protein synthesis and protein turnover. The protein synthesis seems to be of two kinds—one concerns metabolically active protein which is preferentially made from carbohydrate and readily available sources of endogenous nitrogen (e.g., from glutamine); another concerns the formation in proliferating cells of a protein moiety which is inert, is usually rich in hydroxyproline, and embodies certain free amino acids (e.g., proline and arginine) directly into the protein. As the growth factors negotiate the transfer of resting cells to rapidly growing cells they change, not merely one extremely specific reaction, but many physiological processes. Water absorption (properly regarded as a feature of growth) is stimulated; ions are accumulated in two different ways depending upon whether growth is predominantly by self-duplication of organelles or by cell extension; respiratory pathways change from routes sensitive to cyanide and carbon monoxide to others which are less so, or which even become insensitive to these inhibitors; the sensitivity to inhibitors which uncouple phosphorylation, and therefore control the availability of energy to useful work, is increased; protein metabolism and turnover are greatly stimulated; the nucleic acid content of the cells is greatly changed. It is not, therefore, surprising that to accomplish this range of metabolic effects an array, or complex, of interacting, catalytically active, substances is needed. It is within the range of balanced effects caused by this complex of growth substances and their sequential as well as simultaneous action that the possibility of a sensitive chemical regulatory control of the growth of cells exists. Along these lines explanations of plant tumors may be, and are being, sought. The complex of growth substances found in the normal environment of angiosperm embryos is now seen to have the ability to transform the metabolism of resting cells and to engage it, or canalize it, in ways that drive the processes of growth.

chapter five

CELL GROWTH AND CELL DIVISION:
GROWTH FORMS

Why Do Cells Divide as They Grow?

This chapter is more concerned with the way cells grow than with the endogenous and exogenous requirements that must be satisfied if they are to grow.

First, why should cells divide; why can they not expand indefinitely? Very large plant cells are rare. Perhaps the largest single cells of vascular plants, in the sense that they contain only a single protoplast, are the eggs of Cycads. Many structures which are commonly regarded as giant plant cells are often not strictly cells but coenocytic vesicles. Examples are the vesicles formed by species of *Valonia*, marine algae which belong to the Siphonales, but there are many other less dramatic examples (see Fig. 2.13a and b). One such example is a fresh water alga *Botrydium*, which grows on drying mud. In all these cases the relation of the vesicle to a single cell may be somewhat spurious because within a single wall, or cellulose envelope, there are included an enormous number of protoplasts; in fact, the nuclei in these vesicles are about as far apart as they would be in any multicellular tissue composed of uninucleate cells. Moreover, the protoplasm of these vesicles may readily fragment by the methods of cell division that Boegesen (1913) termed "segregative cell division," to form self-contained structures called aplanospores from which the entire organism may grow. There is, however, some apparent advantage in smallness, so much so that the individual meristematic cells of angiosperms especially are apt to be about the same size, whether they belong to a chickweed or a *Eucalyptus* tree, and they (i.e., the cells) are usually more similar in size than either the organisms to which they give rise or the organized growing regions of which they form a part. [A number of shoot apices from vascular plants derived from different parts of the plant kingdom were illustrated by Wardlaw (1965) at the same magnification.]

Among the suggested reasons for division, which preserves cells in a range of size conducive to their efficiency, the following are familiar. With division, new surfaces of exchange, or new boundary surfaces between the cell and its environment are established. The balance between surface and mass is also preserved by division. A less familiar, but perhaps more profound consequence, of the relative smallness of cells concerns the efficiency of diffusion. Diffusion is commonly regarded as a slow process, because it is normally observed over relatively long distances. A diffusion experiment carried out with dyes and a

207

gelatin jelly, as is often done in elementary exercises, may be allowed to run for days or weeks, and the linear distances traversed by diffusing molecules then seem relatively small. The ease with which a given molecule may diffuse in a given medium is measured by its diffusion coefficient. The diffusion coefficient represents the quantity of material that diffuses through unit area in unit time under the influence of unit concentration gradient, and it has the dimensions of a square of a length divided by a time, i.e., cm^2/sec. In consequence, if one compares exactly similar systems which differ in their linear dimensions by a factor of 2, but are identical in every other respect, then the smaller system will achieve *diffusion equilibrium* in a time which is not half that of the larger, but one quarter. Thus, as one reduces the scale of size, keeping all other features of the system similar, diffusion *alone* becomes increasingly efficient in the sense that equilibrium will be established in time periods that are inversely proportional to the *square* of the linear dimensions. Thus, as A. V. Hill pointed out (Hill, 1928), systems that are small can avail themselves of diffusion more effectively than those which are large, and this may explain the familiar impression that, in similar systems, the smallest are the most efficient—a mouse is more agile in relation to its own size than an elephant! A third and obvious idea is that by division the organism has more separate cellular units; if these differentiate there is a greater opportunity for specialization, division of labor, and all the familiar features that lead to the complexities and potentialities of biological organization.

TABLE 5–1   A spectrum of size

Scale	NaCl lattice	Amino acids	Proteins	Viruses	Bacteria	Red blood cells	Plant meri- stematic cells	Human eggs (ovum)	Plant paren- chyma cells	One millimeter
μ	0.0001	0.001	0.01	0.1	1.0	10	10	100	< 500	1,000
A	1	10	100	1,000	10,000	100,000		1,000,000		10,000,000

| X-rays | Ultraviolet | ——Visible —— | Infrared |

The Molecular Complexity of Cells

Smallness of itself, however, is not an unequivocal advantage, for the work that cells have to do is chemically complex. Even the smallest cells are complex in terms of molecules. A "spectrum of size," shown in Table 5–1, indicates the unit of size at different levels of organization and so suggests the minumum unit size which is compatible with life.

Although cells may seem to be small as measured in familiar units of length (millimeters or inches), certain macromolecules may seem large when measured in units appropriate to molecular size. A virus protein with a molecular weight in the millions represents a highly organized structure which can literally be seen with the electron microscope in section (Fig. 5–1) and interpreted in three

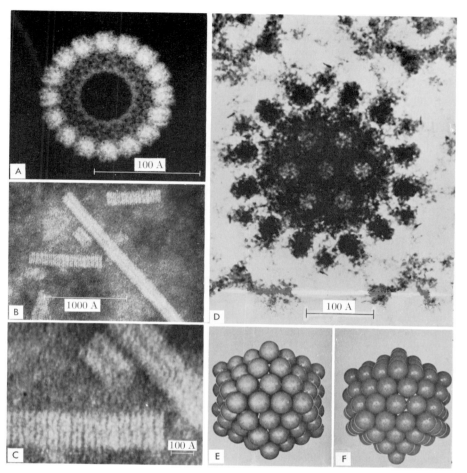

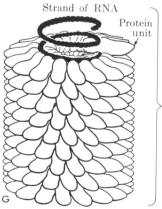

FIG. 5–1. A. Tobacco mosaic virus (TMV) X-protein in the stacked-disc configuration as seen "end-on"; rotated n=16. B. A particle of tobacco mosaic virus, showing the transition from a helical structure to a stacked-disc structure. C. Tobacco mosaic virus X-protein, stacked-disc configuration with pairing of the discs. D. Turnip crinkle virus, rotated n=6. E and F. Models of the turnip crinkle virus as seen along the two-fold and three-fold axes. G. Schematic diagrams for the structure of the TMV rod. The internal helix is the RNA and the external bodies are the protein subunits. (A–F from Markham, Frey, and Hills, *Virology* **20**, 88–102, 1963, as supplied by Dr. Markham; G from Baker and Allen, 1965, adapted by permission of the authors and publisher from W. M. Stanley and E. G. Valens, *Viruses and the Nature of Life*, New York, E. P. Dutton and Co., 1961.)

Strand of RNA

Protein unit

dimensions (cf. Fig. 5–IB). Such molecules therefore approach a size which permits them to be individually rather than statistically appreciated. The smallest of the fibrils of a cellulose wall, as revealed by the electron microscope, seem to be about 20 A thick, whereas in the crystal lattice, which is 8.3 A $\times$ 7.9 A $\times$ 10.3 A, there are 5 parallel cellulose chains. The smallest fibrils therefore represent comparatively small bundles of individual cellulose molecules, whereas the ones more usually seen, being of the order of 100 A or more in thickness, will contain many more strands of β-D-glucopyranose units.

It is, therefore, interesting to speculate on the minimum size and organization which is compatible with life. To detect this minimum size one looks for the minimum organization which has the ability for self-duplication. This minimum unit has often been likened to a gene, or a virus particle, but these units can only work in an already highly organized system. Since the cardinal feature of life is the ability to convert small and random molecules into the "stuff of life," an ultimate unit may be a template surface where synthesis (e.g., of protein) may occur. On present knowledge these events occur at pentose nucleic acid surfaces on particles called ribosomes (Fig. 6–4). However, even the smallest cell with all the characteristics of an organism is very large in terms of molecular size, and to make all the proteins that a cell needs a vast number of template surfaces are required or, as may well be the case, a given template may change its character with time.

Populations of Molecules in Cells

Estimates have been made of the number of molecules of a given kind contained in individual cells. Such an estimate, made by Brooks and Brooks (1941), is quoted below (Table 5–2). It is true that a mammalian red blood cell is a rather special case which, by its lack of a nucleus and of a conspicuous large aqueous vacuole containing dissolved substances, does not remotely represent a typical plant cell.

TABLE 5–2
The numbers of molecules of different kinds present in a single erythrocyte

Water	$980,000 \times 10^6$	Glutathione	52×10^6
Phosphatide	300×10^6	K^+	6300×10^6
Glucose	295×10^6	Cl^-	2800×10^6
Urea	295×10^6	Mg^{++}	70×10^6
Adenine-ribose		HPO_4	70×10^6
nucleotide	68×10^6	H^+	0.0022×10^6

From Brooks and Brooks, *Protoplasma Monograph* **19**, 1-393, 1941

The statement has been attributed to T. H. Huxley that cells, although small, have a degree of molecular complexity that can only be appreciated by visualizing an ocean liner packed with machinery built on the scale of a small ladies' watch. It is obvious, for example, that any cell contains a great range of enzymes; a large number of enzymes are required to break down sugar and convert it to carbon dioxide. While every living cell may be able to do this, it is only one of its many chemical tasks. Any estimate of the total number of enzymes to be found in cells would necessarily be subject to large errors, but such an estimate would probably be of the order of several thousands. If the role of genes is to determine the course of metabolism by regulating enzymatic reactions, on the basis of the "one gene, one enzyme" hypothesis, then it is pertinent to know approximately how many genes a typical living cell contains. This number may be of the order of 50,000. Judging, therefore, by everyday criteria of size one may be impressed by the smallness of cells and by the enormous number of cells that any higher organism may contain; but when considering the cell from the molecular standpoint, it is the degree of complexity which can be encompassed even within this small size that is most impressive. In terms of chemical reactions and of enzymes that make these possible, and of organelles within the cell that are capable of discrete and specialized functions, even the smallest cell is a highly intricate chemical machine.

The number of different molecular species that any living cell may contain, even of such complex molecules as protein, is staggeringly large. This was illustrated above by the kinds of enzyme proteins that each cell may have. But how many individual protein molecules might there be in a single meristematic cell? Sunderland, Heyes, and Brown (1956) gave data from which this can be calculated. They removed the central apical dome from the shoot of *Lupinus* and, after maceration, found the number of cells to be approximately 3500. They also determined the protein nitrogen content, from which they calculated the weight of protein per cell as 10.5×10^{-11} gm. By assuming an average molecular weight for the proteins, the number of molecules per cell can be calculated, since it is known that 6.5×10^{23} molecules are present in one gram molecular weight (Table 5–3). These figures lend point to the aphorism that a cell has the molecular complexity of an ocean liner packed with machinery, built on the scale of a ladies' watch!

TABLE 5–3
Number of protein molecules in a meristematic cell

Estimated average molecular weight	Total protein, mg	Number of molecules per cell
64,000	10.5×10^{-11}	1×10^9 (one thousand million)
640,000		1×10^8 (one hundred million)
6,400,000		1×10^7 (ten million)

Biologists, therefore, should not stand in awe of physicists and chemists in spite of the accomplishments made in these fields of science with systems that are inherently so much simpler. The nuclear physicist is often concerned with the properties of but a very few atomic nuclei, whereas the biologist must be concerned with the workings of a system which even in one cell represents a molecular universe! We should however, be challenged, not dismayed, by this task of interpretation.

From the analysis of carrot cells, similar estimates can be made, once one has determined the protein nitrogen on a known weight of fresh tissue which contains a known number of cells. Representative data are given in Table 5–4.

TABLE 5–4
Protein in tissue explanted from a carrot root

Grams protein/μg fresh weight	4.59×10^{-9}
Micrograms fresh weight/cell	0.10
Grams protein/cell	0.459×10^{-9}

If 6.5×10^5 is the assumed molecular weight of the average protein in the carrot cells, then one molecule of protein weighs

$$\frac{650,000}{6.5 \times 10^{-23}} = 1 \times 10^{-18}$$

grams per molecule of protein, and there would be 4.5×10^8 protein molecules per cell.

There has been an extreme idea that to carry out all the enzymic transformations of the cell, i.e., to maintain an adequate degree of "turnover," virtually all the protein of cells must be enzymatic. This idea, however, loses sight of the fact that some of the protein of cells is quite obviously structural protein; e.g., part of the protein of active tissue cultures has been found to contain hydroxyproline and to be inert (Pollard and Steward, 1959). Moreover, it is inconceivable that the fine structure of cytoplasm could exist without appreciable dependence on proteins which constitute the permanent features of this organization.

The Morphological Complexity of Cells:
Evidence of their Fine Structure

It is not enough, however, to stress the number of molecules of a given species that a cell may contain, for this total number may be variously disposed in many different organelles. To appreciate the complexity and organization of plant cells one should also take account of their morphology as revealed by the electron microscope and described as their fine structure. This fine structure emphasizes that chemical reactions and physiological functions may be geographically isolated in cells and the smooth operation of cells as working machines must be based on the mutual relations of their organelles.

Old ideas of a thin peripheral layer of optically transparent fluid protoplasm, bounded by an external membrane (plasmalemma) and an internal one (tonoplast) and enclosing inclusions of various kinds (aqueous inclusions in the form of vacuoles, living inclusions in the form of plastids and the nucleus), were more incomplete than inaccurate according to present concepts of plant cells.

The electron miscroscope has disclosed structure and organization at levels previously beyond the reach of the eye. The amount of detailed structure within a cell, which can now be revealed by appropriate techniques, reverses the previous dilemma. Earlier the problem was to visualize how such an apparently homogeneous, optically transparent ground substance could function as the "physical basis of life." Now the problem is to understand how such a wealth of finely structured detail in cells can be so accurately regulated and coordinated that it works in a controlled way.

The fine structure of cytoplasm is evident in the form of the unit membranes and lamellae (best revealed by techniques of fixation involving permanganate), the plastids (whether leucoplasts or chloroplasts), and various vesicular structures (such as Golgi bodies, mitochondria, vacuoles). It is now known that there is a great prevalence of granules out of which much protoplasmic organization is built; these granules occur either in the cytoplasm, free or attached to membrane surfaces, or within other cytoplasmic inclusions. Such granules are called ribosomes and presumed to consist of ribonucleoproteins. Lastly, there is the system of ramifying threads or tubules, known as the endoplasmic reticulum. The reticulum, to which some ribosomes are attached, may, on the one hand, be a channel for the transport of metabolites within the cytoplasm and, on the other, may provide surfaces upon which reactions can occur. A structural feature of cytoplasm which has only come to light recently is the system of long rods known as microtubules. In cross section these may have the appearance of hollow tubes but in face view they are long rods or filaments. They are abundant at the periphery of the cytoplasm and also occur in the region of the cell plate—the phragmasome—at cell division. The structural similarity between these tubules and cilia or flagellae has been noted by Ledbetter and Porter (1964), and they may well prove to be crystalline structures composed of contractile protein. Division of labor must occur between the functions of these different cellular organelles, as well as between different plant cells and organs. Anabolic and catabolic functions may be segregated in cells; hence, understanding of the working cells is not achieved by interpretations of their overall nutrition and metabolism alone, for there is also need to see how the separate organelles work together and comprise an integrated whole. As General Smuts perceived long ago (1926), a single cell is an organization which is greater than the sum of its several parts.

Knowledge of the inclusions in cells has increased so greatly since the application of the electron microscope that this should be summarized in general terms as follows.

The cell nucleus, long regarded as a site of regulatory control, is now seen to be bounded by a membrane pierced by relatively large pores. The membranous system, known as the endoplasmic reticulum, which ramifies throughout the cytoplasm as a delicate system of fine threads or tubules, may connect with the outer nuclear envelope and be a channel of transport throughout the

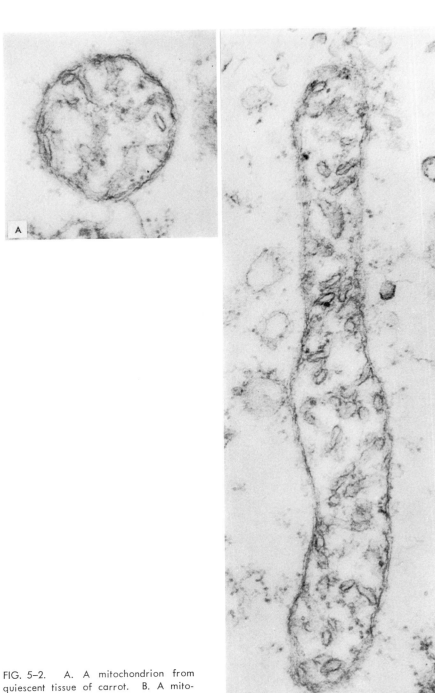

FIG. 5–2. A. A mitochondrion from quiescent tissue of carrot. B. A mitochondrion from actively growing cultured tissue of carrot. (Cf. Israel and Steward, 1966; both × 43,000.)

cytoplasm for substances of nuclear origin. But the reticulum, with its attached granules, may also provide surfaces on which reactions occur.

Plant cells are distinguished by the presence of plastids and these may have varied forms. They may be relatively large and notably free from internal structure, as in the chromoplasts of such quiescent cells as those of the carrot root; they may be active in the internal secretion of starch, as in leucoplasts; or they may assume the form of chloroplasts, as in green cells which have been much studied with the electron microscope. The grana in chloroplasts, seen in sections as stacks or coils of double membranes (thylakoids), the intergranal material, and the even more minute granules now called quantasomes, should all be noted. These characteristics stress that this organelle achieves its role in photosynthesis and in the carbon and nitrogen nutrition of autotrophic cells, not by virtue of its complex biochemical components (protein, fats, pigments, phospho-lipids, etc.) alone, but also by the aid of a physical organization the full implications of which may not yet have been interpreted. In cultured carrot cells (Israel and Steward, 1967) the plastids undergo a complicated developmental history both in the light and in the dark and in relation to their position in the plant body.

Plant mitochondria (Fig. 5–2), like their counterparts in animal cells, are conventionally regarded as the sources of useful energy released by respiration in the form of ATP. Whereas the processes of glycolysis and initial carbohydrate breakdown (cf. Fig. 6–13) are conceived to occur in the ground substance of cytoplasm, the enzymes which take the split products in the form of C_3 and C_2 units and feed them over the coenzyme A system into the oxidative tricarboxylic acid cycle are generally believed to reside in the mitochondria. In resting cells mitochondria (Fig. 5–2A) may be small and have relatively few internal, invaginated surfaces (cristae), whereas in active cells (Fig. 5–2B) they may become larger, and are often more elongate and have much structure and internal surfaces to which enzymes are supposed to be attached. The role of ATP, released by oxidative phosphorylation in mitochondria, or by photosynthetic phosphorylation in chloroplasts (cf. Fig. 3–9), as the applied source of energy to drive the energy-requiring steps of organic and inorganic nutrition and growth, requires that the working of cells needs to be understood at the level of its organelles and membranes.

The vesiculate inclusions known as Golgi bodies (dictyosomes), or Golgi apparatus (Fig. 5–3A and B), consist of lamellae grouped together in a characteristic fashion, and, from these lamellae, vesicles are formed and released into the cytoplasm. These features are especially evident in actively metabolizing or dividing cells (Fig. 5–3B). A currently suggestive idea is that these vesicles release the carbohydrate basis for the formation of the first formed wall, i.e., the non-crystalline, anisotropic, pectin-like material within which cellulose fibrils are later deposited; and, according to Frey-Wyssling and Mühlethaler (1965), the membrane of the vesicle may contribute to the plasmalemma.

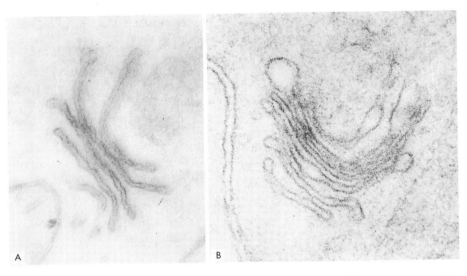

FIG. 5–3. The Golgi bodies (dictyosomes) of carrot cells, as seen in (A) quiescent or resting cells, (B) actively growing cultured cells. A × 46,000; B × 80,000. (From Israel; cf. Israel and Steward, 1966.)

FIG. 5–4. The tripartite unit membrane (plasmalemma) at the surface of the cytoplasm of a cultured carrot cell separating the cell wall (above) from the cytoplasm (below). (From Israel; cf. Israel and Steward, 1967; × 300,000.)

Wherever membranes occur in cells, at the inner and outer surfaces of protoplasm, bordering the reticulum or cytoplasmic inclusions, they have features in common as seen under the electron microscope (Fig. 5–4), thus lending credence to older ideas that such membranes are not mere physical boundaries between immiscible fluids, but definite autonomous organelles of the cell and sites where distinctive reactions occur. Finally, the very large number of granules (ribosomes), free and attached to membranes in the cells, are believed to present the template surfaces against which, when suitably activated, synthesis (e.g., of protein) may occur.

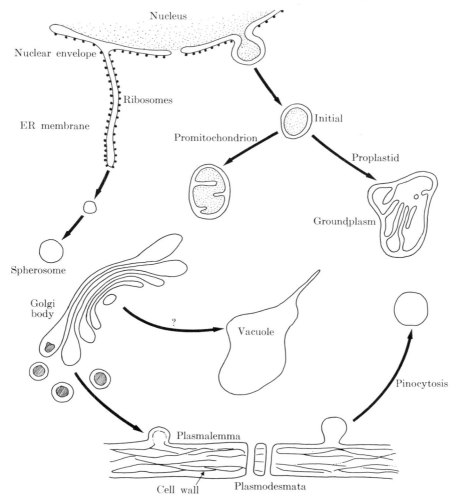

FIG. 5-5. Interrelations of cytomembranes. (From Frey-Wyssling and Mühlethaler, *Ultrastructural Plant Cytology*, Elsevier, Amsterdam, 1965.)

A summarized interpretation of the plant organelles is that of Frey-Wyssling and Mühlethaler (1965) (see Fig. 5-5). The salient features of this diagram are:

1.   The nucleus is bounded by a double (unit) membrane with relatively large pores.

2.   The endoplasmic reticulum extends the outer nuclear envelope throughout the cytoplasm and contains within its vesiculate structure a fluid now termed *enchylema*. The membrane of the reticulum is copiously furnished with ribosomal granules, and it may give rise either to vesicles called spherosomes (as shown) or to vacuoles (as shown earlier in Fig. 2-19).

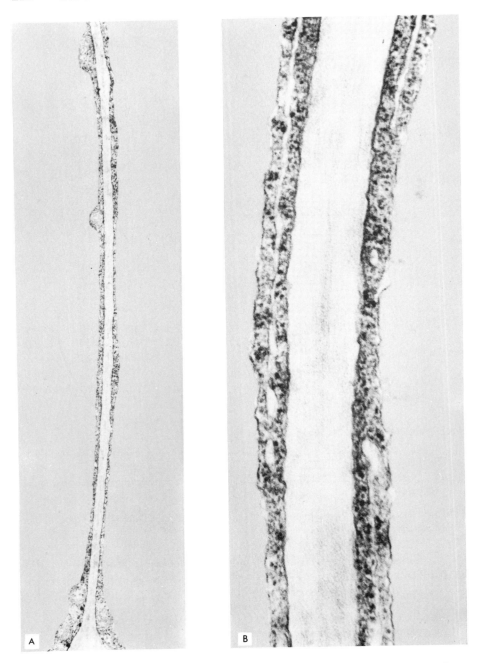

FIG. 5–6.   A. The thin ($<0.25\ \mu$) parietal cytoplasm in a quiescent carrot cell, $\times 8000$.   B. Same as A, but showing details at higher magnification, $\times 57,000$. (From Israel and Steward, *Ann. Bot.* N. S. 30, 63–79, 1966.)

3. Although this interpretation is not generally accepted, Frey-Wyssling and Mühlethaler believe that a second type of vesicle is budded off from the nucleus and contains nuclear groundplasm from within the double nuclear membrane. Such vesicles act as initials and may form, alternatively, mitochondria or plastids.

4. The Golgi body (or dictyosome) is another vesicular, membrane-bounded inclusion which is conspicuous in dividing cells and gives off spherical vesicles into the cytoplasm. These vesicles move to the cell plate at cytokinesis and are presumed to form the matrix of the cell wall, while their membrane substance adds to the outer plasmatic membrane or plasmalemma.

5. To the extent that pinocytosis can occur in plant cells, this is another possible mechanism for the formation of vacuoles and of returning membrane (plasmalemma) substance to the body of the cytoplasm. But at cytokinesis all these structures must be distributed between daughter cells.

Conventional electron microscopy thus extends techniques, long familiar with the light microscope, to a much lower order of magnitude. Preparations can be seen in various planes of sections, and selective staining techniques specifically identify different substances or organelles. A wealth of knowledge about plant cells and their inclusions has been obtained, especially from the relatively unvacuolated cells of plant growing points, for example, the cells of root tips as investigated by Whaley *et al.* (1960). For the often highly vacuolated cells from a carrot root, both in the quiescent condition and as they pass into the growing state, our current knowledge is summarized as follows from the work of Israel and Steward (1966).

i) The quiescent cells are large, and may give rise in culture to some even larger cells, which may be as large as 300 μ. These cells (up to 300 μ) contain very large aqueous vacuoles surrounded by a protoplasmic layer which may be less than 1 μ in thickness. In fact, the parietal protoplasm may be so thin that in places it consists of little more than its two boundary membrane surfaces (Fig. 5–6, cf. 10–2). By contrast, rapidly dividing cells of carrot when in culture are often very much smaller (not more than one tenth the size of mature parenchyma), and their vacuoles are minute.

ii) The nucleus of active cells is commonly to be found in a somewhat central position in the cell; it may be suspended by cytoplasmic strands and is often surrounded by cytoplasmic granules. The perforated nuclear envelope (a double-stranded unit membrane system) of carrot cells may also be attached to the endoplasmic reticulum, which thus may be a channel of transport from the nucleus throughout the cytoplasm; in this way substances that are directly determined by the nucleus (e.g., messenger RNA) may reach their sites of action in the cytoplasm.

iii) All the cytoplasmic inclusions of carrot cells respond to the stimuli (cf. Chapter 4) which make cells grow. The endoplasmic reticulum and ribosome granules (both attached and unattached) become more abundant than in storage cells; some mitochondria assume the branched and lobed condition typical of carrot cells in the actively metabolizing state, in contrast to the spherical form (rather poor in cristae) which is typical of resting or quiescent cells; Golgi bodies are scanty in the cytoplasm of resting cells, have fewer lamellae and fewer vesicles than in growing cells; the plastids (which above all other inclusions distinguish plants from animals) may, when growing in the light, acquire the benefits of the highly organized stacks of lamellae known as grana, which are typical of chloroplasts, in contrast to the large, less structured plastids as they occur in the cells of the storage organ.

But the electron-microscopical evidence from sections can now be supplemented by a technique which is described as freeze-etching; this is applied without either chemical fixation or staining. Though not yet applied to carrot cells, this technique has shown the fine structure of yeast cells in ways which permit the cytoplasm and its organelles to be seen in relief. This occurs because, in effect, the frozen structure is fractured along cleavage planes. The evidence of cytoplasmic streaming suggests that the ground substance of protoplasm is highly fluid. Nevertheless, the content of a very thin parietal layer of cytoplasm (Fig. 5–6), or even a single cytoplasmic strand (Israel and Steward, 1966), in a carrot cell possesses all the fine structural detail described above. By contrast, the technique of freeze-etching brings out highly sculptured surfaces which almost seem incompatible with the high water content and fluidity of active protoplasm. In illustration of this, certain figures from Moor and Mühlethaler, the pioneers of the freeze-etching technique, are reproduced as Fig. 5–7.

FIG. 5–7. Ultrastructure of yeast cells as revealed by the freeze-etching method. A. Total view of a cross-fractured yeast cell, revealing a large vacuole (in surface view), a nucleus (cross-fractured), and several mitochondria close to the cell wall. The "protuberances of the cell wall" are artifacts created by the freezing of the glycerol-containing medium which surrounds the cell (×9000). B. The vesicular systems. The system of flat paired membranes, extending from the upper right to the lower left, is a reduced kind of endoplasmic reticulum. At the bottom, a vacuole in surface view; on the right, a cross-fractured nucleus (×30,000). C. Surface view of a young vacuole, showing circularly arranged particles (ribosomes) (×40,000). D. Surface view of a nucleus derived from an old cell. The pores are concentrated in certain areas (×25,000). E. Inside view of a portion of the cell wall showing rod-like (elongated) invaginations (×20,500). F. Invaginations of the cytoplasmic membrane: top, surface view; bottom, cross-fractured (×30,000). G. A cross-fractured nuclear envelope, showing the structure of the unit membranes. The nucleoplasm is visible on the lower right, the cytoplasmic ground substance on the upper left. Arrows indicate pores (×52,000). H. Cross fracture through a nuclear envelope which is perforated by a pore. The structure of the unit membranes is partially visible (×110,000). I. A large dumbbell-shaped mitochondrion which is probably engaged in division. The upper right shows a surface view of the mitochondrial envelope, the lower left a cross-fracture which reveals the *cristae mitochondriales* (×55,000). (Reprinted by permission of the Rockefeller Press from Moor and Mühlethaler, *J. Cell Biol.* **17**, 609–628, 1963. Photographs supplied by Dr. Moor.)▶

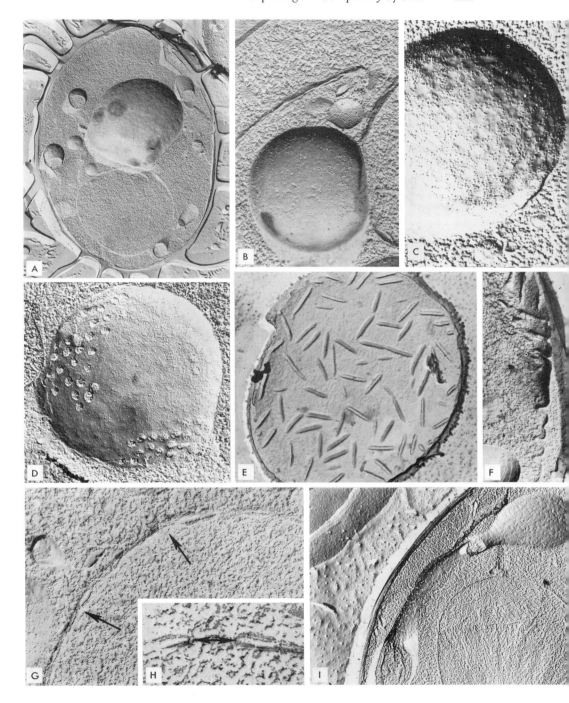

From all this evidence, therefore, the following impressions persist. The chemical reactions which mediate the processes of life in cells are not to be thought of as though they occur in a homogeneous medium, as in a test tube. Protoplasm is so highly structured and compartmented that it almost seems a contradiction in terms to ask, What is the minimum organization at which life exists? For a carrot plant it is clearly a carrot cell; for a yeast plant, a yeast cell, although inclusions that are much smaller than cells may also exhibit some of the attributes of life if they are tested in an appropriate environment in which they can, for a time, survive and function.

The portent that life itself may be created, or creatable, is seen by some in the near ability to make a virus artificially by linking nucleic acid to protein, or in our current ability to visualize the unit steps by which a protein may be made. This seems, however, to underemphasize the difficulties of the sort of "biological engineering" which cells present.

Current enzymology, cell physiology, and molecular biology tell how the individual unit steps in the overall plan may be, and are, feasible; genetics tells us how that feasibility persists from generation to generation both of cells and of organisms. But life is more than just this; it requires a pattern, a design, a milieu without which the feasible cannot become the actual. The evidence of electron microscopy describes organization at the subcellular level and its techniques extend almost down to the level of molecules. But, knowing this, we still seem far from explaining the ultimate organization which is life, whether in terms of the size, or in terms of the complexity, of its minimum viable unit. This gap is even wider than that which existed between the first laboratory experiment to condense amino acid amides into long chain molecules and the synthetic fiber industry as it now exists. Without the evidence of chemical feasibility, the industry would never have been built; without the engineering, no synthetic fibers would be spun or fabrics woven. But the analogy is not an adequate one, for the problems to be faced in cells are far more complicated than those of any synthetic fiber or plastic. Part of our difficulty, and part of the challenge, is to discern how cells and organisms, through evolution, have made a success story of solving the problems of "biological engineering" in the complex setting which we can now see as the fine structure of their protoplasm.

Planes of Cell Division

Granted that growth of cells presupposes their division, what can be said about the principles that determine how this division occurs and how the planes of division so determined lead to the form of familiar plants and organs. New planes of division not only divide cells but they also partition space. Different cell shapes do this with differing efficiency.

If a single cell were endowed with the ability to grow and divide, furnished with all the exogenous nutrients required, and placed in a completely symmetrical environment in which all external stimuli were uniform, what then should

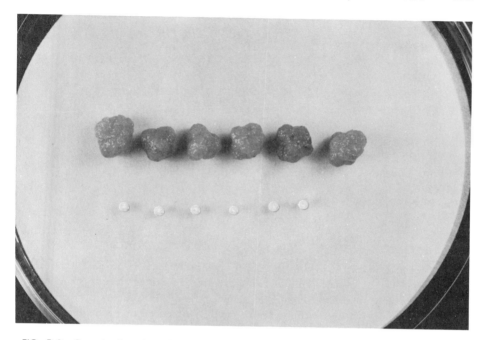

FIG. 5–8. Growth of explanted pieces of carrot root phloem. Upper row: ellipsoidal form of green explants grown in a basal medium supplemented with coconut milk; lower row: cylindrical orange explants in a basal culture medium. Diameter of Petri dish 100 mm.

happen? This condition could only be realized if temperatures were uniform, if the cells were regularly oriented to gravity by the use of a rotating klinostat, if the cells were regularly and uniformly exposed to such stimuli as light and aeration, if waste products were removed, etc. Where they are known the external, or environmental, factors that govern the growth of cells are controllable, and this is best achieved under the conditions of tissue and free cell culture (Steward, Caplin, and Millar, 1952). If by these means a free cell should, in a completely uniform environment, divide at random into two, and if the "daughter" cells remain equally capable of dividing, so that the whole process may be repeated, then a continuously growing globular mass of tissue should emerge. The extent to which this condition is, or is not, achieved lies at the heart of the problem of differentiation and of morphogenesis.

For a brief period some embryos which are fully supplied with food may grow into an almost spherical mass before polarity is established and differentiation occurs. Explanted pieces of uniform tissue can be exposed, by culture methods that need not be described here (Steward, Caplin, and Millar, 1952), to conditions that approximate those postulated above and, if the minute explants are almost spherical or at least cylindrical, and are caused to grow, they form ellipsoidal cultures (Fig. 5–8). If by appropriate means, which have been stipu-

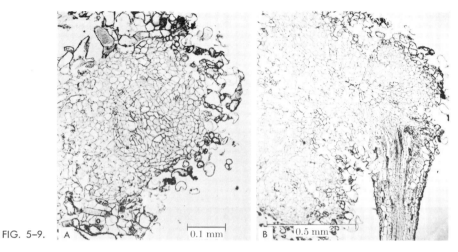

FIG. 5–9.   A   [0.1 mm]   B   [0.5 mm]

lated (Steward, Mapes, and Smith, 1958), such cultures are started from freely suspended cells, or even from minute aggregates of cultured cells, they form even more nearly spherical globules of growing tissue. The indefinite continuation, however, of growth in this way to produce a spherical, or near spherical mass, of tissue quickly encounters certain limitations. As the proportion of surface to mass decreases, all parts of the cultured tissue are not equally accessible to nutrients from the medium nor are they equally able to excrete waste products; hence, local centers of growth tend to arise near the periphery of the cultured mass. This occurs with a minimum of differentiation into organs when explanted pieces of preformed tissue are used to start off such cultures. It seems as though the presence of the older, more mature tissue from the original explant, which is in the center of the cultured colony, tends to inhibit differentiation into such organs as roots. However, the tissue within the cultured colony does promote the division of cells on its surface (Blakely and Steward, 1964), for they divide more rapidly than when they are completely free. While the sowing of free floating cells into a culture medium permits the cultured masses so formed to be more nearly spherical, it is interesting that, lacking a central core of preformed tissue from the organ from which the explants were removed, the culture organizes more readily to form roots; in doing this, certain cells which are at a distance from the surface of the growing culture may often form a pericyclic or cambial-like region within which organized growing points are developed. This is shown in Figs. 5–9A and 5–9B taken from a study of the structure of such carrot tissue cultures (Steward, Mapes, and Mears, 1958). In other words organization often begins spontaneously when there is a cultured mass large enough that within it some internal cells develop, by virtue of their position, in a manner that is different from those that surround them. Although this is a topic for later discussion (cf. Chapters 7 and 10) the organization of a

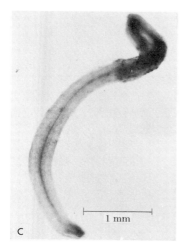

1 mm

C

FIG. 5-9. Organization in cultured carrot cells. A. Section through a nodule, showing a ring of dividing tissue enclosing "nests" of lignified elements. B. Emergence of a root from a nodule. C. An embryoid, with shoot and root, which will develop into a carrot plant. (After Steward, Mapes, and Mears, *Am. J. Botany* 45, 705–708, 1958.)

shoot apex could also occur in these colonies derived from freely suspended cells. Whereas root tips organized readily in liquid cultures rotated slowly about a horizontal axis, the best initiation of shoots first occurred when small cell clusters, already conditioned to form roots, were transferred to a stationary agar medium. Under these conditions "embryoids," i.e., minute plantlets closely similar in form to zygotic embryos, were found (Fig. 5–9C) and successfully grown to whole plants (Steward, Mapes, and Mears, 1958).

Rules of Cell Division

Classical attempts to explain the course of cell division and the eventual shape of cells are few, and the exceptions to the so-called laws which govern cell division are numerous. Nevertheless these laws are worthy of note.

The first such law, or Sachs' law, recognized that when cells divide they tend to do so in such a way that they produce "daughter" cells of equal mass. The second such law, or Errera's law, recognized that the new cell wall tends to be of minimum surface; and a third principle is that new walls often tend to intersect the old walls at right angles. Since liquid surfaces are commonly the seat of surface energy, it follows that any process that spontaneously readjusts the proportions of surface to volume should lead to the minimum of surface and the minimum surface energy. While these laws, which are really only guiding principles, have their value, many exceptions to them are to be recognized. Many of the exceptions, however, are probably due to asymmetry in the environment of the dividing cells due to the very organization of the plant body within which the divisions occur. Lastly, there is the concept that cells would approximate to regular 14-sided figures if they partitioned space completely with a group of regular and similar masses.

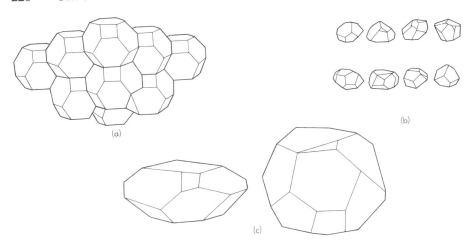

FIG. 5–10. The cell as a tetrakaidekahedron. (a) A set of 14-hedra, to show close packing. (After D'Arcy Thompson, *On Growth and Form*, Cambridge University Press, Cambridge, 1952.) (b) Results of an experiment with plasticine pellets to illustrate the form of the cells of the apical meristem. (After Priestley and Scott, *Introduction to Botany*, Longmans, Green & Co., London, 1938.) (c) Reconstructed models of cells of elder-pith, showing a certain approximation to a 14-hedral form. (After D'Arcy Thompson, 1952.)

When cells multiply under restraints imposed by some limitation of space, when all the cells have approximately the same size, and when their walls remain plastic and in fluid contact during their growth, the conditions for "partitioning space equally and without any leftovers" are satisfied. The regular 14-sided tetrakaidecahedra which achieve this are illustrated in Fig. 5–10(a) from D'Arcy Thompson (1952). If one makes a large number of simulated cells as spheres of plasticene and rolls these in French chalk so that they do not stick together, they can then be packed and firmly pressed into a dome-shaped mold (say the cup of a conventional thermos bottle) to simulate the shape of the central dome of meristem in an angiosperm. The mold can be removed, the unit "cells" dissected, and their margins of contact with neighboring "cells" marked with India ink. If this is done, the shapes in question approximate to the required 14-sided figures (Fig. 5–10b), and a section cut across the mass would show "cells" with sides of unequal dimensions (some longer and some shorter). Rarely, however, are these conditions satisfied throughout the development of cells in a mature tissue. Figure 5–10(c) shows that they may be approximately satisfied for certain pith cells. More commonly, however, the walls of the growing, expanding cells do not remain plastic and in fluid contact, for they become solidified and elastic and then, as they expand, they "round off" at their points of contact as they approach the conditions of spheres, as in many parenchyma which have air spaces (Fig. 5–11a). The oft quoted example of the stellate pith of *Juncus*, which in this water plant achieves the advantage of a highly developed air space system, deviates dramatically from either of the two systems of close packing

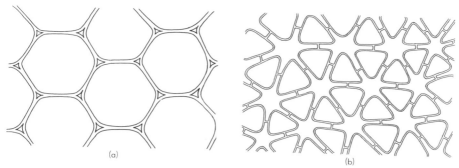

FIG. 5–11. Cell shape and arrangement. (a) Parenchyma of maize showing intercellular spaces. (b) Stellate cells in the pith of *Juncus*. (After D'Arcy Thompson, 1952.)

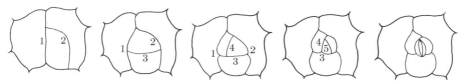

FIG. 5–12. Diagrammatic development of stomata in *Sedum*. (After D'Arcy Thompson, 1952.)

by 14-sided figures (Fig. 5–10a) or spheres (Fig. 5–11a). The impression here (Fig. 5–11b) is not one of growth of the cells as individual units but of the expansion of the tissue as a whole with the behavior of the cells being *constrained and determined by their restricted points of contact*. These points of contact are not only places where the cellulose walls between contiguous cells remain attached, but where protoplasmic connections (not shown in the figure but nevertheless very conspicuous under the microscope) *knit the behavior of the tissue into an organic whole*. In the outcome the pith cells would appear as if, from a sphere, many surfaces had been depressed like the "dimples" in the surface of a Haig & Haig whisky bottle. In this example, however, the emphasis should not be on the independent growth of the pith cells in mutual competition, but on the expansion of the tissue as a whole; not upon the more or less fluid contact of the boundary cell walls, but on their separation as solid, or elastic, entities except at points where there is organic union of cells into a tissue by the presence of plasmodesmata. (The important role of plasmodesmata in the organization of the growth that develops from free cells is to be stressed later.)

There is obvious asymmetry in the size of the cells that arise from the divisions that lead to the formation of sieve tube elements and companion cells, respectively, and there is obvious asymmetry in the divisions that cut off guard cells and accessory cells from the epidermis to form the stomatal apparatus (Fig. 5–12 shows the irregular divisions; their curved walls will be commented upon below). In the hypodermis of *Pellionia* and other plants there are certain

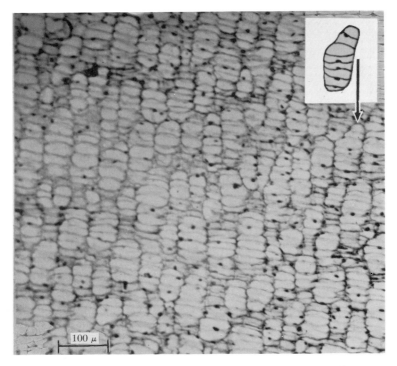

FIG. 5–13.   Region of active cell division at the base of a banana leaf. (From Barker and Steward, *Ann. Botany* N. S. 26, 413–424, 1962.)

very large cells which deform the otherwise regular tissue and give rise to cystoliths. Many similar examples could be found, and yet in large masses of parenchymatous tissue the approximately equivalent size of many cells is often apparent and Sachs' law of equal masses has at least some semblance of validity.

Although Errera's law may be obeyed by a great many divisions in the organized growing points of shoot and root and in the internal divisions which subdivide many elongated cells as in the intercalary growth of some monocotyledons (Fig. 5–13), there are some conspicuous exceptions. The vascular cambium does not divide by walls of minimum area, but by a somewhat oblique longitudinal division which produces a new wall, or surface, of near *maximal* area. However, such a plane of division is in part conditioned by the environment of the cell in which it occurs, as much as by the inherent capacity of the cambium cell to divide. When cambium initials are removed from their normal environment, they divide transversely and repeatedly to form isodiametric cells (Bailey, 1919). In fact, the frequent starting of callus-like cultures from tissue containing cambium elements is evidence that, free from the asymmetry and stimuli of the plant body, more random divisions are the rule. The cambium, however, is the classical example which should induce caution before attempting to predict on geometrical grounds how new divisions should occur; for cell divisions in cambium elements and developing vascular tissue may occur in different ways which lead to the formation of fusiform initials, tracheids or vessels; or, alternatively, the cells may so divide that they form isodiametric parenchyma or ray initials, as the case may be (Fig. 1–19). To state and prescribe the conditions that promote these various modes of division and development in cells that are in such close proximity is obviously difficult, but a full interpretation of the growth of higher plants necessitates that this should eventually be done. Even cork cambium, i.e., the formation of a wound phellogen at a cut surface of such tissue as that of the potato tuber, deviates drastically from Errera's law, for the cambial cells here divide parallel to the cut surface and not anticlinally and the new walls, in consequence, have maximal area. Again, however, these divisions occur under circumstances such that the dividing cells are subject to very asymmetrical conditions.

Errera's law of the minimum area of a new wall, which tends to intersect the old one at right angles, is very clearly satisfied when a filamentous cell divides transversely. This is often seen, e.g., in the formation of new cell walls that are interpolated along filamentous growths originating in some free cell cultures such as those of carrot (cf. Fig. 5–18g) or *Haplopappus* (cf. Fig. 5–21). Even so, the cells at the tip of such filaments may divide more asymmetrically by new walls (cf. Fig. 5–18g) which are curved.

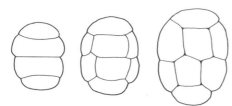

FIG. 5–14. Early development of a liverwort (*Pellia*). (After D'Arcy Thompson, 1952.)

Analogies have frequently been drawn between the behavior of weightless, intersecting liquid films and the behavior of new walls of dividing cells as they form partitions in cells and tissues. Where cell walls behave like such liquid films, they rarely intersect at right angles and never more than three converge at any point. If an original, almost spherical cell elongates and divides, by a septum which is virtually plane, and the two daughter cells divide again while their boundary walls are still fluid, then the second walls will be curved. Such embryonic forms as those of a liverwort were likened to the appearance of soap films in the oft quoted work of D'Arcy Thompson (Fig. 5–14). But where a flattened disc divides equally in this way, first into two, four, and eight partitions, the semifluid partition walls respond to equilibrium conditions and the curved films, intersecting three at a time, assume such forms as those shown in Figs. 5–15 and 5–16. These arrangements may be theoretically continued as shown in the sequences of Fig. 5–17.

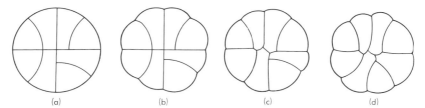

FIG. 5–15. Diagram of flattened or discoid cell dividing into octants, to show gradual tendency toward a position of equilibrium. (After D'Arcy Thompson, 1952.)

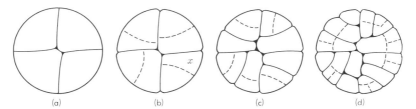

FIG. 5–16. Theoretical arrangement of successive partitions in a discoid cell. (After D'Arcy Thompson, 1952.)

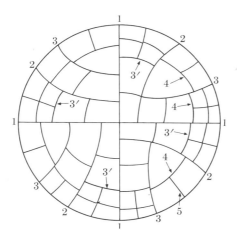

FIG. 5–17. Theoretical division of a discoid cell into 64 chambers, no allowance being made for the mutual tractions of the cell walls. (After D'Arcy Thompson, 1952.)

The glandular hairs of *Mentha piperita* grow in precisely this way. A basal cell is attached to the epidermis and by one periclinal division it cuts off an initiating cell which can now grow out into the free space and, as it expands and grows, anticlinal divisions form eight cells which constitute a flattened disc. Figure 5–18 portrays this development and it also shows that in the eight-celled stage, as seen from above (cf. Fig. 5–18e), the form of the cells and the pattern of intersecting septa conform precisely to the theoretical pattern shown in Fig. 5–15d. Sections through the embryo of a moss, cut at the eight-celled stage, again show patterns (Fig. 5–19a) indistinguishable from those of the mint

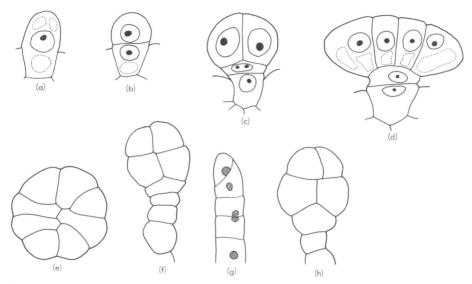

FIG. 5–18. Similarities between hairs and embryos; sequences of cell division. (a, b, c, d) Different stages in the formation of a gland in *Mentha piperita*. (After Howe, 1951.) (e) Surface view of the gland of *Mentha piperita* (after Howe, 1951); identical pattern to that of discoid cell dividing into octants (cf. D'Arcy Thompson, 1952, Fig. 5–15c.) (f) Hair of *Cucurbita*. (After Sachs) 1887.) (g) Filament of carrot cells grown in liquid. (After Steward, Mapes, and Smith, 1958., (h) Embryo of *Nicotiana*. (After Sachs, 1887.) (Entire figure from Steward and Mohan Ram, *Advances in Morphogenesis*, Vol. I, Academic Press, New York, 1961.)

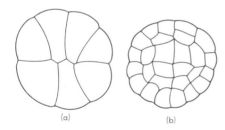

FIG. 5–19.   Sections of embryo of a moss. (After D'Arcy Thompson, 1952.)

gland with its eight cells (Fig. 5–18e). In all these cases, therefore, the growth conforms to a pattern in which the subunits are of equal size and the partitioning walls, or surfaces, behave like weightless films in equilibrium in a system which is free from marked asymmetry or restrictions of space. So long as they satisfy these requirements, such diverse structures as epidermal hairs and embryos grow in almost identical fashion (cf. Fig. 5–18f and h).

The early symmetry apparent in some embryos and their seeming resemblance to a system of liquid films is neither universal nor long continued. Many embryos first grow in a more or less filamentous fashion and produce their globular pro-embryo at one tip of the filament. The carrot embryo in its ovule

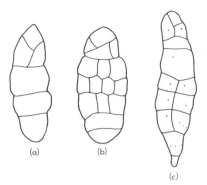

(a)   (b)

(c)

FIG. 5–20. (a, b) Development of *Sphagnum*, after Campbell. (After D'Arcy Thompson, 1952.) (c) Cluster of cells produced in free cell culture (carrot cells). (From Steward *et al.*, in D.Rudnick, ed., *Synthesis of Molecular and Cellular Structure*, The Ronald Press, New York, 1961.) (*Note:* The subdivisions of the terminal cells at one tip tend to be by curved walls and at the other by plane transverse walls, possibly associated with the relatively solid or still fluid state of the walls of the parent cell.)

is a case in point (cf. Fig. 7–2). For one reason or another, one tip of the embryonic axis enlarges to emphasize bulk or volume, whereas the other extremity emphasizes length. This is apparent as a globular embryo gives rise to a heart-shaped one, but it is also very apparent in the embryo-like forms that develop in free cell cultures. [In its later development the aerial shoot becomes dissected (cf. Fig. 1–20), has a large area in contact with the external atmosphere, and its cells receive nutrient (i.e., carbon dioxide) via long internal gaseous diffusion paths; whereas roots increase length, minimize area, and their cells make external contact by short, solute diffusion paths.]

A striking similarity exists, for example, between the form of a *Sphagnum* embryo and a typical embryo-like cluster grown from free carrot cells (cf. Fig. 5–20). *Haplopappus* shows a variety of these cell forms in which one may discern examples of the principal conditions that have been referred to above. Some transverse, more or less plane, surfaces subdivide a filament in which the prior walls have more or less solidified (cf. Fig. 5–21G, H, and J). In other cases,

FIG. 5–21. The form of cells and cell clusters of *Haplopappus* grown freely suspended in liquid medium. A. Free cells showing nucleus and abundant cytoplasmic strands. B. Free cell with papillae. C. Cell after division into two cells, showing nuclei and strands. D. A two-celled group, forming a third as a tubular outgrowth. E. Second division at right angles to the first to form a three-celled cluster. F. Four-celled colony with one terminal cell pigmented. G. Multicellular filament with transverse walls. H. Cell colony with pigmented and non-pigmented cells. I. Planes of division in a compact multicellular colony. J. Transverse walls in a pigmented filament attached to a cell cluster which has divided in other planes. K. Further divisions of a compact multicellular colony. L. Large globular cell with small cells attached. M. Giant cell protruding from the edge of a colony. N. Free-floating cell aggregate, showing intersecting planes of internal division. O. Cluster of isodiametric small cells. (From Blakely and Steward, *Am. J. Botany* **48**, 351–358, 1961.) ▶

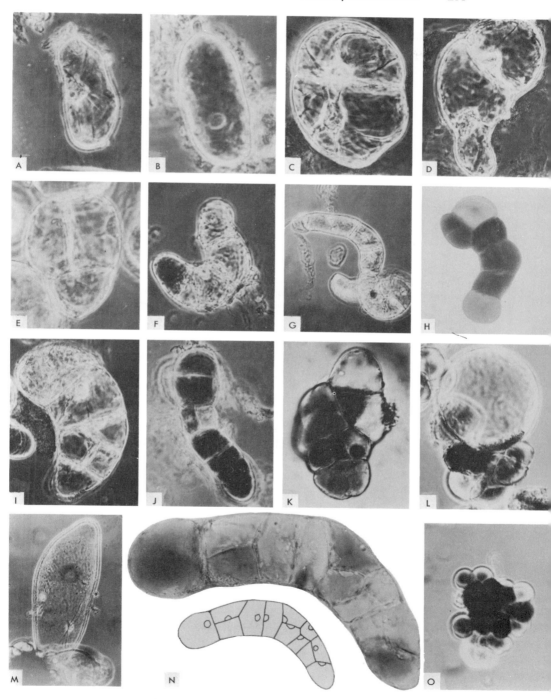

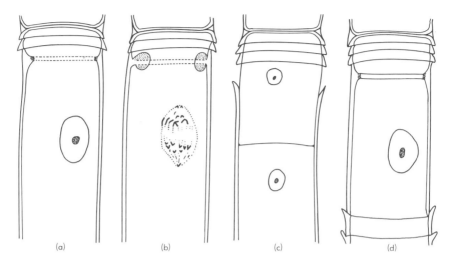

(a)   (b)   (c)   (d)

FIG. 5–22. Cell division in *Oedogonium.* (a) The nucleus has migrated to the upper third of the cell; the dotted lines represent the region at which a ring of wall material will be deposited while the nucleus is in prophase. (b) The nucleus is dividing mitotically; the ring of hemicellulose is several times thicker than the cell wall; a groove has appeared in the ring. (c) The cell wall has split just outside the ring of hemicellulose; mitosis is complete and cytokinesis has occurred. (d) By elongation of the cell the material of the ring has been stretched to form the new cell wall; after a short span of time the process can be repeated.

some septa near the tip of a carrot filament may as obviously be curved (Fig. 5–18g) as they intersect walls which are still somewhat fluid. Commonly cells at one tip of the growing entity enlarge and divide by walls which tend to multiply external surface (Fig. 5–21E and I), while cells at the other end of the incipient axis remain smaller and become internally subdivided in ways which multiply cells with the minimum increase in surface (Fig. 5–21C). Although this condition is recognized as an early expression of polarity in the development of an embryo, it obviously represents a profound and irreversible step in the development toward a shoot, on the one hand, or a root, on the other. But again, it may be noted, it is not any innate differences between the individual cells that induce these patterns of behavior, for it results from their more or less accidental location in the developing cell mass. Having, as it were, committed one tip of an embryonic axis to grow in bulk toward a sphere, it seems as if an irrevocable principle ensures that its other tip must conserve surface and emphasize length.

The mechanics of cell division and new wall formation show a striking constancy throughout the plant kingdom, and indeed, so far as the facts of mitosis are concerned, throughout organic nature. If one considers the division of the protoplast, i.e., cytokinesis, and the new wall formation, some notable exceptions come to mind. The green alga *Oedogonium* possesses a unique method of cell division which has not, apparently, been a successful device, for it is confined to members of this genus; although the genus is widely disturbed, nature seems not to have elaborated upon this method of cell division. In cell division in *Oedogonium* a portion of new wall is interpolated, or intercalated, between the severed portions of the old. The frequency with which this has occurred in a given cell can be noted in the so-called cap cells by the number of ridges, or caps, that occur there (Fig. 5–22).

The curious divisions that occur in the development of the antheridium of a moss are also at variance with both Sachs' law and Errera's law. These and other exceptions to the so-called laws of cell division are familiar. However, when uniform parenchyma tissue from higher plants divides and produces new cells in the freely suspended state by the devices of tissue culture, some curious methods of growth and cell division may occur. These can be shown in such cells as those derived from carrot root phloem, or potato tuber. From some such cells multicellular, filamentous processes develop, while others may multiply by putting out processes, papillae, that present the appearance of budding. Again, some giant cells form in these cell suspensions and within them divisions occur to form a morulloid-like mass of small dividing cells (Steward, Mapes, and Smith, 1958). These somewhat bizarre cell forms are mentioned to show by contrast that *the regularity of the growth of cells which form parenchymatous tissues in the plant body is the result of the control over cell growth and division which is exercised by the milieu in the plant body in which the cells develop.* Therefore, the division and growth of the cells within the organized plant body is limited, not by their innate characteristics, but by extrinsic factors, whereas, when freely and singly suspended in a liquid culture medium, the same cells can respond to intrinsic factors in ways which produce a great variety of cell forms even in the same solution under uniform cultural conditions.

Therefore, in all organized growth, there must be stimuli and controls that restrict the otherwise unregulated expression of the full potentiality of cells for growth and cell division.

The Contrasted Apices of Root and Shoot

In the organized apical growing regions of shoot and root polarity is established early in embryogeny. Thenceforward the cell divisions in the shoot lead to the more superficial origin of lateral organs, whereas the divisions in the root lead to the more deep-seated origin of lateral organs. For convenience, an opposite and decussate shoot will be used to illustrate the shoot, and the root of the same plant (i.e., *Mentha piperita*, the common peppermint plant) will also be considered. The growing regions of *Mentha* are illustrated by median longitudinal and transverse sections for the shoot and median longitudinal sections for the root (cf. Figs. 1–13 through 1–15); reference will also be made to the shoot apex of *Lupinus*, upon which some biochemical data are now available, more perhaps than for the shoot of any other angiosperm.

Next to the fertilized egg or zygote, the completely totipotent cell from which the entire plant body derives, perhaps the most baffling structures in angiosperms are the apices of root and shoot, for in these relatively restricted regions reside all the potentialities for the very different growth of shoots and roots. The development of a fertilized egg into an embryo, with its organized shoot and root tips, and the development of the entire plant body from these apical growing regions, presents a challenge to those who rightly seek biochemical and physiological interpretations of growth and development. Although the subsequent structures formed by the growth of root and shoot apices are so completely different, there is little that is visible under the microscope to distinguish their respective meristematic cells. There seems to be no *a priori* reason why a meristematic cell, if isolated from the shoot apex and put into place in the root apex, should not perform equally well in its new environment, though there seems to be no record that this has ever been done. Therefore, the behavior of the growing apex is the resultant of the potentialities of the individual cells and of their interaction with the environment, or internal milieu, in which they occur. Thus the apices of shoot and root as already organized structures furnish requirements and impose restrictions which freely growing cells, as in free cell cultures, do not encounter.

The presence of a relatively deep-seated zone of active cell division near the root tip, which is followed by a zone of cell elongation and tissue maturation, has often been contrasted with the more superficial occurrence of the dividing meristematic cells of an angiosperm shoot apex. The more deep-seated occurrence of cell division in roots leads to growth in length, unaccompanied by superficial lateral organs. By contrast, the more superficial cells of the shoot divide and so create surface more rapidly than volume, and lateral organs, in the form of leaf primordia, appear first as wrinkles or lobes on the otherwise smooth surface of the apical dome. While at the outset these simple ideas have merit, the true situations are obviously far more complex.

In angiosperm shoots leaf primordia originate along the flanks of an otherwise smooth dome of meristem, and normally they are crowded near the tip. In a transverse section through a shoot apex it can be seen that only a limited number of such primordia can be physically accommodated at the apex. A common situation, therefore, is that leaf primordia tend to originate *as far as possible from each other*, often diametrically opposite to each other. If the next pair occurs at a slightly lower level and below the gaps between the first pair, this produces a familiar situation of opposite and decussate leaves, as in the case of mint.

Leaf primordia seem to make the maximum use of the space available on the tip of the shoot in which to encompass their development, and they obligate for given periods of time the synthetic capacity of the apex. Different arrangements in time and space at the apex result in the geometrical pattern of leaves which is characteristic of the phyllotaxy of the plant in question. After each leaf primordium is produced or cut off from the apex, an interval of time elapses before the next leaf appears. This interval of time is called a "plastochron." In due course another leaf primordium will be formed vertically above the first. Such vertical files of leaves are often united more closely in the vascular system than are the leaves in different files, and they constitute an orthostichy. *Thus there are many reasons for regarding the unit of shoot growth as that portion of the axis (i.e., the internode) which subtends a leaf primordium. There are also reasons to regard the vertical files of leaves, which are closely connected in the vascular system, as constituting a nutritional unit, because solutes and stimuli may pass more readily between these leaves than laterally across the stem.*

A somewhat intermediate condition between a typical root and shoot is to be seen in submerged aquatic angiosperms, like *Elodea** and *Hippuris* (cf. Fig. 5–23); in these plants the submerged leaves are much reduced and the shoot growing point consists of a long cone from which leaf primordia emerge rather far back from the tip. Thus the organization of these shoot tips appears to be somewhat intermediate between the normal apices of angiosperm roots and shoots. The etiolated shoots of dicotyledons, in which preformed leaf primordia do not expand and new ones do not form at the apex, also exhibit a somewhat more root-like habit or organization.

It is well known that the apical growing region of the shoot has different potentialities in regions which are not, however, very sharply delimited. This is shown in *Helianthus* in Fig. 5–24. The central apical meristem consists of rather large, apparently more quiescent, cells. Below this a region occurs in which cells divide transversely to the axis (rib meristem), and this "tapers off" into the pith, though divisions continue through the period of internodal elongation. A cylinder of cells which retain their ability to divide runs back longitudinally from the apex to form the procambial strands which, in dicotyledonous plants, are continuous with the vascular cambium. But the main centers of cell division which lead to leaf primordia are to be found not at the very tip but on the flanks of the shoot apex.

If the whole shoot apex is removed it will reconstitute a whole plant under tissue culture conditions; first, roots form adventitiously, then the shoot develops. If side regions (four in number), consisting of dividing cells together with a small central pedestal, are removed and grown separately, then the side pieces *form leaves only*, probably also some callus, even though they may also root. If the central region only is removed and placed aseptically on a culture medium, it remains alive but will not grow and it may not even form callus.

Therefore, similar, genetically identical cells as they occur in these different regions have very different capacities for growth and development; in the in-

---

* Although *Elodea* is now *Anacharis* it will be referred to under its old name.

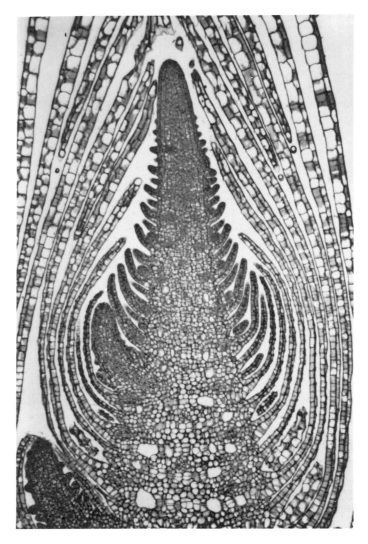

FIG. 5–23. The shoot apex of *Elodea*. (From a preparation by Dr. D. W. Bierhorst, Cornell University.)

tact apex the different regions do not behave as autonomous units, for they are interdependent. It is apparent, however, that these different potentialities for growth in the different regions result not from intrinsic, genetically determined differences between the cells, but are determined by extrinsic factors that are the consequence of the place which the cells occupy in the organization of the shoot tip.

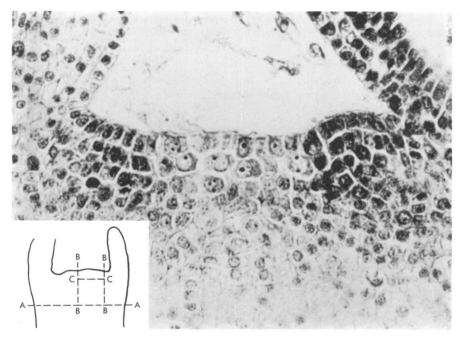

FIG. 5–24. Shoot apex of *Helianthus annuus*, showing young leaf primordia around the apical meristem. The drawing on the lower left indicates how incisions are made in removing the whole apex (cut AA), the flanking portions (BB), and the central core. The small apical piece denoted by CC represents still smaller segments which can be removed for aseptic culture. (Drawing after Wetmore, in D. Rudnick, ed., *Cellular Mechanisms in Differentiation and Growth*, Princeton University Press, Princeton, 1956.)

The Frequency of Cell Division

An old idea that is now dispelled was that the apices of shoot and root are regions in which cell divisions occur very rapidly, or very frequently. R. Brown (see Sunderland, Heyes, and Brown, 1956) dissected the apex of such plants as *Lupinus* and (by applying methods of maceration and counting cells) has estimated the number of cells which comprise the central apical dome and a series of shoot units; these units consisted of the internode and the associated leaf primordium and they extended over seven plastochrons and required 14 days to emerge. Thus, on the average, the time taken to form a leaf and an internode was two days; the number of cells that were formed during the subsequent growth of the initial can be counted. It is of course obvious that all the cells of each of these segments do not divide at the same average rate. Nevertheless, the frequency of division calculated on this assumption is of interest.

The central dome of the shoot apex of *Lupinus* has an estimated volume of 1.6×10^{-3} mm³, weighs only 0.0016 mg, and contains about 3500 cells (Sunderland and Brown, 1956). During an interval of two days (i.e., a plastochron) a growth unit consisting of 2300 cells in an internode and in the first leaf primordium is produced behind the apex. "This suggests for the dome an average rate of one division every third day." Seven plastochrons later the similar growth unit, again consisting of internode and subtended leaf, contained 32,000 cells, and this required about 14 days to be produced. Thus about the same average rate of division was again obtained as in the central dome. Brown also quoted Richards who, in 1951, estimated that the average rate of cell division in the shoot meristem of *Lupinus albus* was one division per cell every five days. While these are admittedly average rates, which would be increased in regions of locally concentrated growth, they certainly do not imply the very rapid rates of division which might earlier have been associated with the meristem of a growing dicotyledonous shoot.

These cycles of division and average frequencies of division of cells in a shoot apex may now be compared with those for a root. It is estimated that the complete cycle of cell division in a pea root occupied on the average about 18 hours at 20° C (Brown, 1951), and Erickson and Goddard, also in 1951, indicated that in a maize root a ten-fold increase in cell volume was completed in about 12 hours. These data indicate, therefore, that cell division and cell expansion proceed more slowly, in fact very much more slowly, in the apical region of the shoot than in the corresponding regions of the root.

It is instructive to compare the rates of cell division in the organized growing points with those rates which have now been achieved under tissue culture and optimal nutritional conditions. As already stated (cf. p. 142), a carrot tissue explant which weighs about 2.5 mg and contains about 25,000 cells will grow in about three weeks to two and a half million cells. This represents about seven cell generations, or a division of every cell once every three days. This is about the same average rate as that quoted above for the unit of shoot growth in the *Lupinus* shoot. However, only the surface cells of the explant participate effectively in the new growth, and it is much more probable that the first situation in the tissue cultures is that equal numbers of layers of cells are formed in equal intervals of time (Steward, 1958). When the data of a typical growth curve are analyzed in this manner, it appears that the maximum rate of cell division under such circumstances would require a minimum average cell generation time in the surface layers of approximately six, or more, hours. While this may well be a maximum and much overestimated rate, there seems little doubt that the rate of cell division which can be achieved under tissue culture conditions may equal or even exceed that which occurs normally in the organized shoot apex. It is now known (cf. Chapter 10), however, that angiosperm cells do not achieve their maximum growth rates when they are completely free, for both division rates and survival of the daughter cells seem better when the cells exist in colonies in which the non-dividing cells stimulate those that are still in a position to divide. All this implies that the cell division rate in the shoot apex may well be limited by some feature of its organization or nutrition. (Parenthetically, it would be interesting to have comparable division rates for cells in the growing points of rapidly growing tropical plants).

There are other indications that the behavior of the shoot may often be modified by the nutrient and other conditions which determine its growth; this may be illustrated by the anomalous behavior of many plants which bear opposite and decussate leaves. Such plants produce, infrequently, anomalous forms in which three instead of two opposite leaves exist in a whorl at each node; these then diverge from the stem at an angle of 60 degrees. This three-whorled condition, in normally opposite and decussate plants, has been observed in mint plants on shoots which emerge from stolons at the end of the rest period (Crane, 1951), and it has been observed in seedling maple shoots grown in the greenhouse at relatively high temperature. The same condition was observed by de Vries (1920) in *Dipsacus*, and it also appears infrequently in *Kalanchoe*. A similar condition was recently noted in a lilac stem which grew as a sucker shoot from a cut stump. In all these examples the anomalous condition of three instead of two leaves at a node seems to be associated with growing points which form on unusually vigorous shoots and at terminal growing points which have a larger than normal central apical dome; indeed, de Vries thought the condition occurred whenever the actual size of the central growing point was larger than normal, due to environmental or nutritional conditions; this permitted more leaves than normal to be accommodated at the same level. This point is mentioned here simply to show that problems of size and geometry arise in the interpretation of the amount of cell division which growing regions can support and of the structures to which they give rise.

But what is the actual distribution of the cell divisions in the apex, and what are the physiological problems inherent in its interpretation? It is convenient to begin with a root. Parenthetically, it may be noted that, although much use has been made of root tips by cytologists who study chromosomes during cell division, there is still much to be learned concerning the factors that determine the distribution of such divisions in root tips.

Growth and Cell Division in the Root Apex

Figure 1–15 shows a typical median longitudinal section of a root of mint, and Fig. 5–25 presents a drawing of the cells in this root at its tip; alongside this are some interpretations which show how the various files of cells may be traced, in their lineage, to the initiating cells at the apex.

If we neglect the root cap, it is clear that there is a quiescent region at the apex of the mint root which consists of relatively large cells; although the cells of this region do not divide frequently they may, nevertheless, release stimuli which may have a formative influence on the apex. In fern apices relatively large apical cells are familiar, but one does not usually expect relatively large non-dividing cells to occur in the midst of the root apical meristem. Recently,

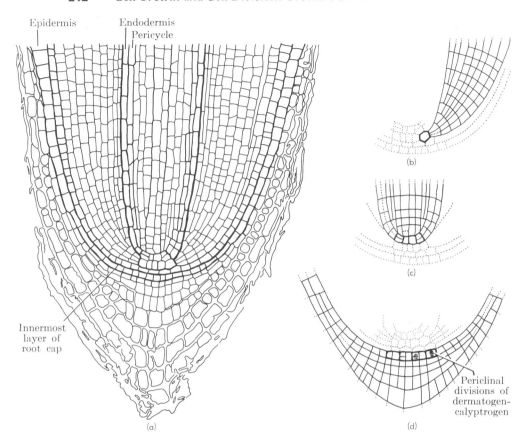

Epidermis   Endodermis
Pericycle

Innermost
layer of
root cap

Periclinal
divisions of
dermatogen-
calyptrogen

(a)   (b)   (c)   (d)

FIG. 5–25. Interpretive drawings of the *Mentha* root apex (a), to show origin and distribution of new cells in cortex (b), stele (c), and root cap (d). (From Howe and Steward, in *Cornell Univ. Agr. Exp. Sta. Mem. No. 379*, 1962.)

however, Clowes (1953, 1954 and 1961) has described such a region in the root apex of various grasses, and he has termed this the cytogenerative region, which implies that it may be a source of stimuli or metabolites that determine the divisions of adjacent cells, although, by the technique of tritiated thymidine labeling, its cells do not divide as frequently as the neighboring ones do (Clowes, 1961, Plate 23). This point of view can obviously be applied to the mint root, in which files of cells are produced along the axis of the root by the orderly multiplication of cells along the diameter of the root by divisions which are parallel to its surface—i.e., periclinally—and by multiplication of cells along the length of the root by divisions which occur at right angles to the axis—i.e., anticlinally. From the diagrams which interpret this root (Fig. 5–25) one may infer that the

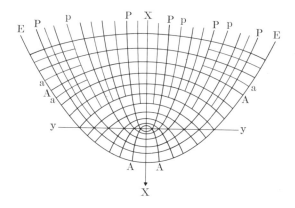

FIG. 5–26. Diagrammatic view of a longitudinal section through a growing point. The outline has the form of a parabola; the partitioning of space within the growing point takes place such that the anticlinal and periclinal walls cut one another at right angles. (*XX*, axis; *yy*, direction of the parameter; *Pp*, all the periclines denoted by confocal parabolas; *Aa*, all the anticlines denoted by confocal parabolas.) (After Sachs, 1887.)

small dome, or cap, of cells at the tip of the meristem seems to control, or direct, the activities of the cell layers to which the tip gives rise. The central dome of cells preserves its identity and the pattern of tissue laid down behind it is indicated in the diagrams. These tissues comprise epidermis (or piliferous layer), a cortex consisting of some five cell layers, an inner cortex which accounts for three more files of cells, and a central stele consisting of some 12 cells (of which two rows arise only by transverse divisions, and two adjacent files of five can each be traced to a single formative cell in the tip). (The root cap is formed from cell layers which divide anticlinally and periclinally in the manner indicated in the diagram.) All this is very reminiscent of an interpretation made by Sachs as long ago as 1878. It is true that Sachs was considering shoot apices, albeit the shoot apex of aquatic angiosperms which are more root-like in character, but he visualized zones of activity and cell multiplication which he represented by a series of confocal and intersecting parabolas (Fig. 5–26). The parabolas which reflected the division of cells parallel to the surface Sachs called "periclines," and other parabolas, which he called "anticlines," indicated the cell multiplication along the axis. Where these parabolas intersect, the "quiescent" or "cytogenerative region" could now be located.

What, then, does this description mean in terms of physiological stimuli and of the nutrition of the growing point? It is hard to visualize these relationships without ascribing some special significance to the distinctive small group of cells in the root apex which seems to regulate and control the flow of tissue growth and differentiation behind the apex. Do these cells elaborate some special nutrients, or is their regulatory control exerted by growth-regulatory substances of the hormonal type? An attempt should surely be made to learn more about the biochemical characteristics of the cells in this region. However, the impression is gained that the individual cells in the root tip do not behave as physiologically independent units, but that the role of each is controlled by *influences which seem to be centered in and emanate from the zone of quiescent or formative cells which has been termed the "cytogenerative region."* Ultimately it should be possible to test whether this regulatory control is exerted by the backward flow of auxins, or by cell division factors of the kind previously discussed (Chapter 4). In fact, recent evidence shows that the larger, non-dividing cells in a cluster of free cells do release stimuli that promote the division of cells attached to them and at the surface of a colony, and they also secrete into the medium substances which promote the viability of free cells in their proximity (see Chapter 10).

A convenient analogy might be helpful. The onward growth of the root apex, clearly determined by food supply via the stele, might be likened to the upward thrust of a rocket or star shell. The fan-wise, parabolic backward flow of cells, radiating from formative centers at the tip, might be likened to the parabolic path of the falling stars released explosively from the center. This analogy focuses the attention upon different kinds of forces—the forward drive which is determined by food supply, the backward "gravitational" fall likened to a wave of differentiation as the tip growth subsides, the lateral thrust determined by cell division and enlargement—and these forces may be used to illustrate the parabolic patterns of Sachs, which are clearly visible in a root like that of the mint. The cytogenerative region at the root apex, therefore, *seems to be strategically placed to be, by its position, the source from which factors radiate backward and outward to stimulate further growth and cell divisions in the files of derivative cells behind the tip.*

Growth and Cell Division in a Shoot Apex

The suggestion that the central dome of the shoot meristem was not, as first thought, the main center of cell divisions but that these occurred more frequently upon the flanks (Fig. 5–27), originated with a French school of botanists. According to this view the formative regions for the vegetative structures of the shoot lie along the flank of the meristematic apex so that the central dome itself may remain relatively inactive until the onset of flowering.

Attempts to culture the root tips of dicotyledons have been frequently successful, but attempts to culture shoot tips have encountered much greater difficulty, the difficulty being greater the smaller the tissue piece that was explanted. Wetmore (1956) particularly has made exhaustive but largely unsuccessful attempts to culture the apex of dicotyledonous shoots in the manner that is readily feasible with ferns. Later Ball (1960) was able to obtain some growth, though it was not indefinitely maintained, when the central apical dome of *Lupinus albus* (diameter 300 μ $\times$ 100 μ high) was nourished by a basal medium

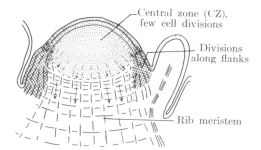

Central zone (CZ), few cell divisions

Divisions along flanks

Rib meristem

FIG. 5–27. The form of and zones of activity in an apex. Schematic interpretation of shoot apex of *Lupinus*. (After Buvat, 1952.)

containing both coconut milk (to induce cell division) and gibberellin (to cause elongation). This sort of work implies that the shoot apex is normally interdependent with the older tissue beneath and that it requires either nutrients in an elaborated form, or stimuli from the older tissue below. It is now familiar that auxin is elaborated mainly in the shoot apex and moves basipetally to invoke cell extension in the maturing organs below; but what is known about the distribution of physiological activities in the apex of the shoot itself?

An old idea was that the shoot apex should be so actively concerned with the synthesis of protoplasm that it would consume its metabolites as rapidly as they could be received from the vascular tissue beneath. To test this idea and to ascertain whether there might be something distinctive about the proteins of the growing point, chromatographic examinations were made of the apex and of the successive leaf primordia of *Lupinus* (Steward *et al.*, 1954). It was possible to show that a wide range of free amino acids occurred in the growing point of *Lupinus*, although their concentration was markedly reduced if the cotyledons were removed from the seeds soon after germination. The range of amino acids in the shoot apex of *Lupinus* was qualitatively similar to that which commonly occurs in many plants. Asparagine, though present even in the apex, was much less prominent in the soluble nitrogen of the growing point than in that of the storage organs of *Lupinus*. A notable feature of the proteins of the growing point was the relative abundance of the more basic amino acids—no doubt attributable to the presence of histones and basic nucleoproteins in the dividing cells.

However, a marked contrast was revealed between the growing point of *Lupinus* and that of the fern, *Adiantum*. Whereas the former had a reasonably complete range of free amino acids in its cells, the latter appeared able to elaborate its protein from a relatively small number of soluble nitrogen compounds, and one of these proved to be a distinctive amino acid hitherto unknown in nature: this was the substance now known as γ-hydroxy-γ-methyl glutamic acid. Figure 5–28 shows amino acid chromatograms for the growing points of these two plants.

A notable feature of the *Adiantum* apex is the outer layer of relatively large vacuolated cells. These were stripped off and separately analyzed, and their nitrogenous composition compared with that of the more meristematic tissue beneath. It was thus possible to show (Steward *et al.*, 1955) that the outermost layer of larger cells had the nitrogenous content of mature, relatively non-dividing cells, which were only encountered in the central axis at a much lower level. This suggests that this outermost layer of the fern apex was not as active in promoting growth by its own cell division as might otherwise have been supposed. It may, however, like the cytogenerative region of the root, be a source of metabolites or stimuli to the dividing region below.

Brown and his coworkers (1956) have measured for the shoot of *Lupinus* the respiration rate, the number of cells, and the protein nitrogen content of different dissected portions of the apex; they have also attempted to compare the distribution of respiration and increase of cell number in the different parts of the apex as they grow. One might expect that respiratory activity per unit weight of tissue would be greatest near the apex, lowest further away. Brown, however, maintains that this idea may be somewhat spurious, with respect to both the root and the shoot, because apical segments that are comparable in size may have a larger number of smaller cells than older segments; consequently, Brown asserts, such comparisons ought more properly to be placed upon either a cellular basis or a protein nitrogen basis. Therefore, Brown draws the following conclusions with respect to the shoot apex of *Lupinus*:

1.   All the tissues of the apex have a relatively high proportion of protein to soluble nitrogen. (In this they resemble the growing cells of tissue cultures). Brown attributes the paucity of soluble nitrogen compounds to the relatively non-vacuolated condition of these cells, and this may limit their activity in growth.

2.   Brown regards the primordium of both root and shoot—that is, the central dome of the meristem—as having a low activity per unit of protein that it contains, and he regards both these regions as probably dependent on metabolites which are drawn from more active regions to maintain their growth. This may account for the great difficulty experienced in culturing minute shoot apices, for they may lack the special nutrients which the subjacent tissues may provide.

3.   Histologically, the shoot growing point has been interpreted as an outer tunica and an inner corpus, and the leaf primordia are supposed to arise from the tunica. In describing the characteristics of these several regions Brown finds that the apical dome and meristem are intermediate between the leaf primordia and the internode. Brown also concludes that "the cells of the corpus are not only larger than those of the tunica, but they have a greater total protein content but a lower concentration of protein and a higher respiration rate per unit of protein. The whole generative system in the apex of the stem may therefore be considered as consisting of a central core with high metabolic activity covered by a mantle with low metabolic activity."

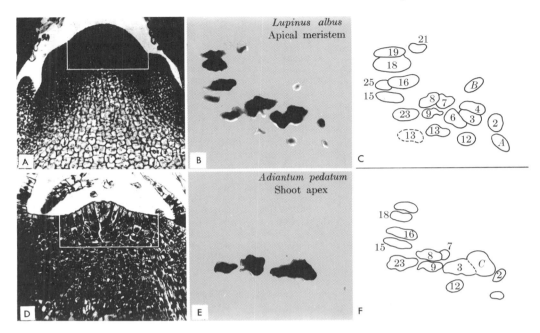

FIG. 5–28. A. Longitudinal section of apical meristem of the vegetative shoot of *Lupinus albus*. B. Chromatogram of alcohol-soluble nitrogenous substances from many apices of *L. Albus*. C. Tracing of chromatogram of B, with numbers, to permit identification of substances. D. Longitudinal section of apical meristem of rhizome of *Adiantum pedatum*. E. Chromatogram of alcohol-soluble nitrogenous substances from numerous portions of non-active apices of *Adiantum pedatum*. F. Tracing of chromatogram of E, to permit identification of alcohol-soluble nitrogenous substances. Key to ninhydrin reactive spots on chromatograms: 2, aspartic acid; 3, glutamic acid; 4, serine; 6, asparagine; 7, threonine; 8, alanine; 9, glutamine; 12, lysine; 13, arginine; 15, proline; 16, valine; 18, leucine(s); 19, phenylalanine; 21, tyrosine; 23, γ-aminobutyric acid; 25, (−)-pipecolic acid; A, spot in the position of glutathione; B, unidentified spot, possibly an ammonium salt—reacts pink; C, unidentified spot later determined to be γ-hydroxy-methylglutamic acid. (From Steward, Wetmore, and Pollard, *Am. J. Botany* **42**, 946–948, 1955.)

Brown goes on to say that "the respiratory activity in the corpus is undoubtedly high, and in it metabolites are probably produced which are not locally consumed. They are transferred to the tunica in which respiratory activity is low and in which synthesis is probably thereby restricted." Whether these ideas will be substantiated by further work is not perhaps the most important point just now; it is rather that by the sort of chromatographic studies made in this laboratory and in collaboration with workers at Harvard, and the respiratory and the cell studies made in Brown's laboratory, a start has been made in interpreting the shoot growing point along combined physiological and morphological lines. Ultimately it will be necessary so to perfect these techniques that the difficult problems of the transition between the vegetative and the floral shoot can also be investigated. Be this as it may, it is now evident that both the apices of the vegetative shoot and of the root comprise regions which are not only morphologically, but also physiologically and metabolically distinct, though probably interdependent, so that each may contribute some essential function to the entire organization of the apex. It is not surprising, therefore, that the separate culture of the most minutely explanted portions of the angiosperm apex has so far failed. The success that has attended the culture of roots may well have been due to the fact that its formative regions are so rigorously confined to a limited area of a few cells at the extreme tip, that the smallest root apex which can be conveniently severed contains the complete generative system.

The centers of growth in the plant body may, however, be areas of intense physiological activity. To some extent this possibility has been examined with respect to respiration. Thus, many of the physiological functions tend to "follow the lead of growth" and to be modified or controlled by the factors which correlate growth and development within the plant body. Such events as the intake of water by cells and organs, and the accumulation of solutes in cell vacuoles, are obvious cases in point. It is, therefore, appropriate to discuss these relationships in a separate chapter devoted to those physiological functions which are closely correlated with, and tend to be determined by, the stimuli which control growth.

Summary

The question is posed why cells that grow need to divide. Various concepts are examined. These concepts are built around the preservation of a critical proportion of surface to mass, the relatively greater efficiency of diffusion in smaller, but otherwise similar, systems, and the fact that with larger numbers of distinct units there are greater possibilities for specialization among them. The minimum size of the organization that is compatible with life is discussed and, by contrast, the molecular complexity of cells of angiosperms is stressed; this is especially evident when one estimates the numbers of molecules of such substances as protein, water, etc., in cells. Cells appear to be as complex, in molecular terms, "as if an ocean-going liner were to be filled with machinery on the scale of a small ladies' watch." Direct evidence of this complexity is, however, obtained under the electron microscope.

Against the background summarized above, certain rules or principles emerge that guide in the determination of how cells grow and what determines the planes along which new walls form. Even when grown in a completely controlled and symmetrical environment, free cells of angiosperms, however, do not obey these laws—less so, in fact, than they often seem to do when in the plant body. Indeed, it is now clear that cells which develop into tissues in the intact plant must have their innate propensities curbed and controlled. Thus the cells *in situ* have their implicit, or innate, characteristics controlled by extrinsic factors peculiar to their immediate place in the plant body. Free cells, on the other hand, behave very differently; they divide in ways which do not necessarily conform to the idealized laws of cell division which apply to systems in equilibrium and, in many ways, the growth of the free cells is subject more to intrinsic, than to extrinsic, limitations.

The distribution of cell growth and cell division in the organized growing tips of shoot and root is discussed. The importance of regions of growth and active cell division on the flanks of shoot growing points is stressed; consideration is given to the relatively few cells which may act as initiating cells from which the files of mature cells of the root diverge; and the presence, in both shoot and root, of a group of relatively quiescent cells which only divide infrequently is noted. A logical unit of growth and nutrition in the shoot is a given leaf and the internode of stem by which it was subtended; the leaves of a given orthostichy are regarded as forming a close, nutritionally interacting system.

Rates of cell division, and the complete cell generation time, are estimated for angiosperm cells growing free, or as parts of different kinds of systems. Rates of cell division in the shoot are relatively low, though the calculated rates are higher in the growing region of the root. In cell or tissue culture there is a role for cells which are part of a small explant or of a small cluster of cells but which do not divide. The role of these non-growing or quiescent cells may be the release of stimuli which cause other cells to divide. This may be the role of "quiescent" or "cytogenerative" cells in the apex of shoot and root.

The distribution of free and combined amino acids in the apices of *Lupinus* and of *Adiantum* is described, and ways in which shoot apices have been dissected and their activity measured are summarized. All this tends to place the greatest metabolic activity, not at the extreme tip of the shoot or root, but somewhat farther back. It is now very necessary to inquire what physiological functions are affected, in their pace, by the correlated way in which growth occurs in the different growing regions of the plant body.

chapter six

PHYSIOLOGICAL FUNCTIONS: THEIR CORRELATIONS WITH GROWTH

This chapter is in four main sections; these deal with:

a) Problems of cell physiology.
b) Problems of metabolism.
c) Problems of absorption and redistribution of salts and solutes.
d) Water and water movements.

Cell Physiology

The control that is exercised over growth in many organs, with its consequential effects upon the intensity of the various physiological functions, is familiar enough in many ways. Organs of perennation are adapted to withstand adverse climatic or nutritional conditions. In lower plants the innate capacity to grow in many resting spores (or the structures to which they immediately give rise) is often reversibly arrested to circumvent an adverse climatic or nutritional period. Examples of such effects are too numerous to mention, and they involve both asexually and sexually produced spores. In seed plants the micro- and megaspores which initiate the gametophytic development commonly do so promptly, but the development of a zygote into an embryo is often delayed (e.g., *Ginkgo, Cocos*; cf. Chapter 4). Factors that delay or induce the onset of germination of seeds are of many kinds (e.g., the need for after-ripening of an embryo; presence or absence of hard seed coats; need for special treatments, as with light in the case of certain lettuce varieties; the presence or absence of specific inhibitors of germination). But once germination occurs the physiological responses and the power of growth go hand in hand. Time-honored studies of respiration, heat production, digestion of carbohydrates, conversion of storage protein into soluble and usable forms of nitrogen, and swelling by absorption of water have been made with germinating seeds; these all reflect the often tacit recognition that growth and physiological activity are interrelated. This is also to be seen in the behavior of the many organs of perennation such as buds, bulbs, corms, rhizomes, and tubers. In the onset of distinct phases of development (e.g., flowering and fruiting), in the events of propagation and regeneration, in the occurrence of wound healing, in such phenomena as apomixis, parthenocarpy, etc., examples are to be seen in which the physiological functions of cells, organs, and tissues are closely regulated by the conditions that incite, or suppress, their growth. While some of these relationships will now be examined, the frequent dilemma may easily be recognized. Where do the master controls lie? Do the physiological functions, by their pace and direction, determine the onset or suppression of growth and development, or are they, in turn, called into play as required to maintain the level of activity which is needed to support that growth and development? These problems arise and need to be considered at different levels of organization—at the cellular and subcellular level, and also at the level of organs as they occur in the organism as a whole.

Physiologists have been loath to invoke the phenomena of growth in explaining their problems and often have preferred to seek systems for investigation in which the complications due to growth and active metabolism can seemingly be neglected. Thus, much traditional plant physiology has been based on the attempt to apply equilibrium criteria to plants. This approach is particularly unsuitable to explain what transpires in the more active growing centers. Therefore, certain salient ideas, some of which have already been mentioned, now need to be developed. These ideas are that:

a) The cells in growing regions constitute centers of synthesis; it is here that the nutrients and metabolites are built into the very stuff of life.

b) In these active centers of synthesis and growth work is done, and energy is used in various ways; consequently there is great interest in the respiration rates in these regions and in the ways in which the released energy is directed toward various useful purposes.

c) Growing cells and growing regions are prominent centers of salt and water uptake and it is in these regions that these processes are most evidently active, rather than passive, and thus depend upon the energy of metabolism.

d) The techniques of biochemistry and enzymology serve best to demonstrate the feasibility of the chemical reactions that may occur. What actually transpires in cells may be very different in their various isolated compartments, phases, or organelles. Therefore, metabolism needs to be seen as a set of interlocking events in which the cellular organization is fully engaged; this organization permits control of the pace and direction of metabolism by the comparative isolation in which particular events occur and in response to the stimuli which determine whether cells grow or remain quiescent.

e) Problems of movement presuppose that solutes and water, released from one center, move to another where they may be stored or used, and consequently these functions of movement are intimately related to, and correlated with, growth in the plant body.

All these concepts now need to be developed and illustrated in the context of systems—cells, organs, organisms—which can grow.

Cellulose and protein synthesis: salient features of growing cells. Two major lines of metabolism that are intimately connected with growth are carbohydrate metabolism (which leads to, and culminates in, wall formation) and nitrogen metabolism (which leads to, and culminates in, the synthesis of protein and the formation of protoplasm and its inclusions). Because these relations of carbohydrate and nitrogen metabolism to the growth and organization of the cells in which they occur illustrate some of the points to be made, they are mentioned here in outline only.

First, the problem of cellulose synthesis and wall formation may be reconsidered. It used to be thought that the synthesis of complicated molecules was achieved in some way by the reversal of their hydrolysis. Indeed, it became almost axiomatic that, under appropriate conditions, the enzymes of hydrolysis were reversible. It is now known that this is rarely so. The enzymes that hydrolyze starch are not the enzymes that synthesize it. Starch synthesis, now easily reproduced in the test tube, occurs not by the removal of water from sugar molecules but by the removal of phosphate from glucose-1-phosphate by the enzyme phosphorylase. This can occur because in glucose-1-phosphate there is already embodied some energy that enables the formation of the new carbon-to-carbon bonds. A major problem is that cellulose synthesis cannot yet be so fully explained in this way. But even the formation of natural starch, in the form of starch grains, requires other enzymes to bring about the branching characteristics that are necessary to account for starch as it occurs naturally in plants.

Earlier (cf. Fig. 3–14) some electron microscope pictures of the organization of a cellulose cell wall were presented, and these demonstrated how cellulose occurs and is formed at a naked protoplasmic surface. Sugar molecules must pass through the cytoplasmic surface in some acceptable form and there, at the surface, be elaborated into cellulose chains; but the long threads which at first can be seen to lie at random in the surface must later mobilize and aggregate and become parallel to form the characteristic rope-like fibrils of a mature cellulose cell wall. Outstanding problems remain to be solved before the architecture of the cell wall can be duplicated *in vitro*. One can, however, be quite sure that it involves, in addition to enzymes which are located in the outer protoplasmic surface, some directive machinery which is invoked as cells grow. Commonly the cellulose fibrils are oriented characteristically along the length of cells as they expand.

However, in the even more challenging problem of protein synthesis a somewhat similar dilemma exists. No one yet has been able to make proteins *in vitro* in quantity and at will starting from the essential raw materials, namely, carbohydrate, nitrate, and ammonia; in fact, this may be beyond the present resources of man, without re-creating life, for protein synthesis in substantial amounts and in the needed variety may only be feasible within an organization as highly asymmetric and as complex as a cell. Although recent work (Fox, 1960) on the effects of heat and pressure on amino acids with the formation of complex, globular bodies is interesting, it is still so far from the *in vitro* origin of true protein that it may be disregarded here. Although more is known about the synthesis of abnormal, non-metabolized virus proteins than almost any others, and although nucleic acid and protein moieties may be put together to synthesize, as it were, "unnatural" nucleoproteins, it still goes too far to say (as is often done) that this evidence presages the creation of life, or the general ability to synthesize proteins.

Two ideas have been prevalent. The first of these was a natural outcome of the knowledge of protein structure. According to this view, the amino acids which comprise a protein are thought to be first synthesized and then chemically tied together to make the protein molecule. And the amino acids which occur free in quantity in cells were first thought to be those from which protein is made. Such ideas are far too ingenuous insofar as the cells of higher plants are concerned. It is important to recognize this because, since angiosperms are currently the predominant organisms on land, most of the *de novo* protein synthesis in nature occurs in just such cells.

When living plant cells make protein *de novo* they use sugar on the one hand and simple sources of nitrogen, like nitrate and ammonia, on the other. When protein is broken down, all the amino acids of the protein molecule are not stored as such, but their nitrogen is stored primarily as nitrogen-rich compounds, i.e., as the amides asparagine and glutamine, and, in some cases, as the basic amino acid arginine or even as such compounds as allantoin or allantoic acid, in which form nitrogen may move in certain trees (e.g., *Acer*). Carbon frameworks so released may contribute to respiration and be respired away. When these mobile and storage forms of nitrogen are reused, there are reasons to believe that their nitrogen is donated at receptive centers and the necessary additional carbon for protein formation *comes more immediately from sugar* than from the amino acids which are present free and in bulk in the cells. This has been shown by experiments in which radioactively labeled sugar and amino acids were used. When the labeled compounds were supplied exogenously it was shown (Steward, Bidwell, and Yemm, 1958; Bidwell, Barr, and Steward, 1964) that the carbon of sugar enters into the composition of protein even more readily than the carbon of certain of the amino acids that existed free in the cells. Hence there seems to exist in active, growing plant cells a cycle in which sugar and sources of nitrogen form protein; protein is then broken down to amino acids, which are reworked and temporarily stored, and, when reused, much of their carbon framework may be respired away while their nitrogen is reconverted to protein. In this reformation of protein, the amino acid intermediates are formed so close to the site of synthesis that they do not mingle with the stored nitrogen compounds which are present in bulk in the aqueous inclusions of the cell (cf. Steward and Durzan, 1965, for a recent summary of these problems).

(a)

(b)

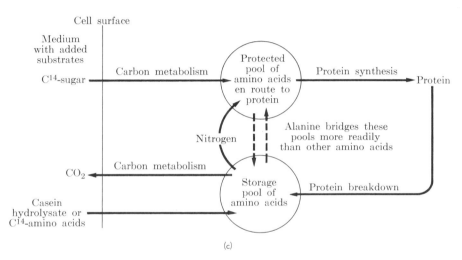

(c)

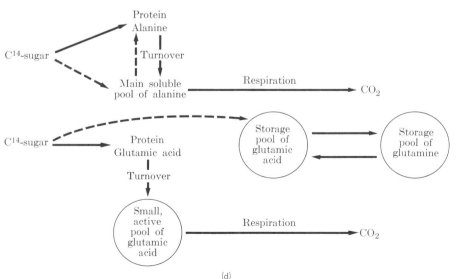

(d)

With respect to their nitrogen metabolism plant cells are fundamentally different from those of animals. Plants economize reduced nitrogen, for they conserve and reuse it; and, more than is commonly realized, the carbon of respiration may have previously passed through the metabolically active protein of the cytoplasm. The process of respiration is usually deemed to involve only the breakdown of sugar in the presence of oxygen and its conversion to carbon dioxide and water; however, it may invoke, to a much greater extent than has been recognized, the processes of nitrogen and protein metabolism, especially in plant cells. But is this not reasonable? If the functions of respiration and energy release were as independent of the processes of nitrogen metabolism as conventional views assume, why is it that cells need to elaborate so much protein—probably one hundred to one thousand million molecules per cell? And why, having manufactured all this protein, should cells maintain much of it in a dynamic state of breakdown and resynthesis? Why is it that cells only negotiate the intricate processes of respiration, smoothly and continuously, in a structured milieu so rich in organelles and composed so largely of protein, especially if the protein is largely enzyme and essentially catalytic? Therefore, the ultimate processes of growth and metabolism need to be seen in their relation to the protein metabolism (to the protein synthesis and breakdown) which, as current use of isotopes shows, is always proceeding. Thus to the classical 19th century ideas of Pfeffer, Schulze (Fig. 6–1a), and Prianischnikov (Fig. 6–1b) others, which are summarized in the interpretive diagrams of Fig. 6–1(c, d), can now be added.

Hence, the physiological functions of growing cells should not be considered in isolation from each other as if they occurred in a static system; on the contrary, they intermesh in a system which is intensely dynamic. Compounds are formed in cells only to be recycled and, as this occurs in respiration (e.g., in the Krebs cycle) or in protein synthesis and breakdown, molecules are made and unmade so that cells may work as "molecular machines."

It is useful, therefore, to summarize some physiological contrasts between mature quiescent cells and those which are actively growing. This contrast is well shown by the behavior of cells, or explants, from mature storage organs (carrot root, potato tuber, artichoke tuber, etc.) under conditions that cause their cells to grow and divide rapidly.

◄FIG. 6–1. (a) Schulze's scheme. (b) Prianischnikov's scheme. (c) The relationships of exogenous sugars and amino acids to soluble pools in the cell and to protein synthesis. (d) The relationships of endogenous alanine and endogenous glutamic acid and glutamine to soluble pools and to protein turnover and respiration. Distinct and immiscible pools are shown encircled. Dotted lines indicate leakage or minor pathways. (From Bidwell, Barr, and Steward, *Nature* 203, 367–373, 1964.)

Contrasts between quiescent and growing cells: dormancy and the induction of growth. It is an apparent paradox that the cells of many organs of perennation become dormant when the external conditions for their further growth seem to be good and when the nutrients (organic and inorganic) which they contain are plentiful. In temperate climates, vegetative buds of deciduous trees (e.g., maple) begin to enter dormancy in the mid to late summer. Such fleshy organs as the potato tuber, the carrot root, and the Jerusalem artichoke tuber illustrate this point very well. Their cells are so richly stocked with carbohydrate (soluble and insoluble), with nitrogen compounds (protein and even larger amounts of non-protein, free nitrogenous compounds), with vitamins, and with mineral salts that the organs in question are nutritious for humans and make good supplements to agar media for the growth of micro-organisms. And yet these nutrients are not utilized by the quiescent cells of the storage organ itself, although they may be so used when the cells are caused to grow again. To a limited extent, this recrudescence of growth may occur during the wound healing which is stimulated at a freshly cut tissue surface exposed to moist air. This response is, however, strictly limited because usually it leads only to those internal cell divisions, within the larger cells of the resting organ, that suffice to form a wound periderm (cf. Fig. 1–17).

By the methods of tissue culture and by the use of stimuli which induce proliferative growth in the cells that otherwise would only respond as in the healing of wounds, the quiescent cells of many storage organs may be caused to grow actively. It is in this chemical induction of growth that such fluids as coconut milk, the fluid from the vesicular embryo sac of *Aesculus*, or the extracts from immature grains of corn (see Chapter 4) have proved to be so effective. In some way these growth-regulating materials re-engage the processes of metabolism so that they again drive the machinery of growth, instead of allowing it to idle and its energy to run to waste. The process of growth induction in its morphological and metabolic manifestations is, therefore, very far-reaching for, like the processes of fertilization, it releases the ability of freely suspended cells to develop into whole plants (Steward, Mapes, and Mears, 1958) which even flower (Steward *et al.*, 1961) and, in their development, they may even recapitulate normal embryogeny to a surprising degree.

Morphological manifestations of growth induction. This subject is only dealt with briefly here (cf. also pp. 212–219). Resting cells of fleshy storage organs are commonly large (about 120 to 150 μ per cell for potato tuber; carrot root cells are somewhat smaller), but the amount of cytoplasm they contain is often incredibly small (Fig. 6–2). The nucleus is usually embedded in a very thin parietal layer of protoplasm in the resting cell and protoplasmic streaming is sluggish or nonexistent. Early symptoms of renewed activity in potato tuber cells are the movement of the nucleus to a more central position and the onset of protoplasmic streaming (Steward, Wright, and Berry, 1932) along cytoplasmic strands; such strands become more conspicuous and now criss-

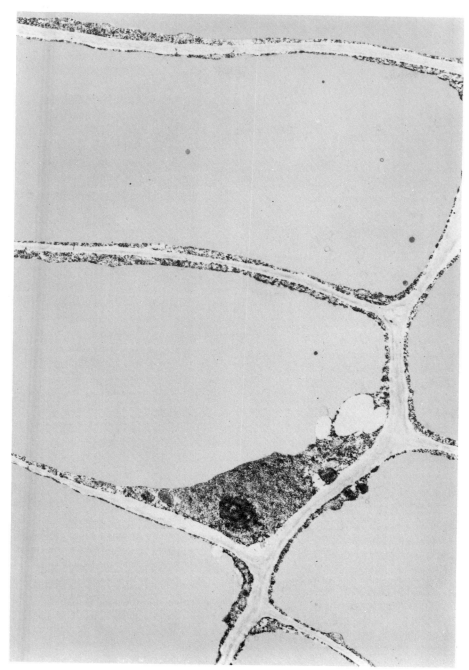

FIG. 6–2. Electron micrograph at low magnification, showing the general appearance of quiescent cells in phloem tissue of the carrot root. Note the very thin layers of cytoplasm along the periphery of the cells. (×5500). (Preparation and photograph by Dr. H. W. Israel, Cornell University.)

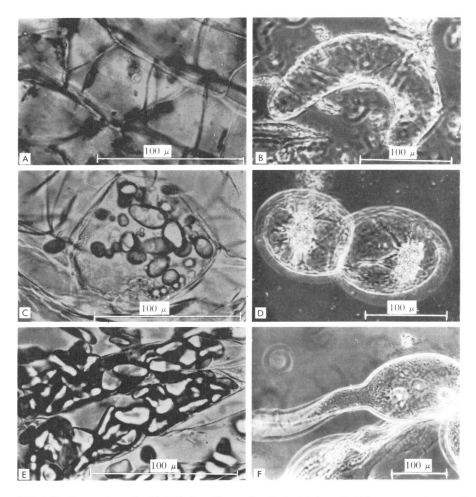

FIG. 6–3. Comparison of cells in their resting and activated states. A. Phloem parenchyma of carrot root. B. Same as A, after culturing in a basal liquid medium with coconut milk. C. Starch-filled cells of potato tuber. D. Cultured cells of potato tuber showing granular inclusions surrounding the nuclei. E. Cells from pulp of the harvested but unripe banana fruit. F. Cultured cell of banana. (Note prominent cytoplasmic strands in B and D. Cells in D and F were grown in a liquid medium containing coconut milk and 2,4–D.) (From Steward, *Canad. J. Bot.* **39**, 441–60, 1961, reproduced by permission of the National Research Council of Canada.)

cross the vacuole. Starch grains and protein crystals of the potato and carotene granules of the carrot disappear whereas abundant minute granules (mitochondria or other inclusions of the order of 1 μ or less) are to be seen, often in motion, under the light microscope (Fig. 6–3) or, in the form of densely packed ribosomes, are visible under the electron microscope (Fig. 6–4). Other cytoplasmic inclusions are plastids and, in the light, these may begin to acquire the form of typical chloroplasts, as in the reactivated cells of carrot (Israel and Steward, 1966). The differences between activated growing cells and the quiescent cells, as seen under phase contrast, are shown in Fig. 6–3A, C, and E. This figure suggests that, whereas the resting cells are packed with food and sluggish in their activity, the activated growing cells, despite their apparent lack of food reserves, are in an intensely dynamic state. The one appearance may be likened to that of a factory with the fires banked down and the machinery at rest; the other to the whole organization vigorously at work. Freely suspended, activated growing cells of many other plants present a very similar appearance to those already described in Fig. 6–3B, D, and F.

As the surface cells of a tissue explant divide internally, or the liberated free cells do so when suspended in liquid, the volume of the "daughter" cells is reduced until the average cell size may be a mere 1/10, or less, of that of the original resting cell. In this condition, which is reminiscent of embryonic cells or cells of the apical growing point, the cell vacuoles are small and the nuclei are relatively large. But, under the electron microscope, there are other very conspicuous changes to be seen, as described by Israel and Steward (1966). All the cytoplasmic inclusions become more prominent; there is a greater prominence of endoplasmic reticulum; mitochondria which were small, rounded, and sparse in the resting cells become elongated even branched, and very much more numerous; Golgi bodies increase in their number and comprise a larger number of their stacked, saucer-like lamellae with more conspicuous vesicles. But the most striking feature of the cells that undergo growth induction, even prior to cell division, is the great increase in the number of their ribosome particles (Fig. 6–4), most of which are free and not directly attached to the reticulum which ramifies between the dense masses of these particles. In other words, the effect which is brought about by the conditions of temperature, aeration, and nutrition which reactivate the cells and make them receptive to the cell division factors that cause them to grow, is not a simple one, for it transforms the cells in ways which affect their organization, their entire submicroscopic fine structure. It is not, therefore, surprising that the physiological functions of the growing cells seem so very different from those of the non-growing; the differences are not merely of degree, they are also of kind. Nor, in light of this fact, is it surprising to find that the non-nutrient stimuli which affect the transfer from the resting to the growing state are numerous and complex in their interactions.

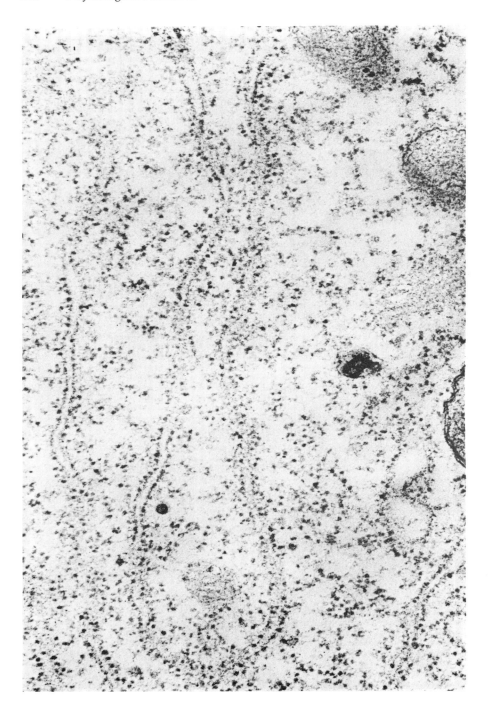

◄ FIG. 6–4. Portion of a cytoplasmic strand, along which streaming occurs, shown in cross section and containing numerous free and attached ribosomes (×82,000). (Preparation and photograph by Dr. H. W. Israel, Cornell University; cf. Israel and Steward, 1966.)

Metabolic manifestations of growth induction. Cultured carrot cells are brought into rapid growth by a complex of interacting factors which act upon fully nourished cells which have been rendered receptive during a lag, or induction, period of some two to four days. The whole coconut milk complex comprises an effect due to reduced nitrogen compounds (replaceable by casein hydrolysate); an effect due to a so-called neutral fraction (replaceable wholly, or in part, by *myo*-inositol); and an effect due to a variety of chemically different substances which release the powers of division in the incipiently dividing cells after the "lag period." In some situations (e.g., potato tuber) the cells require an additional interaction with one of many possible auxinlike molecules (Chapter 4). All this presents a complex picture of synergistically interacting nutrients and growth-regulating substances, examples of which were shown in Fig. 4–35. Moreover, it is now known that the interacting substances of a complex growth-regulating system may be more effective if they are applied sequentially, but in the right order, instead of concurrently (Kent and Steward, 1965; Steward *et al.*, 1966). Nevertheless the tissue must possess some innate or endogenous capacity to respond to the exogenous stimuli for, in organs which pass through a climacteric (Mohan Ram and Steward, 1964), the treatments which effectively induced growth prior to, and up to, the climacteric, failed to do so subsequently (Fig. 6–5). While the contribution of each component of the growth-promoting complex cannot be stipulated, nevertheless it causes some striking metabolic and physiological differences between the resting and the rapidly growing cells; the following summary of these differences is largely drawn from that presented in 1961 by Steward *et al.* in terms of the following physiological functions:

i) *In terms of respiration.* Differences between the resting and growing cells are to be seen in their responses to such inhibitors as cyanide and carbon monoxide, to inhibitors which uncouple phosphorylation, and to effects of the growth stimulus on the sensitivity of the cells to radiation.

Briefly, it was found that the tissue is much more vulnerable to cyanide and to carbon monoxide prior to the growth induction, whereas after growth induction (due to coconut milk, etc.) the metabolism changes in ways that make it less sensitive to inhibitors that affect the terminal oxidation which is mediated by cytochrome. By contrast, the tissue after growth induction was found to be much more responsive to inhibitors that uncouple phosphorylation. Exposure of the tissue to a Co^{60} source readily inactivates the center at which the cell division stimulus acts, for it stops the cell division response due to coconut milk, although it may still allow the cells to expand; but, once stimulated to grow, the cells, which are thereby much enriched with nucleic acid, become *less* sensitive than resting ones to radiation damage.

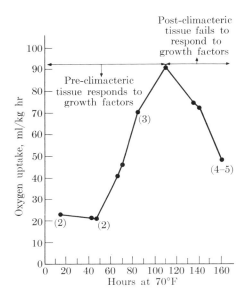

FIG. 6-5. A graphic representation of respiration (ml O_2/kg hr) and color changes (stages 2 through 5) in ripening Gros Michel bananas at 70°F and growth response on a basal medium supplemented with coconut milk and a suitable synthetic auxin as a synergist. (From Mohan Ram and Steward, *Can. J. Botany* **42**, 1559–1579, 1964, reproduced by permission of the National Research Council of Canada.)

Thus the site of the growth induction stimulus is very accessible to radiation damage, to cyanide, and to carbon monoxide, but these agents become less harmful after growth has been activated, for then the tissue is much more affected by the agents which uncouple phosphorylation (nitrocresols). The prior synthesis of ribosomal RNA and the formation of abundant ribosomes may be the definitive feature that is inactivated by radiation damage, by CN^- and CO, and which, if previously accomplished, renders the cells more insensitive to these agents. (Fig. 6-6).

One may now re-examine the converse situation which occurs with the irreversible events of the climacteric and as a prelude to senescence and death. Up to the climacteric banana cells will respond to suitable combinations of growth factors; beyond that point they do not so respond (Mohan Ram and Steward, 1964). [A low-temperature-induced inactivation of the ability of potato cells to divide by wound healing may be of a similar kind (Steward *et al.*, 1943).] One can, therefore, see possible explanations of all these effects if the mechanism that fails at senescence and after the climacteric is the resynthesis of ribosomal RNA so that cells no longer form the abundant ribosomes upon which protein synthesis seems to depend.

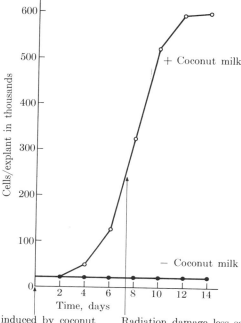

FIG. 6–6. Growth induction in carrot explants; its sensitivity to radiation and metabolic inhibitors. (From work of Holsten and Steward.)

| Growth induced by coconut milk at sites very sensitive to Co^{60} radiation; CN^- and CO. Ribosomes few. | Radiation damage less severe; further growth less sensitive to CN^- and CO; more sensitive to nitrocresols. Ribosomes abundant. |

ii) *In terms of water and salt uptake.* It is obvious that *de novo* intake of water and salt must occur concomitantly with growth. A very early effect of the growth stimulus is to be seen in increased water content. One might, therefore, even say that this water does not merely *move* into the cell; initially it *grows* into it because its entry is an integral part of the growth process. In its sensitivity to oxygen pressure, to potassium content in the medium (contrasted with calcium), water absorption by potato discs has been linked to the processes of growth and metabolism and especially to protein synthesis (Steward and Preston, 1940); this identifies this intake of water with a more physiologically active mechanism than the mere response of the cells as ideal, equilibrium osmotic systems. Moreover, it now seems possible to recognize two consecutive phases, or steps, in the salt intake process—both being dependent on metabolism in different ways.

While the cells are under the stimulus to engage in division, even though they nevertheless remain small, they may multiply self-duplicating structures which range from nuclei to protein. In this phase, the cells can acquire much of their salts (especially cations) by a process of binding to specific sites; this binding is governed by a first-order relationship between external and internal concentrations that applies over a wide range. In this phase, the processes of uptake of an ion (Cs^{137}) and the incorporation of C^{14} proline into protein go hand in hand, both being suppressed by protein synthesis inhibitors (Lyndon and Steward, 1965). However, when the stimulus to division subsides, or gives way predominantly to growth by cell enlargement, the vacuole expands. The type of protein synthesized in the cells is now different, being much less concerned with new formation of organelles; moreover, the ions are now removed from their initial sites to be transferred to the vacuole, where they reach high concentrations and their relative accumulation (accumulation ratio) increases very markedly with external *dilution*. A logarithmic relation to external concentration now holds, for the internal concentration is approximately doubled for a tenfold external increase. In this phase of the process, metabolic energy, presumably mediated via phosphorylated compounds, is believed to be applied in ways that do osmotic work to secrete solutes into the vacuole. Thus water absorption and the absorption of salts and solutes are intimately linked to the growth and devlopment of cells and to the protein synthesis which occurs concomitantly.

The behavior of thin discs of the tuber of the Jerusalem artichoke is interesting in comparison with tissue from a potato tuber or a carrot root. Whereas the respiration of washed discs of potato tuber in aerated water at $23°C$ rises spontaneously to a high and long maintained level (0.20 mg CO_2/gm/hr), that of artichoke tuber tissue rapidly falls off from a similar high initial rate to one which is very much lower (order of 0.01 mg CO_2/gm/hr), but is nevertheless long maintained. This contrasted respiratory behavior was correlated with a rate of potassium bromide absorption which, in the potato tissue, was linear with time, whereas in the artichoke system it fell away from its initially high rate (Steward and Berry, 1934).

At first all efforts to restore the still living artichoke discs to a maintained high rate of metabolism and salt uptake failed until it was also possible to make them proliferate and grow. When this was achieved under tissue culture conditions and by the aid of a complete nutrient medium supplemented with coconut milk (or coconut water), the artichoke cells which seemed to have run their course could be rejuvenated, and their respiration was reactivated. However, the first absorption of ions following upon their reactivation was of the kind that is now more familiar in the relatively non-vacuolated dividing cells (i.e., the accumulation ratios were small as incoming solutes were bound on newly formed sites, and the relation between internal and external concentration was a first-order, not a logarithmic one). Thus cells of the artichoke tuber undergo the full range of effects that have been described above (Fig. 6–7) and this tissue can be placed at will, in the quiescent or the actively growing states, and caused to exhibit appropriately the concomitant physiological functions (Steward and Millar, 1954). It is a moot point, therefore, whether we should give greater emphasis to the factors that unleash the growth of artichoke cells, for their consequential effects upon respiration, water uptake, ion accumulation, and growth,

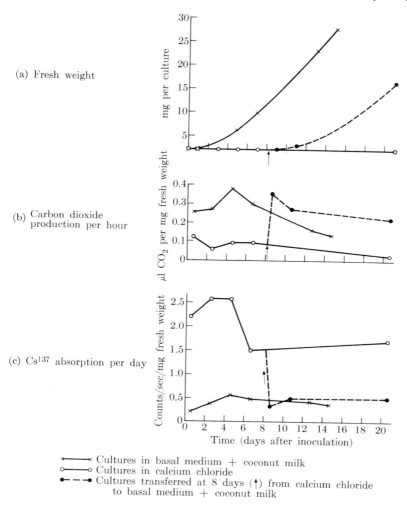

(a) Fresh weight

(b) Carbon dioxide production per hour

(c) Cs¹³⁷ absorption per day

×———× Cultures in basal medium + coconut milk
○———○ Cultures in calcium chloride
●– – –● Cultures transferred at 8 days (↑) from calcium chloride
    to basal medium + coconut milk

FIG. 6–7. Effects of time and coconut milk on fresh weight, carbon dioxide production, and Cs¹³⁷ absorption for artichoke tuber tissue cultures. Note that the recrudescence of growth induced by coconut milk after 8 days in a calcium chloride solution is shown by (a) increased fresh weight, (b) increased respiration, (c) decreased Cs¹³⁷ content per unit fresh weight. The expanding vacuolated cells accumulated high Cs¹³⁷ in the CaCl₂ solution; the dividing cells with small vacuoles reached lower accumulation ratios. (From Steward and Millar, *Symposia Soc. Exptl. Biol.* **13**, 367–393, 1954.)

or to the fact that the conditions under which ions and water are absorbed also contribute to the growth of which these physiological functions are an essential part. What is very clear is that the clue to the behavior of the tissue lies in its maintained ability to grow in an environment which elicits that growth.

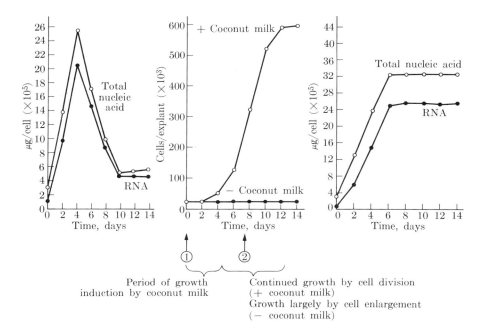

FIG. 6–8. Levels of nucleic acid during growth and growth induction of carrot explants. (After Holsten, Sugii, and Steward, 1965.)

iii) *In terms of nitrogen metabolism.* The cells which have passed through the incipient preparation for growth, which is caused by their activated metabolism in aerated water or in nutrient solution, convert much of their stored soluble nitrogen compounds to protein. The residual soluble nitrogen has very different relative composition; such compounds as asparagine and arginine being much less conspicuous, whereas glutamine, alanine, and γ-aminobutyric acid remain prominent, although at the lower level of soluble nitrogen compounds which the activated cells contain.

A great deal of the synthesis of complex nitrogen compounds which occurs during the lag, or induction, or incipient growth period must be nucleic acid (ribosomal nucleic acid) and nucleoproteins, for these substances may increase very greatly ($\times 20$) in the cells (Fig. 6–8) even as the ribosome granules also visibly increase (cf. Fig. 6–4). However, lacking whatever "master switch" is needed to engage the latent metabolic power of these cells and their inclusions into growth, this greatly increased content of nucleic acid does not alone result in maintained protein synthesis and growth.

The stimulus which makes the cells grow and proliferate, which greatly stimulates overall protein synthesis, also promotes the formation of a structural, metabolically inactive, protein moiety which is rich in hydroxyproline. At first this protein seemed to be a single collagen-like protein moiety but it is now known that it comprises several soluble electrophoretically separable moieties with different ratios of C^{14}-hydroxyproline to C^{14}-proline, ranging from 0.643 to 1.284 (Steward and Chang, 1963). This protein complex is not strictly collagen, for it is not rich enough in glycine. It is also known that this protein moiety passes from the soluble form, where it first appears, into a more insoluble one. High resolution radioautography on sections of cells prepared for use with the electron microscope after they had absorbed H^3-proline has been carried out by Israel, Salpeter, and Steward (in press). The stable substance that is labelled with proline and hydroxyproline distributes itself throughout the cytoplasm but *not* in the cell wall. It occurs in plastids, but not in mitochondria, and appears wherever granules are prominent. Since the extracted ribosomes are not rich in hydroxyproline the substance in question seems to comprise some structural element of the ground plasm (but not the endoplasmic reticulum), with which functional ribosomes are closely associated *in situ* in active growing cells. The H^3-proline first (i.e., at 8 hours) enters the nuclei (especially nucleoli) and later spreads in daughter cells in the cytoplasm wherever there are granules.

But it is significant that the stimulus that causes cells to divide rapidly, that causes protein to be made, also seems to promote the "turnover" of the metabolically active protein fraction. This is only another way of saying that the complex subcellular machinery which is revealed with the electron microscope is put into gear, like a motor previously idling, by the agents that promote the cell division (see below).

Many other aspects of metabolism and of synthesis may be expected to be changed in cells that are actively growing. It is known, for example, that cultured carrot tissue synthesizes carotenoids, but never in quantities and qualities that make them orange-red. The latter condition is a feature of the storage root tissue as it normally develops in the plant body.

A curious feature of the actively growing cultured cells is that they so often fail to make, or accumulate, many compounds that are readily formed by, and which accumulate in, the resting organ from which they were derived (e.g., γ-methyleneglutamine is not recognizably formed in cultured cells of *Arachis hypogaea*). Indeed, it has proved unexpectedly difficult to induce cultured cells to recapitulate the biosynthetic potentialities which are clearly present in the mature organs of plants from which they were derived. This problem has been extensively examined in this laboratory (Krikorian, 1965).

The impression, therefore, is that a growing cell accentuates, or "turns on," one part of its genetically determined biochemical potentiality, whereas resting cells may accentuate other parts. In fact, the products stored in the quiescent cells may often be regarded as due to blocks, or restrictions, which cause some otherwise transient metabolites to accumulate. This is the more feasible when it is appreciated that even growing cells can involve the same metabolite in quite different metabolic paths in different parts of these highly compartmented cells (cf. Fig. 6–13). For example, the specific activity of C^{14}-glutamic acid entering the protein of growing carrot cells may be very different from that which is free in the cell—showing that there are compartments which prevent the "protein-glutamic acid" from mingling freely with the "soluble-glutamic acid" in the cell. Similar conclusions may be drawn from the behavior of other compounds.

iv) *In terms of resistance to infections.* A very curious, but important, feature distinguishes the dormant, resting cells of a potato tuber from those which, being at the surfaces of cut discs, have been metabolically reactivated by access to air and water. This is seen in a marked acquired resistance to bacterial infections to which the inactive cells of a potato tuber are very prone. Since this raises many questions it is worth recording how certain observations came to be made.

The early work on thin discs of storage tissue (particularly the potato tuber) could not be done under aseptic conditions because of its nature and the scale on which it had then to be carried out. It was noted, however, that two key factors reduced the impact of bacterial contamination, maintained the potato cells in viable condition, and permitted the work to be performed without completely aseptic precautions. These were:

a) The use of thin discs only, approximately ⅔ mm thick.

b) The use of *very rapid* aeration to keep the submerged discs adequately supplied with oxygen.

It is now known that the significance of the use of *thin* discs is in part that, at this thinness, *all* the cells of the disc are metabolically changed, when in contact with aerated solutions, from their condition in the intact tuber—there is, in fact, no inactive core of dormant cells in such discs. The significance of the rapid aeration is that it sets up, or reactivates, metabolic processes that were suppressed in the intact tuber (among which are the high respiration and protein synthesis that have been referred to), but there is also a surface browning reaction which involves the phenolic (catechol-containing) compounds that react to polyphenolases.

Immature potato tubers, in which the periderm will still "slip" at the surface because the cambium is still fluid and active, can be shipped without severe loss due to soft rots under conditions of temperature and humidity in transit such that infections of the fully mature dormant tubers would be extensive. (When dormant tubers suffer damage to their periderm an active cambium is not immediately exposed.) The explanation lies in the ability of active growing cells of a cambium to throw off and resist infections that attack the dormant resting cells.

This was dramatically shown when thin (⅔ mm), freshly cut potato discs were inoculated, by either surface or puncture inoculation, with *Erwinia carotovora* (bacterial soft rot) and the incidence of infection was compared with a similar treatment of discs that had been in aerated water for 12 hours or longer.

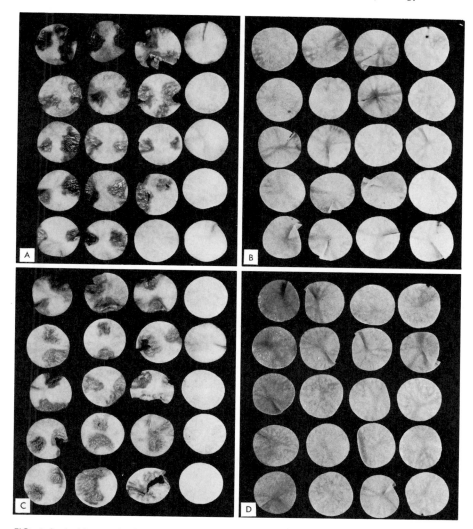

FIG. 6–9. Incidence of infection in thin discs of potato inoculated by either surface or puncture inoculation with *Erwinia carotovora*. Figures A and C, freshly cut slices, show high infection (except in last vertical row, which was not inoculated), whereas B and D, slices which had been aerated in water for 12 hours or longer, were very resistant to infection. (From unpublished work of Steward, 1946.)

As the figure shows (Fig. 6–9), all the centers of inoculation became infected in the resting dormant cells, while they were resisted in the metabolically reactivated, potentially growing cells. There are several lessons to be learned here.

First, there is the important technical point that tissue slice experiments with thin (⅔ mm), well-aerated discs can be carried out with less bacterial contamination than would otherwise seem to be the case.

Secondly, there is the fact that active, protein-synthesizing cells are far less prone to bacterial attack than are quiescent ones. This feature may often render plant tissue culture far easier than it might otherwise be, for the growing cells have "built-in" methods of resistance; they may, in fact, produce their own antibiotics.

Correlated with these observations are others, made on cultured potato cells, which show that actively growing cells are less prone to allow their viruses to multiply than are cells that are, at best, expanding but not dividing (Pollard, Rochow, and Steward, 1958).

The resistance of the aerated, actively metabolizing cells stands in contrast to the susceptibility of their resting counterparts by virtue of features of their organization. The protein synthesis in the aerated discs depletes their stock of soluble nitrogen and changes the composition of the soluble compounds that remain; it may also synthesize other compounds (proteins) with which the bacteria are incompatible. The actively growing cells may be "ploughing back" their products of metabolic turnover by using them in resynthesis, so that these are not as available to the pathogens for their use. (Gates, 1964, showed in this laboratory that a substantial part of the carbon in tobacco mosaic, TMV, protein came directly from protein breakdown in the course of "turnover" in the expanding, but non-dividing, cells of tobacco leaves.)

Having examined some of the physiological contrasts between quiescent and rapidly growing cells, one should now look at the cells of more organized growing regions of plants with a view to understanding how far their physiological processes "follow the lead of growth" in the plant as a whole, and how far the behavior of cells is limited or determined by their location.

Metabolism

Protein in cells of growing regions and mature organs.   The conversion of simple nitrogen compounds to protein in the higher plant body occurs prominently in green leaves in the light and in the cells of growing regions, i.e., the apical growing regions of shoot and root, the cambium, buds, intercalary meristems, etc. Mature storage organs of plants—like the potato tuber, carrot root, etc.—commonly store a large part of their nitrogen in soluble form; as much as two-thirds of the total nitrogen in the potato tuber, for example, may consist of amino acids and amides. When cells of potato tuber are caused to divide and to grow again, as occurs to a limited extent when thin slices are exposed to moist air and large parenchyma cells are subdivided by internal division, there is a reconversion of this soluble nitrogen to protein. Protein synthesis is further accentuated if, by the methods of tissue culture and the effect of growth-regulating substances (cf. pp. 183–185), the cells of the tuber are converted into continuously growing cultures, for in this condition the growing cells may have as much as 90 percent of their total nitrogen in the form of protein; this high protein content prevails even though the external medium contains nitrate, organic nitrogen, and carbohydrate that could be stored in the cells in the soluble form.

The amount of soluble nitrogen in physiologically active green leaves is very much less in proportion to their protein than it is in fleshy storage organs, even storage organs which are modified leaves, like cotyledons and bud scales. Thus, the balance between the free alcohol-soluble nitrogenous compounds and the alcohol-insoluble protein nitrogen (Soluble N $\rightleftharpoons$ Protein N) in these centers of protein synthesis lies far to the right and is strongly in favor of protein. A green leaf, however, does not owe its effectiveness in protein synthesis to the fact that light is used in the synthesis *per se*, as in the case of photosynthesis, but in part to the fact that the intermediates of photosynthesis furnish carbon compounds, particularly keto acids, which can readily accept nitrogen from the reduction products of nitrate.

Furthermore, green leaves in the light are commonly well furnished with carbohydrates and, being active in respiration, they should be rich in the substances that are necessary to donate energy for protein synthesis. However, energy-rich phosphorus compounds are now known to arise directly by harnessing the energy of light in photosynthetic phosphorylation. The leaf then receives what the plant physiologists of the 19th century termed "unelaborated foodstuffs," converts them to the "elaborated" form, and through the mechanisms of digestion and translocation they are then moved to centers of active growth.

There can be no absolute assurance that the mechanism of protein synthesis as it occurs in a leaf is identical with the process as it occurs in shoot and root growing points, in cambium, etc. It was recognized quite early that before nitrogen is translocated from the leaf its protein is broken down, and the immediate products of the breakdown are the amino acids of protein hydrolysis, although the principal forms of nitrogen storage and translocation are fewer "nitrogen-rich" compounds. Classically the substance asparagine was thought to be a storage and translocatory form of nitrogen, and Pfeffer conceived of this substance as streaming up to growing regions, there to combine with carbon frameworks, derived from sugar, to reform protein (cf. Fig. 6–1). As knowledge of the soluble constituents of plants has increased, the possible candidates for the role of translocatory nitrogen compounds has greatly increased; but it still seems that the amides asparagine and glutamine, and possibly the basic amino acid arginine, by virtue of the large amount of nitrogen they contain in each molecule, are frequent storage forms and also possible substances that might move nitrogen efficiently from one organ to another. More recently, however, the occurrence of allantoin, allantoic acid, and ureides in the sap which exudes from some cut stems has attracted attention to these compounds also.

Much evidence indicates that the substances most able to donate nitrogen in an acceptable form at the site of protein synthesis are glutamine and glutamic acid, which, with carbohydrate, readily reform protein. However, modern emphasis on the ready use of the nitrogen of urea, as in the now expanding practice of spraying urea on foliage, raises the possibility that other groups, possibly the carbamyl group ($^-CO \cdot NH_2$), may be readily used in the formation of complex organic nitrogen compounds. This possibility is strengthened by evidence that urea is often used by plants in ways that require the carbon and the nitrogen to be used together and to pass into glutamine (Steward and Pollard, 1956). (It is interesting that when urea is sprayed on banana leaves, allantoic acid appears in the leaf, and it also occurs on chromatograms of the liquid which exudes from the xylem when leaves are severed at their base.) Thus, although simple organic nitrogen compounds may arise in many areas of the plant body by the reduction of nitrate, by hydrolysis of protein, or directly from compounds like ammonia or urea, the bulk of the *de novo* protein synthesis occurs either in the green leaf *in the light* or in the growing centers where new cells are formed. The formation of protein in fruits and seeds, or in storage organs, may be regarded as secondary in that it utilizes translocated organic material which may have arisen after protein breakdown.

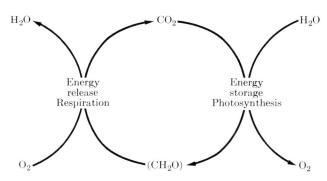

FIG. 6–10
Photosynthesis and respiration.

Carbohydrate metabolism: energy relations

i) *Respiration and useful cellular work.* Wherever plant cells do work, whether this is chemical work in synthesis, physicochemical work in moving water or salts, or mechanical work in raising a substance against gravity or maintaining protoplasmic streaming, etc., energy is used and its presumptive donors arise from respiration. Current thinking could be summarized somewhat as follows.

The ultimate source of metabolic energy is carbohydrate, which stores the energy through photosynthesis and the reduction of carbon dioxide (Chapter 3). A cardinal feature of the reduction of carbon dioxide and of energy storage in carbohydrate is the photolytic breakdown of water, or in some organisms hydrogen sulfide, and the transfer of the hydrogen so released through intermediary hydrogen acceptors to reduce the carbon dioxide. In the release of the stored energy, by reoxidation of the reduced compounds in respiration, the transfer of hydrogen back to water—as it occurs in terminal oxidation—plays an equally important role. Thus a great deal of the complex machinery of life is comprehended between the decomposition and reformation of water, on the one hand, and the reduction and reformation of carbon dioxide, on the other (Fig. 6–10). Similarly a great deal of the organization of cells and organisms is needed to achieve these ends.

ii) *Sequences of carbohydrate breakdown.* The breakdown of carbohydrate proceeds in sequences, each one of which is complex. In one such sequence the molecule of sugar is split, forming at first two carbon fragments, each of three carbon atoms; and this breakdown may even proceed further to give C_2 fragments at the level of acetate. This process, which may proceed without the direct intervention of oxygen, is termed glycolysis. (The breakdown of fatty acids by β-oxidation also yields C_2 fragments.) Thus, since most of the energy which is initially locked up in the sugar molecule still remains in the carbon fragments, the bulk of the energy release comes after glycolysis, when its products are converted aerobically to carbon dioxide and water. The aerobic conversion takes place in a second stage through what is known as the organic acid cycle, or the Krebs cycle. The Krebs cycle utilizes the products of glycolysis and converts the products eventually to carbon dioxide and water but this does not occur directly. In order that the split products of sugar may be rendered compatible with the enzymes that will convert them to carbon dioxide and water, they are first reconstituted into compounds of higher molecular weight which are organic acids. This is necessary to render the organic substrate compatible with the enzymes that bring about its eventual conversion to CO_2 and H_2O. In this prior rebuilding, or anabolic, process molecules of the order of six carbon atoms are reproduced (of the general complexity of citric acid) using some carrier molecule over and over again, the carrier being regenerated with each turn of the cycle. The carrier molecule here in question is the keto acid, oxaloacetic acid. Moreover, the organic acid cycle can only accept the C_2 fragments from glycolysis in a certain form; this is accomplished by a transfer system which consists of appropriate enzymes and coenzymes which together pass on the C_2 fragment as "acetyl-CoA," or "active acetate" as it used to be called. Thus the organic acid cycle reworks the carbon compounds from sugar breakdown into organic acids. The organic acids so reconstituted are then brought under the action of enzymes which bring about (a) decarboxylation, that is, removal of carbon dioxide from organic acids, and (b) dehydrogenation, that is, oxidation by removal of hydrogen. Thus the metabolic fuel from glycolysis (as well as C_2 fragments from other sources) is completely converted to carbon dioxide and water. The hydrogen removed by these dehydrogenase enzyme systems is first accepted by the pyridine nucleotides (DPN or TPN), but it must finally pass to oxygen, and the final stages of this journey are the ones in which oxygen of the air is directly involved. These final steps are termed "terminal oxidation," and they are negotiated by special enzymic machinery which requires the respiratory pigments known as cytochromes. The essential steps are shown in Fig. 6–11.

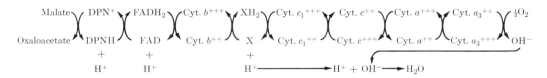

FIG. 6–11. A respiratory chain for oxidation of malic acid. The terminal member of the chain is cytochrome a_3 (cytochrome oxidase). The letter X denotes the factor, possibly coenzyme Q, which mediates electron transport between cytochromes b and c; XH_2 is its reduced form. Note that a proton is liberated in the reduction of DPN^+ but utilized in the reduction of FAD. Two protons are liberated when $FADH_2$ is oxidized by two moles of cytochrome b^{+++}. These may be re-utilized during reduction of X, depending upon the nature of the latter, and are assumed to be liberated upon the reoxidation of XH_2 by cytochrome c_1. It is these protons which react with the hydroxyl ions formed during the aerobic oxidation of cytochrome a_3^{++} to yield the H_2O formed in the respiratory process. (From White, Handler, Smith, and Stetten, *Principles of Biochemistry*, Second Edition, copyright © 1959, McGraw-Hill Book Co.; used by permission of the publisher.)

Thus sugar is only the *ultimate* respiratory substrate, and the overall equation $C_6H_{12}O + 6O_2 \rightarrow 6CO_2 + 6H_2O$ should not therefore imply that the sugar and oxygen ever actually combine. The end result which is of most importance to a cell is not the carbon dioxide released, for this in excess is poisonous and must be eliminated; it is certainly not the relatively small number of water molecules produced, nor is it even the total amount of heat which is released, for this is largely absorbed by the surroundings. The really important consequence for the cell or organism is that, through the processes of aerobic respiration, some special molecules are made which incorporate into their constitution a part of the energy originally present in the sugar molecule, and this is done in such a manner that the energy can be transferred and donated to specific processes in the cell. These molecules are complex compounds of phosphorus of which the substance adenosinetriphosphate, or ATP, is the chief example.* In plants particularly, however, compounds like uridine triphosphate (UTP) play a similar and important role. Be this as it may, the organic phosphorus compounds represent the currency through which energy transactions in the plant body are believed to be negotiated, so that when energy is used, the payment is made in molecules of ATP or of some other phosphorylated compound. Thus the prime function of respiration is to produce these molecules, termed "high energy" phosphorus compounds, in amounts that are directly proportional to the use of oxygen and the consumption of carbon fuel in the Krebs cycle. For each turn-over of a molecule of sugar in the Krebs cycle, many molecules of high energy phosphate, variously estimated at about 38 molecules of ATP, may be made.

---

* Other compounds can "trap" metabolic energy for later use, e.g., guanidine triphosphate (GTP).

iii) *Cells as molecular machines.* Thus we now regard cells not as heat engines but as molecular machines, in which the machinery utilizes the special molecular characteristics of these molecules to make its processes work. In the above account, note has been taken only of glycolysis as the main means by which the carbon of sugar is drawn into the cycle of oxidative breakdown. This is not in fact entirely true, because it is well known that mechanisms also exist for the prior oxidation of sugar to phosphogluconic acid and for the step-wise degradation of this substance by methods (known as the pentose shunt or pentose pathway) that utilize sugars that were hitherto unfamiliar. There are also variants of the organic acid cycle which pass over glycolic acid. The broad outline of these different respiratory pathways are illustrated in the charts of Figs. 6–12, 6–13, and 6–14. (For more detail, reference may be made to Goddard and Bonner, 1960; Beevers, 1961; Beevers *et al.*, 1966; Gibbs, 1966.)

The more complete chart at Fig. 6–14 stresses not only the multiplicity of pathways that may provide routes to carbon dioxide and water, but it also suggests their separate locations. Certainly the enzymes of glycolysis are located in the cytoplasm, whereas those that negotiate the oxidative breakdown are contained in the mitochondria. Thus respiration, like nitrogen metabolism, requires cells that are compartmentalized and which can use these compartments to segregate substances and reaction systems.

iv) *Intracellular compartments and organelles.* Despite the many triumphs of biochemistry which have produced the knowledge of intermediary metabolism which is summarized above and in Figs. 6–12 through 6–14, one should admit that these alone do not give an adequate picture of respiratory metabolism as it occurs *in vivo*. To appreciate this we need to know more about compartmentalization in cells as indicated above.

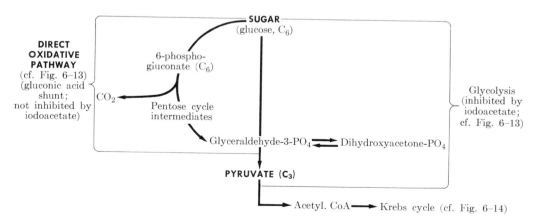

FIG. 6–12. Scheme to show relationship of the gluconic acid shunt to the overall process of preparing the respiratory substrate for oxidation.

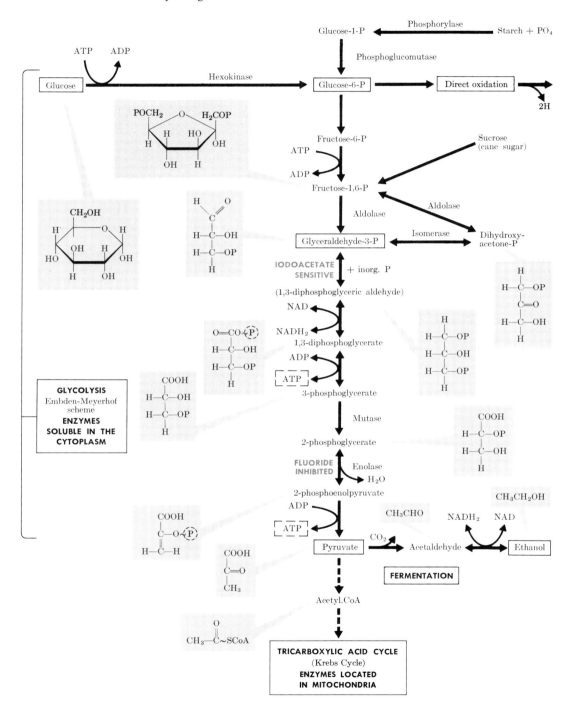

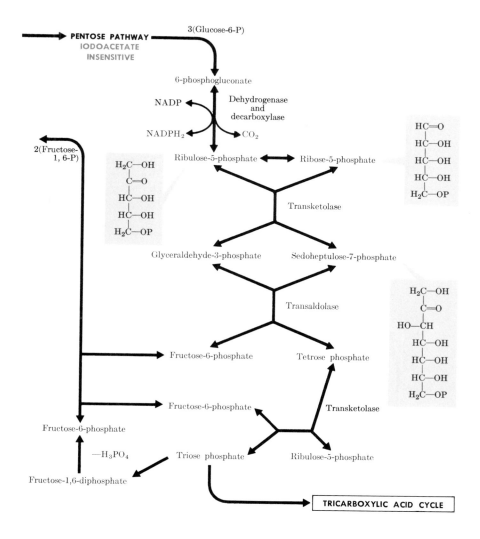

FIG. 6–13. The cytoplasmic reactions of respiration: Glycolysis (Emden-Meyerhof-Parnas pathway) and the direct oxidative pathway (the pentose pathway). The products of glycolysis may be metabolized anaerobically as in fermentation or aerobically as in the tricarboxylic acid cycle (cf. Fig. 6–14). Note the site of action of the inhibitors (iodoacetate and fluoride) and the iodoacetate insensitive oxidative pentose pathway. The pentose pathway, here shown in outline only, is also involved in the path of carbon in photosynthesis (cf. Fig. 3–6).

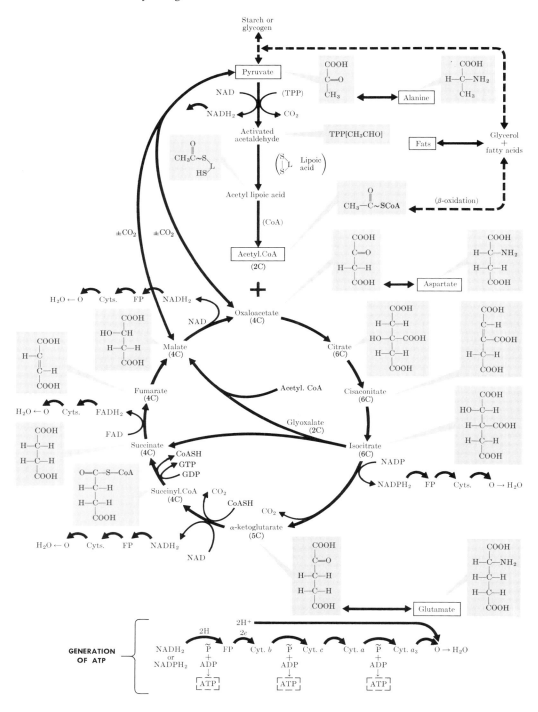

◀FIG. 6–14. The mitochondrial reactions of respiration: the tricarboxylic acid cycle (the Krebs cycle). This scheme shows the entry of C_2 fragments from pyruvate, as acetyl CoA, into the Krebs cycle. Note the role of thiamine (as TPP) and other coenzymes in the decarboxylations; the oxidations by H removal; acceptance of hydrogen by NAD, NADP or FAD which then passes over the carrier system (cf. Fig. 6–11) eventually to oxygen to form water; the removal of CO_2 by decarboxylations; the intermediates of the Krebs cycle (showing the number of carbons per molecule) and the possible bypass via glyoxylate.

The most important organelle for respiratory metabolism is now known to be the mitochondrion. It is here that the complete oxidative processes are believed to be carried out and the oxidatively produced ATP, in which the usable respiratory energy is temporarily stored, is formed. Parenthetically, one may note that it is a real problem to know how the ATP which is formed within a mitochondrion may be made available for useful work in processes that occur elsewhere in the cell.

It was pointed out in Chapter 3 with respect to chloroplasts that the biochemistry of photosynthesis only tells what are the feasible unit reactions; it is the organization of the plastid that enables these consecutive and interlocking steps to work in a smoothly continuous and integrated way. The same is equally true of mitochondria (cf. Lehninger, 1964). In fact, these different organelles merit some comparisons.

Both mitochondria and chloroplasts are to be regarded as autonomous organelles that multiply by division—the one (the mitochondrion) is common to both plants and animals, the other (the chloroplastid) is peculiar to green plants. The origin of both organelles in their minute precursors is still not clear and from time to time it has been thought that they represent dichotomous developments from a common kind of precursor. In particular Frey-Wyssling and Mühlethaler (1965) still speak of a vesicular "initial" which may give rise either to proplastids that form chloroplasts in the light or to mitochondria.

Among the equivalent or homologous functions of mitochondria and chloroplasts are the following. Whereas it is the function of mitochondria to absorb oxygen and to release carbon dioxide with the formation of phosphorylated compounds (ATP) oxidatively and irrespective of light, the role of plastids is to produce the same available forms of chemical energy by almost the converse means. ATP is formed by photosynthetic phosphorylation anaerobically, but only in the light. Whereas the mitochondrion uses heme pigments (cytochromes) to terminate the oxidation of hydrogen removed from reduced substrates by recombining it with atmospheric oxygen, it is a prime chloroplast function to remove hydrogen from water, to release molecular oxygen, to reduce substrates, and to use heme pigments (cyt. *f*; ferredoxin) as part of the catalytic machinery. Both organelles can fix carbon dioxide, the mitochondrion in the form of the malic acid reaction and the chloroplast in the conversion of ribulose diphosphate to hexose in the light. Both organelles use pyridine nucleotides to mediate H transfers, though in the mitochondria DPN (NAD) is the favored substance, whereas in chloroplasts it is TPN (NADP). Both organelles produce intermediate substances (keto acids) incidental to their primary role in respiration (mitochondria) or photosynthesis (chloroplasts) which act as "ports of entry" for nitrogen and furnish the raw material of protein synthesis. Both these organelles—so often related as opposite faces of the same coin—are vesiculate inclusions in protoplasm, and both owe their efficiency to the involvement of their structure and function. In the mitochondria, the outer double membrane is extended by invaginations of the inner surface—these tend to be radial and to divide the organelle into numerous compartments. It is true that mitochondria of metabolically active plant cells present their internal structure much more in the form of contorted threads than in the case of mitochondria in either quiescent plant cells or in animals. It is difficult to conceive of the efficiency of the mitochondrion in the varied steps it performs without involving some internal regularity of arrangement of the various enzymes and catalytic systems which it contains—it is not a mere bag of enzymes present in mixed solutions. In this sense the morphology of the mitochondrion is as important to respiration and the metabolism with which it is linked as is the fine structure and development of a chloroplast to the efficient functioning of photosynthesis. And the fact that isolated mitochondria only retain their activity for very short periods is evidence enough that the functions of respiration are only maintained *in vivo* by virtue of the entire organization of the cell.

Again one sees that the biochemistry tells us what is feasible; the morphology makes it practicable.

The regulatory control of respiration and need for usable energy. In so complex a physiological function as respiration it becomes a problem to know by what factor, or factors, the whole sequence may be regulated. An understanding of the regulation of respiration may also suggest explanations for the control of other events for which respiration provides the needed energy.

All the factors that impinge upon, and determine, the pace of respiration will not be discussed here: some of these now need only passing reference.

i) *Some external factors involved.* The effect of temperature, which largely determines the pace of respiration ($Q_{10} = 2$ to 3) as of all other metabolic processes which are affected by the rates of chemical reactions, may play a more regulatory role over the course of respiration at certain extremes. Low but non-freezing temperatures affect the conversion of starch to sugars (e.g., in potato tubers), and it also exerts far-reaching effects on protein metabolism, which suggests that the coupling mechanism between respiration and protein synthesis has also been deranged (Steward *et al.*, 1943). While these low but non-freezing temperatures may produce what seem to be abnormally high rates of respiration for those temperatures, the rates of respiration are not unduly high when compared to the sugar concentrations which the conditions induce. Such facts have suggested that there are both temperature-induced factors, like sugar concentration, which tend to increase respiration, and other inhibitory factors that tend to suppress it (Barker, 1933). At high temperatures, bordering upon the maximum for biological activity, the denaturing of proteins may introduce special effects. But over a wide range the effects of temperature are on the rate, not the kind, of respiration.

Characteristically plant respiration is more sensitive to oxygen pressure than is animal respiration, which is more apt to be determined by oxygen *supply* than by oxygen *concentration*. Since the cytochrome system is easily saturated at low oxygen tensions, the frequent responses to oxygen concentration (of the order of 10 to 20 percent in the atmosphere) are either responses to other parts of the respiratory process, or to aspects of the organization which restrict oxygen penetration to the sites of terminal oxidation. The main response to oxygen is, however, that which is involved in the balance between fermentation and respiration, i.e., the Pasteur Effect.

It is not enough to know that in the absence of oxygen the course of carbohydrate breakdown is directed to alcoholic fermentation (Fig. 6–13) and toward the organic acid cycle in its presence (Fig. 6–14), for oxygen actually tends to suppress the processes of carbohydrate breakdown by fermentation. The idea of the "common pathway" between respiration in air and in its absence leads to a relationship such that the respiration in nitrogen (NR) should, at the instant of transfer and with instantaneous adjustment, be one-third of the oxygen respiration (OR). However, many plant organs—usually the more massive ones —show substantially greater values of NR than one-third of OR; this led Blackman to postulate that there were other ways in which, in air, the split products of carbohydrate could be metabolized. Blackman designated that part of the metabolized carbohydrate which was not accountable as the CO_2 of respiration as the amount of substrate resynthesized, i.e., by oxidative anabolism (OA), into the more complex, but pre-existing components of the system. Although most of the documented examples of "oxidative anabolism," i.e., where NR − ⅓ OR = OA, are from mature non-growing organs, there are enough of these to suggest that this is part of a distinctive pattern whereby respiration is regulated in these fleshy storage organs. (Reference may here be made to a recent account by Forward, 1965, of these problems.) The levels at which organized structures, like buds, are oxygen-saturated may be a function, not only of the responses of the cells to oxygen, but also of the organization of the whole system of bud scales; this may determine how far fermentative metabolism contributes to the overall process (Pollock, 1950).

ii) *Rate limiting role of energy requirements for growth.* Since there are such different alternative routes (i.e., via glycolysis and the pentose pathway) by which the carbon of sugar reaches the oxidative centers, it has been considered that one or the other may be more used in the systems that can grow. Older ideas that tumor cells could flourish on the proceeds of accentuated aerobic fermentations are not now so widely held. Similarly attempts have been made to ascribe more or less of the respiratory metabolism to the glycolytic or the pentose pathways according as the cells can or cannot grow and divide. Although the general impression is that the pentose pathway is more conspicuous in dividing than in non-dividing cells, so that relatively more of the respiration is mediated in this way, it would be going too far to say that the system grows and divides *because* it utilizes one or other of these routes. A more accurate picture is the following.

Cells must have the resources to furnish the different types of behavior which growth, development, and responses to stimuli entail, with the power that is needed to drive them. Cells must be able to regulate, separately, these sources of power in organelles, and to direct and control them by distinctive stimuli by which they may be called into play as needed. As an end product of respiration, and one which is toxic unless removed, carbon dioxide may be expected to play such a regulatory role. Concentrations of carbon dioxide in the internal atmosphere may suppress respiration, and its prompt removal by efficient aeration may promote it. Therefore, any conditions which promote or suppress decarboxylation reactions (over and above the carbon dioxide tension) may exert a regulatory role; amongst these the balance between oxidized and reduced pyridine nucleotides (DPN/DPNH; TPN/TPNH) in the closely linked dehydrogenase reactions may play their part. In fact the movement of hydrogen along the hydrogen transfer chain may well be limited, or regulated, by any one of the steps mentioned in Fig. 6–11, or by any one of the intermediary metabolic reactions of carbon shown in Figs. 6–12 to 6–14. Alternatively one may see the determining regulatory factor which controls the pace, or kind, of respiration as the need for phosphorylated molecules which donate energy, as it is needed, to the working cellular machine. In other words, it is inasmuch as the $\sim$P, of ATP, UTP, GTP, etc., is drawn off to perform useful chemical work that the respiratory fuel is consumed more rapidly, so that, as required, the metabolic fires burn brighter. Thus respiration may be determined as much by the pace of the overall mechanism for which it furnishes the energy as by an intrinsic or built-in mechanism of its own self determination. This is apparent from several recent accounts of respiration and related metabolic processes (e.g., Beevers, 1961; Forward, 1965; and Gibbs, 1966). This again reflects the dilemma that having determined how the plant biochemistry may function we have also to specify what controls its pace. One cannot here neglect either the organization in cells which permits the various parts of the overall metabolic system to be segregated from each other and, thus, subjected to specific and individual controls; or the exogenous factors which intervene in cells to control the pace and direction of their growth and development and which, thereby, determine their need of the usable forms of energy which respiration yields.

iii) *Respiration and energy requirements in growing cells and organs.* With all this in mind, what do we now know about the respiration of rapidly growing cells and tissues? Resting tissue, even though it is richly stored with food in the form of carbohydrate and soluble nitrogen compounds, as in the potato tuber, may respire at a very low rate (of the order of 0.01 mg CO_2/gm fresh weight/hr). Transfer to the more active, growing, dividing state, as it occurs in cells at the surface of a thin disc exposed to moist air, has long been known to be accompanied by an increased respiration, as shown by carbon dioxide evolution and by the actual production of heat. (For references and discussion see Steward and Sutcliffe, 1959.) These events are, however, strictly confined to the surface cells, and if one studies the respiration of discs of varying thickness, it can be seen that there is a moiety of respiration which can be called "surface respiration" because it occurs at the outside of the disc and is confined to a depth of only a few cells. The limiting value that this respiratory component achieves is of the order of 40 times the respiration of the cells in the middle of a disc, or of the cells as they exist in the intact tuber. The bulk of the energy so released is in fact wasted and is absorbed by the surroundings in the form of heat, but, incidental to this great turnover of carbohydrate and of energy, some is locked up in the high energy compounds which can perform useful work. The salt accumulation and the concomitant protein synthesis that goes on in thin, well-aerated potato slices exposed to dilute salt solutions is an example of this use of metabolic energy to perform useful work in cells.

What then is known about the respiration of the cells of growing regions? Here a digression is necessary to clarify standards of reference and the bases of expressing results.

It is a common practice to refer the intensity of a process like respiration to the total amount, or fresh weight, of the tissue which participates in the process. In so doing the respiration is, in effect, weighted against an amount of water contained in the biological system. For many purposes this device is suitable. Brown and Rickless (1948), however, emphasized that this method may often be misleading if one is thereby comparing pieces of tissue which contain very different numbers of cells of different size; hence it is also desirable to see how these values appear when they are expressed upon a cellular basis. This requires a knowledge of the number of cells contained in a given weight of tissue that participates in the respiratory process.

Comparatively early in the modern study of salt and water uptake by roots it was shown, principally by Prevot and Steward (1936) and Steward, Prevot, and Harrison (1942), that gradients of salt accumulation occur along the axis of the root so that the greatest *concentration* of salts is obtained close to the root apex in regions in which growth, principally by cell enlargement, is also located. Machlis (1944) also showed that similar gradations of respiration, as measured by oxygen uptake and carbon dioxide output, occurred along the axis of the barley root, grading from high respiration near the root tip to lower respiration in the mature regions. Thus, the ability to store salt in the water of the tissue and the ability of the water of the tissue to support respiration were both reflected in these gradients, with the greatest activity occurring near the tip. This was interpreted to mean that the more actively growing cells were also involved as the principal centers of initial salt accumulation, though, as Brown pointed out, this is in part due to the fact that there are a larger number of smaller cells in unit weight of tissue near the root apex.

When these first experiments were made, methods then available did not permit the chemical and physiological work to be performed on segments as small as the morphology of the material really demands, for a segment of a root which is only a few millimeters long encompasses a very wide range in the transition from the meristem to the more mature tissues. In fact, Goodwin and Stepka (1945) showed that the maximum rate of cell elongation in the root of *Phleum* occurs at less than a millimeter behind the root tip. Therefore, the gradients previously referred to simply reflect the approach to this region as the one which is most active in respiration and in salt absorption.

The graded activity in salt accumulation along the root axis may be interpreted more precisely from work which has been done by the use of isotopes and with the unbranched roots of *Narcissus*. In general the results on *Narcissus* confirmed the earlier ones, but the situation at the extreme tip of the root was unexpected. As one approaches the extreme tip of the root from the older tissue, that is, proceeding toward cells which are more active in division than in elongation, *both activities* (i.e., total respiration and ion intake) decline when expressed on the fresh weight basis. Thus the meristematic cells proper may be *less* concerned with the development of high concentration of ions and *less* concerned with the very high rates of respiration than the somewhat older and more vacuolated cells. According to Brown, the primordia—whether of root or shoot—show a respiration per unit of protein that they contain, which is low in the younger primordia and increases steadily as development proceeds. In other words, as the cells increase in volume and become more hydrated by vacuolation and the absorption of water, they also increase in the efficiency of their protein to maintain respiration. The form of the relationship between the respiration and the absorption of water and solutes which occurs at this stage is difficult to specify, but the important point is that these are two interrelated functions of the developing cells.

Another and quite different system suggests that cells in the actual stage of division have lower, not higher, respiration. Erickson (1948) worked with the anther of *Lilium;* he calibrated the anther so that he could prophesy from its length when the two divisions of meiosis should occur. As the anther developed, its respiration per unit weight declined following a rather characteristic, somewhat hyperbolic curve which relates respiration to weight or size. When the two divisions of meiosis were occurring Erickson noted, not an increase of the respiration, but a decrease which was superimposed upon the smoothly falling curve of respiration concomitant with the development of the anther (see Fig. 6–15). It seems, therefore, that during actual division the respiration of cells may be at a relative minimum. Moreover, meristematic cells which are non-vacuolate also seem to have a lower respiration than those which depart different leaves and leaf primordia in a dicotyledonous shoot, in the intercalary growing regions of a monocotyledonous shoot, and in the cambial region of a tree identifies these regions as active centers of growth and of other physiological functions which "follow the leaf of growth."

About 1925 Hoagland first emphasized that the absorption of ions by cells was not a passive diffusion or permeability process, but was an intensely active one in the sense that cells used their own metabolism to perform osmotic work. These now classical ideas were first derived from work on the large internodal cells of *Nitella,* which happened to be responsive to light in a manner that is now believed to be due in part, if not wholly, to their dependence upon light for their growth, predominantly by elongation. Work with storage organs, cut into thin slices, elaborated upon this view and laid the groundwork for the general idea that it is through the oxidative processes of respiration that the energy of metabolism is donated to the *de novo* accumulation of salts. The experiments with slices of storage organs also showed that the mere production of carbon dioxide was not enough to assure maximum ion accumulation, for the accumulation occurs in a system which is sufficiently able to grow in the sense that it is capable also of protein synthesis and, if continued, of actual division of cells. Thus the ability of cells to accumulate salts *de novo* is itself a function of cells which are active enough to grow.

To make a long story short, it now seems that a cell which is able to grow by elongation and by division, able to synthesize protein from simple nitrogen compounds, using a high respiration rate to furnish energy for both of these processes, also takes its salt accumulation "in its stride" and causes ions to move from a low concentration outside into a high concentration inside the cell. These ideas seem as true now as when they were first promulgated, with the additionally suggestive thought that this is really the second phase of the absorption process; for, as cells multiply in the apex by division with but little vacuolation, they also multiply sites where ions can be bound. The binding of ions at self-duplicating sites seems to be a purely chemical process, and it bears quite different relations to the external ion concentrations from those which govern accumulation of ions in the vacuole of larger cells. Thus, as in the case of the tissue cultures described earlier, the salt-absorbing process is now conceived in two steps. One step, described as phase I of the diagram shown as Fig. 6–16, is characteristic of dividing cells, and this may be recapitulated in bacteria, in yeast, and in non-vacuolated forms. The second step, phase II, is characteristic of growing, expanding, enlarging, vacuolating cells in which ions are secreted internally into their vacuoles (cf. Fig. 2–19). The essence of the active process of accumulation, however, is that it is related to energy supply by respiration, and it is sensitive to oxygen pressure in the range of 0 to 20 percent by volume in the gas phase with which the ambient solutions that bathe the cells are in equilibrium. Many examples of such responses to oxygen tension and aeration are now known. (For review, see Steward and Sutcliffe, 1959.)

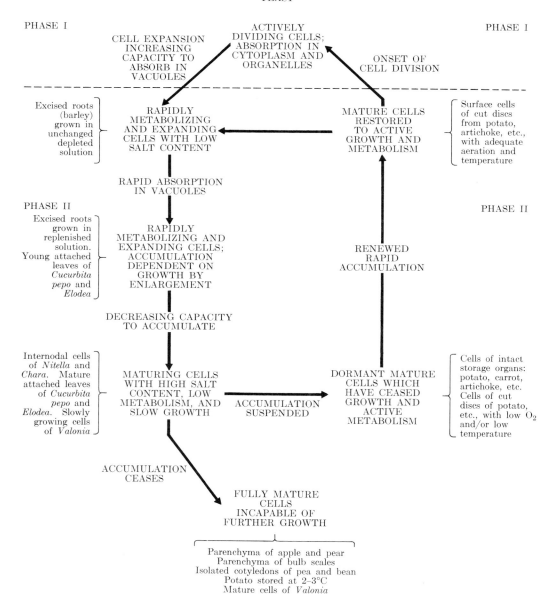

SALT ACCUMULATION RELATIVE TO GROWTH

TISSUE CULTURES
BACTERIA
YEAST

PHASE I   PHASE I

CELL EXPANSION
INCREASING
CAPACITY TO
ABSORB IN
VACUOLES

ACTIVELY
DIVIDING CELLS;
ABSORPTION IN
CYTOPLASM AND
ORGANELLES

ONSET OF
CELL DIVISION

Excised roots
(barley)
grown in
unchanged
depleted
solution

RAPIDLY
METABOLIZING
AND EXPANDING
CELLS WITH LOW
SALT CONTENT

MATURE CELLS
RESTORED
TO ACTIVE
GROWTH AND
METABOLISM

Surface cells
of cut discs
from potato,
artichoke, etc.,
with adequate
aeration and
temperature

RAPID ABSORPTION
IN VACUOLES

PHASE II   PHASE II

Excised roots
grown in
replenished
solution.
Young attached
leaves of
*Cucurbita
pepo* and
Elodea

RAPIDLY
METABOLIZING AND
EXPANDING CELLS;
ACCUMULATION
DEPENDENT ON
GROWTH BY
ENLARGEMENT

RENEWED
RAPID
ACCUMULATION

DECREASING CAPACITY
TO ACCUMULATE

Internodal cells
of *Nitella* and
Chara. Mature
attached leaves
of *Cucurbita
pepo* and
Elodea. Slowly
growing cells
of *Valonia*

MATURING CELLS
WITH HIGH SALT
CONTENT, LOW
METABOLISM, AND
SLOW GROWTH

ACCUMULATION
SUSPENDED

DORMANT MATURE
CELLS WHICH
HAVE CEASED
GROWTH AND
ACTIVE
METABOLISM

Cells of intact
storage organs:
potato, carrot,
artichoke, etc.
Cells of cut
discs of potato,
etc., with low O_2
and/or low
temperature

ACCUMULATION
CEASES

FULLY MATURE
CELLS
INCAPABLE OF
FURTHER GROWTH

Parenchyma of apple and pear
Parenchyma of bulb scales
Isolated cotyledons of pea and bean
Potato stored at 2–3°C
Mature cells of *Valonia*

FIG. 6–16. Salt accumulation in relation to growth and metabolism. In phase I, the main emphasis is upon binding of ions of specific sites which can multiply. In phase II, the main emphasis is upon active secretion into vacuoles. (From Steward and Sutcliffe, in F. C. Steward, ed., *Plant Physiology, A Treatise*, Vol. II, Academic Press, New York, 1959.)

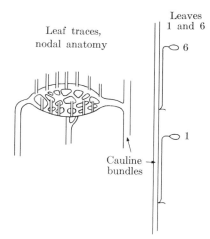

Leaf traces, nodal anatomy

Leaves 1 and 6

Cauline bundles

FIG. 6–20. The vascular pattern of *Cucurbita pepo*, showing direct connection of leaves 1 and 6 via cauline bundles. Each leaf receives three leaf traces which fuse into a network at the nodal plate. Of these three, one springs directly from the cauline bundle.

dicotyledons and monocotyledons, leading to differences in their internal nutrition, can reasonably be interpreted in the light of their manner of growth. Furthermore, what Brown, following Priestley, called a "unit of growth"— namely, a petiole and its subtended leaf—can certainly be thought of as a nutritional unit of salt accumulation.

It is a useful concept that the leaves which are united into one vertical file, or orthostichy (cf. Fig. 6–20), readily transfer salts from one to the other (cf. Fig. 6–21). As upper leaves come into their full intake of salt in the light (Fig. 6–21, Series A), they may deplete, if temporarily, the lower members of the same series. Thus there is a basis for a rational interpretation of nutrition

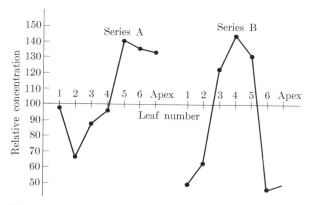

FIG. 6–21. Entry of bromide into the leaf of *Cucurbita pepo* as shown by relative bromide concentration of leaves in an acropetal succession, i. e., from the base upwards. Relative concentration in each leaf equals the concentration in the leaf divided by the average concentration in the leafy shoot as a whole. In series B, contact was made with the bromide during periods of darkness only; in series A, in light only. (From work of A. G. and F. C. Steward; cf. Steward *et al.*, 1954.)

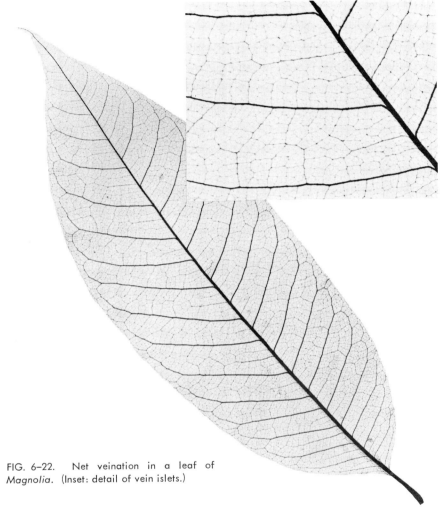

FIG. 6–22.   Net veination in a leaf of *Magnolia*. (Inset: detail of vein islets.)

and metabolism in terms of morphology and anatomy. Nevertheless, when one contemplates the complexity of the vascular system as shown by the bundles of a leaf (Fig. 6–22), or the nodal anatomy and the phyllotaxy of massive monocotyledons like palms (Tomlinson, 1964), or of the banana plant (Simmonds, 1959), one realizes how few facts there are on which to build concepts of the internal nutrition of such plants in relation to the flow of stimuli that determine the way they grow and develop. The backward passage of C^{14}-labeled organic solutes (cf. Fig. 6–23) again shows how numerous are the vascular strands in a leaf base and internode that are concerned with the passage of solutes in phloem from leaf to stem and *vice versa*.

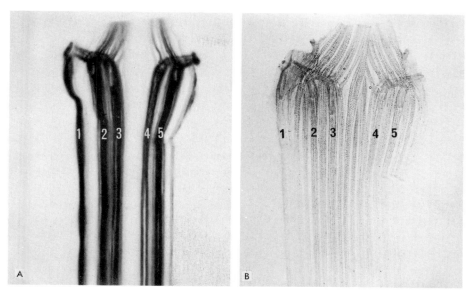

FIG. 6–23. An autoradiogram representing the movement of C^{14}-labeled photosynthate in the phloem of the bean stem. The photosynthate entered the stem from a leaf that had received $^{14}CO_2$. The leaf was removed by a cut at the base of the petiole. A longitudinal slit in the phloem-containing tissue (bark) was then made through the petiole base and the "bark" peeled from the xylem-containing tissue (wood). After dehydration by freeze-drying, the "bark" was (A) exposed to contrast process film, and (B) photographed after fluorescing the sieve plates of the phloem with aniline blue. The path of the photosynthate can be traced through the split petiole base and into the leaf traces numbered 1, 2, 3, 4, and 5. Some upward movement from these leaf traces also occurred. (For details see Biddulph and Cory, 1965.) (From a print furnished by Dr. O. Biddulph, State College of Washington.)

iii) *In Populus.* As a corollary to the accumulation of bromide in the most actively growing regions of herbaceous shoots, it may also be seen to accumulate in the cambial regions of a tree (*Populus*). Here the ion accumulation occurs in the spring in the actively growing cells of the cambial region and from the dilute solution which is present in the stele. If the cambial region in a given area of stem is not in direct contact with developing leaves then its accumulated salt may remain there. But the accumulated salt is more apt to be withdrawn to developing buds; this occurs via the vascular supply to the bud in the current year's growth, in which actively dividing and differentiating tissue (the cambium) occurs (Fig. 6–24) and is in organic contact with the cambial region of the stem, i.e., the growing tissue of the current year. After the buds first begin to "push" there is a brief interlude *before* they accumulate salts appreciably; thereafter salts enter and accumulate in the growing leaf or bud *pari passu* with their growth.

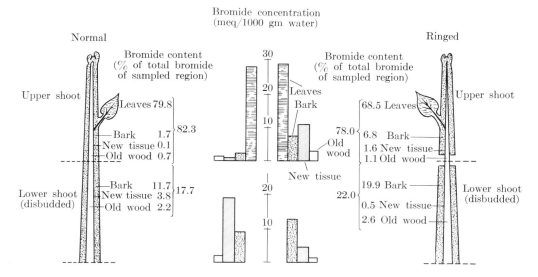

FIG. 6–24. Centers of salt absorption in the shoot of *Populus*. The normal shoot is disbudded below the level shown, but the cambium is stimulated by the growing leaves above. As the buds grow, most of the bromide in the shoot goes to the leaves; the cambium region is depleted of the bromide, which it absorbs from the wood within. In the lower region of the stem (without leaves) the cambium region accumulates markedly more bromide than the old wood within. The ringed shoot is disbudded below the ring. Leaves grow less in ringed shoots. Some residual accumulation of bromide in the cambial region remains even above the ring. Below the ring, the cambium is much less active in the disbudded shoot, so that, even though there are no leaves to absorb it, there is relatively little bromide accumulated in the cambial region. (From work of Harrison and Steward, Harrison, 1938; cf. Steward and Sutcliffe, 1959.)

From such results the cambial region emerges, not merely as a region which lays down new tissue by secondary growth, but as a region composed of active living cells which play a real role in the internal economy of the tree, for they accumulate ions from the xylem sap and distribute them to the shoot. In fact, if Cs^{137} is applied directly to the external cambial surface when it is active, it may be directly absorbed and accumulated by that tissue, but it is also readily supplied to active growing centers directly above the point of application (Fig. 6–25). A radioautograph of a *Phaseolus* shoot, which had received Cs^{137} via the roots, reproduced as Fig. 6–26, shows that the very youngest leaves and buds received Cs^{137} copiously, but it was only prominent elsewhere in the vascular strands where the cambium produced actively growing tissue. With regard to monocotyledons the comparable idea is that the intercalary growing regions at the base of the leaves of monocotyledons function in somewhat the same way; they constitute centers of growth and physiological activity to which solutes are drawn off from the main axis to be supplied to the enlarging laminae of the leaves which are subtended at these points.

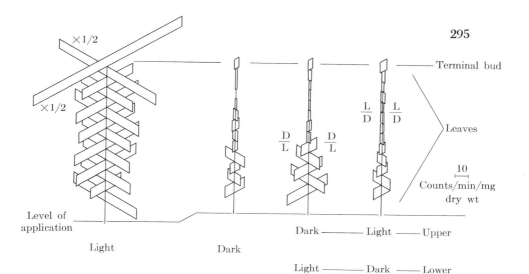

FIG. 6–25. The effect of light and dark on uptake of Cs[137] by cambium of maple (*Acer platanoides*) and its passage into leaves. Concentrations are plotted at right angles to the axis. In view of the high concentrations in the bud, the scale was reduced by one-half for shoots in the light. In the light the terminal bud and the youngest leaves accumulated the highest concentration. In the tree which had its upper leaves darkened, the lower leaves did not accumulate as much Cs as did comparable leaves on the tree in the light. (From work of Pollock and Steward; cf. Pollock, 1950.)

FIG. 6–26. Autoradiogram of *Phaseolus* shoot containing Cs[137] supplied via the roots.

Therefore, the growing regions of shoot and root, the cambium of trees, and the intercalary growing regions of monocotyledons, are important not only as regions where new cells and tissues are formed, but also as centers of physiological activity which regulate the internal nutritional economy of the plant body.

Passive and active water uptake.   But what can be said about the vexed question of water intake by cells and its metabolic basis, if any? Classically the water relations of cells have been interpreted in terms of osmosis, on the assumption that a plant cell behaves as an ideal osmotic system, subject only to the limitation of the elastic, cellulose wall. Since all the early experiments were conducted with mature, already vacuolated cells, it is not surprising that the ideas of water relations were dominated by these equilibrium concepts. However, if cells can perform work by moving ions against a diffusion gradient, may they not equally do so in the case of water? Or, conversely, may not an active flow of water be caused to local regions of solute accumulation? Many examples occur in nature of water movements which are activated by metabolism so that they seemingly occur against, not with, the prevailing osmotic gradients; the functioning of the human kidney is a prominent case in point. Whether active movements of water occur in relatively mature plant tissue remains a somewhat debatable point. It seems, however, inescapable that in the absorption of water *de novo* by the growing, developing cell that this process of water intake is not of a passive equilibrium kind, but is actively motivated by its growth, metabolism, and respiration.

Some years ago Bennet-Clark and Bexon (1940) made the suggestive observation that sap expressed from some storage organs does not plasmolyze half the cells, as one would expect if the range of osmotic concentration of the sap in the cells followed a normal frequency distribution. Indeed some organs furnished saps which behaved as expected from the simple osmotic view of cells; others, which invariably contained cells able to grow, furnished saps in which the cells resisted plasmolysis. Bennet-Clark and Bexon interpreted these observations, which have not passed without criticism, to mean that the cells possessed an internal secretion pressure and were able to absorb water actively by using their own metabolism; they could therefore resist plasmolysis when exposed to a sap that should have been stronger than their own in the case of 50 percent of the cells. It seems clear, however, that the absorption of water by roots to maintain exudation pressures which are a function of oxygen tension, and the passage of water into growing cells, cannot be merely a passive osmotic phenomenon but must be metabolically motivated and maintained by the use of respiratory energy in a manner not unlike that which mediates the accumulation of salts. When the growth of cells is stimulated by the factors which occur in coconut milk, their absorption of water is increased in the same ratio as their synthesis of protein (Steward, Bidwell, and Yemm, 1956). Therefore, both processes are functions of growing cells and require energy to bring them about.

But how is the energy donated to make growing cells do osmotic work in the movement of ions and water? What are the molecular arrangements? This is still one of the great outstanding problems of modern biology. However, the ultimate explanation should take cognizance of the fact that at the time when the cell is growing and synthesizing protein it is also absorbing ions and absorbing water, and metabolic energy seems to be furnished "in one package" for all these processes. In this sense water and salts do not merely *enter* cells but initially they "grow into cells." Paradoxically, a full explanation of water and salt intake by cells requires an understanding of the larger problem of how cells grow.

Movement and storage of solutes. Again it seems presumptuous to embark upon this great problem only briefly. To do so is bound to do it injustice. A general thought can, however, be presented. Problems of solute and of water movement are often treated as if they can be dealt with apart from the manner of growth of the organisms in question. There is talk about movement of water *in* xylem and of organic solutes *in* phloem, as though these tissues came ready-made, pre-endowed with the ability to perform their translocatory functions. However, the problems of the organized plant body cannot be solved in this way, for the functions of translocation of organic solutes and the movement of water must be intimately related to the way the organism grows and develops (cf. Swanson, 1959; and Biddulph, 1959).

For example, solutes cannot be moved from one place to another, released from one group of cells and absorbed by others, without inevitably involving the stimuli that cause cells to accumulate solutes and/or grow at the so-called "sink" and to release them at the "source." The stimuli that negotiate these transfers are quite unknown. It is difficult enough to explain how roots accumulate their salts *de novo*, but it is still more difficult to explain how the shoot stimulates the root to release them again after they were once absorbed. When a potato stolon becomes a tuber and the cells of the tuber grow, they become capable of storing and accumulating salts and organic solutes. It seems as futile to try to explain the movement of the solutes to the tuber, apart from the ability of the growing cells to store them, as it would be to explain the movement of the population of New York City into and out of the subways, apart from the fact that they have waiting the destinations and homes which are capable of accommodating them at the end of the journey. Were it not so, the lines of communications soon would be plugged.

It is usually said that movement of solutes occurs in phloem, and that movement occurs in mature phloem in sieve tubes. Investigators have examined the characteristics of sieve tubes to see the features which are consistent with such rapid flow. The provocative words of one teacher may be recalled, who said, "When I look at a mature sieve tube I wonder whether I see a place

adapted to flow, or, as in a dried-up river bed, a place where flow once occurred." This aphorism was meant to suggest that the growing, developing sieve
tube, at the height of its own metabolic activity, might well be a more potent
agent for the transfer of solutes than the fully mature sieve tube which has lost
its nucleus and much of its metabolic potentialities.* If this idea is tenable, it
is consistent with the hypothesis that the movement of solutes in phloem—
which occurs far too rapidly for any obvious physical or equilibrium explanation—is primarily motivated by living cells which do work in this transfer, even
as growing cells do work in absorption. One can then see how the otherwise
puzzling gap between the differentiated vascular tissue, which terminates well
below the growing point of shoot and root, and the meristematic cells may be
traversed, for the elongated living cells which bridge this gap could function
in a similar fashion. Otherwise sieve tubes would bring solutes, not to the point
where they are ultimately needed, but would deposit them at points which, in
terms of cells and molecules, may be still relatively far removed from where
they are required.

One may therefore re-examine what may be called the "internal nutrition of
a tree" from this point of view. An important consideration is the probable role
of the cambium. While water may move over long distances in a dilute solution
in the xylem, how do solutes reach the place where they are stored in the developing leaves? In other words, how is the solute drawn off and diverted, as it
were, to the lateral organs? Before the availability of radioactive isotopes, this
problem had been investigated by the use of the bromide ion and with reference
to trees of *Populus* (cf. p. 294). The distribution of bromide throughout the
shoot was studied as bromide spread upward, during growth, from the soil in the
dormant period. Briefly, it was shown that the cambial tissue, when reactivated
by the stimuli that pass downward from the buds in the spring, accumulates
solutes from the older xylem within at the time of the spring flush of growth.
However, the activity of the buds in leaf expansion *precedes* the first movement
of salts into the leaf. It is not until growing xylem in the leaf traces spreads
basipetally downwards and connects, *in the current year's growth,* with the cambial tissue on the main stem that solutes pass readily from the main axis to the bud.
When this occurs, a growing bud avidly depletes the cambial zone of the salts
which it has accumulated from the old wood within. Treatments such as ringing,
disbudding, and defoliation, which alter the distribution of active cambium on
the stem and its relationships to growing buds and leaves, also alter the movement and distribution of bromide ion in the tissues, and they do so in ways that
now become intelligible (see Fig. 6–24). Moreover, the exposed surface of the
active cambium will accumulate salts *directly* and transmit them to growing

---

* It is generally recognized that only a very limited layer of phloem (about 0 to 2
mm thick) in the current year of growth suffices to move most of the organic solutes
in a tree, but, by contrast, some believe that sieve tubes in palms may be functional
after 50 years!

buds which are immediately above the point of application, but only if these *young leaves are in the light and thus can grow* (see Fig. 6–25). Therefore, the redistribution of solutes within the plant body is in response to stimuli which determine the growth and development of cells, organs, and tissues. It is cells that are prompted to grow that can store the solutes, depleting other tissues, and it is cells in these active states that can move salts and water far more rapidly than—or even against the direction of—any conceivable diffusion gradients. In short, the distribution of salts and solutes within the plant body follows the lead of growth, for it is where growth occurs that energy is being harnessed for useful purposes.

Translocation: some problems and precepts. One of the oldest ideas on translocation and movement of solutes in plants was based on analogy with the circulation of blood. Stephen Hales' observations recorded in "Vegetable Staticks" were heavily motivated by a search for an analogous circulation of sap in plants. The upward movement of "unelaborated foodstuffs" in the xylem and the backward movement of "elaborated foodstuffs" in the phloem, typical of 19th century knowledge, carried out this idea in part. And ringing experiments— known from the time of Hales—have been prominently exploited ever since to distinguish in woody trees that uninterrupted upward movement of solutes which can occur solely in xylem, from the movement of organic solutes, including much organic nitrogen, which occurs preferentially if not exclusively (and, according to Curtis, both upwards and downwards) in phloem. Abundant evidence suggests that upwardly moving inorganic solutes can pass a ringed region of the stem without the aid of living, or actively metabolizing cells, whereas a killed, anaesthetized, or metabolically inactive region of phloem imposes a barrier to organic solutes which is the equivalent of a ring. Also, there is abundant evidence from the time of de Vries, who speculated on the role of protoplasmic streaming, to Curtis (1935), Mason and Maskell (1928a and b), and such later workers as Nelson (1964), that rates of movement of organic solutes in the path of transport are extremely rapid.

It is as natural to presume that the efficiency of phloem in transporting organic molecules is associated with its characteristic living tissue elements, which are both elongated and specialized (the sieve elements or sieve tubes), as it is to see the problems of water movement in terms of the specialized elements (vessels and tracheids) of the xylem. Nevertheless, some very impressive movements of organic material occur in filaments of fungi (as in the mobilization of material for fruiting and spore formation; cf. Fig. 1–7) which lack any obvious specialization for this function, and effective translocation in some algae must also occur (as in the giant kelps) in elements (trumpet hyphae) which do show some specialized features. The final step of the way in angiosperms, however, must also involve elongated living cells and therefore, in translocation of organic solutes, the cells in the growing regions, which have not yet acquired mature characteristics, must also function effectively in the transfer of solutes. It is cells of this sort that are usually scraped off a ringed surface to ensure that no functional phloem shall remain! Hence ringing experiments which sever the path of phloem also interrupt the whole cambium region and so remove cells from this sheet of developing tissue when they are at the height of their own development and metabolic activity.

Since phloem fulfills its functions as a living system, some reference to its organization is appropriate. The characteristic tissue element which seems to be adapted for translocatory functions is the sieve tube, and this is commonly visualized in the form in which it is familiar in *Cucurbita*. Here the sieve tubes are relatively large and have sieve plates with relatively coarse pores on their end walls, which are accurately transverse. When mature, the individual elements that comprise a sieve tube have no nucleus, have a parietal cytoplasm surrounding a lumen filled with vacuolar sap, and are associated with adjacent companion cells which are more densely cytoplasmic and which retain their nuclei. This picture of phloem is by no means universal or typical. The presence of companion cells is a feature of angiosperm phloem (not of gymnosperms or ferns), but the end walls are not invariably transverse, nor are the sieve plates restricted to them. Figure 6–27 shows the range in the form of sieve tubes that may be encountered.

Whether one examines the vascular bundles of a herbaceous plant, or the secondary phloem of a tree, it is impressive how little phloem there often seems to be, and how infrequently one finds sieve tubes in the complex tissue which is phloem (containing also parenchyma and fibers), and how small is their total cross section. Although this dilemma led Dixon to discredit the ability of sieve tubes to move all the vast amounts of sugar which are translocated, nevertheless it is now universally accepted that this actually occurs. As Curtis showed, very little of the total secondary phloem in a woody dicotyledon will suffice, and Mason and Maskell (1928b) verified this by their work on transport of carbohydrate across a narrow bridge of phloem. Indeed, it was this system which they used to study the "diffusion analogy"—by steepening the concentration gradient as downwardly moving carbohydrates encountered, and accumulated above, a narrow bridge across a ring. Briefly, they were able to show that carbohydrate movement was commonly with a concentration gradient (i.e., from a high to a low concentration), but its rate vastly exceeded (by 40,000 times) anything that diffusion alone could achieve (cf. Canny and Phillips, 1963).

There now seems little doubt that what Mason and Maskell really regarded as concentrations that determine movement in the path of transport were in fact gradients in the storage of carbohydrates which, like other gradients of accumulated solutes, tend to decrease as one passes basipetally downward. Nelson has shown that there is a relatively slow moving component of the translocated sugar, which is perhaps related in direction to these concentration gradients, but there is also a very fast moving component which may not be so related to them. Moreover, the concept of gradients and the diffusion analogy which regards trans-

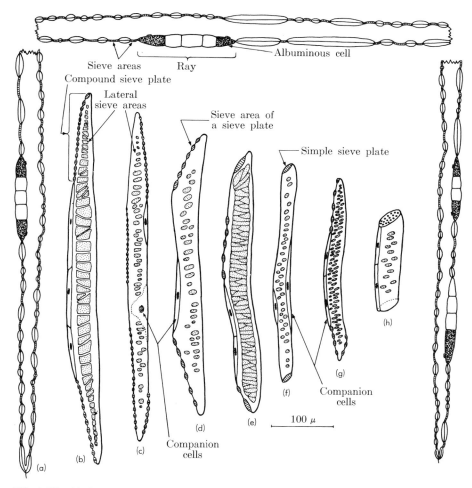

Sieve areas
Compound sieve plate
Lateral
sieve areas
Sieve areas   Ray
Albuminous cell
Sieve area of
a sieve plate
Simple sieve plate
Companion
cells
(h)
(g)
(f)
(e)   100 μ
(d)
(c)   Companion
cells
(b)
(a)

FIG. 6–27. Variations in the structure of sieve elements: (a) Sieve cell of *Pinus pinea*, with associated rays, as seen in tangential section and broken to show total length (1900 μ). Others are sieve tube members with companion cells from tangential sections of phloem of the following species: (b) *Juglans hindsii*; (c) *Pyrus malus*; (d) *Liriodendron tulipifera*; (e) *Acer pseudoplatanus*; (f) *Cryptocarya rubra*; (g) *Fraxinus americana*; (h) *Wisteria* sp. In (b) through (g), the sieve plates appear in side views and their sieve areas are thicker than the intervening wall regions because of deposition of callose. (After K. Esau, *Anatomy of Seed Plants*, John Wiley & Sons, New York, 1960.)

location as a sort of activated diffusion—like it in every respect but the all-important one of rate—though plausible for downward-moving carbohydrates, is less so for nitrogen compounds which often move upward to the shoot apex; and it loses its value when it is recalled that solutes habitually move against concentration gradients as they enter cells. Work and the use of energy must obviously be involved. In fact, there would be no problem of translocation if one could say here precisely how this occurs. Despite over a quarter of a century of work since H. H. Dixon and O. F. Curtis debated problems of translocation, a satisfying answer to them cannot be furnished, despite theories which have ranged from mass flow of fluid in the phloem elements along a positive hydrostatic gradient from "source" to "sink"; to "activated" diffusion; to the movement of solutes along interphases of surface activity; to the recognized ability of living cells to do work by harnessing their metabolism to foster movements which could not occur, either in direction or in rate, by equilibrium means alone.

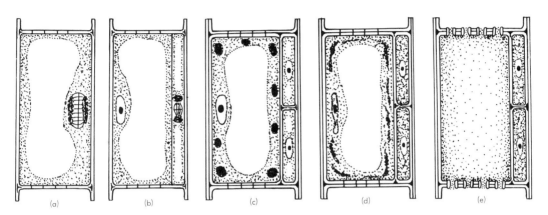

FIG. 6–28. Diagrams illustrating differentiation of a sieve tube member. (a) Mother cell of sieve tube member in division. (b) After division: sieve tube member and dividing mother cell of companion cells. (c) Slime bodies in sieve tube member; two companion cells. (d) Slime bodies, in sieve tube member, are dispersing and nucleus is degenerating. (e) Mature enucleate sieve tube member; callose includes connecting strands. The diagrams show single connecting strands in the form of plasmodesmata. (Photograph courtesy of Dr. K. Esau, University of California, Santa Barbara; cf. Esau, 1960.)

Although one cannot say how translocation of solutes occurs, one can say something about what it involves. The organic solutes can move very rapidly under the driving force of "need" for them at the "sink"—i.e., where they are being consumed in synthesis or stored as solutes. Bidirectional movement of different solutes is possible in the same tissue, if not in the same element, and the activities of living cells are implicated in the activated movement. Hence, one asks what are the characteristics of sieve tubes, or even of elongated parenchyma cells, that fit them for these specialized functions?

The diagrams of Figs. 6–27 and 6–28 tell of the grosser features of phloem structure and development; the photographs of Fig. 6–29 (especially E) show that the sieve plate does not provide wide open channels of communication between one element and the next. At the level of the electron microscope, the fine structure of sieve tubes and of the adjacent living cells may be seen (Fig. 6–29D and E). Whereas the adjacent cells are rich in fine structure and organ-

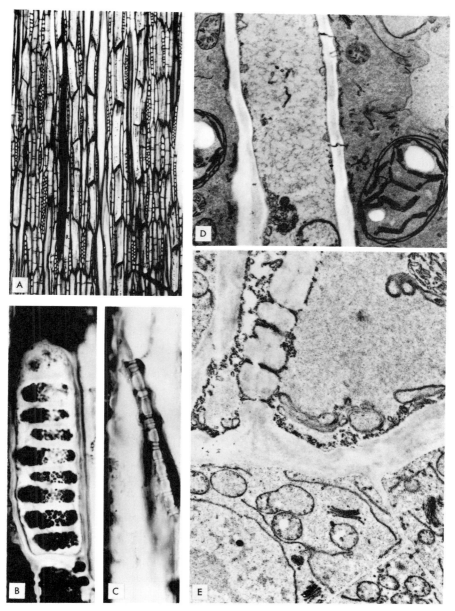

FIG. 6–29. The structure of phloem. A. Tangential section of *Campestris radicans* with sieve tubes (cf. Esau, 1960). B, C. Sieve plates of *Vitis vinifera* in surface view (radial section) and in tangential section, respectively (cf. Esau, 1960). D. Longitudinal section of the phloem from a small leaf of *Beta vulgaris* showing a sieve element in the center with typical clear contents, parenchyma cells to right and left. (From Esau and Cheadle, *Cytological Studies on Phloem, Univ. Calif. Publ. Botany* **36** (No. 3), 253–343, 1965.) E. Cross section of sieve elements and parenchyma cells from the stem of *Elodea*, showing a sieve plate and the fine structure of the sieve tube and adjacent cells. (All photographs courtesy of Dr. K. Esau, University of California, Santa Barbara; also see Esau, 1966b.)

elles, the living but enucleated sieve tube is not so richly endowed. These figures show that any ideas that implicate sieve tubes in rapid translocation must deal with the realities of their structure. The recently revived concept, originally due to de Vries, that protoplasmic streaming activates flow in phloem elements, faces the fact that unequivocal evidence of streaming in a sieve tube that has lost its nucleus has yet to be demonstrated in ways that are universally accepted (cf. Thaine and Preston, 1964). Despite criticisms (Esau *et al.*, 1963), the proponents of streaming in mature sieve tubes still retain their views (Thaine, Probine, and Dyer, 1967).*

The advocates of a downward mass flow of fluid in the sieve tubes of phloem are, in a sense, following out the general idea that Stephen Hales sought to establish. These workers now visualize an upward movement of water in xylem and a downward circulation of it in the sieve tubes of phloem. Only the thickness of cambium and the differentiating phloem and xylem mother cells may separate the contents of vessels and sieve tubes of a tree in which these contrasted movements are held to occur. In a monocotyledonous plant the elements in question may be adjacent and within the same vascular bundle. However, in the upward movement to buds both movements must be in the same direction to furnish the growing regions with *both* solutes and water. This should also apply to the importation of organic substances into succulent storage organs like fruits and tubers.

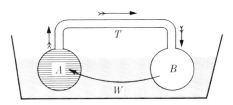

FIG. 6–30.   Diagram to demonstrate basic principle of osmotic flow.   *A*, osmotic membrane with high concentration; *B*, osmotic membrane with low concentration connected to *A* by open tube *T*. Feathered arrows indicate flow of solution from cell or part of cell with high concentration to that with low.   Plain arrow indicates direction of flow of water (*W*). (From Münch, 1930.)

All modern ideas of mass flow in phloem derive from the hypothesis of Münch (1930) based on an essentially simple model (cf. the account by Curtis, 1935, and Fig. 6–30). According to this view it should be difficult to export organic solutes except from regions of high solute concentrations to regions of maintained low concentrations—a view which was originally disputed by Curtis

---

* Thaine *et al.* (1967) have shown, by light microscopy, the presence of transcellular strands in sieve tubes and their association with C[14]-labelled substances believed to be in transit. Later Cronshaw and Esau (1967) describe, in detail, the fine structure of differentiating sieve elements. They show that the mature elements are traversed by linear aggregates of protein fibrils derived from a dense protein body; dense aggregates of these fibrils pass from cell to cell through the pores in sieve plates and may well be the strands seen by Thaine. Even these detailed studies leave the role in translocation of the complex structure of cytoplasm difficult to interpret. This is so because the role of streaming is still not clear, the stage of development at which sieve tubes function is in doubt, nor is it certain that they are the only cells responsible for the movement.

and Schofield (Curtis, *loc. cit.*). Moreover, the mass flow model oversimplifies the condition in the cells. The sources of osmotic pressure are solutions in vacuoles, within cytoplasmic membranes in parenchyma, and there are no open channels over long distances that would allow liquid to flow in the manner originally visualized by Münch. In fact the concept of mass flow places upon the cells of a leaf of a tree when in the light the need to maintain their turgor against an adverse "tension" of up to 10 atmospheres in the elements from which they obtain water directly, while they must simultaneously generate a positive hydrostatic pressure that can be outwardly communicated along unrestricted channels from their vacuoles to the liquid contents of the phloem cells in which the organic solutes are to be transported. It is not clear how these two requirements are rendered mutually compatible.

But it is one thing to postulate a mass flow—it is quite another to prove that it occurs in the intact elements of the phloem. The anatomical barriers to mass flow encountered in the minute strands that cross the primary wall of parenchyma at pit fields, and in sieve tubes at the pores in sieve plates, are obvious enough. Mass flow also requires some degree of turbulent mixing so that fluid shall move *en masse* rather than as individual solute and solvent molecules. Attempts to counter the concept of mass flow by claiming to have demonstrated bidirectional flow, often in the same tissue, but presumptively in the same phloem element, encounter the obvious difficulties inherent in unequivocal proof. But the mass flow hypothesis has hardly fared better in that, if it is correct, water and all solute molecules should be swept along without discrimination between them. Neither have attempts to label the water of phloem (i.e., in sieve tubes) by means of tritium and individual solutes by radioactivity led to unequivocal conclusions. Indeed from all we know about the energetics of solute movements in cells and of active secretions it would be hard to believe that the content of organic carbon, nitrogen, phosphorus, etc., that is actually present at any time in the phloem represents the proportions in which these elements are received and used by the growing cells at the "sink."

The elegant experiments on phloem exudation and the composition of the exudates at first sight seem to go far to establish the primary requirements for mass flow, namely, that (a) the contents of sieve tubes are under pressure and (b) that estimates may be made of the mass of organic matter that must be so transferred. These experiments were first carried out by inserting capillary tubes into the phloem to collect phloem sap and, later, by using the skill with which an insect can insert its stylus for this purpose into sieve tubes (Zimmermann, 1960, 1961, 1963). They are technically very impressive; they have demonstrated both the content and concentration of the sugars in the exudate and its continuing rate of flow. But the fact is that they have as assuredly opened the otherwise closed system of the phloem as the xylem is opened in the tapping of a maple tree. Neither the outflow of sugary sap from the wood of a maple tree, nor the outflow of sugar-containing exudate from the phloem of an ash, is proof that the solute moves in the tissue in question. In fact one may see in the flow of exudate from the phloem equally good evidence of either active secretion of water and solutes into these sieve tubes or a solvent movement that is caused solely by gradients of osmotic pressure in the contents of cells at "source" and "sink."

This discussion is, therefore, unsatisfactory because it leaves the question of the mechanism of solute movement in phloem unsolved. It does, however, relate the primary mechanism of translocation to the living system of the phloem and looks to the cells at the "source" and "sink" as the ultimate source of energy to bring about movements, in cells and tissues that must do work, that are essentially of a non-equilibrium kind, for both their rate and direction are dependent on an expenditure of energy.

What then may be concluded? The phloem as the seat of translocation is still an enigma. The driving force for solute translocation derives from the needs in growing regions where solutes are consumed in growth or actively accumulated in vacuoles. Metabolism along the path of transport must be invoked to furnish energy for a process in which the rates of movement may be stepped up until they are of the order of the rates that could obtain in a gaseous system! Like solute accumulation in plant vacuoles, translocation is a function that cannot be studied apart from the organization of cells and organs, and, like salt accumulation, the problem of translocation has advanced little beyond the recognition that, in transporting solutes at the rapid rates which obtain in living plants, the cells in the system must do work; but the details of the working machine which is inherent in the organization and metabolism of the functional cells, are still obscure. The problem becomes impressive, however, when it is calculated that some 4 to 4.5 tons of organic material are moved yearly into the fruit borne on an acre of apple trees (Swanson, 1959), and that all this is moved within the phloem. A similarly impressive calculation could be made for the movement of carbohydrate along the stolons of potato tubers. The driving force is furnished by the avid use of organic matter in the growing, or storage cells, at the "sink," and its consequential release at the "source." It is this distribution of growth in the plant body, controlled by the morphogenetic stimuli (Chapter 7), that creates the demands that are satisfied by translocation. And the fact remains that whether in sieve tubes along the route, or in elongated parenchyma cells at its limits, the solutes are moved at baffling rates, for which there is neither a satisfying physical explanation nor an obvious basis in the organization of the phloem cells where the movement occurs. The correlation of the process with growth and development is, however, beyond question.

Water and Water Movement:
Correlations with Growth and Organization

Problems posed.   The cohesion theory is well known, for it purports to explain the forces that lift water to the top of a tall tree solely in terms of the forces of evaporation from the leaf and of the properties of water. In consider-

FIG. 6–31. The lifting power of growth. A basidiomycete which has raised an asphalt surface. (Photo supplied by Dr. A. D. Krikorian, Cornell University.)

ing alternatives, or supplements, to the cohesion theory as it is usually presented, forces of evaporation are still regarded as of great importance. However, it seems futile to interpret water movement in a tree without recognizing that a tree grows, and without also recognizing that the water which reached the top of a tall tree in the first place did not merely move there—it surely grew there!

In each annual increment of growth a new cone of active, living cells is laid down by the cambium outside the older tissue within, and this constitutes a layer of active growing cells which can remove water and solutes laterally, can accumulate them there, and can readily pass them into the growing tissue of the current year's growth. Thus the essential problem is not to lift water 300 feet into the air, as it were in "one fell swoop," but in each season of growth to take water and solutes from the old wood within to the new growth above, and also to maintain the system in which the water and salts, if removed, may be replenished. In this sense, the problem of water movement is also closely related to growth and development, and to the activities of cells behind the shoot apex. A highly provocative article by Priestley (1935) promulgated this point of view.

Since so much of the substance of living cells and living organisms consists of water, the water economy in the plant body must loom large in the interpretation of growth and development. In this sense water is a nutrient (cf. Chapter 2). Whether it is absorbed actively, or passively, the intake of water is a prominent part of the growth of cells by expansion. The pressures that are exerted during growth (cf. Fig. 6–31) are traceable to the volume increase that occurs when water is initially imbibed, as in seeds, or is drawn osmotically into a more concentrated internal fluid across a membrane, as in vacuolated cells.

FIG. 6–32. Volume changes of imbibition. Dry mustard seeds were sealed with water into a medicine bottle; after the seeds had swollen, the pressures exerted were enough to break the bottle. (Photographs from a film by F. C. Steward, *Plant Growth and Development*, A. I. B. S., McGraw-Hill Book Co. Biology Series, Film No. 12.)

Stephen Hales notes the "great force with which vegetables imbibe moisture," and describes in his Experiment XXXII (p. 102) of "Vegetable Staticks" his experiments to demonstrate this with peas.

I filled near full with Pease and water, the iron pot and laid on the peas a leaden cover, . . . I then laid 184 pounds weight on them, which (as the peas dilated by imbibing the water) they lifted up. The dilatation of the peas is always equal to the quantity of water they imbibe . . .

Being desirous to try whether they would raise a much greater weight by means of a lever with weights at the end of it, I compressed several fresh parcels of peas in the same pot with a force equal to 1600, 800, and 400 pounds in which experiments, though the peas dilated, yet they did not raise the lever, because what they increased by the great incumbent weight, pressed into the interstices of the peas, which they adequately filled up, being, thereby formed into pretty regular dodecahedrons.

This is in short a very early (1726) example of the experiment which demonstrates the form of regular solids which by mutual compression fill space completely (cf. Chapter 3), and of the experiment to demonstrate the pressure of swelling seeds by which mustard seed, sealed with water into a bottle, will break a stout medicine bottle (Fig. 6–32).

Conventional physical and equilibrium concepts go far toward satisfying explanations of the relations between *established* cells, tissues, and organs, and their environment with respect to water. For this reason little has been made of the equally obvious need to recognize and explain the involvement of water while the system is being developed and, conversely, of the impact of growth and development upon the absorption, movement, and retention of water.

Water relations of cells and tissues: the classical background. The role of osmosis and osmotic pressure, and of the back pressure of elastic cell walls in the interpretation of cells at equilibrium with their environment, needs no emphasis here. This is conventionally interpreted by the classical osmotic theory of solutions (which in its development owed so much to work on plant cells) applied as in the concept of suction pressure (or diffusion pressure deficit), to the physical conditions that plant cells present; this is often summarized by Höfler's familiar diagram. This being so, all movements of water would be passive. Water should move into cells that have a positive net suction pressure (or diffusion pressure deficit) measurable in atmospheres (i.e., if they absorb water from pure water, in doing so they exert an initial pressure measured by their suction pressure). Alternatively, water should move from one region to another inasmuch as a given tissue system, or organ, is composed of cells that have a greater suction pressure than another. While these concepts may go far to explain what occurs after cells, tissues, and organs are mature and established, problems arise when one asks how did the system arise *de novo?*

Active water movements? Interpretations of the water relations of cells that merely regard them as responding passively in their environment imply that all movement of water is along a positive gradient of vapor pressure. This presents difficulties, either of rate or direction, if there is no physical evidence that the required vapor pressure gradients actually exist. Continuing positive secretion of liquid water to a saturated atmosphere, familiar in many examples of guttation or exudation, implies an active machinery to maintain the uptake. Contractile vacuoles (admittedly rare in plants) which take in and eject water exhibit a mechanism of this kind. In his early experiments on transpiration and evaporation Darwin (1916) was led to postulate what he termed transpiration (i.e., loss of water as vapor) to a saturated atmosphere, and he correlated this with such factors as light and oxygen that might regulate the vital activities of the cells in question. Whether or not these early and simple experiments satisfy more fastidious modern standards, it is clear that simple osmotic interpretations do not suffice to explain all problems of water-holding capacity and retention. The undoubted differences between young and senescent leaves when they are exposed to moisture stress presents problems on any simple osmotic view. It is an evident fact that ultimately the retention of water against evaporation is as much a feature of the cytoplasm, i.e., of the membrane system, as it is of the osmotic value of the cell contents: the simple direct consequences of anaesthesia or even killing the cells testifies to this. The absorption and secretion of water by submerged aquatics, as in the case of *Ranunculus fluitans* as studied by Wilson (1947) seems again to require active machinery of a non-equilibrium kind. Studies of localized uptake and secretion of water along the axis of roots as made by potometer methods reveal gradients, even in isolated segments of roots. There is commonly a greater intake of water nearest the tip than at points more remote and, therefore, a metabolically driven circulation of water, with intake at one end of a root segment and loss at the other, may be maintained. This is after all only a special case of the backward secretion of water into the stele that results in the familiar phenomenon of root, or exudation, pressure but it nevertheless has a biological, as well as a physical basis. According to Cailleaux, who has successfully devised and applied a root hair potometer, a gradient in the intake of water to, and loss from, a single root hair can be demonstrated along the length of a single hair! And if all we have to work with in the explanation of water uptake by cells is to be represented by the simple osmotic view of it, then some growing systems present difficult problems. Elongated cells grow at their tips; their walls are then incredibly thin and their cellulose consists of a loose random weft of cellulose fibrils in a non-cellulosic matrix (cf. Fig. 3–14). Such a plastic wall, by contrast with the later-formed wall with its evident "ropes" of cellulose, is ill-equipped to exert an elastic back pressure. This being so, why does the osmotic intake of water along the older portions of a still growing elongated cell (say a fiber) fail to expel the cell contents at its own tip? In fact, the prevalent condition of the first-formed cellulose in angiosperm cells is hardly consistent with the ability of the cells to withstand swelling, if it is their own osmotic pressure that causes the initial driving force for cell enlargement. While the evidence has not been generally accepted, Mason and Phillis (1939) and Bennett-Clark and Bexon (1939) have questioned the time-honored concept that regards the large aqueous angiosperm vacuoles as inevitably the seat of high solute concentrations; it has in fact been claimed that in leaves, more local solute concentrations may occur in the cytoplasm, so that the vacuolar sap may be dilute. Were this the case, the dilute sap would need to be internally secreted.

Despite the fact that more attention has been paid to the water relations of guard cells and the mechanism of the opening and closing of stomata—which clearly involves the volume of the guard cells and the controlled entry and egress of water—than to the water relations of any other cells, no completely satisfying simple equilibrium explanation has been advanced and proved. And the fact that minute traces of such physiologically active substances as auxins so greatly modify the water balance of water ("auxin-induced" water intake*) cautions against too facile physical explanations of this aspect of the water economy of cells, on the one hand, or of the action of the auxins, on the other

---

* One of the earliest recorded observations of the effect of IAA on the fresh and dry weight of potato tuber discs was that of Reinders, 1938. Much later the effect of IAA on water content came to be known as "auxin-induced water uptake" (Hackett and Thimann, 1950; Hackett, 1952).

(Ch. 5). Both these problems involve a complicated system to be considered under conditions suitable for growth.

All this points to problems which the osmotic relations of cells present, problems which can only be resolved by a more intimate understanding of their organization and the involvement of their growth (what Blackman called "organizational resistance") in water uptake and retention than the simple osmotic view of cells entails.

Dramatic problems which require a closer understanding of the involvement of growth and organization of plants in the economy of water, are presented by the ascent of sap in trees and by the phenomena of root, or exudation, pressure.

Water relations of land plants: absorption and evaporation. Land plants, adapted to obtain their organic nutrition via photosynthesis from the air, expose a large absorbing surface to an atmosphere that is rarely saturated with water vapor. In order that carbon dioxide may enter cells it must first dissolve in water, for it must enter as a solute. Inevitably, therefore, the exposure of so much wet cell surface to an atmosphere that is not saturated leads to evaporation. Characteristically, aerial shoots restrict that water loss by the protective layer of varnish-like cuticle, or by the presence of a cork periderm in older regions in which, by secondary growth, the epidermis and cuticle have disappeared. But leaves must absorb gas (CO_2) and cannot, therefore, be completely protected against loss of gas (water vapor) by evaporation. The devices by which stomatal pores, often responsive to light so that they show diurnal rhythms of opening (by day) and closure (by night), provide for the intake of carbon dioxide during a light period (when it may be fixed) and also protect against losses of water during a dark period (when carbon dioxide cannot be used) are familiar. Also familiar is the diffusive efficiency (carrying power for gases by diffusion) of the system of small pores that the stomatal apertures in a leaf present. Without entering into the many different kinds of stomatal behavior, or touching upon the evident fact that physiologists are still not agreed upon the mechanism of stomatal opening and closing, nevertheless the fact of the diffusive efficiency of the stomata of a leaf, and the physical facts of the evaporating power of a leaf surface in air and by day, are obvious enough. Equally obvious are the extensive absorbing surface of a root system and, when the shoot is removed, the impressively demonstrable power of a root to exert hydrostatic pressures.

According to the classical concept of water relations, and of the ascent of sap, the problems of water movement in tall trees can be physically explained in terms of the evaporating power of their leaves, the absorbing power of their roots, and the physical property of cohesion in the water in their conducting strands. Thus, according to this theory—the cohesion theory of the ascent of sap—the organization of a tree is not involved except insofar as it provides for this interplay of the events of evaporation and absorption. In other words it is only important in the explanation that the tree should have grown because it must be there, but how it grew seems irrelevant under the cohesion theory, for this does not enter in any intimate way into this interpretation of the ascent of sap. It is because the interpretation of sap ascent in a tree seems to have gone so far (in the cohesion theory) toward a satisfying physical explanation that it is profitable to ask whether this is really as complete as it seems and whether sap ascent can be explained without an understanding of how a tree grows and of the extent to which its water economy is bound up with the way in which it develops.

Roots or exudation pressure. The discussion of water movement, or water relations, in a tree logically begins with root or exudation pressure, even as it began historically with Stephen Hales. Following upon his experiments which demonstrated the pressure of blood in the arteries of a horse, a dog, and a fallow deer, Hales actually compared these with the force of the rising sap as measured by a "mercurial gage." When such a gage was fixed "near the bottom of a Vine" the "mercury was raised by the force of the sap 38 inches, equal to 43 feet + 3 inches to ⅓ height of water." Hales noted that this force "is near five times greater than the force of the blood in the great crural artery of a horse; seven times greater than the force of the blood in the like artery of a dog; and eight times greater than the blood's force in the same artery of a fallow doe."

But Hales did more than this, for he showed that the phenomenon in question was a variable one—there were diurnal fluctuations and seasonal variations and, most significant of all, he recognized that the phenomenon was not confined to roots. To illustrate these points, as well as Hales' technique, the following reference to his experiment XXXVII and his Fig. 19 (here reproduced as Fig. 6–33) has merit.

Experiment XXXVII

April 4th, I fixed three mercurial gages [cf. Fig. 6–33] *A*, *B*, *C*, to a *Vine*, on a southeast aspect, which was 50 feet long, from the root to the end *ru*. The top of the wall was 11 + ½ feet high; from *i* to *k*, 8 feet; from *k* to *e*, 6 feet + ½; from *e* to *A*, 1 foot 10 inches; from *e* to *o*, 7 feet; from *o* to *B*, 5 + ½ feet; from *o* to *C*, 22 feet 9 inches; from *o* to *u*, 32 feet 9 inches.

The branches to which *A* and *C* were fixed were thriving shoots two years old, but the branch *oB* was much older.

When I first fixed them, the mercury was pushed by the force of the sap, in all the gages down the legs 4, 5, 13, so as to rise nine inches higher in the other legs.

The next morning at 7 a.m. the mercury in *A* was pushed 14 + ¼ inches high, in *B* 12 + ¼, in *C* 13 + ½.

The greatest height to which they pushed the sap severally was *A* 21 inches, *B* 26 inches, *C* 26 inches.

The mercury constantly subsided by the retreat of the sap about 9 or 10 in the morning, when the Sun grew hot; but in a very moist foggy morning the sap was later before it retreated, *viz.* till noon, or some time after the fog was gone.

FIG. 6–33. Experimental design from Hales to show pressure. "Expt. 37 April 4th I fixed 3 mercurial gages *A, B, C* to a vine which was 50 ft. long . . . The branches to which *A* and *C* were
fixed were thriving shoots 2 years old and that to which *B* was fixed was much older. When I first
fixed them the mercury was pushed by the force of the sap in all the gages down the legs 4, 5, and
13 so as to rise 9 inches higher in the other legs." Hales noted that the mercury rose still higher
next morning and reached a maximum height of 21, 26, and 26 inches respectively in *A, B,* and
C. He also noted diurnal fluctuations in this pressure. (From Stephen Hales, 1738, *Statical
Essays:* Vol I, *Vegetable Staticks,* 3rd Edition; cf. Fig. 19, p. 115.)

About 4 or 5 o'clock in the afternoon, when the Sun went off the Vine, the sap began to push
afresh into the gages, so as to make the mercury rise in the open legs; but it always rose fastest
from the sun-rise till 9 or 10 in the morning.

The sap in *B* (the oldest stem) play'd the most freely to and fro, and was therefore soonest
affected with the changes from hot to cool, or from wet to dry, and *vice versa.*

And *April* 10, toward the end of the bleeding season, *B* began first to suck up the mercury
from 6 to 5, so as to be 4 inches higher in that leg than the other. But *April* 24, after a night's
rain, *B* pushed the mercury 4 inches up the other leg; *A* did not begin to suck till *April* 29, *viz.*
9 days after *B; C* did not begin to suck till *May* 3, *viz.* 13 days after *B,* and 4 days after *A. May* 5
at 7 *a.m. A* pushed 1 inch, *C* 1 + ½, but towards noon they all three sucked.

I have frequently observed the same difference in other Vines, where the like gages have been
fixed at the same time, to old and young branches of the same Vine, *viz.* the oldest began first
to suck.

In this Experiment we see the great force of the sap, at 44 feet 3 inches distance from the
root, equal to the force of a column of water 30 feet 11 inches + ¾ high.

From this Experiment we see too, that this force is not from the root only, but must also
proceed from some power, in the stem and branches: For the branch *B* was much sooner influenced
by changes from warm to cool, or dry to wet, and *vice versa,* than the other two branches *A* or
C; and *B* was in an imbibing state, 9 days before *A,* which was all that time in a state of pushing
sap; and *C* pushed 13 days after *B* had ceased pushing, and was in an imbibing state.

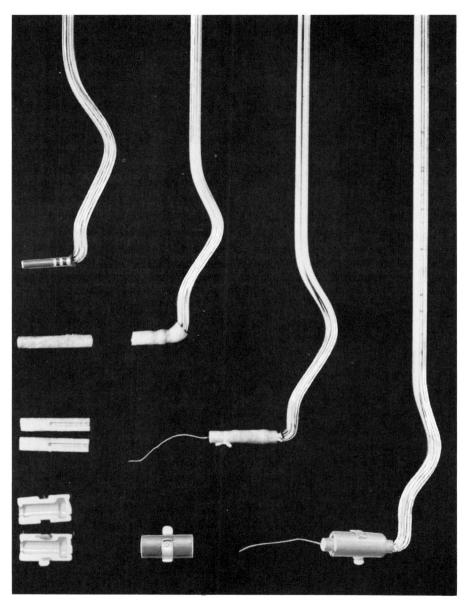

FIG. 6–34. Assembly, consisting of glass manometer, rubber connecting tube, and metal clamp, by which a single tomato root can be attached to a recording apparatus and its secretion pressure measured. (From White, *Am. J. Botany* **25**, 223–227, 1938.)

From Stephen Hales, in 1726, to modern times root or exudation pressure has figured in interpretations of the internal water economy of land plants. While it may suffice in some herbs to carry water to the tips of their shoots, its maximum values commonly were small in comparison with the pressures needed to carry water under pressure to the tops of tall trees (300 feet or more, i.e., the equivalent in a water column of about 10 atmospheres). But the argument that seems to discount root pressure as a potent factor in water movement is its seasonal character and the fact that when the needs for water movement are acute, i.e., after the buds have opened and a canopy of leaves exists, it is rare to find that water issues under pressure from a cut stem. On the contrary, the contents of the stem under these conditions may be under tension as shown by the familiar facts of injection; moreover, some plants, like gymnosperms, are notoriously poor in showing root pressure. Nevertheless, root or exudation pressure is demonstrably a vital activity, it is a property of a growing root, it requires aeration and oxygen supply, it exhibits diurnal rhythms, and it is inactivated by inhibitors of respiration. If root pressure is simply due to osmosis, then it raises a baffling problem, because it is so hard to demonstrate the osmotic concentrations of solutes in the contents of the stele that seem adequate to pull in the water from the surroundings and to yield the pressures that are observed; this is so even though the observed pressures (of the order of 1 atmosphere or less) seem small in relation to the pressures needed to take water to the top of a tall tree.

A dramatic experiment of P. R. White, described in 1938, restored interest in root pressure as an "unappreciated" force in the ascent of sap.

White had learned how to culture the growing tips of certain roots, like tomato roots, and he was led to mount the growing tips of the roots in a suitable device to which a manometer could be attached (Fig. 6–34). Thereafter, he maintained the root tips aseptically in a medium in which they could continue to grow indefinitely while he studied their ability to secrete water backward and to develop what is usually termed a root pressure. Much to the surprise of White and the scientific audience of the day, these tiny root tips, which had no conceivable need to move water 200 feet high, nevertheless continued to secrete water backward into vertical tubes which needed to be made longer and longer to accommodate the secreted sap. Eventually, to demonstrate the maximum pressures against which the water could be secreted, White introduced mercury into the manometer system or allowed the secretion to be opposed by pressure from a gas cylinder with a recording gage. By this means it was shown that the growing root tips of the tomato could secrete water backward against pressures of the order of 8 to 10 atmospheres; i.e., they developed pressures which would have sufficed to push the water as high as a tall tree. Moreover, the backward secretion was a diurnally rhythmic phenomenon (Fig. 6–35). Thus, White recognized root pressure as an "unappreciated force in the ascent of sap." The fact remains, however, that under many circumstances in which water must

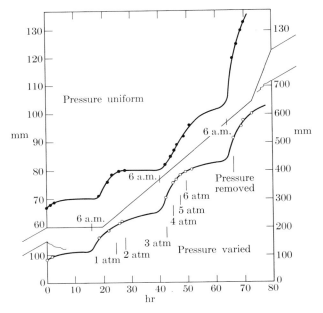

FIG. 6–35. Curves showing the rates of secretion from two similar tomato roots, recorded over a period of 3½ days, one against uniform (atmospheric) pressure, the other against imposed pressures up to 90 lb in². (From White, *Am. J. Botany* **25**, 223–227, 1938.)

move over these long distances the xylem vessels do not, in fact, contain liquid water under positive pressure. But this does not mean that the mechanism so ingeniously demonstrated by White could not operate in ways yet to be mentioned.

Evaporating power: transpiration "pull." Stephen Hales demonstrated not only root or exudation pressure; he also showed that plants could "suck in" or imbibe fluids, and, in so doing, he demonstrated what later came to be familiar as "transpirational pull." Hales attached shoots, even stems of young apple trees with wood two, three, or four years old, to water manometers in which the tips dipped under mercury. He noted that when the leaves were in the light of the sun their "perspiration" caused water to be imbibed and the mercury to rise in the mercury gage or manometer to heights which would have represented considerable lengths of water columns. Hales was familiar with the ebb and flow of this "pull" due to evaporation—he was also familiar with, though did not circumvent, the loss of air from the ends of the cut shoot which often terminated his experiment. Nevertheless Hales recognized the forces of imbibition, demonstrated in this way, by observations on branches of a young apple tree, on an apple shoot with both fruit and leaves, as well as on other shoots lacking alternatively the fruit and the leaves. In this way Hales convinced himself that the force which raised the mercury in one of his mercury gages, or manometers, resided in the leaves. Even "a sprig of Mint, treated in the same manner, raised the mercury 3 + ½ inch, equal to 4 feet 5 inches of water."

In modern terms the experiments to demonstrate the "pull of transpiration" are carried out as follows.

One cuts off the shoot, preferably under water, so that any cut elements of the xylem inject with water rather than with air bubbles. To the base of the stem is attached a manometer which is filled with water, and its tip dips under water or, better, under mercury. If one then turns a fan on the shoot, water is evaporated from the leaves and is then replaced by the water in the mano-meter which, in turn, pulls mercury up the tube. It is comparatively easy to show that the mercury can rise by these means to substantial heights. This ex-periment usually ceases, however, when air is pulled back out of the stem system into the manometer, terminating that phase of the experiment. Plants that have tracheids and few or no vessels are often better adapted to demonstrate the so-called "lifting power of transpiration" in this way than are the ring-porous, broad-leaved plants, with large vessels in their spring wood. In fact, conifers often work better than dicotyledonous shoots.

But how do the living cells of the leaf obtain the water that they need when there may be, in effect, a column of water 300 feet long tending to pull water, as it were, out of the leaf cells with a pull also equivalent to approximately 10 atmospheres? This situation may be explained as follows.

When the leaf has open stomata and is in bright sunlight, and possibly in wind, the wet cell walls evaporate water efficiently. The free interstitial water, i.e., water which is free to flow over the whole surface of the wall, evaporates first. Subsequently, the water films retreat into the minute pores of the cellulose wall, and, as they do so, their menisci become increasingly curved. It is a physi-cal fact that the vapor pressure over a curved water surface is very different from that over a plane surface. Therefore, the more the films retreat into the internal structure of the cell wall, the harder it is for this water to be evaporated. This condition was called *incipient drying* by the earlier plant physiologists. Meanwhile, however, the living cells of the leaf will have given up some water; as they do so they tend to shrink and to develop a positive suction pressure, or diffusion-pressure deficit. So long as the green cells of the leaf have a suction pressure, or diffusion-pressure deficit, which is greater than the back pressure due to the column of water from leaf to root, they can retain, or obtain, water from the tips of the xylem strands. H. H. Dixon, a pioneer investigator of the ascent of sap, illustrated this principle by what he called the analogy of the weight lifter.

Dixon diagrammatically placed (see Fig. 6–36) the weight lifter on a raised platform and visualized him as lifting a weight suspended from a long rope beneath the platform. As the weight lifter raises the weight, there is of course a thrust from his body to the platform on which he stands, and the physical work of lifting the weight is done by the muscles. If, however, a spiral spring balance on which the weight lifter stands is placed on the platform, then, when the weight is at rest on the ground, the tension in the springs of the balance merely reflects the weight lifter's own weight. But as he tenses his muscles and raises the weight gently off the ground, the coiled springs must take the additional strain.

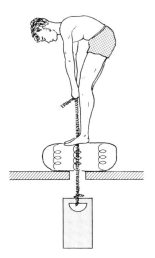

FIG. 6–36. The analogy of the weight lifter. The "pull" exerted by the youth represents the process of evaporation. The rope represents the unbroken water columns under tension. The compression of the springs, and the cushion, or balance, represent the suction pressure (DPD) of the parenchyma cells which, as it were, "take the strain." (After Dixon, 1930.)

By analogy, Dixon visualized the parenchyma cells of the leaf in a saturated atmosphere as merely being "tense enough" to take water from the xylem strands when there is no great pressure of evaporation. But when evaporation becomes greater, these cells "take the strain," and it is their suction pressure which enables them to obtain water from the columns in the xylem which hang backward, as it were, from the films, or menisci, by which they adhere to the parenchyma cell walls. Thus, the cells of a leaf, however high in the tree, can obtain water from the xylem provided that they develop, by evaporation, the equivalent of a diffusion-pressure deficit which is greater than a water column equal to the height of the tree. In fact the maximum height of trees is about the same whether the tree is a *Eucalyptus*, a *Sequoia*, a palm, or a pine. The probability is that this height reflects the maximum tension against which leaf cells can obtain water and their walls remain wetted and wettable, capable of being "tensed" by evaporation and desiccation and also, reversibly, capable of recovery. Thus the maximum tension to which the leaf cells may be subjected and still have access to free water should depend on a physical property of their cellulose walls, just as the conditions for the success of the Askenasy experiment demand that water shall completely wet the walls of its glass tubes and that air should not enter the capillary spaces of the surface from which the water is evaporated.

There are, however, two major problems: How does the water get to the top of a tall tree *in the first place?* And, secondly, having achieved this, how is it continuously moved to those heights as the demand arises?

First, the best purely physical theory to explain the ascent of sap in tall trees should be mentioned.

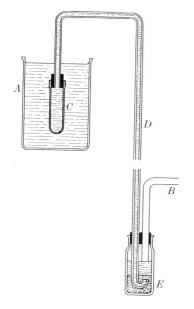

FIG. 6–37. A later version of the Askenasy experiment. The porous pot C is immersed in a beaker of boiling distilled water A. If the water is boiled, hot water will siphon through the apparatus and out B. The apparatus is then allowed to cool, the system being now free of air. Upon removing the beaker, evaporation proceeds and mercury E will rise in the glass tube D above a barometric height. (After Thut, 1928.)

The cohesion theory. This theory was elaborated by a botanist, H. H. Dixon, and a physicist named Joly. These men applied to the problem a previously somewhat unfamiliar property of water attributed to Boehm in 1893. Dixon and Joly also knew about what came to be called the Askenasy experiment after its author who discussed the rise of sap in 1896. [The Askenasy experiment was repeated by Thut in the 1930's, but essentially he modified an experiment done by Livingston and Lubin (1927) after Askenasy (1896)]. In this experiment a vertical manometer tube has attached to it an efficient evaporating surface in the form of a porous pot, or an atmometer cup. If one inverts a sealed tube containing water over water, or more conveniently one containing mercury over mercury, the liquid in the tube will be maintained to a barometric height, and above that the vacant space in the tube is occupied by a Torricellian vacuum. If, however, above the mercury surface one has a water connection with an evaporating surface (e.g., a porous pot) and if one takes special precautions that no air bubbles can leak back from the pot into the manometer (i.e., by first soaking the pot in alcohol, then replacing the alcohol with water), some interesting consequences may be observed. If efficient evaporation from the pot is promoted by turning a fan upon it, then the water will be evaporated and will pull the mercury up to a level near barometric height (Fig. 6–37).

If performed carelessly, the experiment will break down because air will come out of the water or the pot and, being freely expansible, will quickly produce the equivalent of the Torricellian vacuum above the mercury surface. The experiment may also break down if the tube is not clean, or if the water failed to wet either the tube or the interstices of the pot effectively. But, if these consequences do not arise, it may be shown that, by the evaporation of water from the pot, the mercury surface will rise even *above a barometric height*. In these circumstances what is the condition of the water in the tube and in the porous pot? Here the water is under great tension, and it is because water molecules adhere to each other so effectively that they can perform the seemingly impossible task of pulling the mercury, which is also under tension, to a level above a barometric height. The Askenasy experiment created the circumstances in which water would evaporate off from the pot and produce the tension in the manometer column, and then, by having water restored to the surface of the porous pot, the mercury would sink back again to the normal barometric height.

Dixon and Joly measured the tensions which unbroken water columns would sustain without breaking and showed, by various devices, that the available tensions were very great indeed. From time to time there have been changes in the magnitude of the tensions which could be reliably demonstrated but, be that as it may, they are very much larger than the pressure needed to retain the water at the top of a tall tree.

FIG. 6–38. Diagram of flask as used by Dixon and Joly to demonstrate cohesion of water. When cooling sets in, tension in the contracting water increases the curvature of the helix.

A device which Dixon and Joly used to demonstrate this "cohesion of water" may be described as follows. By skillful glass blowing, little flasks were made and shaped as shown in Fig. 6–38. The flasks were completely filled with water near boiling temperature, from which air was removed, and then the pointed tips were sealed off. When the water in the flasks was allowed to cool, its volume would shrink, but if it wetted the tube effectively and there was no air in the system to expand freely, the water pulled back and caused even the volume of the glass vessel to shrink. This produced a curvature in the glass vessel, which could only be simulated by very high pressures superimposed from outside. By means of this sort, Dixon and Joly showed that there was in unbroken water columns, capable as they are of withstanding tension without breaking because of the great cohesive forces that reside in water, a possible means of assisting water to reach the top of a tall tree.

Briefly, they visualized the leaf as an efficient evaporating surface. Water in the xylem vessels connects leaves with roots so that, as evaporation occurs from the leaf, tension develops in the contents of the xylem. Without breaking the column, this tension can reach a figure high enough, in Dixon's view, to pull water from the root system up through the xylem elements to the leaf surface. Before discussing this concept any further, it is interesting to mention another instructive example of the role of the cohesive properties of water.

The cohesion of water and its role in a fern annulus.   The shape of a fern sporangium is shown in Fig. 6–39(a), with the annulus as a sort of ring, or crest, of unequally thickened cells. As the sporangium shrinks in dry air the stomium breaks. Previously full of water, the dead cells of the annulus lose water and tend to pull the cell walls of the annulus inward. Since the outer tangential walls are thinner than the inner ones, the cells as they shrink adopt the shape shown in Fig. 6–39(b), and this causes the split sporangium to bend slowly backwards like the aim of a thrower about to fling a spear. The back-

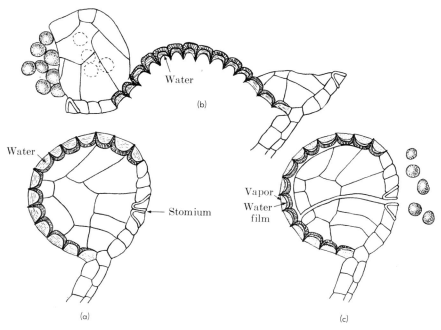

FIG. 6–39. Diagrammatic representation of spore discharge from a fern sporangium.

ward movement is slow and, of course, spores are attached to the broken parts of the sporangium. There comes, however, a point when this system becomes unstable, for further loss of water becomes difficult if the walls of the annulus are to be indefinitely caused to shrink. At this point (Fig. 6–39c), therefore, the liquid under great tension in the cells of the annulus is suddenly and almost explosively released *from contact with the wall* and almost instantly the residual water is converted into vapor. Since the water vapor is freely expansible, the walls of the annulus cells previously under tension are released like a spring. Thus the annulus, having been slowly bent backwards into the posture indicated in the diagram, is now forcibly and violently caused to move in the reverse direction, thereby flinging the spores to some considerable distance. If the annulus is put back into water almost immediately, before air has entered into the cells, this movement can be repeated time and time again. But once the annulus cells have become filled with air the mechanism cannot be repeated. This, then, shows an example in which the cohesive properties of water are harnessed to bring about a mechanism of spore dispersal. Other, but less conspicuous, examples occur in the coiled shape of elaters and in their subsequent violent spring-like movements which disperse the spores from certain capsules, as in mosses.

The cohesion theory in relation to the contents of the xylem. The crucial test of the cohesion theory of water movement rests upon the demonstration that, at the critical period, the content of the xylem in trees is really compatible with the supposedly unbroken water columns under great tension.

Dixon and Joly pointed here to the injection of the xylem of transpiring or wilted plants with dyestuffs. Later investigators have often used India ink. The evidence of rapid injection, both up and down, when India ink or dyes are introduced into the xylem of a rapidly transpiring plant, is very impressive indeed. But in point of fact the evidence is almost *too* good for the purpose because, although the water columns are capable of being under great tension, their volume should change hardly at all. Thus, on cutting a manometer (as in the Askenasy experiment) under a dye solution, even when the tension was actually great, very little dye would enter merely to restore the volume in response to the release of the tension. The evidence of injection, however, quickly shows that the entire volume of the xylem system can on occasions inject, and in fact dye will move very rapidly to the extreme tips of shoot and root.

This must mean one of two things: Either the xylem did not have in it any liquid at all, so that entering liquid could rapidly fill the whole space—i.e., the content of the xylem was really water vapor at low pressure—or else the entering liquid, after cutting, displaced liquid previously under tension which was then withdrawn very rapidly from the vascular system after the cutting to be absorbed somewhere else, i.e., by living cells released like the tensed spring in H. H. Dixon's weight lifter analogy (cf. Fig. 6–36b), if one suddenly severed the rope which held the weight.

However, is it physically feasible for the xylem vessels in a plant, with their permeable lignified walls, to contain a gas at pressures which may be almost as low as that in a vacuum, i.e., merely the saturated vapor pressure of water? At first, this does not seem feasible, but it is a physical possibility. So long as the walls of the xylem vessel are kept wet, they in effect constitute a tube of water, and the only possibility of allowing air to leak into the system will be through the pores of the closing membranes in the bordered pits. These pores are so small that even colloidal particles, like India ink, cannot pass. Water films across such minute pores can actually hold a pressure of one atmosphere without breaking into a bubble. One recalls here that the pressure in a soap bubble is greatest when its curvature is largest. The excess pressure in a bubble is related to the surface tension of water by the formula $P = 4T/R$, where T is the surface tension of water, and R is the radius of the bubble. One can, therefore, calculate that pores as small as those that exist in the closing pit membranes of xylem elements would require a pressure greater than that of one atmosphere if one were, as it were, to blow a bubble through so small a hole. It is, therefore, entirely possible for all the water inside the xylem to be evaporated by an actively transpiring surface; then the content of the xylem would not be liquid water at all but *gas at low pressure*. Haines (1935) peeled off the bark and examined the large vessels of a ring-porous tree (ash or oak) in the early summer. By a series of simple tests he showed that xylem vessels in a tree may conform to any of the following conditions. They may contain liquid water under pressure, so that when punctured by a hypodermic needle liquid will actually flow out. They may also contain liquid water under tension so that, when cut beneath the surface of a dye, liquid will enter until the tension is relieved. Yet again, they may contain gas at low pressure, so that if dye or India ink is introduced, without air contamination, the whole system will fill instantaneously. And yet again the vessel may contain air at atmospheric pressure, in which case it is extremely difficult to reintroduce liquid into such a xylem vessel.

Evidence and views of this sort, more mathematically treated by Preston (1952), have therefore tended to call in question the unmodified cohesion theory as the sole explanation of the ascent of sap in tall trees. But the main question that the cohesion theory alone does not explain is the very important one, how did the water get up there in the first place? At best the cohesion theory seems to explain how the system, once established, can be maintained intact under fluctuating stresses of evaporation by day and recovery at night.

Ascent of sap and how a tree grows.   One normally tends to think that the water which rises from soil to the shoot tip in a *Sequoia* or a pine tree, makes the journey, as it were, in one operation. However, it did not happen this way, because the *Sequoia* tree may be as much as 3000 to 4000 years old. Thus, in the first instance the water did not ascend 300 feet; it moved there as the tree grew. The main limitation in the cohesion theory is that it says nothing about the bearing of this growth on the mechanism of water movement.

FIG. 6–40. Willow shoot shown injected with India ink. A clean cut was made under ink through the bark shoot into the cambium region when it was active. (c) The bark was then stripped to reveal the white surface of the cambium and the injected xylem elements which radiate downwards from the bud to form part of the current year's xylem. (a, b) Since the ink cannot pass a cross wall, this shows how far below the bud a given xylem strand had formed when the injection was done.

In the first season of its seedling growth, the first year's xylem is established, and as shown by the experiment of P. R. White there is no problem in explaining how the water may be secreted backward from the root tip to keep full the first-formed xylem system. However, over the first period of rest and dormancy the cambium remains quiescent. In the next spring, spreading backwards from the buds there is a signal that "tells" the cambium to begin to grow again. In fact, the xylem to be formed in that second year is the xylem that will supply the second year's crop of leaves, even though they formed in the buds of the preceding year. The cambium, however, is an active layer of living cells which divide, vacuolate, differentiate, and in effect grow. This sheath of living cells draws off water laterally from inside the stele in the older xylem, in which it had been stored up to this point.

In the layer of developing cells just within the cambium, one can actually see the new xylem elements of the current year's growth when they begin to form. These appear first as long chains of living cells. Then, as they lose their permeability properties, their contents are free to move upward and outward to cells that can absorb this liquid and its solutes. In fact, in the early part of the season this growth and development in the vascular strand may actually produce a transient positive pressure, so that liquid may exude from the punctured surface. But, when the leaves have become sufficiently expanded, they make a greater drain on the conducting power of the new vascular strand than it can easily supply. Tension then develops in these xylem elements of the current year's growth. At this point, if injected with India ink, the new xylem elements may fill completely (Fig. 6–40). This is easily demonstrated if one peels off the bark of a willow shoot, for the new xylem elements which pass downward beneath the axillary buds will very beautifully inject with India ink. This shows that they contained, not liquid under pressure, probably not even liquid under tension, but actually gas at such low pressure that their entire volume can be replaced with the entering fluid.

Therefore, one can visualize that water rises in the first instance to the top of a tall tree in a series of annual steps. Thus, the problem is not to raise water 300 feet high in the first instance, but in each annual period of growth to take water from last year's cone of vascular tissue, via the new growing tissue of the active cambium and xylem, into the current year's growth (cf. Fig. 6–41). The "pull" for this step comes initially *from the growing cells at the tip of the shoot and in the leaves.* With the onset of dormancy, this preformed xylem can fill up with liquid and, as long as the xylem elements remain wet, as long as they fail to be injected completely with air, this process of emptying and filling and refilling can go on repeatedly. Moreover, there may be diurnal changes in the contents of the xylem in the summertime; in fact, an instrument known as a dendrograph may be used to record both daily and seasonal changes in the diameter of a tree which in part reflect these events. Accurate dendrographic measurements, of the kind originally made by MacDougal (1924) now show that the wood of trees shrinks when water loss begins after sunrise and it does so

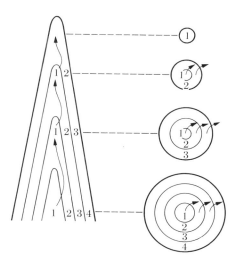

FIG. 6–41.   Diagram to show successive lateral movement in a four-year-old stem from the wood of one year into the newly differentiating vascular tissue of the next.

first at higher points on the axis (cf. Zimmerman, 1963). At night the diameter of the trunk recovers as water is again stored therein. The wood of a tree is also a seasonal storehouse for water.

There is no doubt that there is a place in all this for the cohesive properties of water, but it is an oversimplification to regard, as Dixon and Joly did, that the whole system of a growing tree merely behaves like the Askenasy experiment shown in the diagram (cf. Fig. 6–37). The actual processes of growth have much more to do with the initial movement of water to the top of a tall tree than the cohesion theory alone implies.

This extensive excursion into the discussion of water and its absorptive movement in a tree has been made to show that, however good the physical evidence, the physiological function to which it relates must be interpreted in the context of a living, growing plant. In this sense the water that reaches the top of a tall tree in the first place did not merely move there—it grew there along with the tree. The essential problem is not to lift water 300 feet high in the air, as it were in "one fell swoop" but, in each season of growth, to take the water and solutes from the old wood within to the new growth above and also to maintain the system in which both water and salts, if removed, may be replenished. In this sense even the problems of water absorption and movement are closely related to growth and development, and to the activities of cells in the growing regions of shoot and root. Thus at crucial stages the control of the internal economy of water tends to follow the lead of growth.

In the relationship between transpiration and the ascent of sap the stomata present a special problem to the extent that the role of the guard cells either may be interpretable on simple equilibrium grounds or it may involve more active mechanisms.

The mechanism of guard cells.   The posture of guard cells during the opening and closure of stomata and their change of shape with volume is a classic case, dating back to Schwendener (1881), of a motor cell system in which the power of movement is brought about by the water relations of the cells and, in this case, it is predominantly related to light.

Since guard cells are relatively isolated cells of the epidermis and also have chloroplasts, theories of stomatal movement and regulation have moved progressively through the following sequence. The osmotic pressure that causes swelling of the guard cells was first sought in their net photosynthesis in the light. This proved to be too slow and it became clear that the photosynthesis acted more as a trigger than as a *de novo* source of osmotically active carbohydrate. Lloyd (1908) then pointed to the unusual starch $\underset{dark}{\overset{light}{\rightleftarrows}}$ sugar equilibria of guard cells but even this, triggered by the light-dark pH changes in the guard cells, activating the then known hydrolyzing enzyme (diastase), was deemed too slow a mechanism. Scarth (1929) then turned attention to the possibility that colloidal imbibition, responsive to the pH changes caused by alternating exposure to light and dark, might cause the required response. Later knowledge that reversible starch ⇄ sugar changes are brought about by phosphorylase and that this enzyme system is pH-sensitive led to osmotic theories based on this principle. However, even these ideas must face the dilemma that the conversion of starch and phosphate via phosphorylase does not achieve the needed net increase of osmotic pressure unless it goes further than the formation of glucose-1-phosphate to glucose and free phosphate. However, when this is done the system is not reversible, for energy must be furnished and a different enzyme sysitem (hexokinase + ATP) invoked to remake starch. New views, stated by Zelitch (1963, 1965), implicate the formation of carbohydrate (stimulated by the low carbon dioxide concentrations and high oxygen which could occur in stomata at high light) by a pathway from such starting points as pentose cycle intermediates via the following steps: Phosphoglycolic → glycolic → glyoxylic → glycine serine → glyceric acid → carbohydrate. Inhibitors of the oxidation of glycolic acid, as shown, affect stomatal movement (closure) in a manner consistent with this hypothesis. Nevertheless, the problems of the rate of movement remain.

At this point (circa 1958; cf. Heath, 1959) it was natural to suggest (cf. Steward, 1964) that the stomatal movement might involve more active mechanisms, and that the processes of opening and closing might be very different. Closure can be conceived as a process that might require energy of metabolic origin, as in the compression of a coiled spring, and opening, triggered by light, as a more spontaneous process of relaxation.

In very recent times photosynthetic phosphorylation could be invoked to furnish energy (ATP) that might be harnessed to stomatal regulation. However, if one were to postulate a contractile mechanism in stomata, as for example a system of long fibrous molecules (such as protein chains or membranes in cytoplasm), and if one were to "anchor" these to cell walls, the following plan could work.

Long molecules can perform work as they coil and uncoil (Kuhn *et al.*, 1950). A working model has been built on this principle which does mechanical work (Steinberg, Oplatka and Katchalsky, 1966, also see Lear, 1966). Long fibers of a sort of pseudo-collagen maintain an open, straight, relaxed condition when they are charged. When the adjacent charges are removed, or neutralized, the fibers contract. In the model described in *Nature* (Steinberg *et al.*, 1966) and in the *Saturday Review* (Lear, 1966), the fibers are exposed to a salt bath in which they become charged and relax, and are then physically moved over pulleys into a water bath, in which they become uncharged as their salts are removed when the fibers contract. The continuously working machine then moves salt in one direction and water in another and its continued operation depends on the maintained chemical potential of the two states (i.e., contact with stronger and weaker solutions alternately) to which the moving fibers are thus exposed.

In the stomatal system, however, the differences in chemical potential to which the contractile system is exposed can be attributed to light (more alkaline reactions in the light, proteins more ionized with negative charges, and exposed to possible phosphorylation with ATP from photosynthetic phosphorylation). Under these circumstances the activated volume changes could occur as shown below, and the starch $\rightleftharpoons$ sugar and osmotic changes which follow may then stabilize the stomatal posture so created.

Light	*Dark*
Stomatal pore open; guard cells large	Stomatal pore closed; guard cells small
Contractile system relaxed	Contractile system tensed
Fibers or proteins negatively charged on alkaline side of IEP	Fibers or proteins discharged, more nearly isoelectric
Volume increases spontaneously; water taken in	Volume contracts; water pumped out
Starch$\rightarrow$sugar; osmotic pressure builds up	Sugar$\rightarrow$starch; osmotic pressure falls

Thus, the stomatal mechanism could be conceived as a much more active piece of metabolic machinery than hitherto, not, it is true, dependent on harnessing the growth of cells, but using the metabolic responses of cells to light and dark to bring about responses that are not due *in the first instance* to the passive osmotic flow of water. However, once the more active movement of guard cells has occurred, motivated by light or darkness, the slower changes in osmotic value of the guard cells may follow to stabilize their posture *after* the mechanically activated movement of water and the consequential volume changes have occurred. It remains, however, to confirm that either the whole cytoplasm of guard cells behaves as a contractile system or else that contractile cytoplasmic fibers do exist!

Epilogue

It should now be clear that all reactions, processes, and functions of plants accomplish more by their interactions and interdependencies than each achieves separately; the whole is indeed greater than the sum of its parts. Therefore, many of the problems of the physiology of flowering plants can hardly be separated from their organization and the way they grow and develop. The physiological functions are, in fact, seen more clearly when they can be interpreted in terms of organization at all levels: at the subcellular and cellular level, at the level of organs and of the whole organism, and in terms of the interrelationships and correlations which regulate the growth and development of plants. The task of the plant physiologist is, therefore, incomplete until, having prescribed each physiological function, he can also visualize how it interrelates with others and how all are correlated and controlled in the smooth flow of events that we recognize as growth and development. Seen in this way, plant physiology must persist as an essentially biological discipline until the life and growth of plants is fully understood.

Summary

Traditionally, plant physiologists have attempted to apply the knowledge of chemistry obtained *in vitro* and the concepts of equilibrium to the interpretation of cells and plants. They have often treated each physiological process and function separately, almost as if each operated independently in a system which is in a steady state—or even at rest. For this simplified approach the favored systems for investigation have often been mature, quiescent cells or organs. During their growth, however, cells do work; they depart from equilibrium, and various physiological functions work together in a controlled and integrated way. The contrasts between quiescent and actively growing cells, therefore, need to be recognized in both their morphological and metabolic manifestations. In the impact of growth on water and salt intake, and the coupling of energy to useful purposes, one must take account of respiration, nitrogen metabolism, and protein synthesis, and the interactions between these several processes. In the final analysis, however, it is difficult to maintain only that the factors which regulate respiration will have a determining effect upon growth; it is equally true that the factors that regulate growth also affect respiration because growth draws off the compounds, produced in respiration, which donate energy in chemically usable form. Metabolism is, therefore, to be seen not only as a consequence of biochemical reactions and their respective enzymes but in the context of a system that has organization and congruity.

In the interpretations of centers of synthesis and growth, additional relationships are to be considered for metabolism, and the movements of water and solutes are correlated with, and subject to, the stimuli by which growth and development are regulated within the plant body as a whole. These points are considered with respect to certain examples drawn from investigations on angiosperms. In discussing these examples, which included a herbaceous monocotyledon, and a dicotyledon, as well as a tree, one has to take full cognizance of the way the organism in question grows and develops, for this determines where the centers of both growth and physiological activity lie, and the orderly way in which they are called into play.

Lastly, the water economy of plants is considered, for in this area plant physiology has contributed heavily to the classical understanding of the physics and physical chemistry that are involved, and it is in this area that satisfying physicochemical explanations are most commonly accepted. Nevertheless, there is need, where growing plants are concerned, to invoke considerations that require a knowledge of how plants grow and develop and the ability to recognize sites where metabolic work is done. This is illustrated with reference to sap ascent in tall trees and the postulated mechanisms of stomatal movement.

In the understanding of the interrelations between physiological functions with each other and the way they so often follow the lead of growth, plant physiology remains an essentially biological science, though it must draw to the full on physics and chemistry in the understanding of the means by which highly organized cells and plants both function and grow.

chapter seven

MORPHOGENETIC STIMULI

In the 19th century, plant physiologists were much concerned with mechanisms of stimulus and response. They regarded the response to stimuli as a fundamental characteristic of protoplasm. The property which conveyed this ability was termed "irritability." Several classes of stimuli can be distinguished. First, there are those stimuli responsible for tactic movements, i.e., the stimuli which cause movement of the whole organism or of independent cells. The free-swimming movements of *Chlamydomonas,* notable for its sensitivity to light, and of motile gametes in non-flowering plants are of this kind. Secondly, there are the stimuli responsible for tropisms, in which the organism responds by a change in the direction of growth. Also, there are a variety of morphogenetic stimuli which determine the nature, or the kind, of growth. Neither tactic stimuli nor tropisms will be discussed here. However, it was the study of tropisms that was largely responsible for the hormone concept in plants (cf. Fig. 4–2) when it was realized that there was a region of perception, a motor region in which the response occurred, and that the "action at a distance" was brought about by the transfer of substance from the region of perception to the region of response. This area of plant physiology, concerned largely with the phototropic response of such structures as the coleoptile and the geotropic response of primary roots, yielded the body of information now familiarly associated with the auxins. A variety of stimuli cause other responses, morphogenetic responses, in which the effect of the stimulus is upon the nature, or the kind of growth which results.

This large problem may be subdivided as follows:

1. Morphogenetic effects in early embryogeny.

2. Morphogenetic effects on vegetative growth, notably the effects of light.

3. Morphogenetic effects involved in the phenomena of rest, dormancy, and perennation, i.e., responses to seasonal cycles.

4. Morphogenetic effects of plant development in response to diurnal variations, notably the effects of photoperiodicity and thermoperiodicity.

Morphogenetic Effects in Early Embryogeny

The development of an embryo from an egg, which occurs in angiosperms in the specialized environment of the ovule, comprises a range of morphological changes in time which are unequaled in later development. Plant embryologists have been largely preoccupied with tracing these changes in form (Wardlaw, 1955; Maheshwari, 1950; Johansen, 1950), although in animal embryology there has been more attempt to describe early embryogeny in chemical terms (Needham, 1931). It is a problem to know how far the development of the egg is the inevitable unfolding of its innate characteristics and how far this development is fostered by the specialized nutrition which it receives in the environ-

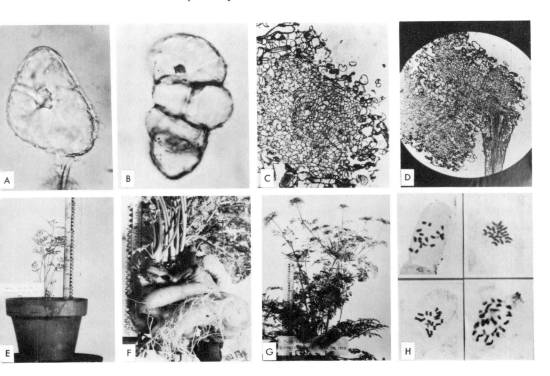

FIG. 7–1. From carrot cell to carrot plant. Sequence in the development from (A) freely suspended carrot phloem cells to (B) cell aggregates, (C) colonies with organized growth centers or nodules, (D) roots. E. Plantlets grown first in tubes on agar, later in pots in vermiculite. F. Plants with massive storage roots with normal carotene content. G. Plants with flowers in the second cycle of biennial growth. H. The 18 chromosomes of a normally diploid carrot root (upper left) which remain diploid in proliferating cells around a preformed explant (upper right) and, despite the chromosomal aberrations (lower right)—polyploidy—in the free cells, are again diploid in the reorganized root (lower left) developed via a cell colony from the free cells. (From Steward *et al.*, in *Synthesis of Molecular and Cellular Structure*, edited by D. Rudnick, copyright © 1961, The Ronald Press, New York.)

ment of the ovule. Until fertilized eggs of angiosperms can be isolated and cultured, these questions may remain largely unanswered. Nevertheless, the *nurture* as well as the *nature* of the embryo may play a significant part in this morphogenetic process of embryonic development. This is suggested by the growth-promoting stimuli located in the regions which nourish young embryos, as summarized in Fig. 4–9.

Some embryos, freed from the constraint of an archegonium, grow in a random proliferating fashion (Wetmore and Morel, 1949). Immature embryos of *Datura* (Van Overbeek, Conklin, and Blakeslee, 1942), cultured in a medium which permitted them to grow, could form either plantlets or tumors, according to the balance of the growth factors that the medium contained. As mentioned earlier, the fluids which nourish immature embroys in the coconut (*Cocos*), in horse chestnut (*Aesculus*), and in maize (*Zea*) are sources of powerful stimuli which promote division in otherwise resting and mature cells. When the extracts act upon already differentiated tissue explants the first cell divisions occur at random over their whole surface and the resulting growth is comparatively unorganized. However, if the same fluids nourish freely suspended cells (cells which may be stated to have undergone some dedifferentiation—whatever that may mean), the results may be quite different.

Cells derived from mature carrot root phloem grow and divide when freely suspended in a medium which contains coconut milk, or other fluids from comparable sources or solutions which contain similar constituents, and they do this in various ways that are different from those that obtain in the intact plant body (cf. Chapter 5 and Fig. 5–17). The suggestion is that the free cells are not subject to external restraints and, when supplied in non-limiting amounts with the factors that promote growth, they can respond to intrinsic rather than extrinsic factors. However, the first loose, randomly growing cultures, raised from free cells, may quickly organize, producing first roots, then shoots, to form complete plantlets (Steward, Mapes, and Smith, 1958; Steward, Mapes, and Mears, 1958), and indeed such plantlets produced massive storage organs and also flowers (Steward *et al.*, 1961). In so doing there is often organized within the proliferated cell culture a multicellular "nodule" or "growing center" which, in its behavior, replaces the zygote or pro-embryo, since it gives rise to a minute embryo-like structure which develops entirely from vegetative cells without the stimulus of fertilization. These events are shown in Fig. 7–1. When the parallelism between this developmental sequence and normal embryogeny was appreciated, it was also seen that stages in the growth from free cells strikingly resemble the normal growth of the carrot embryo (Fig. 7–2). From this standpoint embryogeny represents the development from a cell (the fertilized egg) which is preeminently able to grow; and the course of the development may be, in part, a response to the specialized nutrition furnished in, and the external restraint imposed by, the ovule. In the case of the carrot plant the physical environment of the ovule is more dispensable than the nutrition it provides

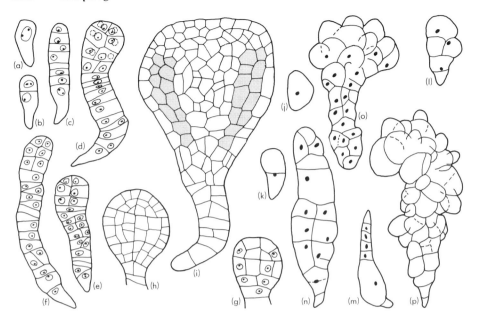

FIG. 7-2. Embryo-like formations in the growth of free cells of carrot in a liquid medium which contains coconut milk. (a)–(i). The normal embryogeny of *Daucus carota* as illustrated by Wardlaw, 1955 (after Borthwick, 1931). (j)–(p). Growth forms in the outgrowth of single carrot cells, of secondary phloem origin, in liquid medium. (From Steward *et al.,* in *Synthesis of Molecular and Cellular Structure,* edited by D. Rudnick, copyright © 1961, The Ronald Press, New York.)

(cf. Steward, Mapes, and Mears, 1958), for the fluids that nourish immature embryos may be potent sources of chemical stimuli to morphogenetic development. However, the most important requirement in order that cells may grow like embryos instead of merely proliferating, is to start that development from free cells.

The course of development from cells of carrot root explants to carrot plants, as this first occurred in media which contained coconut milk, was marked by certain salient events. These were:

i) Division and proliferation in the otherwise quiescent carrot cells was accompanied by protein synthesis and the formation of a particular protein moiety which, like collagen, is rich in hydroxyproline and is not metabolized.

ii) Within the resultant mass of dividing cells, grown from a free cell, the stimulus to orderly division and organized growth often emanated from a central "nest" of cells, some of which lignify and lose their contents; these seemed to furnish the stimulus to the formation of a "nodule" of dividing cells within a peripheral layer of cells cut off by divisions which are tangential to the radial stimulus from the center of the nodule.

iii) Within the nodule, or growing center, cells had more restricted, instead of free, access to the coconut milk growth factors, and under these conditions they readily formed roots in liquid, rotated cultures, whereas cultures formed shoots more readily when they were stationary and exposed to air.

These early observations stressed the inherent totipotency of cells of the carrot root. They also stressed that the release of that totipotency springs, in large measure, from the isolation of the totipotent cells from their neighbors. In fact it seemed that the morphogenetic significance of severing all organic contact between initiating cells and neighboring cells may not have been adequately realized in the past. This is significant because spores and zygotes, which initiate new phases of development in angiosperms, do so as free cells which commence their development as isolated cells. The course of development from such free cells of carrot has already revealed marked similarity to normal embryogeny (Steward and Mohan Ram, 1961; Steward, 1961) but, in a later chapter (cf. Chapter 10) it will be shown that cells which originate from embryos can stimulate embryogeny even more closely and directly; clusters of cells grown from free cells may then form a normal, though non-zygotic (or adventive) embryo even without the stages in the nodule which "walled off" the generative cells from the external medium in the example first described.

Morphogenetic stimuli are more familiarly seen in the later response of growing plants to external and environmental stimuli. The environmental factors which, above all others, exert morphogenetic effects of this kind are light and temperature. It is true that a number of morphogenetic responses, which are directly attributable to chemical substances, or to types of nutrition, are known. Some of these have been mentioned, notably the responses to the crown gall organism; such effects surround the inception of tumors or galls, or other abnormal growth which may be brought about by chemical agents of one sort or another. Knowing that such chemically induced morphogenetic effects occur, it is natural to presume that the morphogenetic effects of light and temperature, of the kind now to be described, also operate through some chemical machinery which is yet to be identified.

Morphogenetic Effects of Light on Vegetative Growth

The range of morphogenetic effects of light on growth is remarkable. An outstanding response is that which is detected when shoots are grown in the complete absence of light; that is the phenomenon of etiolation. This was a prime subject for study in the 1920's, and both in Holland and in England much was done to describe the effects of growth in complete darkness and the subsequent effects of small additions of light to catalyze the removal of the most extreme symptoms of etiolation. Much of this work was done with legumes, which, by the formation of the so-called "plumular hook," are very favorable plants for the study of this response. However, to see the extreme effects of etiolation, the growth must be in continuous darkness—darkness which is complete and absolute. The plants need to be treated with the same care as photographic plates. Under these circumstances the following events occur:

a) Internodes become long, stems rounded, and the distribution of the vascular tissue in the stem is much more like that of a root than of a shoot (i.e., it is more deep-seated, with a broader cortex); lignification is suppressed; no new leaves are initiated from the growing point; and the growing point itself assumes a more root-like character and develops the plumular hook when the shoot apex is recurved in a characteristic fashion. Exposure to light of very low intensity, or for a very brief duration each day, is enough to eliminate the most characteristic features of complete etiolation. A feature of etiolated dicotyledonous shoots is the presence of a functional endodermis with Casparian strips, which usually is not present in normal shoots but is a characteristic of roots. The effect of light is catalytic in the sense that minute exposures eliminate the most drastic symptoms of etiolation. Since no new leaf primordia are formed in darkness, over and above those already in the seed, it is evident that light is necessary for the *initiation* of new leaves as well as for the expansion of their laminae.

b) A pronounced effect of light is that by which internode length is suppressed. Extreme examples of this effect are found in alpine plants which normally, at high altitude and with high insulation, develop a rosette habit with very shortened internodes but which, when grown at lower light intensities, develop more elongated stems, reduced leaves, and longer internodes. The *Sempervivums, Sedums,* etc., show these phenomena very readily.

c) Enlargement of the leaf lamina is an effect due to exposure to light. It is noteworthy, however, that the effects of growth in the absence of light—i.e., etiolation—are much less pronounced in the case of monocotyledons than in the case of dicotyledons. The linear leaves of corn or wheat develop much more normally in the dark than the shoot of a broad leaf plant. The morphology of leaves, however, is also affected by light, as seen in such examples as sun and shade leaves, in which leaf area, thickness of lamina, and to some extent the distribution of stomata, are all responsive to light intensity.

d) A special case, however, which may also involve light as the primary stimulus is the well-known morphogenetic response which results in the dimorphism of the leaves of aquatic plants. The submerged shoots of aquatics often resemble etiolated shoots, with laminae which tend to be reduced and leaves which tend to be inconspicuous, whereas the floating or aerial leaves assume the expanded form more typical of land plants. The change in the composition of light, after absorption by water, may well be a contributory cause of these differences. It is, moreover, extremely suggestive that the growing points of submerged aquatic plants, like *Hippuris* and *Elodea*, are much more root-like in form than those of normal land plants (cf. Fig. 5–19). It is also suggestive that submerged aquatic plants (such as *Veronica beccabunga* or species of *Potamogeton*), like etiolated plants, commonly possess a functional endodermis with Casparian strips in their shoots, and they also have stems with poor development of lignified xylem.

Periodicity in Plant Growth and Response

There is now widespread recognition that growth does not normally proceed at a steady pace under uniform environmental conditions, but that it involves certain discontinuities, and the essential contributions that are made in environments which fluctuate. Organisms, in short, are adapted to the alternations of light and dark, as in night and day; and they are also adapted to the changing seasons. When time is an obvious parameter it is as though organisms have built-in "biological clocks."* Seedtime and harvest, springtime, summer, and winter rest are biological realities and not mere poetic phrases. The effects of temperature on growth and morphogenesis are especially obtrusive, because they are not confined to the effects of temperature on the rate of growth that may be observed under controlled and constant temperatures, for temperature fluctuations in the environment often play an essential role in determining the kind of growth and development that occurs.

The recent emphasis on photoperiodicity (which resulted from the classical works of Garner and Allard) and on temperature effects (which flowed from the interest of "vernalization," i.e., the flowering-fruiting phenomenon as it occurs in normally biennial cereal grains, and from the thermoperiodic responses of a variety of biennial and greenhouse crops) has tended to obscure the fact that the mounting knowledge of periodicity in development antedates many of these later observations.

As an indication of early knowledge of periodic phenomena in growth and cell division, reference may be made to Sachs (1887); to an interesting book by W. L. Balls (1912), *The Cotton Plant in Egypt;* and to a paper by R. C. Friesner (1920); and of course to many other sources. There is even a passage in the writings of Liberty Hyde Bailey which has been construed to mean that he appreciated the phenomenon of photoperiodism as early as 1891 (cf. Bailey, 1891, 1892).

In the 19th century (for example, see Sachs), it was already recognized that alternating periods of light and darkness cause many plants, like *Dahlia* and *Fritillaria*, to show their maximum of elongation shortly after sunrise, and their minimum shortly after sunset. Prantl, in 1873, recognized that leaf expansion occurred at a maximum rate at 6 to 9 a.m., and at a minimum at 6 to 9 p.m.; but the timing of these maxima and minima could be altered by changing the periods of light and darkness.

---

* A book on this subject by Bünning is now available in translation (1964).

Various workers were cited in the middle and late 19th century, for the recognition that cell divisions in such plants as *Spirogyra* occurred predominantly
at night; and later, those who fixed material for cytological purposes have done
so at various inconvenient hours when the frequency of divisions was supposed
to be at a maximum. Zoospores of *Vaucheria* are supposed to shed in the early
morning. Those who, especially in Britain, may have attempted to show the
fertilization of *Fucus* eggs under the microscope to a class may know that this
occurs much more readily by day than it does by night. This was impressed
upon the writer when conducting evening classes in elementary botany; for,
although the materials were collected with oogonia and antheridia ready to shed
eggs and sperms respectively, they performed with far greater difficulty at night
than they normally do by day. Among rhythmic phenomena involving biological
"clocks," the remarkable example of the Palolo worm, which inhabits coral
reefs, may be cited (Burrows, 1945; Caspers, 1951). The reproduction of this
organism occurs at a specified time in the lunar cycle in a given month, and, by
an appropriate formula, it can be anticipated to occur on a given day—almost
at a given tide. Thereafter, the organism retreats into its coraline fastnesses
until another year! Having recognized these biological problems, which involve
periodicity in greater or lesser degree, the question arises, how is the periodicity
in behavior determined?

Balls (1912) made one of the first studies of this sort on a higher plant.
He investigated the factors that determine the growth of the cotton plant,
and noted that in strong sunlight growth was suppressed; Balls questioned
whether this was due to "an overheating" of the growing point. However,
by inserting thermocouples he showed that young leaves and buds rarely
showed a higher temperature than the typical shade temperature of the environment. Nevertheless, the growth by elongation in the stem was shown to
occur at night; and Balls stressed that light suppressed, even stopped, the
elongation of the cotton plant; he also obtained similar results from *Helianthus*
in Egypt.* Balls recognized, even as early as 1912, that in the early part of the
growing season night temperature is the prime factor which limits the growth
of the cotton plant; i.e., growth occurs better by night and it is then temperature-
limited. Balls regarded the need of the growing shoot for water as a factor
that, along with light, tended to retard growth during the day. During the day,
a water deficit occurred, and water loss from the leaves diverted it, as it were,
from the growth processes of the shoot.

Friesner showed, as early as 1920, that mitoses in the roots of pea and corn
seedlings grown in the dark occurred with maximum frequency at night; between 9:30 p.m. and 2:00 a.m. for pea, and at 4:00 a.m. for *Zea*. This rhythm
in cell division in a root tip is already induced in the seedlings at germination,

---

* Modern work in Japan attributes this suppression to a chemical substance which
has been isolated and termed *heliangine* (cf. p. 152).

and, once established, it becomes relatively independent of light and temperature, and tends to continue. Friesner also believed that cell elongation proceeds
in a wave-like fashion in all the plants he studied, with several such waves in a
24-hour period. He recognized that individuals of the same species were not all
alike and suggested that this diurnal rhythm is set up when the seed germinates,
and, once established, it tends to persist. Friesner regarded the process of cell
division as occurring with cyclic frequency, the exact time of the maxima and
minima being dependent on the initiation of the activity, not on the exact time of
day, although elongation tended to subside when division was at a maximum.

The so-called autonomic rhythms in the behavior of excised roots may be
recalled. It was noted in Hoagland's laboratory that roots exude liquid by guttation when severed from the shoot; this occurs very readily in aerated nutrient
solutions. If barley plants are grown under controlled conditions, they continue
to exude this liquid in a cyclical fashion and, once the rhythmic pattern is established, it continues after the leaves are removed and irrespective of the time
of day or exposure to light. Such work was described in well-known papers by
Grossenbacher (1939).

The point, however, is that cyclical, rhythmic, periodic phenomena may
occur in many ways through the frequency of cell division and elongation in
the growth and behavior of a variety of organs. It is obvious that, before
divisions can occur in a growing point at the apex of shoot or root, the growing
region needs to mobilize material, and time is necessary for this to occur. The
essential materials, organic and inorganic nutrients, derive ultimately from the
external environment. Temperature and light are factors in the overall nutritional
processes which make these available. But even if these factors do not limit
the supply of the raw materials of growth to plants, these have still to be mobilized and fabricated in the growing regions for the events that there occur. None
of these events proceed uniformly in time or throughout the growing region.
Cell divisions are localized, primordia develop sequentially in predetermined
order, tissues form and internodes elongate. Therefore, there will be recurring
cycles in the supply of, and in the demand for, essential metabolites in and to
the apex. If the essential metabolites, or the stimuli, for any or all of these developmental events become a function of the external environment (e.g., of day
or night temperature; of the length of day or night), this should subject the
periodic events of growth to external control. Thus, morphogenetic stimuli
frequently affect the balanced events of vegetative growth, as for example in the
differences in form between long- and short-day plants (Fig. 1–16) or in the
events that lead vegetative organs of perennation through rest and dormancy.
But the most dramatic morphogenetic transformations are those involved in the
shift from the vegetative to the reproductive state. These discontinuities in
growth, which can often be related to fluctuations in the environment, will now
be mentioned.

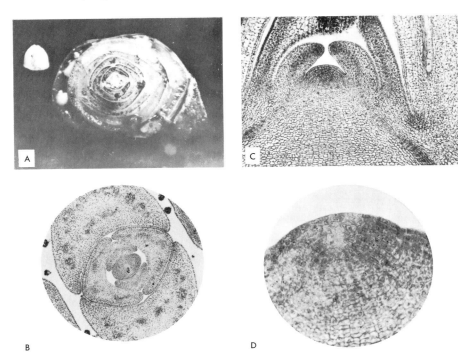

FIG. 7–3. The shoot apex of *Acer platanoides*. A. The apical meristem flanked by two pairs of very young leaf primordia. The heavily shaded areas are scars left after the older primordia and bud scales were dissected away. B. A transverse section through the shoot apex at the base of the meristem. Note the elliptical shape of the meristem in this section and the regularly opposite and decussate arrangement of the leaves. C. A median longitudinal section of the shoot apex. In the leaf primordium on the right, the procambium of the leaf can be seen as a region of heavily staining cells from the apex of the primordium to the elongated, dividing cells of the procambium in the axis. D. A median longitudinal section through the apical meristem of the bud. A two-layered tunica covers the corpus of irregularly dividing cells. The swellings on the flanks of the meristem are new leaf primordia. (From Pollock, 1950.)

Rest Period, Dormancy, and Perennation

These are phenomenona of the temperate zones, with their marked alternation between summer and winter. The characteristics of the rest period are very evident in trees, although such organs of perennation as tubers, bulbs, corms, and rhizomes illustrate the same principles. Bulbs, corms, and rhizomes are storage organs, in the genesis of which the photoperiodic stimulus often plays a part. Garner and Allard (1920) showed that a photoperiodic stimulus is also involved in the dormancy of the buds of many trees.

Dormancy in trees is a characteristic feature of the cambium as well as of the buds. The cambium is remarkable because it is a cell layer endowed with the ability for continuous division, but this layer may also assume a winter rest and dormant condition. One of the most remarkable phenomena in plant development is that which causes the onset of cambial activity in the springtime, after the period of winter rest. Buds of trees pass into rest in the summer when all the conditions for their continued growth are ostensibly at their optimum. At the height of summer conditions in July and August in north temperate latitudes, many buds begin to be dormant, although temperature, light, and the availability of food to the tree are still conducive to continued growth. It requires a subsequent exposure to cold, of specified duration and of a certain degree of severity, to permit the buds to emerge from the dormancy which is primarily located in the meristem itself. True, the foliar organs in the bud change somewhat in preparation for the dormant condition, and leaves become increasingly modified as scales, but the remarkable thing is how little visible evidence distinguishes the meristem in its active and dormant states. A meristem of an actively growing bud of maple, as shown in Fig. 7–3, is astonishingly similar to that of a dormant bud. A number of chemical substances can break dormancy in buds, e.g., thiourea, ethylenechloryhydrin (Crocker, 1948); these need not be itemized here, for it is the mechanism that normally operates in the tree to induce and dispel dormancy that is of paramount interest. Pollock (1950) studied this phenomenon in the author's laboratory as he investigated the respiration of maple buds and their parts. Pollock came to the conclusion that the problem of dormancy could be, in part, explained if one considered the respiration of the buds in relation to the oxygen tension which saturates the system. Pollock conceived that dormancy was induced by the accumulated products of partial anaerobiosis, since the dormant bud is not completely oxygen-saturated even at concentrations near to 100 percent oxygen, whereas the non-dormant bud is oxygen-saturated at concentrations of the order of 20 percent.

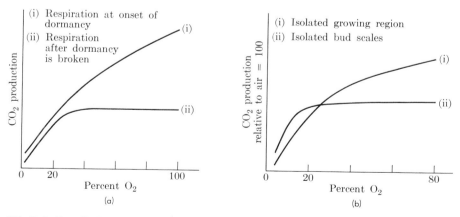

FIG. 7–4. The effect of oxygen concentration and seasonal changes on the respiration of excised *Acer platanoides* buds at 25 C. (After Pollock, 1950; see also 1953.)

At the onset of dormancy a whole maple bud is not oxygen-saturated even in air, because the form of the CO_2-production/pO_2 curve is that shown in Fig. 7–4(a) at (i); this shows that if the bud in air could receive more oxygen it would respire at a much higher rate. For this reason, products of partial anaerobiosis may be expected to accumulate in the bud as a whole. Later in the year, and after the exposure to cold, this condition changes, for the whole bud is now oxygen-saturated at very much lower oxygen concentrations, in fact at concentrations which are much closer to those of air [Fig. 7–4(a) (ii)]. Thus products of partial anaerobiosis should now tend to be respired away. The respiratory behavior of the bud is controlled, however, not only by the innate respiratory capacity of its component parts, but by factors which follow from its organization. Due to the tight overlap of the bud scales (Fig. 7–5) and other physical effects, like the presence of gummy substances, the bud scales *in situ* are more apt to be operating at a sub-optimal oxygen supply than when they are dissected and in freer contact with air. But of all the component parts of the bud, it is the central growing region which, even when it is isolated, is most difficult to furnish with enough oxygen so that it can exercise its full respiratory capacity unlimited by oxygen. This point is illustrated by the diagrams at Fig. 7–4(b) (i) and (ii). It was considerations of this kind that suggested that the onset and breaking of dormancy in maple buds might be conditioned by the prior accumulation of products of respiration at sub-optimal oxygen concentrations and by their subsequent disappearance when the bud later respires under conditions more nearly approaching those of oxygen saturation.

mm

FIG. 7–5. An early stage in the spring bud opening of *Acer platanoides*. All five pairs of bud scales are visible, but the leaves have not yet emerged. In the winter condition only two pairs of scales would be exposed. The bud is flowered by a pair of lateral buds and the leaf scars from the preceding year's terminal leaves are visible. (From Pollock, 1950.)

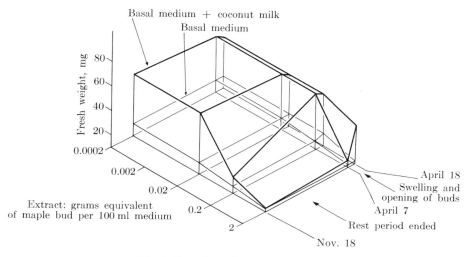

Effect of maple bud extracts on growth
of carrot root explants in media
with and without coconut milk

FIG. 7–6. Evidence for specific substances which inhibit the action of coconut-milk growth factors on carrot. (1) Extracts of maple buds never show positive growth-promoting activity which may replace coconut milk in the growth of carrot. (2) Dormant maple buds do, however, yield extracts which have inhibitory activity towards the growth of carrot tissue under our standard procedure. (3) As the rest period advances and after winter chilling there comes a point beyond which the inhibitory activity is much reduced; it then becomes evident only at much higher concentrations of the maple extract than hitherto. (4) When the buds begin to swell, the inhibitory substance for the growth of carrot seems to disappear almost entirely. (From Steward and Caplin, *Ann. Botany* N. S. 16, 477–489, 1952; after work of Pollock.)

Another approach to this problem arose from the application of the tissue culture technique. Using carrot assays to detect inhibitors of cell division, extracts of maple buds were tested for their ability to suppress the activity of the cell division factors that are present in coconut milk. This was done at different seasons of the year. It could be shown that dormant maple buds yielded extracts which were strongly inhibitory to the cell divisions which are induced by coconut milk; and that this inhibitory mechanism persisted until, by the effect of temperature, the buds emerged from dormancy. At this latter point the inhibitory qualities of the maple bud extract for the growth of carrot cultures in coconut milk declined rapidly and eventually disappeared. There-fore, some process of metabolism, perhaps caused by partial anaerobiosis in the growing regions, due to the development of more impervious bud scales, causes some inhibitor of growth to accumulate. Such inhibitors of growth may be found in extracts of certain storage organs, such as potato tuber and onion bulb (Steward and Caplin, 1952), and also in the effect of added substances

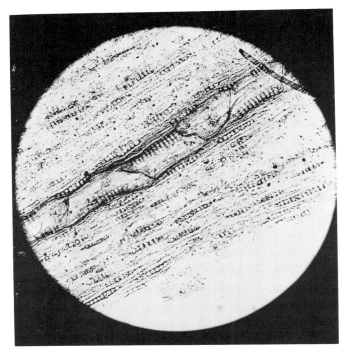

FIG. 7–7. *Acer platanoides* developing xylem in "xylem strips" from first internode beneath developing buds (×790). Very early vessel development in spring; leaf expansion nearly complete. (From work of Pollock, 1950.)

like hydroxyproline. If, therefore, the progressive growth in the apex is in part prompted by cell division factors, its suppression by flooding the system with a metabolically produced inhibitor could account for the onset of dormancy. In the maple tree there is experimental evidence to suggest that this is so (Fig. 7–6).*

Buds normally begin to grow, to "push," in the spring before the activity of the vascular cambium is resumed. Water can first enter a bud via vascular tissue which was laid down in the preceding summer. However, the main entry of solutes and water into a growing bud often awaits the differentiation beneath it of vascular strands in the current year and their integration with the vascular tissues of the main stem. Following upon the initiation of activity in the bud, cambial activity and differentiation are evoked below the bud by stimuli that

* Later work has revealed a substance, variously called dormin, abscisin II, or ter-polinic acid, that is held to be responsible for dormancy (cf. Chapter 4). This substance has been isolated, identified, and synthesized through the respective works of Addicott, Wareing, and Cornforth and is now to be called abscisic acid.

pass, mainly basipetally, from the growing bud. This wave of cambial activity can be followed, particularly in ring-porous trees like ash, oak, and beech, by observing xylem differentiation. In ring-porous trees a few large vessels— large enough to be visible to the naked eye—are formed in each spring flush of growth. It is often stated that the stimulus that emerges from the buds to incite the cambial activity in the tree is the familiar plant auxin, indoleacetic acid, and it is true that papers on this subject have been written (Avery, Burkholder, and Creighton, 1937). A later view is that indoleacetic acid plus gibberellic acid, or some endogenous substance which acts like gibberellic acid applied exogenously, more nearly resembles the natural stimulus in the cambial region (Wareing, 1958). Auxin obviously is involved in the normal hormonal balance of plants, and it may well be that flooding the system exogenously with auxin may upset this balance in ways that lead indirectly to cell division. However, this effect is so different from those that auxin normally controls that its role in the control of cambial activity should be re-investigated. It seems much more probable that the stimulus that passes basipetally from the shoot apex and which incites xylem differentiation in the cambial region (cf. Figs. 6–34 and 7–7) is one of the now numerous substances that seem to be concerned—much more directly than indoleacetic acid—with the catalytic induction of cell division (cf. Steward and Shantz, 1959). It has been reported (Hillis, 1955) that there is an abundance of leucoanthocyanins in *Eucalyptus* in the cambial region at the spring flush of growth, and this relates to the observation (cf. Chapter 4) that these substances have growth-inducing properties and are prominent in such natural growth-promoting fluids as coconut milk, *Aesculus* fruits, etc. The problem of rest period and dormancy, therefore, needs further investigation in the light of current thought on the control and induction of growth as this has emerged from work on tissue cultures.*

Dormant potato tubers contain a powerful inhibitor of cell division (Steward and Shantz, 1959), which can be revealed by the carrot tissue culture assay system; this example—one of several—suggests why so many storage cells cease to grow at the time when they are replete with the food (salts, amino acids, etc.) which should be conducive to further growth. Therefore, the old problems of rest period, dormancy, and perennation can be reopened for biochemical investigation. The thought here is that the variables that induce dormancy, or break dormancy, operate through some chemical machinery which controls the ability of cells to divide and grow. There are, therefore, two major problems. First, what are the chemical, catalytic, causal agents that control the growth? Second, how does the external variable in question—whether photoperiod or temperature—bring the activity of these causative agents in the cells under regulatory control?

---

* It is in fact now established that the substance known as dormin will suppress the growth of tissue cultures as this is stimulated by coconut milk growth factors (unpublished work in the author's laboratory).

Among the possibilities to be considered here are the following. The mechanism of control may operate, not only by direct inhibition of the growth-promoting substances, but alternatively by blocking a key metabolic process without which the induced growth cannot occur. Such a process is protein synthesis. It has been seen that hydroxy-L-proline inhibits protein synthesis in carrot explants even in the presence of the coconut milk growth factors; so much so that it could be regarded as an "anti-coconut milk growth." The hydroxy-L-proline acts at the site where proline is made available for, and incorporated in, protein. Azetidine-2-carboxylic acid may also act as a proline antagonist. Thus protein amino acid analogues which are not themselves directly incorporated in protein may function as inhibitors of protein synthesis and of growth in storage organs or organs of perennation in which they occur. This is, however, only one example of the more general case in which anti-metabolites may block any of the synthetic pathways that are vital for growth.

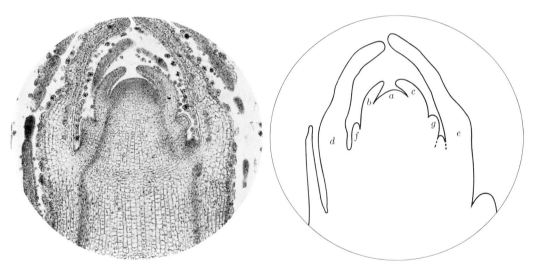

FIG. 7–8. Photograph and interpretive drawing of a longitudinal section of the stolon apex of *Mentha piperita* L. Diagram shows: *a*, the apex proper; *b*, *c*, the first pair of leaf primordia; *d*, *e*, the third pair of leaf primordia; *f* and *g* represent the leaf bases of the second pair of leaf primordia with evident node formation. Note gland initials on the first visible pair of leaf primordia and their profusion on successive leaves. (From Howe and Steward, *Cornell Univ. Agr. Exp. Sta. Mem. No. 379, 1962.*)

The vegetative growing point of mint (*Mentha piperita*) enters a dormant condition which is photoperiodically induced by short days. Under these circumstances, the mint plant produces prostrate rhizomes, or stolons, with reduced scaly leaves, and the stolons function as organs of perennation during the winter. By contrast, the same plant under long days produces erect leafy shoots which branch copiously and eventually flower. The only visible feature that distinguishes the vegetative from the dormant growing point (cf. Figs. 1–10 and 7–8) is that the growing point of the stolon is relatively broader and flatter, the leaves are more scale-like, and the leaf primordia are soon separated by longer internodes. The main stimulus to the inception of this dormant condition is photoperiodic, although it is now known that low night temperatures will override the effects of long days and form a short-day type of plant (Howe, 1956). It is also known that the biochemistry of mint under short days is different from that under long days (Steward *et al.*, 1962); this opens the possibility that some as yet unidentified metabolite may be the chemical trigger which switches the growing point from one type of development to the other.

A treatment which breaks the rest period and which has received a biochemical explanation is that due to Goddard (1939). Dormant spores of *Neurospora* can be brought into growth by heat, and they owe their reactivation to a heat stimulation of the enzyme decarboxylase. Presumably, therefore, an inhibitor of metabolism in the dormant spores suppressed the enzyme decarboxylase, and the heat treatment removes this block. An equally direct explanation of the onset and breaking of dormancy in buds of woody trees as that suggested for *Neurospora* would be of great value, because it might lead to a much needed regulatory control over this phenomenon.

The Photoperiodic Response

The main credit for the discovery of, or more accurately for focusing attention upon, photoperiodism goes to Garner and Allard (1920), two workers in the U.S.D.A. in Washington. The remarkable thing is that so interesting and important an environmental factor in biology should have been discovered so late. Briefly, Maryland Mammoth Tobacco always continued vegetative through the growing season in the vicinity of Washington, D.C., and it flowered only when its growth was prolonged in the greenhouse into that part of the year when the days became short. Similarly, all Biloxi soy beans tended to bloom at the same time, irrespective of the day of planting. These observations directed attention to the season at which the flowering occurred, and Garner and Allard clearly differentiated between the daily *duration* of light as the causal factor which incited the onset of flowering and the *amount*, or *intensity*, of light which the plants received. While the main credit goes to Garner and Allard, many previous indications also pointed the way. Klebs, in 1913, especially recognized that *Sempervivum* will flower in the winter only with extra artificial light, and he seemed to have the idea that this was associated with the balance between day (i.e., the length of the light period) and night (i.e., the duration of darkness).

In summary, we now recognize short-day plants, induced to flower by the short days of fall or of spring in temperate latitudes, and long-day plants, which are induced to flower by the days, longer than 12 hours, which occur in summer.

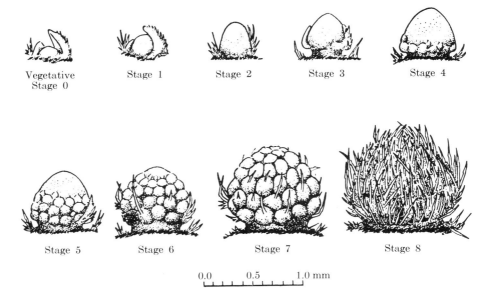

Vegetative   Stage 1   Stage 2   Stage 3   Stage 4
Stage 0

Stage 5   Stage 6   Stage 7   Stage 8

0.0   0.5   1.0 mm

FIG. 7–9. Floral induction in *Xanthium*. Drawings of the developing terminal inflorescence primordium (staminate) of cocklebur, illustrating the system of flowering stages described in Table 7–1. (From Salisbury, *The Flowering Process*, Pergamon Press, New York, 1963.)

There are many indeterminant plants whose flowering and fruiting is insensitive to day length, though it may well be determined by other causal factors. It is known that this phenomenon is not peculiar to plants, for many animals also respond to day length by their sexual or mating behavior, which is often induced by long days. In plants leaves usually receive the stimulus—not the stems or buds—but the stimulus moves and will pass across a graft union to the region in the growing point where the stimulus elicits the response. In animals too there is usually a localized seat of response; in certain birds it is the eye, and by hooding or removing the eyeball or by removing the optic nerve, it can be shown that this is not a matter of vision but that light affects particular structures in these organs. It would take too long to pass all the phenomena of photoperiodism in review; this is well documented in textbooks, notably the one by Murneek and Whyte (1948), in many recent review articles (Bonner, 1959; Borthwick, Parker, and Hendricks, 1950), and in recent books by Hillman (1962) and by Salisbury (1963). All we need to note here are the following essential facts. The first point is that the stimulus is exerted by the balance between day and night. It is the daily period of illumination that is involved, not the total amount of incident energy. More strictly, it appears that short-day plants, like *Xanthium* (the cocklebur, cf. Fig. 7–9 and Table 7–1), should really be regarded as plants that require long nights. Flowering has been induced in

TABLE 7—1

Criteria for the determination of flowering stages in the apical bud
(to become staminate) of *Xanthium pennsylvanicum* (cocklebur)

Floral stage	Criterion
0	Vegetative. Shoot apex relatively flat and small.
1	First clearly visible swelling of the shoot apex.
2	Floral apex at least as high as broad, but not yet constricted at the base.
3	Floral apex constricted at the base, but no flower primordia yet visible.
4	First visible flower primordia, covering up to the lower one-quarter of the floral apex.
5	Flower primordia covering from one to three-quarters of the floral apex.
6	Flower primordia covering all but the upper tip of the floral apex.
7	Floral apex completely covered by flower primordia. Slightly to moderately pubescent.
8	Very pubescent and showing some differentiation of flower parts. At least one millimeter basal diameter.

From Salisbury, 1963

Xanthium after exposure to a single long night, and if, in such a single long night, the plants are exposed to a brief light flash in the middle of the dark period, the effectiveness of that dark period is eliminated. The photoperiodic stimulus can travel from a treated leaf to all parts of the plant, so that it is not necessary to stimulate photoperiodically the whole plant, but only the effective region.

The Mechanism of Light Action in Photo-Responsive Growth

The action of light presupposes a pigment system by which the radiation may be absorbed. There is abundant evidence that this is not the same pigment system which is involved in photosynthesis. Etiolated plants are almost devoid of such pigments—certainly devoid of the green ones—and yet the response of the etiolated plant is a cardinal example of the morphogenetic effect of light. Also, as indicated, light has morphogenetic effects on fungi as well as on flowering plants. The idea that the morphogenetic effects of light are mediated by some mechanism common to all these diverse responses gains credence from some very elegant work done at the United States Department of Agriculture at Beltsville by Hendricks and Borthwick (1954). These authors have used a spectrograph which spreads the spectrum of visible light over about 1.7 meters of length and permits relatively large objects to be exposed to monochromatic radiation.

Hendricks and Borthwick have investigated two dissimilar systems. The first of these is the effect of light on the floral initiation of the cocklebur, and the ability of a single flash of light to break the effect of a long night. The second system is of an entirely different kind. This system is based on a much earlier observation of MacAllister (Flint and MacAllister, 1937) to the effect that the germination of seeds of lettuce (*Lactuca sativa*) is greatly influenced by light, and on Withrow's first (1936) recognition that the effects of red and far red light are opposed. It was Hendricks and Borthwick however, who many years later correctly attributed these effects to the same light-reversible pigments (Table 7–2).

TABLE 7–2
Photo-reversal of promotion and inhibition of *Lactuca sativa* var. Grand Rapids seed germination in a series of irradiations alternating between red and far red at two temperatures

Number of irradiations		Final irradiation	Percent germination at 20°C with irradiation at indicated temperature	
Red	Far red		26°C	6 to 8°C
1	0	Red	70	72
1	1	Far red	6	13
2	1	Red	74	74
2	2	Far red	6	8
3	2	Red	76	75
3	3	Far red	7	11
4	3	Red	81	77
4	4	Far red	7	12

From Hendricks and Borthwick, 1954

If lettuce seeds have previously imbibed water in complete darkness and remain continuously in darkness, the seeds do not germinate; but if they are exposed to certain wavelengths of light from a few seconds to an hour, germination is influenced. In red light germination is promoted; in far red light, curiously enough, this effect is reversed; so that, if the seeds are exposed to a sequence of radiation treatments, first with red, then with far red, with red and far red again, the germination reflects the type of radiation used in the final treatment. The seeds germinate to about 70 percent if the final radiation is with red light, and only to about 6 to 13 percent if the final radiation is with far red light. It is remarkable, however, that the action spectrum which reflects the amount of energy needed for each wavelength to bring about a good biological response, shows that *the same wavelengths that are effective in promoting the germination of lettuce seed are also the wavelengths which are able to inhibit floral initiation in the growing point of the cocklebur.* Furthermore, the wavelength which tends to reverse this effect most effectively in lettuce—i.e., about 720 μ— also promotes floral initiation in cocklebur. These remarkable results are shown in Fig. 7–10. The fact that both these responses are evoked by a specific type

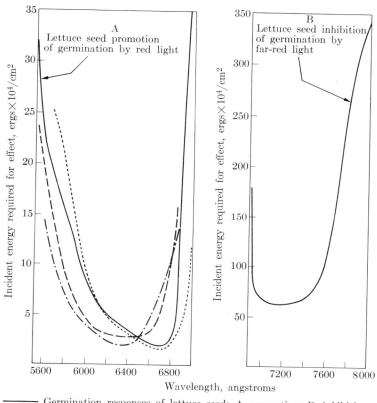

Germination responses of lettuce seed: A, promotion; B, inhibition
········· Promotion of elongation of etiolated pea leaves
– – – – Inhibition of flowering of cocklebur by light in a dark period
–·—·— Control of flowering of barley (a long-day plant)

FIG. 7–10. These diagrams show how different responses that are brought about by light are related to wavelength. The ordinates show the amount of energy at each wavelength which is needed to achieve the response. This type of diagram is called an action spectrum. The low points on the curves indicate wavelengths which are easily absorbed by the plant and very effective in producing the responses indicated. (After Borthwick and Hendricks, 1954.)

of radiation and reversed by another, and that these two effects may be repeatedly applied, suggests strongly that *the same type of pigment system detects the radiation in both cases.* However, the comparison goes even further. The action spectra show the similar efficiency of light in stimulating the recovery of etiolated peas, in *inhibiting* flower formation in the cocklebur, which is a short-day or long-night plant, and also for the *promotion* of flowering in a short-night or long-day plant, namely barley. The similarity of all these action spectra suggests that a widely distributed pigment system in plants is involved, and this idea was extended by Hendricks and Borthwick to include the development of color in the ripening of tomato fruits, which again has a similar action spectrum.

A response which is mediated by light, stimulated by wavelengths of 6500 angstroms, and reversed by wavelengths of 7300 angstroms, suggests that the pigment either forms a modified substance when stimulated at these wavelengths, or else it reacts with some other reactant to produce a distinct substance which evokes the morphological response. Ultimately both pigment* and its reaction product will need to be identified, and it will be necessary to know how they affect the metabolic behavior of the plants in question. But, according to Hendricks and Borthwick, there is now a very long list of plant responses such as seed germination, elongation of the seedling stem, leaf enlargement, unfolding of the plumular hook, epinasty, leaf abscission, bulb formation, rhizome production, Casparian strip formation, floral initiation, flower development, pigmentation of ripening fruits, succulence, sex expression, root development, and response to day and night temperature, all of which are areas of behavior which are linked with this light-activated mechanism. However, the interpretation has more recently been complicated by the views of Mohr (1962). According to Mohr, the essentially low energy light-activated mechanism of Hendricks and Borthwick, which operates through the pigment called phytochrome, may not be the only one involved. Mohr believes that a high energy system is also implicated in the morphogenetic response. Nevertheless the chemistry of phytochrome is a salient problem.

By about 1959–1960, and subsequently, the workers at the U.S. Department of Agriculture (Borthwick, Hendricks, and Siegelman) upheld the following views on the phytochrome of oats. Phytochrome is water soluble, contains a protein moiety believed to be of high molecular weight, has an absorption in the visible spectrum which matches the action spectrum of the photomorphogenetic effect, and the pigment moiety seems to be a tetrapyrrole (which probably resembles allo-phycocyanin).

Subsequently, Shropshire and Correll at the Smithsonian Institution in Washington have succeeded in obtaining pure phytochrome (Correll *et al.*, 1966). These workers used annual rye and a routine procedure in which the grains are scattered on thick paper, in fiberglass trays in light-tight carts. The dark-grown seedlings are ground with an active grade of alumina and ground glass, and the optical density of the extracted pigment is measured spectrophotometrically while the protein content is followed by the Lowry method. Although the phytochrome is pH-sensitive, it is stabilized between pH 7 and 8 and by mercaptoethanol. Isolates contain about one-tenth of the estimated phytochrome content of the rye plants. Contact with non-polar solvents like acetone or alcohol is avoided because they denature the product and, of the two forms, the red-absorbing one is held to be the more resistant. According to this school, the

---

* In the work of Siegelman, now being done at Brookhaven National Laboratories, the purification of the pigmented moiety of phytochrome is now far advanced, and Mumford and Jenner (1966) at The Central Research Division of E. I. DuPont Co. have characterized phytochrome with respect to its protein moiety.

protein moiety of phytochrome consists of a monomer (about 34,000 mol. wt.) which yields 34 recognizable entities in a "fingerprint" of a tryptic digest. Each such protein subunit is believed to contain at least one chromophore and to exist, as seen in the electron microscope, in a complex of five subunits (180,000 mol. wt. and about 50 Å in size) arranged as in a pentagon. This complex is in equilibrium with a heavier aggregate in which the pentagons are assembled into an even larger complex (of the order of 1.2×10^6 mol. wt.). When a solution of pure phytochrome is converted to the far-red absorbing form and is then maintained in the dark it slowly reverts to the thermodynamically more stable, red-absorbing form. The kinetics of this reaction are complex (greater than second order) but in less than one hour the reaction has gone half way to completion. This reaction is believed to be the mechanism of the photoperiodic control of flowering in plants. (The above summary is based on personal communication from Dr. D. L. Correll.)

The mechanism of the morphogenetic action of phytochrome is still not known. It is obviously a long way from the absorption of light (red or far red) by phytochrome to the varied events that morphogenesis involves. The phytochrome seems to be a light-activated trigger which sets the morphogenetic events in train. Different schools favor different ideas. The Borthwick-Hendricks-Siegelman group have upheld the view that the protein moiety may function as an enzyme whose activity is regulated by the chromophore. Others (e.g., Hans Mohr, 1962), following the prevalent thinking of molecular biology, have latterly espoused the view that it may act by regulating gene repression and depression and thus ultimately act through mRNA-mediated mechanisms. This, however, is not specific to phytochrome for *all* morphogenetic factors could fit, and many biologists suppose they do, into such a scheme. Moreover the protein of phytochrome seems not to be a histone, the class of proteins which are supposed ultimately to "cover" or "uncover" the genes. A view attributable to the Smithsonian group is that the role of phytochrome, located in mitochondria or in chloroplasts, may be that of a "redox trigger" which acts, as it were, by saying "yes" or "no" to electron transport and so may determine the course of metabolism.

It is at least indisputable that great interest attaches to the chemistry of phytochrome and its mode of action, even though neither question can be categorically answered. The morphogenetic role of phytochrome will not be fully understood until it can be seen in terms of its behavior *in situ* in the cells and organelles in which it occurs. Furthermore the role of phytochrome should be seen in a perspective which recognizes that there are many morphogenetic responses in which it may play no part (e.g., those regulated by temperature) and that it often occurs in quantity in situations in which it may not be implicated in morphogenesis. Even in those situations in which morphogenetic events are catalyzed by light the responses are rarely motivated in nature by conditions which are as sharply contrasted as the red-far-red mechanism would seem to imply.

Temperature Effects in Floral Induction

The morphogenetic effects of temperature on plants of the temperate climates are almost as varied as are those of light. The necessity for exposure to cold to break dormancy in vegetative buds has already been mentioned. An entirely different effect, however, is that by which the potentiality to flower in normally biennial plants is released through exposure to a characteristic temperature, usually a low temperature, and may be suppressed by exposure to temperatures which are too high. This phenomenon in cereal grains has become well known under the name of vernalization, but it was known in such biennial plants as beets, celery, onions, etc., before the term "vernalization" derived from the Russian word "jarovicija" (hence *yarovinization*) meaning "to make spring again," became so frequently used.

Winter-grown cereals behave as biennials because the grain germinates in one season and makes a substantial amount of growth, which is the essential prerequisite to the formation of a flowering spike in the second cycle of growth. A similar behavior is familiar in such plants as the beet and onion, and in many biennials in which there is a normally rosette-like shoot formed in the first cycle of growth, with a massive storage organ which, after rest and dormancy and exposure to cold, will form an elongated flowering shoot in the second season of growth. Vernalization of cereal grains is the pre-treatment of the grain, at a suitable temperature and at a suitable moisture content, so that changes that normally obtain in the first growth period will occur *prior to the emergence of the shoot* from the grain, the winter sowing being thereby circumvented. This technique, which was applied in Russia, became common knowledge in the early 1930's. However, long before this, certain essential observations led to its perfection. Temperature regulation of the behavior of cereals was already beginning to be known when, in 1918, Gassner chilled cereal grains and when later, in 1928–1929, Lysenko noted the need for exposure to low temperature to promote the flowering shoots and also noted the converse phenomenon of "hibernalism," a term which describes the tendency of cereal plants to remain vegetative if they are kept at too high a temperature. All this was part of the background which led to the recognition that the flowering behavior of cereal grains could be sensitively regulated by temperature. In fact, under appropriate conditions of dryness and temperature, the phenomenon of devernalization of some cereal grains may occur.

In bulb plants, however, similar phenomena were also well known, for as early as 1926 work by Blaauw, Luytens, and Joustra, as described in a book by Murneek and Whyte (1948), had shown the sensitive temperature regulation of flower induction which obtains in the tulip. When the bulbs are lifted after flowering, the growing point is entirely vegetative, and the tulip bulb thus presents a very favorable organ in which to study floral induction and flower development, because this occurs progressively during the resting period. Blaauw

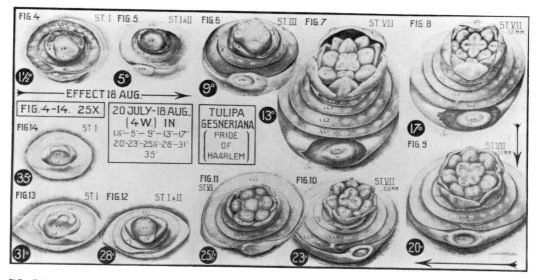

FIG. 7–11. Temperature effects in terms of bud development. The state of the growing point of a tulip bulb after a four-week storage at constant temperatures ranging from 1.5°C to 35°C. The figures show what can be observed at ×14 after all bulb scales and enclosing leaf bases have been removed around the growing point. The scars of the removed foliage leaves are indicated and marked LL1, LL2, etc. The main vegetative growing point producing the shoot for the next year is marked VP; the lateral growing point which would have developed two years later is VPA (with its bulb scales R_1 and R_2). After the fourth or fifth foliage leaf (LL4 or LL5) was initiated, the growing point widened and the petals (T1 and T2), stamens (M_1 and M_2), and carpels (VD) were initiated. At 1.5°, 31°, and 35°C no change in the growing point had taken place during the 29 days' storage; the growing points were in stage I (vegetative). At 5° and 28° the fourth or fifth foliage leaf had developed, and the growing point was just advanced to where it changes to the flowering condition. At 9° the growing point was in stage III (only petals initiated); at 25.5° it had reached stage VI (all flower parts, except carpels, well developed); and between 13° and 23° all flower parts were in the same advanced stage of development (stage VII). Another interesting fact can be observed concerning the effect of temperature on flower initiation. When the temperature is high, the normal trimerous flower is formed (23° to 25.5°), but at low initiation temperatures (9° to 13°) the flowers are predominantly tetramerous. At intermediate temperatures (17° to 20°) intermediate numbers of flower parts are found. (From F. W. Went, "Thermoperiodicity," in *Vernalization and Photoperiodism*, edited by A. E. Murneek and R. O. Whyte, copyright © 1948, The Ronald Press Company, New York. After Luyten, Joustra, and Blaauw, 1926.)

et al. showed that this process had critical temperature limitations, for it could be arrested by both too high and too low a temperature during the storage period. This can be seen in Fig. 7–11. At such low temperatures as 1.5°C the growing point remains in the same vegetative state as when the bulbs were lifted. At a temperature of 5°C, after four weeks, the last foliage leaf had developed, and the growing point had come to the stage of flower formation. At 9°C petals only were initiated, and the flower parts were in whorls of four instead of the normal whorls of three. Between 13°C and 23°C all flower parts were being formed, and at 23°C petals and anthers with flower parts in the normal whorls of three were established. At temperatures above 25°C, abnormalities again occurred. Therefore, in the tulip, as indeed is well known to floriculturalists, the formation of the flower during the storage of the bulb is most critically conditioned by temperature.

In New York State, however, these general ideas were already well known in another context. Professor H. C. Thompson, working in the Vegetable Crops Department at Cornell University, had studied the bolting, or premature seeding, of onions and similar crops. Thompson was, in fact, one of the pioneers who showed that exposure to temperatures which are too low in the early stages of development of the seedling caused the plants to enter the floral phase prematurely. This change was irreversible when temperatures were raised, and the plants grew as flowering, or bolting, plants instead of in the vegetative condition. For example, two days at 40°F to 50°F caused celery to initiate flowers, even though the subsequent growth of the flower required temperatures of 60°F to 70°F.

In all of these responses, therefore, temperature makes an impact upon the normal processes of growth and development to influence the kind of behavior which the growing apex achieves. It seems obvious that the external variable temperature must operate through the control of some metabolic process and the effect must be mediated by some chemical substance, or agent, in the tissue. This thought is compatible with all we know about the chemical regulation of growth. Indeed, an example first quoted by Dr. James Bonner shows that this idea may be well on the way to proof. The substance gibberellin or gibberellic acid, which was previously mentioned, has the ability to stimulate elongation in normally dwarf or rosette plants. The plant *Hyoscyamus*, or the henbane, produces during its first season of growth a fleshy root and a crown, or rosette, of leaves. Elongation of the flowering shoot, however, fails to take place, even though it is initiated, until after the *Hyoscyamus* plant has been subjected to a sufficiently long period at low temperature. This occurs normally in the winter, and, if this is prevented by growing the plants indoors, the elongation of the flowering shoot may not occur. Dr. Anton Lang, working first at U.C.L.A. and later at the Earheart Laboratory of the California Institute of Technology, has shown that failure of these high-temperature-treated *Hyoscyamus* plants to send up their flowering shoot may be relieved by the application of the substance gibberellin (Lang, 1956). The presumption is that the low temperature treatment releases a block by the production of some substance, gibberellin or its equivalent, which is needed to promote the elongation of the flowering shoot. It is also reported from the California Institute of Technology that in perennial rye, which normally requires the stimulus of cold in order to flower, cold-treated seeds can release to water an active agent that will promote flowering in grains not so treated. (More detailed hypotheses on the chemical control of flowering are taken up in Chapter 8.)

All these examples suggest that the morphogenetic stimuli of photoperiod, and thermoperiod, which are exerted on the flowering response of plants of temperate zones, are exerted through—or mediated by—chemical substances that control metabolism and growth at the active sites of the plants in question. However, not all flowering plants are sensitive to length of day or even to periodicity in temperature. For examples of striking morphogenetic events triggered off without the apparent aid of either photoperiodic or thermal effects, attention is conveniently turned to some tropical plants. The polycarpic perennial banana plant will serve as a convenient though somewhat unusual example.

Growth and Morphogenesis in a Polycarpic Perennial

The banana plant of commerce (*Musa acuminata*), one of the most ancient of crop plants (cf. Simmonds, 1959), develops its fruit parthenocarpically, but during its growth it also shows a remarkable sequence of other morphogenetic events. These are described here to show that endogenous controls or stimuli must determine and correlate the incidence of growth in the various regions of this plant and, so far as is known, it is improbable that the environmental periodicities that are conspicuous in controlling growth and morphogenesis in plants of the temperate zones are effective in this tropical plant. Therefore, the chemical stimuli in question must originate during the normal development of the banana plant.

The banana plant forms a perennial rhizome or corm. The growing point which produces the vegetative shoot forms at a near-ground level in a shallow depression in the corm. The large visible shoot, with its enormous leaves, is not a true stem but a hollow "pseudostem" made up of a succession of encircling leaf bases. The true stem is the axis of the inflorescence which grows up within the pseudostem.

The formation of the pseudostem illustrates the very anomalous way in which the vegetative plant body of the banana is formed. Commonly leaf primordia arise on the flanks of a vegetative growing point, one or more at the same level. In order that the next leaf or whorl of leaves may form, the shoot tip usually grows upward by the distance of an internode; then leaf and internode grow independently to form an axis with leaves at a series of nodes. In the vegetative banana the vertical displacement of the shoot tip is virtually nil; leaves as they develop from the shoot apex are displaced laterally so that a large number of developing leaves appear in a section cut at the horizontal level of the central dome of meristem (Figs. 7–12 and 7–13). Although the upward growth of the vegetative shoot tip is virtually nil, the growth of the leaf primordia is nevertheless very great, for the production of the vegetative plant body is taken over entirely by its lateral organs. The leaf primordia grow very vigorously in two ways—they completely encircle the axis and overlap at their margins, and they grow radially outward forming massive structures which very quickly exceed the central growing region in size and, by growing regions

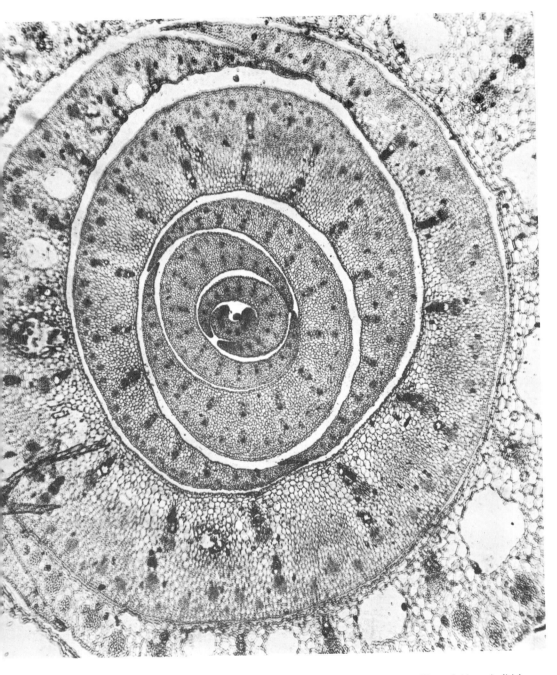

FIG. 7–12. Transverse section of the shoot apex of a seedling of *Musa balbisiana*, showing the apical meristem and successive leaf primordia. The outermost leaves show conspicuous air chambers. (From Barker and Steward, *Ann. Botany* N.S. 26, 389–411, 1962.)

500 μ

FIG. 7–13. Median longitudinal section through the shoot apex of *Musa acuminata* cv. Gros Michel, showing the central apical dome and the encircling and overarching leaf primordia, which are extended upward as the precursory appendages. (From Barker and Steward, *Ann. Botany* N.S. 26, 413–424, 1962.)

500 μ

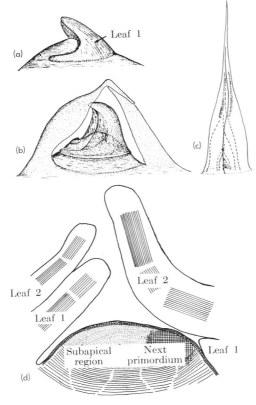

FIG. 7–14. The shoot apex of the banana: interpretive diagrams. (a) The central apical dome with the youngest leaf showing sufficient growth to begin to encircle the axis and overarch the apex. (b) The central apical dome, showing the origin of leaf primordia and a completely overarching primordium. (c) The apex completely enclosed within a series of hollow cones formed by the encircling leaf bases. The stippled area shows the location of the marginal meristems that build the laminae.   The precursory appendage is shown as the extended tip of the outermost leaf.   (d) Diagram to interpret the median longitudinal section through the shoot apex of *Musa acuminata* cv. Gros Michel. (From Barker and Steward, *Ann. Botany* N. S. 26, 389–411, 1962.)

at their bases, they grow upward and outward to form a succession of hollow cylindrical leaf bases (Fig. 7–14).

There are several unusual features of the vegetative plant body of the banana which require explanation in terms of the morphogenetic stimuli which are involved. These are:

i) The almost total lack of participation of the shoot tip in the growth of the vegetative plant body except to cut off the lateral appendages as primordia.

ii) The tremendous growth of leaf bases tangentially around the axis, radially outwards, and upwards to form the pseudostem.

iii) The presence of marginal leaf meristems at the overlapping tips of the leaf primordia which eventually build the lamina of the leaf (Figs. 7–14 and 7–15).

iv) The complete lack of buds in the axils of these encircling leaves. In fact, when buds eventually do arise they do so adventitiously and as far away from their normal position (as in dicotyledons) as possible, on the outer surface of the pseudostem. Therefore the normal dominant growth of a shoot apex is

FIG. 7–15. Meristems on the overlapping edges of an encircling leaf cut in transverse section: these will form the two halves of the lamina. A precursory appendage is shown in transverse section at the lower right of the figure. (From Barker and Steward, *Ann. Botany* N. S. 26, 389–411, 1962.)

here lacking; this is taken over by the leafy appendages and vegetative buds which also seem anomalous in their formation. This implies a quite unusual set of growth correlations and morphogenetic stimuli.

v) However, the most dramatic morphogenetic event occurs when the vegetative plant body switches over to a floral development. This occurs when the plant body has produced, as primordia or expanded leaves, a given number of appendages (over 40 in the cultivar Gros Michel), by which time the central dome of the shoot apex has slowly increased in size (Fig. 7–16). Apparently all that is accomplished in the central dome of the apex over the many months that elapse prior to this event is the production of enough cells to build slowly the necessary bulk upon which the floral development can be based.

vi) At the point of transition from the vegetative to the floral shoot a complete transformation occurs in the apex. The central tip grows, advances up the pseudostem, and forms a succession of lateral organs (bracts), the growth of which is relatively suppressed; but vigorous "buds" now occur in the axils of the bracts. The buds form double, crescent-shaped rows of meristematic regions

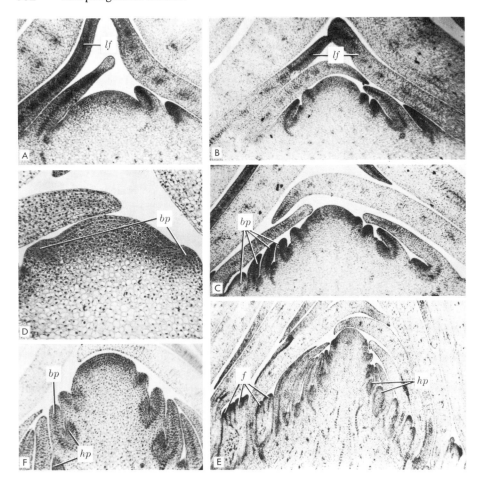

FIG. 7–16. Origin and development of the inflorescence. A. Longitudinal section of the vegetative shoot apex showing leaf primordia (*lf*). Note the broad apical dome. B. Longitudinal section of the apex at transition from the vegetative to the reproductive state. Bract primordia (*bp*) have already appeared. C. Longitudinal section of the transformed apex. Note the gradual elongation of the apex and the numerous bract primordia (*bp*) with axillary meristematic regions. D. The terminal part of C, if enlarged, shows three mantle layers, the subapical region, and the bract primordia. E. Same as C but including the well-formed bracts at the base of the figure with hand primordia (*hp*) in their axils. F. Central apex of E enlarged. (From Barker and Steward, *Ann. Botany* N. S. 26, 389–411, 1962.)

the spring of the year, when temperatures are lower, are richer in asparagine, and fruits that develop in the summer contain more of their amide as glutamine. Moreover, most, if not all, of the asparagine is in the central, carpellary regions (Steward *et al.*, 1960).

Metabolism and Morphogenesis

It is difficult to separate the metabolism which is the *cause* of morphogenetic events from that which *results* from the changed growth which a given morphogenetic stimulus initiates. In fact, insufficient use may have been made of metabolic criteria in tracing the course of growth and morphogenesis. Earlier reference has been made to the changed metabolic patterns, as shown by the complement of nitrogen compounds, that accompany growth and development (cf. Chapter 6). The stimuli that cause modified leaves of the tulip to assume the form of bulb scales or such floral parts as sepals, petals, stamens, and carpels, also modify greatly their nitrogen metabolism. Differences in the composition of leaves, stems, and tubers, whether these are to be seen in mint (Steward *et al.*, 1962) or the potato (Steward and Durzan, 1965), reflect, not the total innate genetically determined biochemical potentiality of the cells in question, but the way this is modified by their position in the organ in which they occur. In other words, morphogenesis and metabolism are here controlled by similar stimuli. Moreover, environmental factors that are known to determine morphogenesis also affect metabolic patterns (Steward, 1963). Assuming that a given

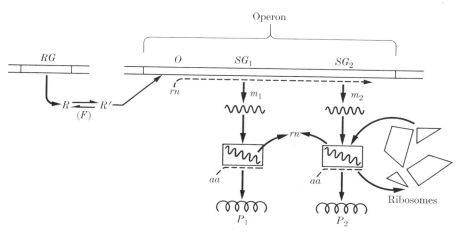

FIG. 7–17. General model of the regulation of enzyme synthesis. (*RG*, regulator gene; *R*, repressor converted to *R'* in the presence of effector *F* (inducing or repressing metabolite); *O*, operator; *SG*$_1$, *SG*$_2$, structural genes; *rn*, ribonucleotides; *m*$_1$, *m*$_2$, messengers made by *SG*$_1$ and *SG*$_2$; *aa*, amino acids; *P*$_1$, *P*$_2$, proteins made by ribosomes associated with *m*$_1$ and *m*$_2$.) [After Jacob and Monod, 1961.]

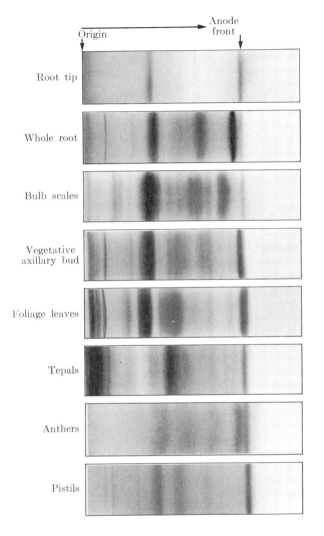

Origin → Anode front

Root tip

Whole root

Bulb scales

Vegetative axillary bud

Foliage leaves

Tepals

Anthers

Pistils

◄FIG. 7–18. Electrophoretic separations on acrylamide gels of the soluble proteins (pH 8.3) of *Tulipa*. (From Barber and Steward, unpublished data.)

FIG. 7–19. Electrophoretic separations on acrylamide gels of the soluble protein (pH 8.3) of three-day-old pea seedlings. (a) Segment, 0–1 mm from the top of the root. (b) Segment, 5–6 mm from the tip of the root. (c) Hypocotyl. (d) Epicotyl. (e) Plumule. (f) Cotyledons. (Cf. Steward, Lyndon, and Barber, 1965.)►

morphogenetic stimulus is to exert its effect through some metabolic step, where should one look for the causally important metabolite? Since so much is now known about the mechanism of protein synthesis (cf. Fig. 3–20) and the genetic determination of protein structure, it is not unreasonable that morphogenetic stimuli may intervene to modify or modulate the genetic determination of protein structure. In other words, may the morphogenetic stimuli act through special genes which are modifiers and repressors (in the sense of Jacob and Monod) and thus be able to turn on or off functional genes, or groups of genes (cf. Fig. 7–17)? If one approaches problems of development and morphogenesis

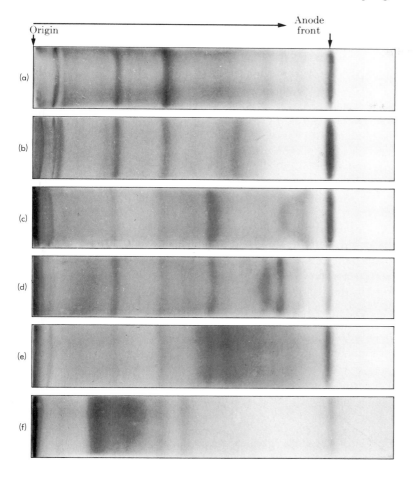

in this way, one might seek distinctive protein complements as the immediate consequence of the morphogenetic stimuli and these, through their role as enzymes or as special structural moieties, could greatly affect the course of metabolism and thus of development. The technique of acrylamide gel electrophoresis now permits a range of soluble mobile proteins to be scanned in ways that reveal differences between organs of the same plant. Figure 7–18 shows that one can ascribe particular protein complements to the morphologically distinct regions of the tulip plants; one can also trace changes which occur during differentiation in the pea plant (Fig. 7–19). At this point, however, these results only arouse the hope that it will be possible to relate morphogenetic stimuli more closely to metabolism than hitherto, and through their ability to modify genetically determined mechanisms of protein synthesis, to the proteins which are important in growth and development (cf. also Chapter 8).

Morphogenetic Effects in Organisms Other Than Angiosperms

The morphogenetic problems of plants are, however, not confined to plants with a highly organized apical growing region, for they are equally prominent in the thallophyta. In *Coprinus*, for example, darkness causes the stipe to be elongated and the pileus to be smaller. Other striking effects occur in the fungi. [Light-stimulated morphogenesis, Gutter (1957), in *Trichoderma* may be suppressed by 5 fluorouracil (Galun and Gressel, 1966).] Bisby (1925) even claimed that a fraction of a second of light exposure was enough to permit the formation of conidia in certain fungal colonies. In the work of Raper on *Achlya* (1940–1966), extremely sensitive chemical mechanisms have been detected, which evoke the formation of the sex organs and cause the attraction of the gametes. (See also Machlis, 1966)

In the U.S.A. *Marchantia* is often used in class demonstrations to show sex organs in the gametophyte, and to do this in winter, plants may be placed under the greenhouse bench in flats with supplementary light. On one occasion an enterprising graduate assistant used fluorescent lights for this purpose, only to find that they were ineffective, and so the interesting observation was made that the red light of a Mazda lamp was essential for the formative effects which evoke this response. (Perhaps this may be another case where the effect of red light may be reversed by far red!)

Dr. Armin Braun of Rockefeller University (cf. Pringle *et al.*, 1960 and Pringle, 1961) has investigated the formation of antheridia on the gametophyte of a fern, particularly of *Aspidium*, and there is in prospect a chemical description of the mechanism by which these structures are induced. *Aspidium* gametophytes will form antheridia if they are treated with an extract of the medium on which the bracken fern (*Pteridium aquilinum*) has been grown. There is, therefore, something in the culture fluids on which the bracken fern has grown that induces antheridia on *Aspidium*. This is not, apparently, a growth-inhibiting effect, as shown by cell counts, and it is not an effect which is easily reproduced by a variety of normally growth-promoting substances or extracts. It seems, therefore, to be a highly specific effect, for antheridial cells can only be induced in the first 14 days after the germination of the spore. Apparently this is a fairly general effect, because related species of fern all show antheridial induction from the material produced by *Pteridium*. Apparently then we have here another example in which the cells of the antheridium-forming gametophyte are endowed with a potentiality to form the sex organs, *but it requires a highly specific stimulus to evoke their formation.* In a lecture, given at Cornell University, Dr. Braun (1954) described how, over a period of years, he had grown spores in some thousand flasks in the light, at 23°C for seven weeks, producing in each crop 25 liters of material to be extracted. Five hundred liters were obtained, and from this was isolated *about one-half milligram of active substance for every 25 liters of medium;* but this one-half milligram of substance is active in producing this morphogenetic response at the incredible dilution of 10^{-9}, i.e., *one part in a thousand million*. The substance in question is apparently stable, sparingly soluble in ether, soluble in ethylacetate, has a characteristic absorption at 200 μ, and so on. It has some of the characteristics of an unsaturated acid but it is not, as yet, identified.

The above examples, arbitrarily selected, indicate that the same general principle may be expected to operate, probably at all levels in the plant kingdom. Individual cells or organized growing regions are endowed with certain innate potentialities, but the extent to which these are expressed is subtly determined by chemical regulation in which substances which specifically unleash this potentiality produce a biological response out of all proportion to the minute amount of the catalytically active substance that is involved. It is clear, therefore, that there is here a very rewarding area for biochemical investigation of the morphogenetic stimuli and of the causally active substances for their action. Moreover, the basic observations on which such research is based may often be made, as already indicated, very simply by well-informed observers.

In principle the control of growth, development, and morphogenesis must operate at different levels. In any given organism, the tolerable range of morphogenetic responses, and its limitations, have already been set during evolution; modern genetics prescribes how this information is conserved and transmitted. The problems of development and morphogenesis require an understanding of the means by which this information is transcribed for use. In the first instance organ specificity must operate by calling into play a prescribed part of the genetic machinery. But even this control over the behavior of the cells during development may be exogenous to them and take the form of specific agents which, as growth-regulatory substances, operate at the level at which cell division, or cell enlargement, is determined. Or the vital activities of cells may be mediated in peculiarly organ-specific ways, inasmuch as cells in distinctive positions in the plant body, or which are destined to play a prescribed role, perform their metabolism in distinctively organ-specific ways, and to do this, cells mobilize organ-specific proteins to mediate their metabolism. As seen, the versatility of the protein complement, which may be produced within a given and constant genetic constitution, seems more than equal to this task. But within the feasible range of morphogenetic adaptability the environmental stimuli hold further sway over the course of development. Where these effects are in response to light, the organism needs to "see" by a pigment system (e.g., phytochrome) and subsequently to respond to it; where the responses are to temperature (whether during periods of light or darkness), a temperature-sensitive recording device (in the form of the products of chemical reactions) is needed; if the responses to either light or temperature involve critical settings along the variable time, then the equivalent of a "biological clock" is also involved; and where gravity is a morphogenetic stimulus, then the organism must detect that stimulus by some aspect of its organization which responds by virtue of its mass.

The problem of morphogenesis is to understand, ultimately, how all these various stimuli converge upon the organization of the living cells that *in situ* compose the organism, to modify a pattern of development which already operates subject to some measure of inherited control. The following chapter selects a particular problem—the onset of flowering and fruiting—to show how far our current knowledge may be equal to this task.

Summary

The ability to respond to stimuli is a fundamental property of living organisms. Tactic movements and tropisms are responses to particular stimuli. The morphogenetic stimuli exert their effects by determining the kind of growth which ensues. Morphogenetic effects in the early growth of embryos are examined from the standpoint that they may be in part a response to the special nurture which the embryo receives in the ovule. The extent to which free somatic cells, furnished with the appropriate nutrients, may recapitulate the growth of embryos (i.e., exhibit totipotency) is discussed with special reference to carrot cells. On this evidence, the zygote is not to be regarded as a unique cell, but as a diploid cell which can grow, in a medium which makes it grow, and in a space into which it can grow. Cell forms that result from growth and cell division of free somatic cells are described. Thus the physical separation of cells from their neighbors, which disrupts the influence of the tissue within which they developed, has immediate morphogenetic consequences. The morphogenetic effects of light, or complete darkness, on the vegetative growth of plants are summarized. Emphasis is placed upon the responses of plants, not to constant conditions, but to periodicities of light or temperature. Some early observations upon these phenomena are summarized, leading to the recognition that morphogenetic consequences flow from such stimuli as the balance between day and night temperatures, the daily duration of light or darkness, etc. The responses of plants to these stimuli are described by reference to the phenomena of rest period and dormancy, and their possible causation; alternative ways of approaching these problems that are suggested by work on tissue cultures are also described. The significance of events that occur in the cambial regions of trees in the springtime and that accompany the onset of xylem differentiation are discussed, as well as the role of growth-regulatory substances and their inhibitors in the dormancy of such fleshy storage organs as the potato tuber. Examples of photoperiodic phenomena are presented to illustrate the nature of the responses to this type of stimulus and the mechanism of the action of light in photo-responsive growth is examined with special reference to the work of Hendricks and Borthwick and others on the pigment system (phytochrome) which is involved. Various temperature effects, especially those due to exposure of young seedlings to lower temperatures than normal, are mentioned. The effect of temperature on the initiation of flowers in tulip bulbs is described, as well as the work of H. C. Thompson on the induction of flowering due to temperature treatments (i.e., the phenomenon usually termed vernalization). Whether a morphogenetic response is triggered off by the daily duration of light (or of darkness) or the temperature that prevails at night, it must surely make its impact upon growth in the growing regions by the intervention of some chemical substance, or substances. The role of gibberellins is briefly mentioned in this context. Long or short days and low temperature are morphogenetic stimuli that elicit responses in plants of temperate regions. Therefore, and by contrast, the morphogenetic responses that occur during the growth and development of a banana plant are described, for these can hardly originate in cyclic features of the environment and must surely originate within the plant as it grows. Some very unusual features of the vegetative growth of this plant are described, for these must be evoked by powerful morphogenetic stimuli which are nevertheless reversed or modified when flowering ensues. The parthenocarpic development of fruits and the formation of different types of flower on the same inflorescence are again morphogenetic responses which should be explained in terms of the stimuli by which they are evoked. Stress is laid upon the evident fact that the fortunes of a large agricultural industry may ultimately turn upon the behavior of a few highly specialized but minute growing regions as in the banana plant. Some morphogenetic responses of non-flowering plants to external stimuli are also described. Finally, it is to be concluded that individual cells are endowed with certain innate potentialities; these are modified, or controlled, by their presence within a growing region. The extent to which these potentialities may be expressed is ultimately determined by chemical regulation, i.e., by the substances that prompt cells to divide, to enlarge, or to differentiate, and by the interactions of these substances with each other and with their respective synergists or inhibitors. Attention is also drawn to the possibility that among the many metabolic events that flow from, and are parallel to, morphogenetic responses there may be some that are more causally significant than others. In this context, the association of characteristic soluble protein complements with morphologically distinct regions is significant, for it arouses the expectation that morphogenetic stimuli may intervene to modify otherwise genetically determined protein complements and these, as enzymes or structural proteins, may determine both metabolism and the course of growth. Flowering and fruiting is reserved for discussion as a separate morphogenetic problem.

chapter eight

THE ONSET OF FLOWERING AND FRUITING: CONTRASTS IN VEGETATIVE AND REPRODUCTIVE GROWTH

The primary topic of this chapter is the transition from the vegetative habit to the flowering condition and the nature of the stimuli which bring this about. As part of the background against which the floral stimulus may be judged it is profitable to see how leafy appendages are arranged on the axis of vegetative shoots and, in the contrasting organization of a flower, to appreciate the magnitude of the transition which occurs with the onset of flowering and fruiting. (Such other transitions as those from juvenile to adult leaf forms are referred to in Chapter 10.)

Growth and Cell Division in Vegetative Shoot Apices: Phyllotaxis

A conspicuous and impressive feature of angiosperm shoot organization is the way leaves are arranged upon the axis. This arrangement (i.e., the phyllotaxis) necessarily derives from the way the leaf primordia originate on the shoot apex. Since buds most commonly appear in the axils of leaves, branching habits are also related to phyllotaxis.

The first point to be made about phyllotaxis is the least controversial. It is essentially a problem of shoots—the arrangement of leaves on the axis of any vascular plant. It is the prime function of shoots to expose a large surface or canopy of leaves to air and light but it is not cell surface alone that needs to be efficiently arranged, for, at its extremities, a shoot performs nutritional and physiological functions which, in the "division of labor" of the plant body, require that substances (nutrients, water, and stimuli) be effectively moved to and fro. Indeed the ramifications of the vascular system in shoots are as impressive a feature as the way shoots proliferate and enlarge their surface and arrange it in space. This may be seen in any cleared or macerated preparation which shows the internal detail of the vascular skeleton of a flowering plant (Fig. 6–22). Hence, to increase surface and bulk without internal communication is of little avail.* This is the condition in the "*Cladophora* balls" (Fig. 1–4).

---

* J. B. S. Haldane says in an essay on "Being the Right Size," in a volume entitled *Possible Worlds* (1928), that comparative anatomy is largely conditioned by, and the consequence of, the struggle to maintain surface with increasing volume.

Hence any discussion of leaf arrangement (phyllotaxis) also involves the vascular system. Indeed it may often seem baffling to decide whether a given leaf primordium develops where the vascular supply permits, or whether the vascular elements are caused to grow by the developing leaf primordia! Nevertheless, during evolution, the various phyllotactic patterns that have emerged must have endowed the plants in question with overall physiological efficiency, especially in photosynthesis, in the situations in which they grow. The baffling problems do not only concern the origin of the phyllotactic patterns in evolution; they also relate to the means by which during development they are reproduced, and to the nature and mode of action of the causal stimuli which govern the behavior of the shoot apex to achieve these ends. It is hardly enough, though self-evident, to say that phyllotaxis is inherited and genetically determined, for it still needs to be explained developmentally. One should, however, see the problem of phyllotaxis as the ultimate outcome of that first very obvious tendency in the shoot, evident as soon as polarity is established in the embryo, to grow in both volume and surface, in sharp contrast to roots, which emphasize their growth in length. The phyllotaxis and branching habit of an angiosperm shoot therefore achieves efficient means to discharge the functions of a shoot even as the structure of a root furnishes the effective means for it to absorb water and solutes (Fig. 1–20). The problem of phyllotaxis, therefore, boils down to the way in which the growth at a shoot apex is dissected into discrete units, with its consequential implications for both leaf and branch development and vascular communication.

The literature that describes the various types of phyllotaxis that are encountered, and the ways of representing these geometrically and in terms of mathematical formulae, is far beyond the scope of the present discussion. Reference may be made to the papers of the Snows (1955, 1959, 1962) and of Richards (1951, 1956), and to both longer (Wardlaw, 1965, pp. 1027–1044) and shorter (Clowes, 1961, pp. 86–96) recent summaries of such works in relation to discussions of this subject. All that is done here is to relate the patterns of leaf arrangement in angiosperms to the shoot apex in which they originate, so that phyllotaxis may be seen as a problem of vegetative growth and organization that requires physiological interpretation, and so that it may also serve as the background for a description of the events that precede flowering.

There are two obvious and related approaches to phyllotaxis. How may the variety of phyllotactic systems be described? How is the growth of the vegetative shoot apex locally controlled to achieve the patterns which are observed?

Wardlaw (1965, p. 1029) illustrates nine selected types of phyllotaxis (*A* through *I*) as shown by the ground plan of their leaf arrangement (which is also shown in transverse sections). The growing points of mint (Fig. 1–13) conformed to the decussate type, *E;* the growing points of banana (cf. Fig. 7–12), to the spirodistichous condition as in type *I*.

A convenient device emphasizes the arrangement of leaves by their points of insertion on the axis. Leaves that are morphologically above or below each other form part of the same orthostichy in the stem. The interval that separates one leaf from the next is a plastochron. A shoot with all its leaves in two opposite ranks possesses two orthostichies; a shoot with opposite and decussate leaves, in which the angle of divergence between successive leaves is $90°$, would have four orthostichies. When leaves alternate on the axis their angles of divergence may be various, and, in accordance with this, the line connecting successive points of insertion will trace a spiral path around the axis. The number of such turns that intervene between successive leaves in the same orthostichy describes the spiral phyllotaxy in question; namely A turns around the stem include B internodes. On this convention the fraction of the circumference which is obligated by each leaf is A/B, and the divergence of successive leaves, measured by the angle between them, is $A/B \times 360°$. Common phyllotactic systems, according to this classification, fall into the series $A/B = \frac{1}{2}, \frac{1}{3}, \frac{2}{5}, \frac{3}{8}, \frac{5}{13}, \ldots$. (An example of $\frac{2}{5}$ phyllotaxis is considered in Chapter 6, Fig. 6–20.) This series, in which both numerators and denominators consist of numbers that represent the sum of the two preceding members, is known as the Fibonacci series. Many authors have yielded to the charm of more or less precise mathematical description, in one or other of these ways, of the observed patterns of leaf arrangement. At best, however, these devices describe phyllotaxy; the more major question, which is relevant here, is the way in which a given leaf arrangement arises and is determined during development.

In order that any leaf primordium may form in the apex there must be a local center of growth; i.e., some cell, or cells, must divide more frequently than its neighbors. If essential metabolites are furnished from within a growing mass, their supply becomes progressively less efficient to the surface as the mass grows. Under these circumstances the growth breaks up into a series of local proliferations. This effect may be seen even in the contrasted growth patterns established in carrot explants cultivated on a stationary agar medium, as opposed to those grown in liquid. Although both types of culture are ultimately nourished by a basal medium containing coconut milk and have equal potentialities for growth, the conditions of nutrient supply are very different. In rotated liquid cultures the surface cells are regularly oriented to light and gravity, and are evenly bathed by the nutrient medium; such cells receive their nutrients externally with a minimum contribution from the central core of the explant. When similar small explants are implanted upon a stationary agar medium the nutrients are transmitted to the surface cells via the stalk-like explant. In the former case the explants turn green and they grow in an elipsoidal, nearly spherical, form with a minimum of local and irregular proliferation; in the latter case they remain colorless, proliferate irregularly, and the surface breaks up into discrete centers of growth [cf. the appearance of explants cultured in liquid and on agar as in

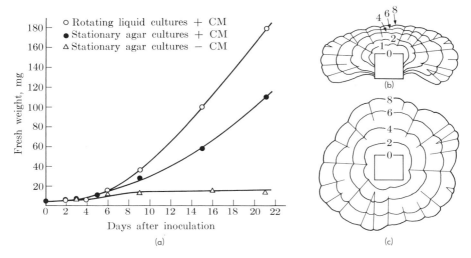

FIG. 8-1. (a) Growth of carrot root phloem explants in the presence and absence of coconut milk in rotated liquid aseptic culture or in stationary solid culture. (From early work of Caplin and Steward). (b) Diagrammatic section through culture illustrating morphological changes during eight weeks' growth. Section perpendicular to nutrient agar surface. (From Caplin, *Botan. Gaz.* 108, 379–393, 1947.) (c) Section parallel to nutrient agar surface. Cubes changed into somewhat flattened hemispheres by growth of knobs in which proliferation of cells occurred in and near surface. Concentric lines represent the shape of the culture after indicated number of weeks growth. Radial lines indicate surface of contact between adjacent knobs. Points of radial lines nearest center are sites at which the knobs have divided. Where two lines radiate from such points, new growing centers have been formed. (From Caplin, *Botan. Gaz.* 108, 379–393, 1947.)

Fig. 8–1(a) and also see Caplin (1947) for the form of the cultures as they are grown on agar, Fig. 8–1(b,c)]. This contrast in the form of the early growth of cultivated tissue is unaffected by vascular supply from within the culture, although Wetmore (Wetmore and Rier, 1963) has studied the effects of supplies of sugar and auxin upon the differentiation of scattered vascular elements within a cultured tissue mass. One may see, therefore, in the early formation of discrete growth centers in embryonic shoots, which become leaf primordia, the evidence that endogenous nutrients and stimuli are more effectively furnished to the cells in question. But, having embarked upon such localized growth, every new center of activity that arises on the shoot apex [unlike the condition in the proliferated tissue-cultured mass of Fig. 8–1] arises in time and space in ways that bear clearly discernible relations to the first such centers to form; this is the problem of phyllotaxis.

The dilemma of phyllotaxis is the dilemma of any attempted interpretation of growth—one should not confuse descriptions (even mathematical descriptions; cf. Chapter 9) with causal explanation. To account for phyllotaxy and leaf arrangement the following general ideas have been advanced:

1.   That the development of a leaf begins when the surface of the shoot apex, growing at the surface more than in bulk, wrinkles and throws itself into folds, the folds becoming leaves.

2.   That the site of a new leaf is determined by the development of a preexisting leaf trace below it.

3.   That the site of a new leaf is never at the summit of the shoot apex proper and that each new leaf is as far removed from its predecessor as possible, thus implying that, by this mode of origin and by the development of the internode, the subsequent leaves will not compete with each other so that, in their origin, they even appear to exert mutual repulsion.

4.   That each new leaf as a local center of growth preempts, as it were, a portion of the apex and, therefore, that new leaves arise whenever there are vacant, unobligated spaces large enough for them on the shoot apex.

Point 1 loses much of its force when it is realized that new leaves arise much more on the sides, or flanks, of the apical meristem than at its dome-like extremity. Point 2 presents the difficulty that, while leaf primordia and developing leaf traces are closely interrelated, it is hard to distinguish which initiates the other—on balance, it seems that stimuli from the developing leaf more often initiate basipetal xylem differentiation in an existing procambial strand. Indeed, various workers (M. and R. Snow, Ball, and Wardlaw) have concluded that the site of a new leaf initial is not in fact determined by the pre-existing leaf initials. The experimental methods they adopted required careful incisions to isolate the presumptive sites of future leaves from any connection with procambia and, in *Lupinus albus*, all the authors agree that leaves which may be normal in size and position develop despite such incisions. So much is clear from the surgical experiments that Clowes (1961) writes: "The conclusion of M. and R. Snow (1947, 1948) was that the leaf traces played no appreciable part in determining the positions of the leaf. In this they have been supported by Ball (1948), working also on *Lupinus albus*, and by Wardlaw (1949a and b), working on *Dryopteris dilatata*." One must therefore pass on to points 3 and 4, which may usefully describe what occurs in the apex even if they do not prescribe the stimuli by which this localized growth pattern is regulated. Thus the problem of phyllotaxy reduces to the physiological stimuli which can locally incite such active growth centers to form leaves and which control their interaction.

The idea that a developing leaf needs to obligate a given amount of space in the growing point in order that it may develop is attractively supported by the evidence, cited earlier, that many opposite and decussate plants may abnormally produce alternating whorls of three leaves at a node instead of two. As stated previously (Chapter 5), this occurs when, for reasons that can only be surmised, the apical dome is unusually large. The idea that slight differences in level between the opposite leaves at a node may sufficiently imbalance the system, so that normally opposite and decussate plants may adopt a spiral habit, is an attractive explanation for what may also occur in mint (Crane, 1951) when it exhibits a spiral torsion in its stem. The prevalence of opposite and decussate phyllotaxis in dicotyledons is also attractively related to the theories of both repulsion between leaf initials and needed space on the apex because, with two opposite cotyledons, their influence should predispose the shoot to produce its next leaves in pairs. Similarly, the greater frequency of spiral arrangements in monocotyledons bears an obvious relation to the overriding influence at the outset of a single leaf-like cotyledon. These ideas are attractive in a general sense, but they lack the precision that will come when it is known by what means the permissible area for leaf development is defined (i.e., the means by which cells that might produce competing leaf centers are inhibited) and the precise way in which the cell divisions that initiate each new leaf primordium are in turn incited and controlled. The mechanisms that were discussed in Chapter 5 should contribute ultimately to this end, but, whatever the means of growth regulation and integration that apply in a vegetative angiosperm shoot, they are very drastically altered by the stimuli that cause the shift toward flowering and fruiting. This will now be discussed.

It may seem unnecessary to ask, "What is a flower?" Some answers come readily to mind and may receive general agreement; but, as with all questions of comparative morphology, when the homologies and relationships are pushed to their ultimate, difficulties and differences of opinion arise. Even so, it was disturbing to see some years ago in the columns of a popular weekly an article, replete with colored pictures, entitled "The Sex Life of the Gladiolus," in which flowers were displayed with their anthers and pistil referred to as sex organs and with the implication that the pollen grain was the counterpart of an animal sperm. While this may make for saleable copy, the true homologies are far less apparent. Thus, one of the problems implicit in the physiological interpretation of flowering and fruiting is a clear appreciation of what is to be explained.

What then is a flower? A flower may be, and has been, described as an "axis beset with sporophylls." The anther, as the microsporophyll, gives rise to microspore mother cells, and by meiosis to microspores which initiate the male sexual cycle of the angiosperm. In turn, the carpel with its ovules gives rise to megaspore mother cells which arise in the nucellus and, through meiosis, give megaspores which in turn initiate the female sexual cycle of the angiosperm. Flowering, then, does not comprise a single morphological event, but, in the average hermaphroditic flower with both male and female sexual cycles represented, there appears in succession a baffling array of highly specialized structures, completely different in form from those of the vegetative plant body.

Flower-Forming Substances or Hormones: The Concept of a Flowering Hormone

The viewpoint outlined above has an important consequence. When considering a given treatment, whether it is photoperiodic or a vernalizing low-temperature treatment, or a treatment with a chemical substance regarded as flower-forming, the prevalent tendency is to believe that the treatment acts at one point to induce the actual *formation* of the flower as a whole. This idea is implicit in the concept that there is a single flower-forming hormone or "florigen." It is always easier to name a hormone than to isolate or identify it, but the question can be raised whether there is any evidence that a "florigen," in the sense of a flower-forming substance, actually exists. If the role of florigen is to act upon the purely vegetative apex, which normally forms leaves, internodes, and vegetative buds in regular succession, and miraculously to induce this apex to desist and to form, instead, a regular succession of more or less leaf-like organs (sepals and petals), followed by whorls of quite different organs (the stamens), then whorls of still different organs (the carpels), and finally, to set in motion the intricate machinery of meiosis and of development, then it seems that these diverse actions are far beyond the resources of what we normally consider a hormone to be. How could one chemical substance induce effects which are so varied? Is it reasonable, in short, to invoke a single formative chemical control over a system which is clearly subject to unit genetic controls at many key points in its development, as in the case of maize (Postlethwait and Nelson, 1964)?

The Innate Capacity to Flower of the Angiosperm

What is the reasonable alternative? Surely it is the destiny of flowering plants to flower, form fruit, and set seed. This is inherent in their genetic constitution; it is as much a "built-in" characteristic of the zygote as its ability to grow. The charted instructions are already present in the zygote for all the development that may intervene between zygote and the next meiosis, when spores are again formed. However, reduction division, an essential feature of meiosis, is not confined to the environment of anther and ovules, for, under appropriate conditions which need to be more closely defined, free somatic cells will undergo reduction and even exhibit pseudochiasmata (Mitra and Steward, 1961). Therefore, in the morphogenetic responses of flowering and fruiting we are concerned with the way in which these innate, genetically "built-in" characteristics are modulated and worked out—not with their initiation *de novo*.

The "destiny to flower and fruit" may be released and consummated in a chickweed within a few weeks after its germination; in a biennial it may require two seasons of growth; and in some plants flowering may not be achieved for many years. Klebs formulated the concept of "ripeness to flower" to express the conditions which evoke flowering.

An alternative to the florigen theory, therefore, is that the innate ability to form flowers is present from the start but cannot be expressed until there is a multicellular organization of a sufficient degree of complexity. Thus at a very early stage of embryogeny a portion of the meristematic tissue is set apart to this end. This does not mean that the cells in question are spontaneously changed, for they, like any other living cells of the plant body, retain all the genetic information of the whole. It is rather that the fact of their being where they are exposes them to a physical and chemical environment which promotes one kind of development while it suppresses another. Thus, what we normally conceive to be the floral induction stimuli could be regarded as stimuli which do not initiate the *formation* of the flower initials *de novo* but rather release meristematic potentialities that are already there. Thus, a chickweed may flower uninhibitedly because there is nothing in its vegetative plant body to suppress the potentiality to flower. A century plant (*Agave americana* L.) goes many years without flowering, because the potentiality to flower is inhibited in the early stages of growth, and some protracted events must occur before this inhibition is removed. In a Gros Michel banana plant the vegetative growing point is either prompted to, or released to, flower after many months and the prior formation of over 40 leaf primordia (cf. Chapter 7). It is conceivable that a single substance may remove an overall block to the growth of an organ, or a series of organs; thus, when development eventually ensues, growth occurs according to the potentialities of the initiating cells or regions, but not, in any real sense, because the stimulus acts in a formative way to determine the course of that development. Hence, the capacity to flower should be inherent in an angiosperm from the start; this being so, we should be concerned only with the mechanism which evokes that development—the mechanism which unleashes it, as it were, and removes whatever blocks or hindrances exist to suppress its earlier expression.

What then do we know about the conditions that elicit this flowering response? Annuals complete all the requirements for flowering in their first cycle of growth and, having set seed, they often consume a large part of the dry matter of the plant body, so that the vegetative plant body is unable to weather the winter and has, therefore, run its course. In a biennial plant, on the other hand, the first cycle of growth may result in the formation of a storage organ of one sort or another, often with a rosette of leaves, and the plant does not normally complete the requirements for flowering until after it has been exposed to one winter period. Often exposure to cold is the factor that unleashes the ability of a biennial to grow in its second cycle and to form flowers.

Perennial plants are of two broad kinds. Monocarpic perennials may exist in the vegetative state for several years until a suitable mass of tissue is formed; if then there is an adequate supply of whatever materials evoke flowering, the plant flowers once, but only once, consuming thereby some essential features of the plant body, which then dies.* Polycarpic perennials, on the other hand, having once achieved the ability to flower, do so repeatedly, although, as horticulturalists are only too well aware, this capacity may not be equally well expressed in every season of growth. In temperate climes many cultivated fruit trees often exhibit the phenomenon of alternate bearing, suggesting that a heavy set of fruit, or seed, in one season tends in some way to consume reserves of materials that are needed for the flowering-fruiting process in the next cycle of growth. These events, therefore, suggest that the potentiality to flower is present in angiosperms from the initial organization of the shoot, even with the formation of the embryo, and that the ease with which this potentiality is unleashed depends upon catalytic events that remove whatever block represses the otherwise free growth of these flower-forming initials or tissue.

If floral growing points are examined with the high powers of the microscope and compared with vegetative growing points, it is impressive how little difference may be seen. In the central regions, which consist of the apical dome of meristem with its surrounding primordia, there is astonishingly little to suggest a subsequent development so radically different from the formation of leaves and branches as the development of flowers, fruit, and seed. Ultimately, however, these different growth patterns must have a biochemical and material basis; there must be some point at which the biochemical or metabolic characteristics of the two types of meristem diverge.

Visible Effects on Growing Points at Floral Induction

The signs that distinguish shoot apices in their floral and vegetative states concern their form. The individual meristematic cells and the broad way in which primordia originate seem surprisingly similar in the two cases; however, the results of their growth are quite different. The phyllotactic patterns of dicotyledonous plants are relatively simple; leaves may be opposite, or opposite and decussate, or they may alternate on the axis with a type of phyllotaxis designated in the Fibonacci series by a fraction such as ⅖. However, angiosperm flowers commonly have a whorl of sepals and a whorl of petals, one or two whorls of stamens, and an ovary which may have one or several carpels; all these appendages arise on the axis in whorls in rapid succession with very short internodes between. Consequently, as a vegetative shoot apex becomes a floral apex, it must

---

* Medvedev (1966) sees flowering, as indeed "aging" generally, as part of a morphogenetic trend. Whereas many plants seem to undergo a slow and progressive "wearing out" of their productive capacity with age (and they often do so after flowering), this is probably to be attributed to the decline of protein synthesis and the ascendancy of breakdown (Medvedev, p. 556). However, in monocarpic plants rapid decline after flowering is complete. While speculation designed to fit these behavioral patterns into conventional views of DNA/RNA regulation are possible, convincing evidence is not at present available.

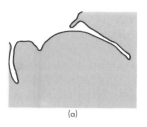 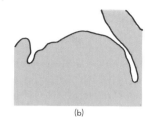 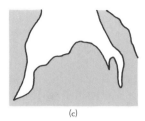

(a)   (b)   (c)

FIG. 8–2. *Vinca* shoot apices undergoing responses to floral stimulus. (a) Vegetative. (b) Transitional. (c) Floral condition. (After Boke, *Am. J. Botany* **38**, 433–439, 1947.)

accommodate itself to the formation upon its surface of many *more* lateral organs than normally appear in the vegetative state of a dicotyledonous plant. Therefore, when flowering occurs, the central dome of meristem of dicotyledons often becomes broader and flatter, as seen in median longitudinal section; this is in contrast to the more rounded, conical, and narrower shape of the vegetative apex. This condition has been illustrated by such authorities as Boke (1947), working on *Vinca* (Fig. 8–2), and Engard (1944) with *Rubus* (Fig. 8–3). And when a vegetative shoot apex is entirely transformed into a head of flowers, as in the capitulum of a composite, this type of change is accentuated.

A typical monocotyledon may present a somewhat different situation. The phyllotaxy of monocotyledonous plants is usually more complex, internodes are short, and the vegetative growing point produces in very rapid succession a large number of leaf primordia. Monocotyledonous flowers, however, commonly have fewer floral parts in each whorl, and the number three, of course, recurs

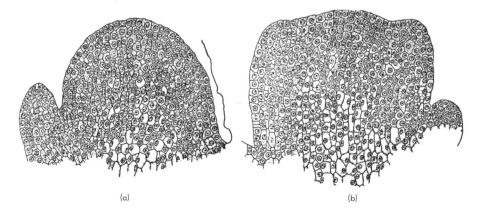

(a)   (b)

FIG. 8–3. *Rubus* sp. (a) The vegetative shoot apex. (b) The same during transformation into a floral apex. The dome-shaped apex (a) undergoes a characteristic flattening and widening. (After Engard, 1944; reproduced by permission of College of Tropical Agriculture, University of Hawaii.)

frequently. Consequently, when a monocotyledon shoot apex is converted into the floral state, it often bears on its surface *fewer* primordia than when it was in the vegetative state; thus, the apex may change its shape as the growing point becomes floral, and it often becomes narrower and more pointed in so doing. This seems to be the visible event which occurs in an orchid, as in the description published by Rotor and MacDaniels (1951), shown in Fig. 8–4. The central apical dome of the shoot of a banana plant plays little or no direct part in forming the vegetative plant body, for this role, as described in Chapter 7, is taken over by the leaves. By the time of flowering the central part of the apex of a banana shoot has become broad and somewhat flattened and it includes beneath it a sufficient bulk of tissue to be transformed into the massive inflorescence. When this occurs a very large number of floral buds occur in the axils of bracts but the immediate effect on the shape of the banana apex as it grows upward is that it becomes narrower and more pointed (Fig. 7–13). This type of transition is very evident when, as in grasses, the vegetative apex is transformed into an elongated flowering spike which bears along its axis many growing regions which form spikelets and individual flowers.

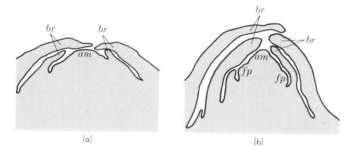

(a)   (b)

FIG. 8–4. (a) Outline drawing of apex of *Cattleya*, prior to flower formation. (b) Outline drawing of apex of *Cattleya*, at the time of differentiation of floral primordia. (*br*, bract; *am*, apical meristem; *fp*, floral primordia.) (After Rotor and MacDaniels, *Am. J. Botany* **38**, 147–151, 1951.)

A well-documented system is the growth of the tip of the cultivated wheat plant; this has been analyzed by Williams *et al.*, in a group of papers (1965). The first leaf to originate as a primordium after germination (i.e., the fourth) has received attention, especially with respect to its development prior to emergence.

In wheat each leaf primordium passes through a similar time sequence. The relative growth rate of the primordium (i.e., relative to that of the apex) begins slowly; it then rises to a maximum just before the leaf emerges and as it seemingly escapes from some prior limiting factors to its growth; subsequently, the relative growth rate falls. Hence, each leaf assumes, for a period, a dominant role in the growth of the apex.

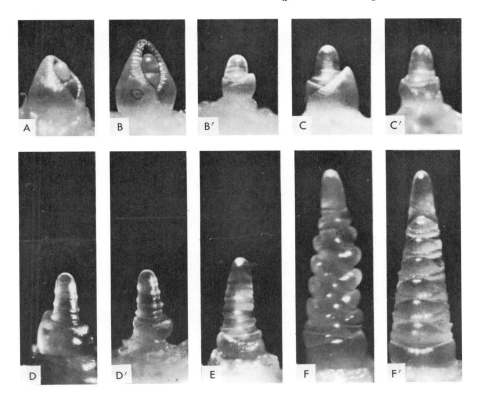

FIG. 8–5. Dissected apices, mid-April to the end of May. A–C', vegetative; D–F', just prior to and after inflorescence initiation. A. Apex from rhizome with outer scale leaf and next four in the bud removed. B. From shoot with fourth leaf lamina fully exposed. B'. Same with next outer cowl-like leaf (eighth on shoot) removed. C. Similar apex from slightly more mature shoot. C'. Same apex with next leaf (ninth on shoot) removed. D. Apex just prior to inflorescence production from shoot with seventh leaf lamina fully exposed. D'. Same with next leaf (twelfth) removed. E. Apex at inflorescence initiation from shoot with seventh or eighth fully exposed leaf and four others in bud removed. F, F'. Two views of young inflorescence with seventh or eighth fully exposed leaf and four others removed. (From Sharman, *Botan. Gaz.* 106, 269–289, 1945. Photo supplied by Dr. B. C. Sharman.)

The change in the form of a wheat shoot tip on the transition from the vegetative condition to the reproductive may be seen in Fig. 8–5, from the photographs of Sharman (1945). Williams stresses that this transition is first associated with a progressive decline in the relative importance of the growth rates of leaf primordia and a shift in emphasis "culminating in an almost explosive growth of corpus-derived tissue." This shift from a primary emphasis upon foliar growth in the vegetative state, to more cauline growth in the floral, is accompanied by a change from a rather flat cone in the terminal vegetative apex

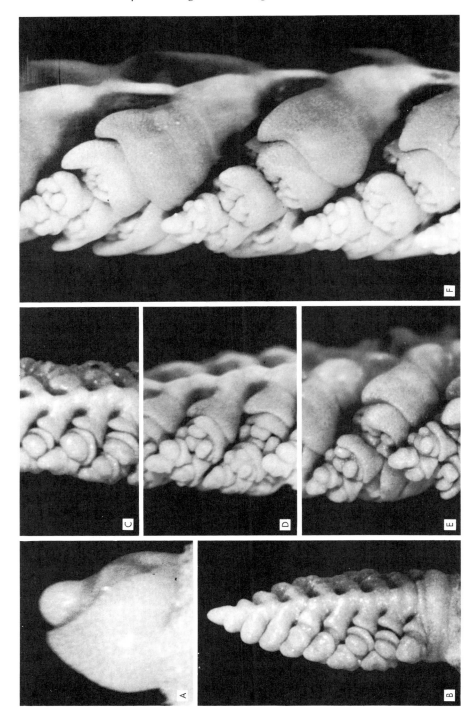

FIG. 8–6. Development of the inflorescence of wheat, induced by soaking the grain under long-day conditions (16-hour day): A. Vegetative apex 16 days after soaking—the apex has begun to elongate (×60); B. Apex 28 days after soaking—total length is 1.8 mm from foliar ridge to tip (×25); C. Thirty days after soaking (×50); D. Thirty-two days after soaking (×25); E. Thirty-four days after soaking (×25); F. Thirty-six days after soaking (×25). (Photographed by C. Totterdell; courtesy of Dr. R. F. Williams, C. S. I. R. O., Canberra.)

to an acute one, with many meristematic lobes or ridges along its length, in the reproductive state. In this respect the wheat and banana plants are somewhat similar. The factors which control the relative ascendancy of growth in the leaf primordia, or in the central axis, are fundamental in both plants to an understanding of the first events of floral induction. An evident change occurs as the apical dominance which suppresses lateral centers of growth near the vegetative apex gives way to a condition in which such lateral growth centers can freely develop, subdivide, and multiply in the formation of flowers. The full range and complexity of the subsequent events that lead to the development of a flowering spike, with its many distinct and crowded growth centers, which form the spikelets and individual flowers, is well shown in the series of photographs which comprise Fig. 8–6.

It would be far too presumptuous to claim that there is any current basis for a full understanding of all the controls which determine the smoothly integrated development of so complex an inflorescence as that of wheat. It is, however, noteworthy that the only visible signs, in this and other plants, which may offer clues to the first events of floral induction, concern the redistribution of growth in the central apical dome of the shoot apex and the consequential changes in its size and shape. External as well as internal (i.e., inherited) factors bear upon the way these changes are brought about. To illustrate this, reference may again be made to the floral growing point of tulip (Fig. 7–11). If the tulip flower develops in the bulb at different temperatures, it permits varying numbers of floral parts to form, and the characteristic whorls of three of the perfect, normal flower require a severely restricted temperature range, such as 23°C, for their formation.

But is it enough to attribute the whole business of flowering to a change in the size and shape of the central dome of meristem? If the potentiality and ability to flower is already present as formative embryonic initials or regions, long before this tissue develops and grows, is there any way in which it might be identified? Some speculative ideas (cf. Buvat, 1952), mainly from France, suggested that the main centers of growth in the formation of leaf primordia and internodes of the shoot lie along the flanks of the apical meristem, and that divisions in the central part of the shoot apex are far less frequent than had earlier been supposed (cf. Fig. 5–27). This gave rise to the idea that the central part of the apex of an angiosperm consists of quiescent cells, more or less "going along for the ride" until the conditions permit flowering, at which time they spring into activity and transform the shoot so that it produces a flower or an inflorescence. So drastic a revolution in thought may initially have been too extreme, and those who have considered this hypothesis do not give it unqualified support (cf. Clowes, 1961). However, this should not discourage the attempt to identify, in the apex of the shoot, those regions which, in the form of initiating cells, express the inherent capacity to form flowers, since these are almost certainly laid down and set apart at an early stage in development. But this inherent capacity is not solely in the cells—which may ultimately be totipotent— but it also resides in the milieu of the cell in the growing region. Randolph (1950) has drawn attention to some genetic and cytological effects in *Zea*, which are relevant. When studying the cytogenetic effects of ionizing radiation on corn, he noted certain abnormalities in the subsequent development of the tassel, which suggested that these abnormalities arose by lineal development from initiating cells that *must have been in the embryo when it was in the grain that was irradiated.*

Randolph also points out that the seeds which were irradiated produced abnormalities in leaves, some of which were already present as primordia in the seed:

These sectors obviously consisted of tissue derived from single cell initials which were present in the seed at the time of irradiation. The amount of tissue derived from an affected cell during ontogeny determined the size of the sectors which ordinarily varied in width from about 1 to 30 millimeters, and in length from a few centimeters up to the full extent of the leaf and leaf sheath.

However, chromosomal alterations were detected in the examination of the staminate spikes or tassel branches from a large number of the radiated plants, and these abnormalities were described. The frequency of these abnormalities again suggested that they derived from initiating cells in the growing point which were already committed *as they occurred in the seed.* Thus the initiating cells, which had been affected by the radiation, transmitted the abnormality in the formation of the tassel. Therefore, this cytological evidence is consistent with the view that in the growing point of the shoot, even as it exists in the seed, there are present initiating cells, or regions, which eventually grow to form the flowers. This is also consistent with the idea that there are, in the shoot growing point, localized areas which are not dissipated in vegetative growth but which remain more quiescent and which only burst into activity when floral growth occurs.

This problem has been under scrutiny at Harvard University. Wetmore has attempted to see whether the photoperiodic stimulus redistributed cell division in the shoot apex of photoperiodically sensitive plants. One may quote from Wetmore (1956):

Recent experience with three species of plants: *Chenopodium album* (lamb's quarters), *Xanthium saccharatum* (cocklebur), and *Glycine max* (Biloxi soybean), with known photoperiods, indicates that towards the close of the induction period, buds killed, fixed, and sectioned show the large-celled central region to be cut up into small, actively dividing cells. *In other words, as the vegetative bud is induced to become a flowering bud, the latent central part of the vegetative bud is activated and contributes to the inflorescence and flower production.* Our work has not yet progressed far enough to permit me to say whether there is a definite contribution to any *particular* part of the reproductive axis from that portion of the apical meristem. If it is found that a similar situation exists after investigating more angiosperms with varying patterns of organization in their apical meristems and with different induction periods, one may be in a better position to interpret the zonation of the angiospermous apex. If one were rash enough to extrapolate beyond the existing facts, one might hazard a statement that there is in the center of the angiospermous apex, and perhaps in the apices of similarly organized higher gymnosperms as well, a column of tissue which takes part in the reproductive phase of the life history only, a kind of Weismann's Germ Plasm.

Thus at least one experimental morphologist, looking anew at the floral growing point, saw some indication that the area that will eventually form the flower is set apart for this function in a localized region of the apex. In essence, therefore, the flower-forming potentiality is there from the start, but it springs into activity only when the stimulus to flowering occurs. That stimulus could well be the removal of the inhibition which prevents those potential flower-forming cells from growing when the plant is in the vegetative state. In the banana plant, only scattered cell divisions occur in the subapical region of the shoot meristem prior to flowering; these are only enough to build its own bulk. But with the onset of flowering much greater activity occurs in this region (Barker and Steward, 1962).

The changes that occur in the relatively quiescent cells of the central shoot apex as they are transformed into actively growing cells at floral induction are reminiscent of those that have been studied in the growth induction of carrot cells. In both cases an exogenous chemical stimulus to cell division is required. Recent studies on both systems by the use of the electron microscope reinforce the general similarity in the responses that culminate in cell division. Gifford and Stewart (1965) described changes in the central cells of the apical meristem of *Chenopodium album* three hours after one photo-inductive cycle. These changes included an altered endoplasmic reticulum (which became more complex and distributed through the cytoplasm), more active forms of plastids (which more nearly resembled those to be seen in the dividing cells along the flanks), and a great increase of ribosomes. Changes such as these, affecting virtually every feature of the cytoplasm, have also been seen to follow the transition from the quiescent to the active state in carrot cells in response to the naturally occurring cell division factors (cf. Chapter 4), as in the work of Israel and Steward, 1966 (cf. Figs. 5–2, 5–3, 5–6). The changes in the fine structure may also be correlated with the concomitant changes in nucleic acids and the inception of protein synthesis. All this suggests the kind of biochemical and morphological events which a floral stimulus must evoke in these otherwise quiescent cells as they become activated as a prelude to flowering.

Against this general background the factors which evoke flowering may now be examined, whether these factors are regarded as formative, with the actual induction of flowers, or whether they are regarded as releasing the inhibition of the growth of preexisting regions which, when they develop, can form flowers.

The Stimuli That Evoke Flowering

A suggestive observation was made by Gregory and Purvis (1936) on the vernalization of winter rye. They interpreted the morphology of the cereal spike and showed that behind a tapering meristem there is a series of ridges which represent leaf or bract primordia (cf. Figs. 8–5 and 8–6). According to Purvis, no treatment will induce the formation of flowers in these cereal grasses until *a definite number of leaves have appeared on the axis* and, as Williams later showed (pp. 382–5), the relative importance of the contribution of leaves to the growth of the apex suddenly declines when these plants flower. Spring-sown varieties, which grow to flower under long days, only require a small number of leaves to be preformed; this number is often seven. Under long days and short nights seven preformed leaves will release the potentiality of the growing point of rye to flower. Under short days the number of leaves required to permit flowering is much increased, to 22 to 25; i.e., flowering is very much delayed. Thus under short days and long nights it takes many more preformed leaves to release the potentiality of the apex to flower.

Winter-sown varieties, if grown in the spring, do not flower because they must normally lay down a large number of leaves prior to flowering, i.e., more than they have time to acquire before the long days arrive. Therefore, they remain vegetative and produce tillers but not flowers. Winter rye, on the other hand, when germinated and *grown at high temperature*, also requires the formation of a large number of leaves before flowering. If, however, the rye is germinated at 1°C, it is able to form flowers after the initiation of a smaller number of leaves—now not more than 12—*and these leaves can develop as leaf initials in the vernalized embryo.* Thus, according to Gregory and Purvis, winter rye will flower after 14 weeks at 1°C when it has formed as few as seven leaves. Therefore, what vernalization does is twofold: (a) It allows the effects of, or the stimulus from, preformed leaf initials, which are the photoperiodically responsive organs, to act with fewer leaf primordia; (b) it provides conditions in the seeds such that these leaf primordia can develop *before the grain is planted.*

Two other features of the vernalization response may be mentioned. First, the response is *normally* irreversible; i.e., although the response is brought about by exposure to cold, it is not usually reversed if the plants are subsequently placed at higher temperatures favorable to growth, for they then produce only floral shoots—the growth of which had been unleashed by the low temperature. Some cases have been reported in which, immediately after the vernalization treatment, its effect may be nullified by abnormally high temperatures applied before floral development. This seems to be the case in carrot and *Hyoscyamus* (Lang and Melchers, 1947). However, once the apex has begun to form floral parts it is committed and does not reverse. Secondly, the region of perception is the growing region, though the stimulus may be transmitted to other parts of the plant body. Some plants (e.g., *Lunaria biennis*), which may be propagated by leaf or petiole cuttings, may receive the floral stimulus from the cutting even if it is removed from a plant which has been exposed to cold; in this event the new shoot which develops does not need a cold stimulus in order to flower (Wellensiek, 1961, 1964). This principle was well shown in earlier experiments conducted by Curtis and Chang (1930) which were based on observations by H. C. Thompson (cf. Thompson, 1953). Plants that were normally vernalized at low temperature could be grown in the *perpetually vegetative state at high temperature*. This was conspicuously true of cabbage and of celery. Thompson illustrates a cabbage plant, which was grown by Miller (1929) at a temperature well above that which is normal for its growth; this plant remained vegetative, producing one vegetative head after another, until, eventually, it reached the full height of the greenhouse! This maintained vegetative condition in cabbage can be obviated not merely by chilling the whole plant but by *chilling only the shoot growing point*. Curtis and Chang (1930) showed this with celery by circulating water of known temperature through three millimeter rubber tubing wound around the base of the petioles near the growing point; in this manner they chilled, not only the apical growing point, but the entire growing region. In a cool greenhouse, cabbage plants in which the growing point was kept warm did not go to seed. By contrast plants in a warm greenhouse, with the growing point kept cool, did go to seed. These observations suggest that some substance is produced locally under these conditions and is capable of eliciting the flowering response.

The extreme localization and irreversibility of the vernalization response was shown by Gregory and Purvis (1936) when they emphasized that vernalization of cereal grains could be brought about by localized chilling of the ear. That is, the grain could be vernalized *before it was even mature*. Other requirements for the vernalization response are oxygen during the chilling treatment and carbohydrate. Gregory also introduced the use of excised embryos into the study of the vernalization response (1938). (A brief account of Gregory's work in this field will be found in the *Biographical Memoirs of Fellows of the Royal Society*, 1963, pp. 131–153.)

Phasic Development

Note should be taken of the phasic hypothesis of development as enunciated by Lysenko. According to this hypothesis, development can only be completed if plants pass in sequence through phases, each of which requires for its completion the elapse of time under prescribed conditions. Thus phases may be distinguished by characteristic alternations of light and darkness, and, if this condition is paramount or limiting, the plant is a strongly photoperiodic one; otherwise, the phase of development which has prescribed temperature limitations may be the distinctive one and the plant then appears as one which is sensitive to thermal periodicity. But in either case, according to the Lysenko hypothesis, light and temperature evoke in sequence certain necessary steps in the developmental process.

Is there any evidence whatsoever concerning the nature of the substance, or substances, which the growing region uses to control and evoke these responses? A well-known case of chemically induced flowering, which is a basis of commercial application, is the use of synthetic auxins (NAA or 2,4-D) to induce flowering in pineapple (*Ananas comosus*). Whether this signifies a normal need for the stimulus of high levels of the natural auxin (IAA) or that the synthetic analogue acts by antagonizing the natural substance may still be a moot point (Bonner and Liverman, 1953; Gowing, 1956). Work on gibberellic acid is suggestive here. In *Hyoscyamus*, the release of the floral shoot by gibberellic acid, which substitutes for cold, suggests that this substance, or some natural equivalent of it, is the chemical molecule that unleashes flowering in the growing point. However, the plants that respond to gibberellin by flowering may be those which have a vegetative axis with a rosette habit and which give rise to an inflorescence with elongated internodes. The effect of gibberellin may therefore be on internodal growth rather than on floral induction *per se*.

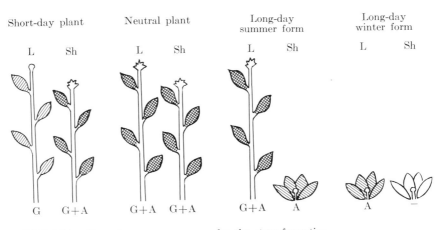

Short-day plant   Neutral plant   Long-day summer form   Long-day winter form

L   Sh   L   Sh   L   Sh   L   Sh

G   G+A   G+A   G+A   G+A   A   A   —

▨ Gibberellins—hormones necessary for the stem formation
◩ Anthesins—hormones necessary for the flower formation
▦ Florigen—gibberillins+anthesins, necessary for flowering

FIG. 8–7. Scheme of formation of flowering hormones in various plant species. (L, long-day conditions; Sh, short-day conditions; G, gibberellin-producing; A, anthesin-producing.) Reproduced by permission of the National Research Council of Canada from Chailakhian, *Canad. J. Bot.* **39**, 1817–1841, 1961.)

Chailakhian has formulated a concept of flowering in terms of the need for dual stimuli to evoke flowering. These are represented by a gibberellin-like substance, on the one hand, and a substance called anthesin, on the other. In some plants (e.g., certain cold-requiring plants in which gibberellin effectively replaces the need for cold) one of these stimuli may be limiting, and in others anthesin may be the limiting substance. Chailakhian has interpreted (Fig. 8–7) the behavior of plants which require short and long days to flower under the different day length conditions, and has shown that one could explain the range of behavior in terms of the dual need for a gibberellin and anthesin for flowering.

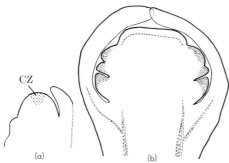

CZ

(a)   (b)

FIG. 8–8. Apices of *Papaver somniferum.* (After Wetmore *et al.*) Note the central zone (CZ) of large cells. The shoot (a) and floral apices (b) are shown to the same magnification for comparison. Note the broadening of the dome and the disappearance of the central zone of large cells in the latter. (After Wetmore *et al.*, 1959; from Steward and Mohan Ram, *Advances in Morphogenesis,* Vol. I, Academic Press, New York, 1961.)

This concept, which has been skilfully applied to some typical examples by its originator (cf. Chailakhian, 1961), might also apply to the banana plant (cf. Chapter 7). The gibberellin-like stimulus, which causes the floral axis of the banana to elongate, could be contributed by the large number of preformed leaves, while the anthesin could be the analogue of the stimulus that causes the cell divisions in that part of the shoot apex in which floral initials arise. On the other hand, the flowering of *Papaver* (cf. Wetmore *et al.*, 1959, and Fig. 8–8, in which the apex is transformed in flowering into a more massive shoot tip) might be explained as due more particularly to "anthesin." A hypothesis which depends upon dual stimuli to flowering, each determined by different controlling factors, is obviously more flexible, but it only becomes more credible with the identification of the substances in question. In the known gibberellins there is a possible exogenous counterpart for one part of the system, but the chemical identity of anthesin is still unknown and it can only be considered in relation to the various cell division factors discussed in Chapter 4.

Specificity of the Light Effect in Long- and Short-Day Plants

The release of the flowering response is obviously not a single or simple event, even as it is controlled by photoperiodicity. It is now known that short-day plants, or more strictly, long-night plants, such as the cocklebur and the Biloxi soybean, require two types of light response. The main stimulus to flowering comes from exposure to long nights and this may be nullified by brief flashes of

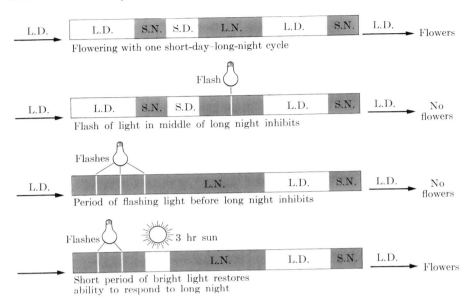

FIG. 8–9. The kinetics of the interplay of light and dark of short-day plants. (From Bonner and Liverman, reproduced by permission from *Growth and Differentiation in Plants*, edited by Walter E. Loomis, © 1953 by the Iowa State University Press.)

light which interrupt the long night. This light response is obtained at very low light intensities and is of a catalytic kind. But, as K. Hamner (1940) showed, there is also another type of light response, and this occurs at relatively high light intensity and is the effect of light which prepares the plants to respond to the long night. Thus, for the long night period to be effective in bringing about photoperiodic induction, it should be preceded by an appropriate period at high light intensity.

To demonstrate this latter requirement with the cocklebur, it is necessary to make use of the flashing light experiment. Cocklebur plants are subjected to a long continuous dark period, interrupted at three hourly intervals by three minute flashes of light. During this dark period the plants are apparently depleted of substances which are produced during the preceding light period, for they are prevented from flowering by the interruptions of the dark period. When plants which have been subjected to such flashing light for 12 to 24 hours are subsequently given a long uninterrupted dark period, they do not respond by flowering. If, however, after exposure to flashing light, the plants are exposed for two to four hours to intense light and then returned to a period of uninterrupted darkness, they do respond by flowering. These relations are aptly summed up in Fig. 8–9, from Bonner and Liverman (1953), or in a different type of figure taken from Lang (Fig. 8–10).

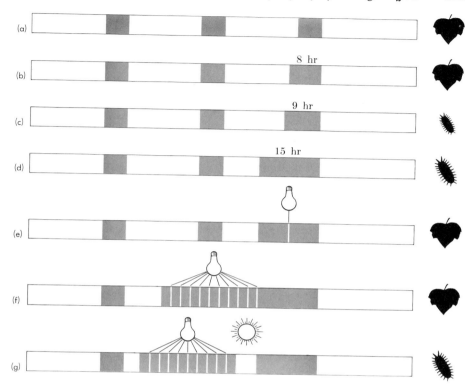

FIG. 8–10. Photoperiodic phenomena in plants. This summarizes the interplay of light and dark on a short-day plant. (a) Vegetative growth of cocklebur occurs with short nights. (b) Vegetative growth of cocklebur occurs with an 8-hour night. (c) Some flowering and fruiting of cocklebur occurs in a 9-hour night. (d) Pronounced flowering and fruiting of cocklebur occurs in a 15-hour night. (e, f) Effect of a long night interrupted by brief light flash or flashes; the growth remains vegetative. (g) When a long night is interrupted by brief flashes of light and is followed by a short period of bright light, this restores the ability to respond to a long night, and flowering and fruiting occur. (After Lang, *Biochemistry of Morphogenesis*, Pergamon Press, New York, 1958.)

It is now known that the flowering response of some long-day plants also involves the temperature during the night period to a far greater extent than was at first realized. This can well be shown with the mint plant, to which frequent reference has already been made. If mint plants are grown under long days (up to 18 hours) but exposed at night to low temperatures (down to 50 to 55°), then, as shown by Howe (1956) in this laboratory, the normal long-day condition gives way to a short-day type of growth, with the comparative absence of flowers and the formation of stolons. Other examples are also known in which the otherwise clear-cut long- and short-day behavior may be greatly modified by exposure to different temperatures during the night.

Hormonal Control in Relation to the Photoperiodic Stimulus

The sequential process that is visualized in the interpretation of the behavior of short-day or long-night plants may be illustrated by Fig. 8–11, which is taken from Bonner and Liverman (1953). A somewhat similar figure, in which the effect of night is interrupted, not by low light intensity in the otherwise dark period, but by low temperature for long-day plants, could be conceived. To what extent, however, can these stimuli now be identified with the effect of known substances?

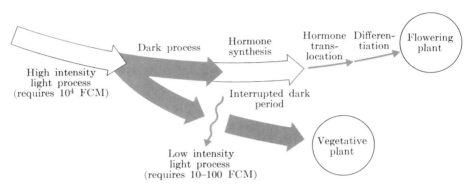

FIG. 8–11.   Resolution of the photoperiodic response of short-day plants into its component partial processes.   The upper sequence is that which leads to flowering.   In the lower sequence, effectiveness of the dark period is suppressed by a light flash, and the plant remains vegetative. (From Bonner and Liverman, reproduced by permission from *Growth and Differentiation of Plants*, edited by Walter E. Loomis, © 1953 by the Iowa State University Press.)

Workers at the California Institute of Technology have related most responses of angiosperms to auxin, i.e., indoleacetic acid, and they identify the auxin economy in the leaf with the flowering response.

This school of investigators showed some time ago that the application of auxin during the dark period eliminates the photoperiodic induction due to the dark period in a short-day plant like cocklebur. Auxins, whether IAA or a synthetic substitute like naphthalene acetic acid, 2,4-D, 2,4,5-T, etc., are all active in this respect. Thus the application of auxin acts like light in that it *interrupts the effect of darkness*; and, in fact, if auxin is added at the beginning of a dark period, a subsequent short flash of light during the long night has no effect.

Another effect which links auxin to the flowering response is that of known auxin antagonists, like 2,4-dichloranisole (DCA), which counteract the effect of a brief light flash in a dark period which would normally stop the cocklebur plants from flowering. Thus the auxin added prior to a dark period acts like light, and an auxin antagonist acts in opposition to light during the dark period. It is not believed, however, that the ultimate flowering hormone is auxin itself.

On the contrary, it is thought by the California Institute of Technology school to be a distinctive and probably more complicated, more subtle, type of hormone than any other yet known; perhaps of a protein nature, rather than a small molecule of an organic substance which would be readily extractable. In fact, Bonner and Liverman presented an analogy with the effects of virus; they likened the photoperiodically stimulated plant to one which has become irreversibly affected by the equivalent of a virus disease—the symptom in this case being flowering! The natural auxin acts in the leaf at the site of the production of the flowering response, and appears merely to "permit the leaf to produce the floral stimulus, an illusory material which has thus far eluded capture and study."

This is, more or less, where this complex problem now rests in the literature of plant physiology. It is recognized that some material stimulus to flowering exists; it is transported out of leaves, readily through living tissue, but it is difficult to extract from, or reintroduce into, the living plant. The stimulus will pass across a graft union from plant to plant, and it is transmitted by grafting more readily than by extraction; but, despite all claims, no repeatable observation has been made by which the stimulus to flowering, whether engendered by photoperiodic treatment, by temperature treatment, or by vernalization of seeds, has been successfully extracted, identified, and reintroduced into a vegetative plant to produce an unequivocal flowering response where it would not otherwise have occurred. The distinguished work on phytochrome, the pigment by which a light-activated stimulus is "perceived," concerns the mechanism of perception— it still leaves unanswered the problem of the mobile substance and the means by which it activates the growth response at the active site.

Endogenous Rhythms

When plants can flower only under the stimulus of short days it is biochemically attractive, as indicated above, to regard the flowering stimulus as a response to darkness, and especially so when it may be so precisely nullified by a brief light flash, as in the case of the cocklebur. However, Hamner stresses that even in short-day plants the primary mechanism that generates the ability to flower must be light-controlled. According to Hamner, there is a "built-in" rhythm (or "biological clock") which releases or suppresses the flowering response. Granted correct exposure to light in a critical light period (8 hours in soybean), the organism can "tell time" in the ensuing dark period. Thus the proneness to flower, which is light-conditioned, is rhythmically expressed according to the length of the ensuing dark period. The rhythm, like so many others in biology, is "circadian" in that it displays maxima and minima which recur at intervals that comprise a 24-hour cycle. In the soybean the stimulus of the critical 8-hour days are without avail until the ensuing dark periods comprise a 24-hour day but, if the day (one light plus one dark period) is artificially lengthened by extending the darkness, flowering is suppressed at a total of 36 hours and is restored at 48 or 72 hours. Thus the 8-hour light period "winds up the biological clock" but the soybean can subsequently "tell time in the dark." According to Takimoto and Hamner, who published in 1965 extensive papers in Plant Physiology on the Japanese morning glory (*Pharbitis* or *Ipomoea*), there is a timing phenomenon which originates when the light is turned on (i.e., a "dawn effect"), and another (the "dusk effect") which originates when the darkness begins. The end result is circadian in that effects recur cyclically at intervals of approximately 24 hours. Although work on endogenous, circadian rhythms, summarized by Bünning (1964), in his book on the biological clock, has produced many fascinating observations that affect a great range of organisms, their interpretation faces the overriding dilemma that the nature of the timing mechanism is unknown. This is especially true of the rhythmic flowering responses in plants.

Sex Determination or Sex Expression in Flowering Plants

Having recognized that the act of flowering comprises a sequence of morphogenetic events, one can approach the problem of sex determination, or sex expression, as a closely connected morphogenetic activity for which a causal explanation is again required.

Angiosperms may bear flowers which may be bisexual or hermaphroditic (monoclinous), with both anthers and ovules, or they may be unisexual (diclinous) and bear either stamens or pistils. Plants which have unisexual flowers may be either monoecious, bearing both staminate and pistillate flowers on the same plant, or dioecious, bearing them only on different plants. Thus, it is not enough to know what causes the transition in the shoot apex from a vegetative to a floral state; one should also be able to stipulate the factors which govern the kind of flowers that form.

The first factors to be considered are of course genetic. The sexual fusion of morphologically similar gametes is common in lower plants, i.e., in algae and fungi, although, even so, differences in their size and mobility may be construed as some measure of sex determination. In higher organisms, however, with marked functional differentiation (i.e., division of labor) between sexes, this may be determined by the segregation at meiosis of the members of a given chromosome pair which, though homologous, are not identical, for they may be distinguished as X and Y. Thus the flowers to be borne eventually upon a dioecious plant would be potentially male or female according as the egg was fertilized by a Y or an X chromosome-bearing gamete. In the familiar and widely studied case of *Drosophila*, the sex of the insect is determined by the presence of two X chromosomes in a female and one unpaired X in a male. But even in organisms where males and females are normally distinct, each may have genes for both sexes and sex may eventually be determined hormonally. Thus, cases of sex reversal are not unknown in higher animals, e.g., in chickens. In *Lychnis* (*Melandrium*) the genetic basis of sex determination is the segregation of an XY

chromosomal pair so that an *XY* plant bears staminate flowers and an *XX* one bears pistillate flowers (cf. Warmke, 1946). Thus, the biochemistry which is triggered by either the *XY* or the *XX* chromosomal condition determines whether flowers, once they are initiated, will develop into staminate or pistillate ones. The sex of the flowers of monoecious plants must, however, be determined in another way; it is from plants of this sort that the evidence for the effect of environmental and nutritional factors, and of auxins and auxin-like agents, on the morphogenetic activity that results in sex expression has been obtained. Even in hermaphroditic flowers the androecium and the gynoecium form at well-defined levels; therefore, distinct zones of the floral apex must receive endogenous stimuli that determine whether given primordia form stamens or carpels.

Two sources may be consulted for the details of work on sex determination in flowers; these are the comprehensive account by Heslop-Harrison (1957) and the shorter summary by Hillman (1962, pp. 130–136). Within limits set by the genetic control over development, Heslop-Harrison recognizes examples in which sex expression may be modified by effects of mineral nutrition, light, temperature, changes in the internal economy caused by removing parts of a storage organ (e.g., of a corm), or by changes in leaf area, the removal of existing flowers or fruits, etc., and, finally, by the artificial application of growth-regulating substances (auxin, naphthaleneacetic acid, etc.) and of treatments which alter the economy of endogenous auxins.

Heslop-Harrison's paper contains the essential information. Among nutritional factors, the level of nitrogen supply was most influential on sex determination. When nitrate was added to low nitrate soils, cucumber (*Cucumis sativus*) plants increased their production of flowers of *both* sexes, particularly under long days, while the excess tendency to form pistillate flowers due to the extra nitrogen was small (55 percent increase of pistillate flowers and 45 percent of staminate flowers). Under short days the total response to extra nitrate by flower formation was less, but it was almost exclusively in female flowers (20 percent increase of females and 3 percent of males).

The light regime to which many plants are subjected determines their sex expression as well as the induction of flowers. In some plants (e.g., *Xanthium*), short days induce flowering and also promote their development; they also cause a shift toward female flowers, and may even cause a trend to carpellate flowers in species (certain cucurbits and tomato) which do not require short days to flower. The effect of temperature during the dark period on the sex expression of *Cucurbita pepo* was investigated by Nitsch *et al.* (1952). Low temperatures during the early stages of development promoted femaleness and depressed maleness of flowers, while high temperatures had the reverse effect. In monoecious plants, which normally first form female flowers followed by male ones, the premature removal of female flowers caused maleness to be suppressed in later-formed flowers. This has been observed in both cucumber (*Cucumis*) and plantain

(*Musa paradisiaca*). Also, the reduction of leaf surface and the removal of parts of a storage organ (corm) curtailed the formation of female flowers in an aroid (*Arisaema*).

Chemical controls over the balance between male and female flowers of cucumber are traced by Heslop-Harrison to observations of the effects of gases from incomplete combustion in wood stoves; the treated plants had a much greater proportion of female to male flowers than the controls. But the most important effect is that which was observed by direct application of 0.1 percent naphthaleneacetic acid, indoleacetic acid, or dichlorophenoxyacetic acid on the number of female flowers at the first ten nodes of cucumber. The effect observed was strongly in the direction NAA→IAA→2,4-D→controls. In cucurbits a high auxin level caused the early appearance of female flowers and increased their preponderance over males. According to work by Galun (1959) the gibberellins, unlike auxin, may accentuate the trend toward maleness and balanced effects of an auxin (NAA) versus a gibberellin can be visualized.

The complexity of the interacting variables which determine sex expression is reminiscent of those which affect and determine floral induction in otherwise vegetative shoots, and it is also strongly reminiscent of the range of factors that determine metabolic patterns as shown by the soluble nitrogen compounds which plants form and contain (cf. Chapter 6). This suggests that these morphogenetic responses of flowering and sex expression, though they may be seemingly evoked by and seemingly triggered by relatively simple and direct effects, are actually responses of the growing apex to a complex internal biochemical milieu which affects its growth. Since Bonner and Liverman have likened the flowering stimulus to a high molecular weight substance, i.e., a protein which, virus-like, affects development, Heslop-Harrison has also ascribed to such nucleoprotein-like agents plasmagene-like properties which may determine floral morphogenesis.

Metabolism of Long- and Short-Day Plants and Low-Night-Temperature Plants

The many unavailing attempts to extract an active principle from florally stimulated plants has led to the rather despairing point of view that nothing unusual is to be seen in the metabolism of plants in these two contrasted states. However, many differences can be demonstrated by chromatographic techniques. For the mint plant this became known some years ago, although never fully published, except in the thesis of Dr. F. Crane from the University of Rochester (1951) until the summarized version of 1959 (see Steward *et al.*) and the somewhat more complete account in the Cornell Memoir No. 379 which deals with the physiology, nutrition, and metabolism of mint (Steward *et al.*, 1962).

Briefly, it was shown that *greenhouse-grown* mint plants (now known to have been high-night-temperature plants) differed drastically in their nitrogen metabolism according as they were short- or long-day plants. These effects were

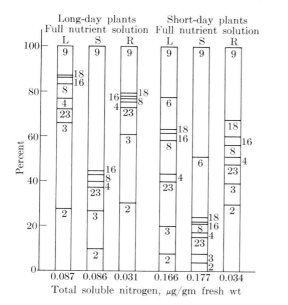

Long-day plants   Short-day plants
Full nutrient solution   Full nutrient solution

1. Cysteic acid (from cysteine)
2. Aspartic acid
3. Glutamic acid
4. Serine
5. Glycine
6. Asparagine
7. Threonine
8. Alanine
9. Glutamine
10. α-amino-n-butyric acid
11. Histidine
12. Lysine
13. Arginine
14. Methionine sulphoxide
15. Proline
16. Valine
17. Methionine sulphone
18. Leucines, chiefly isoleucine
19. Phenylalanine
20. Tryptophan
21. Tyrosine
22. β-alanine
23. γ-aminobutyric acid
24. Hydroxyproline

0.087 0.086 0.031   0.166 0.177 0.034
Total soluble nitrogen, μg/gm fresh wt

FIG. 8–12. Relative composition of soluble nitrogen of leaves (L), stems (S), and roots (R) of *Mentha piperita* L., grown under long and short days in greenhouse (70°F); nitrogen of each amino acid expressed as percentage of total soluble nitrogen determined by reaction with ninhydrin. (From Steward *et al., Cornell Univ. Agr. Exptl. Sta. Mem. No. 379*, 1962.)

due to long-continued growth under these conditions; they were not the catalytically induced effects that might result from one, or a few, photo-inductive cycles. As Fig. 8–12 shows, long-day mint plants rarely contain much asparagine in their leaves, though abundant glutamine occurs. The general effect of growth under long days is to foster the formation of the C_5 amino acids (glutamic acid, glutamine, and a substance that might be related to it, namely, γ-aminobutyric acid). Similarly, the short-day plants emphasize the C_4 compounds and contain asparagine in some quantity. Carbohydrate metabolism and nitrogen metabolism are linked together via keto acids, and the suggestion was therefore made that light, like potassium nutrition, tends to foster the metabolism of C_5 compounds by affecting or stimulating the enzyme systems which cause carboxylation. Thus, in long-day plants, the keto acids which act as "ports of entry for N" tend to be the C_5 keto acids (α-ketoglutaric acid), whereas otherwise there is a predominance of the C_3 or C_4 keto acids (pyruvic or oxaloacetic acids).

With these results in mind, a further investigation was planned and undertaken by Dr. R. Rabson, also of this laboratory. The mint plants were grown mainly in the open by methods worked out by Dr. K. J. Howe, and arduously transferred to dark rooms in which night temperatures were controlled for the purposes of the experiments. The object of these experiments was to verify that

TABLE 8–1. Amino acids and amides of *Mentha piperita* after one diurnal cycle and a dark period under different photoperiods and night temperatures (amino acid expressed as μg/gm fresh weight of tissue). (From Rabson and Steward, *Cornell Univ. Agr. Exp. Sta. Mem. No. 379,* 1962.)

Amino acid	Leaves			
	Short days (8 hours)		Long days (15 hours)	
	50°F	80°F	50°F	80°F
Aspartic acid	160	105	72	113
Glutamic acid	390	224	378	282
γ-aminobutyric acid	29	26	38	41
Serine/glycine	35	13	13	21
Threonine	6	5	*	6
Alanine	48	23	52	45
Valine	*	21	38	27
Leucines	—	22	*	28
Proline	*	*	*	*
Asparagine	*	11	*	46
Glutamine	441	55	510	128
	Stems			
Aspartic acid	26	60	76	42
Glutamic acid	77	112	232	96
γ-aminobutyric acid	132	159	94	129
Serine/glycine	28	23	*	20
Threonine	1	5	—	3
Alanine	61	46	29	39
Valine	25	38	25	17
Leucines	33	37	—	*
Proline	—	*	—	13
Asparagine	112	105	94	106
Glutamine	867	192	918	460

*Trace

the nitrogen metabolism was affected by photoperiod and to extend these effects into the study of the night temperature; and also to obtain information on the keto acids which actually occurred in the mint plant, and the way in which they were affected by these treatments.

These experiments showed that night temperature is the most striking and overriding variable which determines the composition of the leaves of mint plants. In fact, the results of exposure to one low night temperature on the composition of the leaf have been detected (Tables 8–1 and 8–2). Furthermore, the effects which have been detected in the nitrogenous composition of the leaf can also be extended to the keto acids of the leaf. As always, however, when one obtains data over a wide area of metabolism, it seems as though there is a complex interplay of variables in the metabolism of the plants in question. Nevertheless, it may be seen that the effect of these environmental variables is exerted in that area of metabolism which links the products of carbohydrate breakdown, through the Krebs Cycle and the keto acids, to nitrogen metabolism and to the synthesis of

TABLE 8–2. Keto acids of *Mentha piperita* plants grown under different photo-periods and night temperatures (keto acids expressed in micromoles/gm fresh weight of tissue). (From Rabson and Steward, *Cornell Univ. Agr. Exp. Sta. Mem. No. 379*, 1962.)

Keto acid	a) After 1 diurnal cycle (1 dark and 1 light period)			
	Short days (8 hours)		Long days (16 hours)	
	50°F	80°F	50°F	80°F
	Treatment 1	Treatment 2	Treatment 3	Treatment 4
	Leaves†			
α-ketoglutaric	1.14	0.88	0.70	1.09
Pyruvic	0.13	0.14	0.07	0.12
	Stems			
α-ketoglutaric	4.70	4.21	2.72	4.17
Pyruvic	0.30	0.09	0.09	0.26
	Roots			
α-ketoglutaric	0.12	0.01	0.13	0.24
Pyruvic	0.02	0.00	0.01	0.02
	b) After 2 dark periods and 1 light period (1 diurnal cycle and a dark period)			
	Leaves†			
α-ketoglutaric	0.21	0.93	0.25	0.11
Pyruvic	0.02	0.00	0.03	0.01
	Stems			
α-ketoglutaric	3.83	0.92	1.34	3.73
Pyruvic	0.06	0.02	0.04	0.07
	Roots			
α-ketoglutaric	0.02	*	0.02	0.00
Pyruvic	0.00	0.00	0.00	0.00
	c) After 4 diurnal cycles (4 dark-light cycles)			
	Leaves†			
α-ketoglutaric	1.50	0.23	1.99	0.45
Pyruvic	0.11	0.04	0.14	0.05
	Stems			
α-ketoglutaric	11.35	0.84	7.63	0.91
Pyruvic	0.08	0.02	0.19	0.02
	Roots			
α-ketoglutaric	0.39	0.00	0.03	0.02
Pyruvic	0.02	0.00	*	*

*Trace

†The figures expressed here represent duplicate analyses of samples of leaves from different plants.

protein. There is every reason to believe that some specific product, or reaction, at the level of the keto acids may be the important means of transmitting the effect of length of day, or night, to the behavior of the growing cells. This approach seems the more plausible, because a salient feature of cultured cells, which are caused to grow by the effects of coconut milk, is a great increase in the amount of, and the balance between, the keto acids which they contain; this was shown in the work of Towers (1954) in this laboratory (Tables 8–3 and 8–4).

TABLE 8–3
Comparison of the keto acids of three different cultures of carrot tissue explants growing in coconut milk. A. Tissue cultures grown for 30 days. B. Tissue cultures grown for 57 days. C. Tissue cultures grown for 28 days. (From Towers, 1954)

Keto acid	Amino acid by hydrogenolysis	Amount of keto acid,[†] μg/gm fresh wt		
		A	B	C
α-ketoglutaric	Glutamic	10.8	9.8	19.9
α-ketoglutaric	γ-aminobutyric	—	—	—
Pyruvic	Alanine	0.5	2.6	3.4
Oxaloacetic	Aspartic	0.2	*	—
Glyoxylic	Glycine	*	0.6	0.8
Unknown No. 1	Unknown No. 1[‡]	—	—	16.2
Unknown No. 9	Unknown No. 9[§]	—	—	13.9

*Trace
†Estimated as corresponding amino acid
‡Estimated as γ-aminobutyric acid
§Estimated as leucine

TABLE 8–4
Comparison of the keto acids of carrot root tissues and carrot tissue explants growing in coconut milk. (From Towers, 1954)

Keto acid	Amino acid by hydrogenolysis	A	
		Amount of keto acid[†], μg/gm fresh wt	
		Normal root tissue	Cultured root tissue
α-ketoglutaric	Glutamic	4.2	10.8
α-ketoglutaric	γ-aminobutyric	—	—
Pyruvic	Alanine	0.2	0.5
Oxaloacetic	Aspartic	0.2	0.9
Glyoxylic	Glycine	*	0.1
		B	
α-ketoglutaric	Glutamic	0.9	9.8
Oxaloacetic	Aspartic	*	*
Pyruvic	Alanine	0.1	2.6
Glyoxylic	Glycine	0.1	0.6
Unknown No. 1‡	Unknown No. 1[‡]	0.8	—
Unknown No. 0§	Unknown No. 9[§]	0.2	*

*Trace
†Estimated as corresponding amino acid
‡Estimated as γ-aminobutyric acid
§Estimated as leucine

In summary, the effects of the nutrition and environment (photoperiod and night temperature) upon the metabolism of the leaves of the mint plant could be represented by the simplified schemata shown in Fig. 8–13. The basis of these schemata is that light (long days), high potassium nutrition, and low night temperatures all foster protein synthesis or conserve the protein so synthesized; whereas darkness (short days, long nights) and high night temperatures promote more breakdown of protein than resynthesis. Asparagine arises preferentially as an ultimate nitrogen-rich compound as the products of breakdown of protein are reworked; whereas glutamine is more conspicuous under conditions of protein synthesis. It is possible, therefore, that the photoperiodic and night temperature effects are due to their control over the metabolism through the balance in the amount and the kind of nitrogen compounds that the plants contain. The most probable compounds through which these effects may be negotiated are the keto acids (α-ketoglutaric; oxaloacetic; pyruvic; succinic semialdehyde), probably by controlling the balance between carboxylation and decarboxylation. It is not conceived that the pool of substances in which changes due to photoperiod and night temperature have been detected in mint are necessarily the actual substances which *per se* cause the morphogenetic responses, but rather that they represent the changed internal metabolic environment to which the shoot apex responds by growth in different ways. Leopold and Guernsey (1953) somewhat prematurely located—but Leopold and Price (1956) subsequently retracted—the photoperiodic effect in the acetyl-CoA mechanism as this may be affected by light through lipoic or thioctic acid. While there is as yet insufficient evidence to identify one specific reaction or substance as the causal agent of the response, it is now clear that there are far more metabolic, as well as morphogenetic, responses to these stimuli than were at first recognized.

What is now needed is a ready method of assaying the efficiency of extracts to affect the behavior of the growing points. A serious limiting factor is that the minute growing point of angiosperms, relatively free from subjacent tissue, cannot be easily and separately cultivated. If this were possible it would enable extracts from photoperiodically or night-temperature stimulated plants to be tested directly upon uniform growing points in tissue culture. This, unfortunately, is not yet feasible. However, the general trend of this work on the metabolism of photoperiodically and thermoperiodically stimulated plants is to suggest that in due course a substance will be isolated, probably from leaves, and shown to be the agent which evokes the mechanism by which the plant growing point is modified, prompting it to remain vegetative or to develop flowers, or to grow continuously, or to form organs of perennation, as the case may be.

Somewhat similar ideas emerge from work done at Harvard, U.S.A., and Imperial College, England, by Gregory, Spear, and Thimann (1954). These workers arrived at the idea that photoperiodically stimulated *Kalanchoe* plants have their dark CO_2 fixation changed in such a manner that the response is irreversible, and they believe that the organic acid metabolism is changed in ways

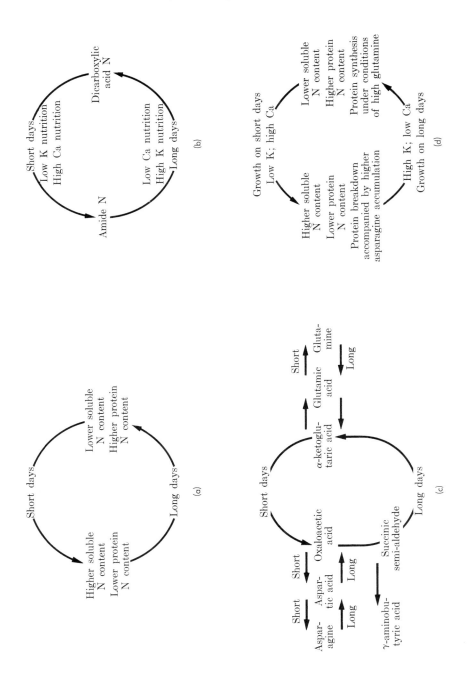

FIG. 8–13. Effects due to day length, potassium, and calcium on nitrogen metabolism of *Mentha piperita.* (From work of Crane, 1957; cf. Crane and Steward, 1962.)

that are related to the flowering response. In this context the work of Cantino (1961) is also of interest. Cantino relates certain morphogenetic responses of fungi, members of the Blastocladiales, to metabolic reactions which are triggered by carbon dioxide and which operate through DPNH and reactions which involve amino acids (e.g., glycine).

Rabson (1956) made a direct attempt, using $^{14}CO_2$ to find out whether the path of CO_2 fixation in the light and dark could lead to chromatographically detectable substances that could be correlated with the behavior of mint. There is at least the suggestion that this technique, if pursued, should be profitable, for the pattern of ^{14}C-fixation products was different under long- and short-day conditions. Some unidentified substances were more strongly labeled at low night temperature; asparagine was labeled only in plants that received a dark period *after* exposure to light, and the labeling of α-ketoglutarate was more conspicuous in the light. These and other differences point to the rather far-reaching consequences of the environment on metabolism.

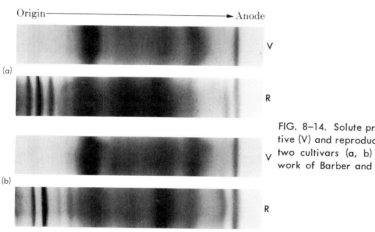

FIG. 8–14. Solute proteins of vegetative (V) and reproductive (R) apices of two cultivars (a, b) of tulip. (From work of Barber and Steward.)

A very promising biochemical development that may link the flowering response with metabolism concerns the effect of flowering on protein and enzyme complements as investigated by acrylamide gel electrophoresis. This work, part of a general study of soluble proteins in relation to morphogenesis in the author's laboratory, was carried out by J. Barber (for summary see Steward and Barber, 1965). It was observed that the floral organs of the tulip, while still within the bulb, showed additional and characteristic protein bands not found in the vegetative organs (bulb scales, axillary buds, roots). Even in the dissected shoot apices, *long before the floral organs were mature*, the temperature conditions that induce flowering had caused the protein bands characteristic of floral parts to appear. This is shown by the use of a general protein stain, amido black, on the gels (Fig. 8–14). However, the effect of the flowering response can also be

Origin ———————————————→ Anode

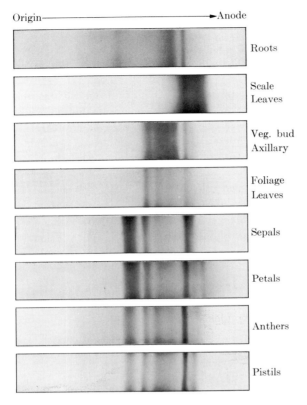

Roots

Scale
Leaves

Veg. bud
Axillary

Foliage
Leaves

Sepals

Petals

Anthers

Pistils

FIG. 8–15. Soluble proteins of tulip: the esterases. (From work of Barber and Steward.)

seen in the behavior of enzymes, notably a general class of esterases (Fig. 8–15) and, perhaps even more interestingly, in malic dehydrogenase (Fig. 8–16). As in the case of other dehydrogenases (lactic) malic dehydrogenase exists in the form of several "isozymes," i.e., distinct electrophoretically separable proteins which can mediate the enzymic effect. The total number of such isozymes detected in the tulip (as also in a hybrid trout!) is nine. The immediate interest of this work is its bearing on the hypothesis that the floral induction stimuli mediate the response through distinctive proteins in the growing cells. The more general interest is that morphogenesis may be mediated by characteristic proteins and that plants may exploit the isozymes of metabolically important enzyme systems to carry out their metabolism in organ-specific ways. If malic dehydrogenase, like lactic dehydrogenase in the work of Markert (1963), is built of two or more polypeptide monomers into complexes (dimers, tetramers, etc.) which are enzymically active, a large number of isozymes could be potentially built from the polypeptides (AA;BB) that are controlled by a very few

Origin——————————————————————→ Anode

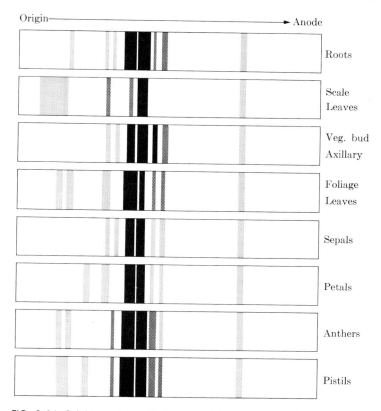

Roots

Scale
Leaves

Veg. bud
Axillary

Foliage
Leaves

Sepals

Petals

Anthers

Pistils

FIG. 8–16. Soluble proteins of tulip: malic dehydrogenases.   (From work of Barber and Steward.)

(two non-allelic) genes. If the isozyme complexes (AAAA; BBBB; AAAB; ABBB; AABB, etc.) are controlled at their site of formation in an organ-specific way, and in flowers are determined by the floral induction stimulus, metabolism may be given an "epigenetic" control within an overall genetically determined plan. Within currently accepted concepts of molecular biology, however, the floral stimulus should be transmitted through characteristic proteins only inasmuch as it elicits characteristic messenger RNA's. Although Cherry and Van Huystee (1965) demonstrated a greatly increased production of total informational RNA in *Xanthium* buds, in response to the photoperiodic stimulus, the desirable evidence that *distinctive* mRNA's were formed seems still to be lacking.

Thus ideas on the biochemistry of the flowering response have come a long way since it was first thought there was an essential antithesis between vegetative and reproductive growth and that vegetative growth was fostered by high nitrogen supply and reproductive growth by a preponderance of carbohydrate (i.e., by the C/N ratio). It is true that the seeming antithesis between vegetative and reproductive growth is frequently seen in microorganisms, in which sexual re-production is often the means to generate spores which surmount conditions that are adverse for growth. Much evidence now shows that flowering involves changes in metabolism at the site of the response: accompanying the release of these specific metabolic patterns growth is also released in cells which, though totipotent, may function as initials in the development of floral organs by virtue of their position. The problem currently rests here and awaits further experimental evidence in this important field.

Metabolism and Parthenocarpic Development

Another link in the chain of evidence that relates nitrogen metabolism to morphogenesis and fruit development may be seen in a case in which the stimulus to fruit formation arises, not from known environmental factors, but through the inherent genetic causes of parthenocarpy. Such an example is the fruit of the banana cultivar Gros Michel (*Musa acuminata*). In response to an innate or "built-in" growth stimulus which is present in the inner pericarp of the fruit, probably similar to that which occurs in coconut milk (Steward and Simmonds, 1954), the fleshy pulp of the fruit develops. As it does so, it consumes nitrogenous compounds faster than they can be mobilized, so that the developing fruit primordium passes from an initially soluble-nitrogen-rich condition, characteristic of the floral shoot apex, to a soluble-nitrogen-poor condition, characteristic of the fruit in the stage of Sachs' Grand Period of Growth. Thereafter, soluble nitrogen accumulates again as maturity approaches. However, fruit that develops in the winter and early spring does so slowly and contrasts sharply in many of its characteristics with fruit that develops more rapidly in the summer. It has been found that these two types of parthenocarpically developed banana (cv. Gros Michel) fruit can be distinguished by their soluble nitrogen compounds, for the one type (summer-grown) is glutamine-rich, high in histidine, and very poor in asparagine; whereas the other (winter-grown) is relatively less rich in glutamine in relation to the other soluble compounds, and it is particularly notable by its lack of asparagine. During post-harvest ripening the summer-grown fruit carries out certain changes which, in the slower growing winter-grown fruit, have already commenced on the plant and are, therefore, less prominent in the post-harvest phase—these changes are the increase in histidine at the expense of amide-N, particularly glutamine (work of Barr, 1963; also see Steward *et al.*, 1960).

Therefore, it is now possible to detect certain stages in the nitrogen metabolism of the developing and ripening banana fruit and to see the effects of the season of the year upon their respective duration and intensity. Initially the floral organs in the shoot growing point are rich in soluble nitrogen, which is almost exclusively amino acids (alanine, arginine, proline, α-aminobutyric acid, which together with the dicarboxylic acids comprise 80 percent of the soluble nitrogen).

Subsequently, as development proceeds, asparagine, glutamine, and histidine become conspicuous in the soluble nitrogen of the fruit, and the amino acids correspondingly decrease. The proportion of glutamine to asparagine in the amide-N complement seems to be determined by the season of the year at which development occurs, even more than by the variety of the fruit, and it is suggestive that greater asparagine accumulation occurs in the winter and spring months when night temperatures should be lower. (This effect should be compared with the effect of low night temperature in mint, for this also fosters asparagine over glutamine.) Furthermore, the asparagine accumulation in the banana (cv. Gros Michel) is almost entirely confined to the central, or carpellary, region in contrast to the fleshy pericarp. Therefore, one can recognize stages of development, probably temperature-limited or controlled, which are also characterized by recognizable biochemical characteristics that are to be seen in the nature and the proportions of the soluble nitrogen compounds which are contained in the fruit. The problem here is, as in the case of the analysis of leaves, that of distinguishing between the composition which is the *result* of the way in which the fruit grows and develops, and the biochemistry which exerts a causal effect by predetermining the morphogenetic development from the growing point. In the banana, floral induction seems to be a consequence of the prior formation of a given number of leaves and of a previously quiescent central shoot apex which has reached a critical size (cf. Chapter 7). The subsequent stimulus to the formation of seeded or parthenocarpic banana fruit is genetically determined. This genetic determination having been made, the normal growth of fleshy fruit is precluded by the stimulus of fertilization and the presence of seeds. The stimulus to parthenocarpic development of fleshy, non-seeded fruits can be located in certain formative regions of the young fruit where a prescribed balance of growth regulators incites cell division in otherwise more mature cells. But the composition of the developing fruit may only describe the biochemical consequences of these morphogenetic events; it does not necessarily, as yet, reveal its causation.

In flowering and fruiting the problems of morphogenesis appear in a peculiarly dramatic form. Nevertheless, the responses which have been described should be seen as the behavior of essentially totipotent cells (cf. Chapter 10) in the milieu they occupy within the organization of the growing region of a shoot. A single cell may have all the genetic information to form a flower, but no flower can begin to emerge until such cells exist in a formative region of an already organized growing point, which is in turn part of a plant body. It is when such cells are subjected to influences, chemical and physical, by virtue of their position, that their behavior is determined, namely their comparative dormancy at some stages and the manner of their growth when they spring into activity. In the larger context of differentiation and morphogenesis Paul Weiss has used the phrase "molecular ecology" to describe the way in which cells as populations of molecules can respond to the chemical environmental stimuli that control, epigenetically, the behavior of cells which undergo differentiation and which participate in morphogenesis. The analogy between ecology, which describes the interplay of all environmental factors on populations of organisms in their habitat, and the responses of cells as they exist in the developing populations that compose an organism, is an apt one. Cells within an organism, like organisms in a population or an ecological system, are subjected to a complex of chemical and physical factors which determine their response and behavior. Essentially this complex of epigenetic factors derives from *where* cells are. In Chapter 10, after considering the knowledge gained of the totipotency of single angiosperm cells by free cell culture, the problems of cell diversification and of morphogenesis will be reconsidered. However, one may recognize here that the problem of floral induction and development resolves itself into a closer definition than has yet been possible of the environment, of the chemical and physical milieu within the organization of a shoot apex, which controls and triggers the behavior of the cells in the formative regions which are to become floral organs. It can be said without fear of contradiction that the *parameters* that define that milieu are neither single nor simple.

Summary

Flowering and fruiting are the culmination of the angiosperm life cycle but this is not to be thought of as a single morphogenetic event. In the transition from the vegetative to the floral state the vegetative shoot growing point which had produced leaves, buds, internodes, etc., gives way to one which produces quite different structures such as sepals, petals, anthers, and ovules. The sequential growth and development of these floral parts essentially follows "instructions" which were inherent in the zygote, although in their expression they may be greatly modified by other "epigenetic" factors. Even the reduction division of meiosis, which halts the predestined development from the previous zygote, is not confined to the reproductive organs, for it may be initiated in isolated somatic cells, though without as yet giving rise to gametophytic development (e.g., an embryo sac). Following meiosis, very different development occurs. Therefore, it is the destiny of flowering plants to flower and set seed—this innate capacity is there from the start. One can conceive of a single stimulus that may either unleash, or suppress, this entire course of development but not of a single stimulus which acts in a formative way to produce this entire array of different organs and events. The innate capacity to flower may be expressed in different ways and on different time scales, as in annuals, biennials, monocarpic and polycarpic perennials. Remarkably little difference can be detected at the outset between the vegetative growing point and one which is already committed to flower, although certain changes of shape, *brought about by growth in bulk or elongation, as the case may be,* of the otherwise rather quiescent subapical region of the shoot meristem are noticeable. Evidence suggests, however, that floral initials are already committed *before* the stimuli that irreversibly activate this subapical region by cell division to create more bulk, or cell enlargement to create an elongated axis, take effect. Different stimuli evoke the transition to flowering. In some monocotyledonous plants it is associated with the prior formation of a sufficient number of vegetative leaf primordia, where time is the paramount variable, and this in turn may sometimes be controlled within the seed prior to its germination by temperature and moisture conditions, as in the vernalization effect. Premature exposure of seedlings of biennials to cold often stimulates their flowering (i.e., "bolting"), and in biennial bulb plants (tulip, narcissus) critical temperatures control both the inception and the development of flowers. Specific substances seem to be engendered by the cold stimulus and their effect may be simulated by such substances as gibberellin. Hypotheses have been developed to suggest that flowering requires the sequential effect of several phases of plant development, time being an essential parameter, in each of which a given factor (temperature or light) predominates, and, no doubt, each developmental phase may contribute chemical substances through which their effect is mediated. Even the effect of light (or darkness), which has been the most studied under the term photoperiodism, is not a simple phenomenon, for there are responses to a high energy light stimulus, which conveys the propensity to flower, and to a low energy light stimulus which catalytically releases or suppresses it. In short-day (long-night) plants, auxin acts like a light flash to nullify the effect of dark period, and auxin antagonists will counteract the effect of a light flash during a dark period. However, auxin is not itself a "flowering hormone." Auxin, as well as the pigment "phytochrome," by which the light stimulus is perceived, may act in the leaf in ways which permit it to produce an illusory floral stimulus. The sex of flowers, i.e., whether they are staminate or pistillate, is a morphogenetic response which is susceptible of experimental investigation because the effect of a variety of external and internal factors can be both observed and measured. The essentially genetically determined potentiality of the growing regions may thus be modulated by a number of stipulated factors, and these include auxin levels, which regulate the kinds of flowers that form. Nevertheless, one cannot ascribe the maleness or femaleness exclusively to a single factor which may evoke, or trigger, a given kind of floral development. The response at the morphogenetic site is probably to a biochemical milieu which has to be defined in more precise, though perhaps complex, terms. In fact, there are many often unrecognized metabolic differences that at least accompany, even if they do not incite, the change from vegetative growth to flowering; some of these are described with special reference to effects upon the balance between nitrogen metabolism and carbohydrate metabolism which may be negotiated at such "ports of entry for nitrogen" as the keto acids. The fact that artificial, or genetically determined, parthenocarpy may initiate the development of fruits and replace the need for stimuli normally received by pollination and the presence of seeds, encourages the belief that ultimately all the morphogenetic events that result from the release of the "innate capacity of an angiosperm to flower" may be brought under chemical regulatory control. These chemical regulators seem to act through their control over the ability of cells in localized regions of the shoot growing point to divide, to elongate, and to grow.

Essentially the initiating cells, from which the development of floral organs stems, are endowed, like other cells of the plant body, with all the genetic information for the whole organism. The floral initials are, however, unique in their location within the organization of the shoot apex and it is in this location, where they are subjected to a complex of factors, that they embark on the events that lead to flowering. Much is known about the features of the external environment which are conducive to flowering when the whole plant or growing region is exposed. It still remains, however, to translate all this into a precise definition of the environment of cells in the formative regions of the shoot—for it is this which sets them apart as floral initials and primordia—and of the various stimuli which promote their growth and development. "Epigenesis" after Waddington may be invoked as a useful concept to stress that the controls of this morphogenetic response cooperate with, but are not solely determined by, the genetic constitution. "Molecular ecology" after Weiss is a useful concept to emphasize that the formative cells are subject to, and responsive in, a complex internal environment which determines their behavior. But these concepts, useful as they may be, still require to be translated into precise physical and chemical terms. Recent work on proteins and enzymes in vegetative and florally induced growing regions holds out hope that the floral stimulus may be causally linked to special proteins and enzymes at the active site, and this in turn leads to the expectation that it may be mediated by molecules (mRNA's) which act at the sites of protein formation.

chapter nine

QUANTITATIVE INTERPRETATIONS OF GROWTH: GROWTH CURVES AND CONTROL SYSTEMS

The problems of growth have now been approached from different standpoints. Whether growth is regarded as increase of size, of substance, or complexity, or however it is measured or observed, growth is essentially a process that occurs through time. To the extent that this behavior is orderly, it can be described in mathematical terms, though whether such an analysis will illuminate the biological problems may be a question. In the equations to the curves which describe growth it is recognized that any two determinations in the ascending series of weights, of linear, area, or volume measurements, of cell numbers, or of other parameters that describe an organism, or even a population of organisms, will differ by amounts which are related to the time that has elapsed. For the purposes of analysis, growth is usually considered as though it proceeds smoothly and continuously in time. But the successive increments by growth are also related to the organic mass which produces them. In other words, the ratio between the increments due to growth, and the size of the system which grows, is a measure of the productivity of the growing system in question. The aim now is to show with what success the time course of growth has been mathematically analyzed. This method of approach, however, will only be meaningful inasmuch as biological significance can be attached to the constants in the derived equations.

Growth Curves

Growth curves may take different forms. First, they may relate the quantity (W), suitably measured, to the time which has elapsed during growth. Secondly, the first derivative (dW/dt) of this growth-time curve relates the velocity, or rate of growth at any point along the course of the growth, to time. Again, the second derivative (d^2W/dt^2) of the growth curve relates the acceleration (or deceleration) in growth at any point along the growth curve to time. Each of these concepts may have its use.

The curve which describes the size of an organism, organ, cell, or cell population at any time is sigmoid in shape (Fig. 9–1a). The sigmoid size/time-growth curve is characterized by a point of inflection when the first rising pace of growth

413

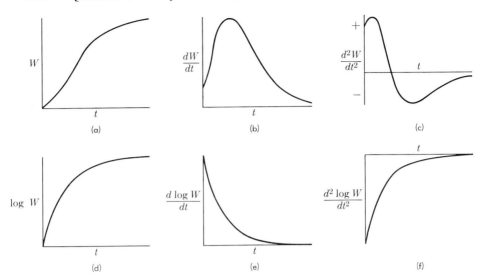

FIG. 9–1. (a) The curve of growth; (b) of growth rate; (c) of acceleration. (d) The curve of *specific growth*; (e) of *specific* growth rate; (f) of *specific* acceleration. The curves have been plotted from an equation for the Gompertz function, but the scales of the ordinates have been so adjusted as to make the height of each graph uniform. (From Medawar, *Essays on Growth and Form,* edited by W. E. Le Gros Clark and P. B. Medawar, Clarendon Press, Oxford, 1945.)

gives way to a decreasing pace. Figure 9–1(b) shows that there is a maximum in the curve of the velocity of growth, and the curve of acceleration (Fig. 9–1c) reflects first the increase to a maximum in the accelerating phase, the decrease to minimum acceleration (or maximum deceleration) in the decelerating phase, and the final approach to zero change as growth finally ceases. As Medawar (1945) shows, the concept of growth and its derivatives (velocity and acceleration) may be replaced by the concept of specific growth and its derivatives. Specific growth is simply the growth per unit of growing substance. The form of the curves which relate specific growth and its derivatives (velocity and acceleration) to time take the form of Fig. 9–1(d, e, f), and, it will be noted, these curves lack the points of inflection and the maxima and minima of the curves of growth and its derivatives.

In the sigmoid curve of growth, it is increments (dW) which are being plotted in the integral quantity $\int dW$ against time. The curve of specific growth plots dW/W against time, i.e., the $\log_e W$. The curve of specific growth describes not the absolute increments due to growth but the *multiplication* due to growth, and correspondingly the rate and acceleration of specific growth are represented by $d \log_e W/dt$ and by $d^2 \log_e W/dt^2$, respectively; these relationships take the general form of Fig. 9–1(e, f). These curves emphasize that the rate of multiplication is highest at *the outset*, and the *rate of multiplication de-*

clines progressively from the point at which the living matter itself was formed. The advantage of the analysis in terms of specific growth is that it "distracts attention from a prominent but not perhaps significant feature of the curve of growth, namely its point of inflection." Despite these evident advantages of curves of specific growth, curves of growth are more familiar and more commonly interpreted.

The sigmoid growth curve (Fig. 9–1a) can, for convenience, be considered in three parts. First there is the accelerating phase in which the products of growth also catalyze further growth; in short, each part of the whole system grows at a maximal rate, virtually unlimited by external factors. This is the part of the growth cycle to which the concept of the "Compound Interest Law" applies. Second, there is a phase, more or less protracted, in which the course of growth is more or less linear with time—i.e., the increments made by growth per unit of time tend to be constant, irrespective of the size of the system which grows. In this phase, specific growth continues to fall with time (cf. Fig. 9–1d). Third, there is a decelerating phase in which the system becomes less and less effective in growth until, in the course of time, growth ceases for one reason or another. The tangent to the time-growth curve has maximum slope when the velocity of the growth is at a maximum, and this identifies what came to be called Sachs' Grand Period of Growth (cf. Fig. 9–1b). Sachs' Grand Period of Growth is also recognizable if the first derivative of the time-growth curve is plotted against time (cf. Fig. 1–25, which shows the distribution of the rate of elongation growth along a root axis, from Goodwin and Stepka, 1945).

Auxanometers

As already stressed (Chapter 1), much of the analysis of growth has been in terms of the measurement of size, often using units of length as the most convenient. In classical plant physiology, instruments which measure growth came to be known as auxanometers. These were largely devices to magnify the growth in length of an organ so that it could be more easily discerned. Descriptions of the "pulley" and "lever" type shoot-recording auxanometers are familiar (Sachs, 1887). In Sachs' series of lectures (1887) an optical device was described which permitted the growth in length of the sporangiophore of certain fungi to be sensitively determined: this device was an auxanometer (Sachs, l.c., p. 561). By direct observation, the elongation of a root tip along a capillary tube has often been recorded by a microscope equipped with appropriate eye piece scales and vertical adjustments. However, a simple but sensitive form of "root auxanometer" was devised by Nielson Jones and, in its simplest form (1920), deserves to be better known. This device measures the vertical displacement of a root tip, attached to a seedling, by the volume of a movable rod which it is necessary to submerge to raise the level of water until it just touches the root tip (Fig. 9–2).

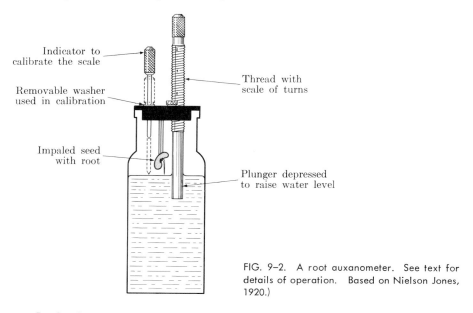

Indicator to
calibrate the scale

Thread with
scale of turns

Removable washer
used in calibration

Impaled seed
with root

Plunger depressed
to raise water level

FIG. 9–2. A root auxanometer. See text for
details of operation. Based on Nielson Jones,
1920.)

In the diagram, a seedling root (e.g., *Vicia faba*) grows down over water. The position of the rod may be adjusted until the water surface just touches the root tip. The rod may then be withdrawn, the root grows down, and after an appropriate time the process is repeated. The change in the position of the movable rod is recorded. It will be apparent that the magnification factor (vertical displacement of the rod/vertical displacement of root tip in a given time) is the ratio of the diameter of the circular vessel which contains the water to the diameter of the movable rod, and this ratio may be made very large. Recording forms of root auxanometers have also been devised, and the growth of entire root systems has been determined by devices which measure the change with time in their submerged volume (Priestley and Pearsall, 1922). The dendrograph of MacDougal (1924) is a special case of an instrument designed to record the changes in the girth of a tree. The optical method of Goodwin and Stepka (1945) made it possible to observe the rate of displacement of the outermost cells of the root past a reference point and was in this sense a type of root auxanometer. One may note the use of film records (cf. Fig. 1.5 from Green), which are especially useful when recording the behavior of shoot tips (cf. also Soma and Ball, 1963) or the growth from free cells as shown by Ball (1963).

Having recognized that growth in size may be recorded by various devices, and that growth regarded as increase of substance may be measured by fresh or dry weights, or the accretion of particular compounds, e.g., protein or cellulose, and that the increase in the number of cells may be determined either directly by counting (after maceration) or indirectly by the increase in DNA, there still remains the problem of interpreting the data so obtained. Some equations that have been fitted to growth curves, therefore, will now be noted.

The Compound Interest Law

This is the law which is applicable to the first part of the sigmoid curve in which any new product of the growth is as effective in growth as that from which it was derived. All parts of the system are growing, in this phase, as rapidly as they can and unlimited by external factors. Lord Kelvin recognized in many natural phenomena that the rate of change of a given quantity is proportional to the quantity itself. The rate of cooling of a hot body is a case in point; the hotter the body relative to its environment, the more rapid is the rate of its cooling. Lord Kelvin coined the phrase Compound Interest Law to cover such relationships. In the case of growth, the size of the system that grows is the analog of the starting principle, and the rate of growth per unit time per unit amount of growing material is the analog of the rate of interest. The growth of seedlings may be usefully analyzed in this way for a longer time than would at first sight seem profitable. While each organ (a leaf, a root, an internode) rapidly passes out of the exponential phase of its own growth, it is nevertheless true that, as growth proceeds, new centers of growth (axillary buds, lateral roots, etc.) are formed as part of the product of the growth. As the newly formed centers of growth contribute to nutrition (photosynthesis by leaves, absorption by roots) the approximately exponential phase of the whole continues longer than it otherwise would.

V. H. Blackman (1919) led a school of thought that developed at the Imperial College of Science at South Kensington, London, which was mainly responsible for the attempted interpretation of the growth of seedlings of angiosperms in terms of the Compound Interest Law.

If W_0 is the initial weight of the seed (or should it more strictly be the weight of the embryo?), if W_1 is the final weight after growth during time t, if r is the rate at which the material present at any time t is employed to produce new material (i.e., the percent increase per unit time), then, if growth occurs smoothly and continuously, $W_1 = W_0 e^{rt}$. In its more convenient logarithmic form, this expression becomes $\log e\ W_1/W_0 = rt$; and, using $\log_{10}$ instead of natural logarithms, the expression becomes $2.303 \log_{10} (W_1/W_0) = rt$. In types of growth which seem to obey this expression, it is to be noted that what seem to be small differences at the outset appear to cause disproportionally large differences as growth proceeds. A relatively slight change in the value of r, which could be caused by circumstances that tend to favor assimilation rather than respiration, may cause a seemingly disproportionate effect on the final product. For example a 6 percent increase in r, when $r = 0.115$, will double the final weight at 100 days if the growth obeys the Compound Interest Law.

An early hope was that the constant r in the compound interest equation could be used as an "efficiency index" to measure the effectiveness of the substance of a given type of plant to produce new substance by growth and that the "efficiency indices" would become characteristic of each plant in question. When oats and maize were grown in water culture, the indices proved to be

7.76 percent and 7.45 percent respectively per day over a growth cycle of 100 days. The indices for *Helianthus* and *Nicotiana* were much higher (17.6 percent and 20.5 percent respectively). The limited usefulness of this concept when applied to the entire growth of a plant was quickly realized, because it was pointed out that (a) the efficiency index is not in fact constant throughout the life of the plant, and (b) the growth is too complex a process to be represented throughout by a single equation of exponential increase. This is, indeed, recognizable from the sigmoid nature of most growth curves, and the evident fact that the early requirements of the growth as it occurs under the Compound Interest Law are not met throughout; the growth falls short of the requirements of this law as time goes on. Moreover, it is not satisfying to describe the growth, *after* it has occurred, by an average rate of increase which is calculated for the whole period.

Growth Analysis after Blackman and Gregory

After their first preoccupation with the Compound Interest Law, the school under V. H. Blackman and F. G. Gregory developed certain simple concepts which came to be known as "Growth Analysis"; the chief virtue of this form of analysis is that it permits relatively simple measurements, that can be made under natural conditions, to be interpreted in ways which shed some light on growth as the accretion of substance (i.e., dry weight). For a concise treatment of this subject, reference should be made to G. E. Blackman (1961).

A number of terms that have been used need to be defined. These are:

1. Relative Growth Rate (or the Efficiency Index), i.e., the rate of production of new material (e.g., dry weight) per unit weight per unit time.

2. Net Assimilation Rate (or the Unit Leaf Rate), i.e., the rate of increase of dry weight per unit time per unit area of leaf.

3. Leaf Area Ratio, i.e., the ratio of leaf area (A) to weight (W) of plant (usually excluding roots).

The relationship between relative growth rate (RGR), net assimilation rate (NAR), and leaf area ratio (LAR) is

$$(RGR) = (NAR) \times (LAR),$$

or, more usefully,

$$\frac{1}{W} \cdot \frac{dW}{dt} = \frac{1}{A} \cdot \frac{dW}{dt} \frac{A}{W},$$

if the weight and the leaf area vary exponentially with time.

This type of analysis lends itself to interpretations of measurements which can be made in the field, or on plants growing under natural conditions, and especially to effects on vegetative growth that are induced by light. The three diagrams from G. E. Blackman (Fig. 9–3) compare the effects of light intensity (shading, where 1.0 denotes natural daylight) on the three parameters in question. Blackman points out that the lower net assimilation rate of buckwheat than of sunflower is offset by its higher leaf area ratio to give a better relative growth rate at all light intensities.

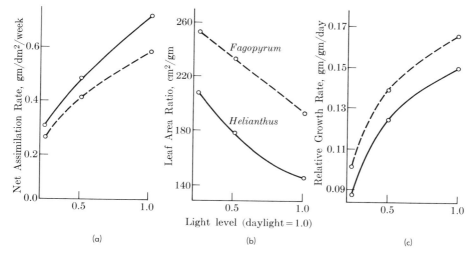

FIG. 9–3. The influence of shading on (a) the net assimilation rate, (b) the leaf area ratio, and (c) the relative growth rate of *Helianthus annuus* and *Fagopyrum esculentum*. (From Blackman, in *Growth in Living Systems*, edited by M. X. Zarrow, Basic Books, Inc., New York, 1961.)

Two further figures show the effects of shading on plants from different habitats and with different growth habit. The English bluebell, *Endymion non-scriptus*, or perhaps more familiarly known by its earlier name *Scilla non-scripta*) produces its leaves as part of the pre-vernal flora in woodlands and forms its leaves as primordia in the bulb in the preceding season. By contrast the leguminous crop (*Medicago sativa*) grows in open situations and has a high light requirement. Although these plants respond similarly to shading by their net assimilation rate, *Endymion* is relatively indifferent to shading as shown by the effect upon its relative growth rate and its leaf area ratio, while *Medicago* responds by wide changes in both these parameters.

By the use of an aquatic angiosperm (*Lemna minor*) and a fern (*Salvinia natans*), Ashby and Oxley (1935) and later G. E. Blackman (1961) interpreted the interacting effects of light and temperature by the methods of growth analysis. In summary it was shown that the weight per frond (e.g., of *Lemna*) reached a maximum under a low (10°C) temperature and a relatively high light (500 to 1600 ft candles) intensity, whereas a minimum frond weight appeared under high (20°C) temperatures and low light (80 to 150 ft candles). The frond area was determined mainly by light (up to 500 ft candles) and was little affected by temperature in the range studied. The interacting effects of temperature and light on *Salvinia* fronds are shown by the response of its leaf area ratio in Fig. 9–4.*

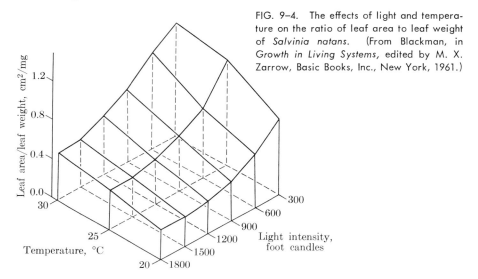

FIG. 9–4. The effects of light and temperature on the ratio of leaf area to leaf weight of *Salvinia natans*. (From Blackman, in *Growth in Living Systems*, edited by M. X. Zarrow, Basic Books, Inc., New York, 1961.)

The interpretation of growth in accordance with the Compound Interest Law, and its sequel in growth analysis after Blackman and Gregory, depends upon the ability of the product of growth to support more growth—which in green plants is dominated by the production of leaf area and the consequential effect upon accretion of dry weight. Useful as these concepts are, they are nevertheless relatively crude. Photosynthetic assimilation of carbon dioxide determined by leaf area and light is only one of the many parameters that regulate and limit anabolism; others are nitrogen, phosphorus and potassium supply, other nutrients including trace elements, and the many morphogenetic stimuli that determine how the products of anabolism shall be used (cf. Chapter 7). Also, the concept of net assimilation rate makes only the minimum concession to catabolism, and it fails to distinguish between assimilates that are usefully employed in new growth and those which are merely accumulated as inert storage substances of all kinds.

---

* Fig. 9–4 represents the interactions of two variables and one parameter. Another potentially useful device (Hutchinson, 1936) allows many such parameters to be represented in the form of a polygon, the shape of which defines the system for each combination of several variables.

The Autocatalytic Equation

The utility of this concept is that it permits one to recognize, and account for, the sigmoid shape of the typical curve of growth. This was first given prominence by Brailsford Robertson, who analyzed the growth of the common pumpkin (fruit of *Cucurbita pepo*) in this way. Much later Brody treated the sigmoid curve in two parts; the accelerating phase from the origin to the inflection point, and the decelerating (or self-inhibitory) phase from the inflection point to the asymptotic value which growth finally approaches. The autocatalytic equation of Robertson (1923) combined both these phases into one curve which is symmetrical about its midpoint in time. In his book on population growth, Pearl (1925) stressed the similarity in the growth of organs, organisms, and populations and showed that the sigmoid curve of growth could be fitted by the so-called logistic expression, of which the autocatalytic equation can be regarded as a special case. The logistic equation may be written in the form

$$W_t = a/ (1 + be^{-kt}),$$

and Pearl and Reed (1923) provided for the degree of asymmetry to fit curves which have their inflection point "off center" by introducing a series involving many terms in t into the exponent, thus:

$$W_t = \frac{a}{1 + b \cdot e^{-(k_0 + k_1 t^1 + k_2 t^2 + k_3 t^3 + \cdots + k_n t^n)}}.$$

An example was given for the increase in the body weight of male white rats which was represented as follows:

$$Y = 7 + \frac{273}{1 + e^{4.3204 - 7.2196x + 30.0878x^2 - 0.5291x^3}},$$

where Y is the body weight and x is the age in units of 100 days. The growth curves of the fruit of *Cucurbita pepo* (Fig. 9–5) and of a population of yeast cells

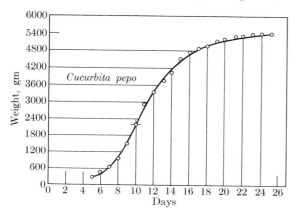

FIG. 9–5. Growth of *Cucurbita pepo*. (Reproduced by permission of the publisher from R. Pearl, *The Biology of Population Growth*, Alfred A. Knopf, Inc., New York, 1925.)

(Fig. 9–6) were also interpreted in a similar manner. In the former case, the increase in weight was represented by

$$y = \frac{5190}{1 + e^{10.3148 - 16.3399x + 8.1028x^2 - 1.6667x^3}},$$

where Y is the weight in grams and x is the time in days. In the latter case, the population increase was represented by

$$y = \frac{66.5}{1 + e^{4.1896 - 0.5355x}},$$

where Y is the crop of yeast and x is the time in days.

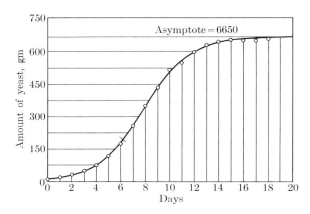

FIG. 9–6. The growth of a population of yeast cells. Reproduced by permission of the publisher from R. Pearl, *The Biology of Population Growth*, Alfred A. Knopf, New York, 1925.

The form of expression adopted by Brailsford Robertson (i.e., the autocatalytic equation) is a symmetrical form of the logistic curve. These concepts were early applied by H. S. Reed (1920) to the analysis of certain growth phenomena in plants.

The characteristics of an autocatalytic reaction are that:

1.   The quantity of starting or reacting material is fixed or determined (e.g., the quantity of an ester that may be hydrolyzed).

2.   The reaction proceeds slowly at first but gathers momentum because the products of the reaction catalyze the reaction (in the case of ester hydrolysis the fatty acid so produced is catalytic, for the reaction is a function of the acidity or pH of the medium in which it occurs).

3.   The reaction rate slows down as the unreplenished active mass of the substrate declines (i.e., as the quantity of ester available for hydrolysis decreases).

A process which follows the autocatalytic pattern conforms to the following expression: $\log [x/(A - x)] = K(t_1 - t)$, where $A =$ the maximum amount of initial substrate to be converted, $x =$ the quantity of reacted material at time t_1, $t =$ the elapsed time necessary to convert half of the initial substrate. In its integral form this expression represents a special case of the more general logistic equation. In the example cited (hydrolysis of an ester), these quantities may easily be identified; the inital amount of substrate A is the quantity of ester available, the quantity x represents the amount of fatty acid produced. When the process is catalyzed only by acid (instead of the enzyme lipase), the autocatalytic equation fits the hydrolytic behavior.

In the application of the autocatalytic equation to growth curves, several points are immediately apparent. In the analogous physicochemical system a defined amount A of initial substrate is eventually all converted. In a growing biological system the amount of eventual product is initially represented by the *latent potential* of that which will grow, and it cannot, *at the outset*, be measured, for it can only be determined *after the growth has fully occurred*. However, the final product of growth (number of cells in a yeast suspension, length or weight of an organ when growth is completed) may be used to substitute for A in the equation with the recognition that there is no quantitative measure at the outset for the amount of growth that has yet to occur.

It is characteristic of the autocatalytic type of equation that it represents a sequence of events which are symmetrical about their midpoint in time. While biological time-growth curves are indeed sigmoid, they are rarely as symmetrical as this, for no innate significance may be attached to the midpoint in time of the growth process. Even so, the autocatalytic equation may be useful. In essence, the interpretation of growth as an autocatalytic reaction implies that there was a latent, or initial, amount of substrate (or energy) already present in the system that could grow; and when this was completely used, or converted, the growth would be complete.

H. S. Reed (1920) analyzed the effects of the severity of pruning on the annual growth of apricot shoots in this way. As expected, the shoots grew more on the heavily than on the lightly, or unpruned, trees. Reed used the autocatalytic type of growth curve in its differential form, in which the rate of growth (dx/dt) is proportional at any time to the amount of growth $(a - x)$ *still to be achieved*; thus $dx/dt = k(a - x)$, and in its integral form this equation becomes $x = a(1 - e^{-kt})$. The initial length of the shoots on the trees which had been severely pruned was 8 cm, and their mean annual growth in length was 210 cm, the total growth achieved was 218 cm, and, according to Reed, the growth was described by $x_2 = 218(1 - e^{-0.11t})$. For the trees subjected to mild pruning, the equivalent data were 6 cm for the initial shoot length and 94 cm of mean annual growth; so that the growth was described by $x_1 = 100(1 - e^{-0.11t})$, and the constant k $(= 0.11)$ was the same in both cases. Thus Reed concluded that the growth in length at any point in time is a function of the final length of the shoot, i.e., of the growth still to be done. Therefore, whatever limitations were set upon the growth of these shoots must have been there at the outset of the growing season, and in some way the growing points of the shoot on the severely pruned trees had to "become aware" of this and to "decide," as it were, in advance to achieve the larger growth! This type of analysis is, in the first place, of limited use. It may describe growth after it has occurred; it does not, however, foretell the growth, or in any sense explain it, beyond the implicit assumption that the growth as it will occur is, in some way, predetermined in the shoot apex of the pruned and unpruned trees.

While the capacity to grow is, as it were, "built into" the shoot apex, it is very clear that in its expression it is very subject to external control. Temperature and nutrition are obvious factors, and there is evidence that, apart from the intervention of variables which determine either the onset of flowering or the onset of rest and dormancy (see Chapters 7 and 8), the growth of shoots may, like the growth of root tips, be potentially unlimited. By the repeated propagation of cuttings of shoots, or the repeated removal of root tips, they may grow indefinitely. Potentially unlimited growth of tissue cultures and of free cells derived from shoots must also be accepted. It is true, however, that the growth only becomes potentially unlimited when it is periodically renewed by removing a part which can grow (shoot or root tip, tissue explant, or free cells) from whole which has grown. One may interpret this effect in terms of the removal from the growing region of inhibitors which emanate from the mature tissue it has produced. Even so, it is not helpful to conclude only that a given shoot growing point makes a strictly limited amount of growth which is predetermined at the outset of that particular "stanza" of its growth.

One can, however, regard the shoot apex as capable of growing and forming its lateral organs at a rate which must have a physically determined maximum, but the actual rate achieved may be the consequence of competition for endogenous and exogenous nutrients as well as the subtle interaction of all the external variables that make their impact on growth. The autocatalytic equation does not, therefore, offer a very useful interpretation of growth curves, because one cannot in any given system obtain *at the outset* a quantitative measure of the final amount of growth which will be achieved. As a first approximation to a type of expression which will fit a sigmoid growth curve, it has, however, some interest.

The Growth of Cuttings: The Case of Mint

A given shoot apex, adequately furnished with all the requirements for growth, should be able to achieve the formation of a prescribed number of leaf primordia and internodes in a given period of time: the rate at which this is achieved would be expected to be a function of the external conditions, the nutrition, etc. This appeared to be the case in the early growth of mint cuttings as found in the experiments of Crane (1951). It was found, empirically, that the opposite 4 leaves at 4 internodes (8 cm long) promoted maximum growth of the shoot and adequate rooting in water. Such cuttings could be grown in a plentiful supply of Hoagland's solution for some weeks prior to the complications of flowering (especially on short days).

As a measure of growth of mint plants, the length of the main shoot, the length of the longest lateral shoot, and the length of the longest roots could all be recorded. These data, plotted against time, yielded Fig. 9–7. From this the behavior of the shoot apex may be interpreted as follows.

Lacking roots, there was a lag period in the growth of mint cuttings. Four pairs of leaves on a 7 to 8 cm cutting, however, will quickly generate an adequate crop of roots. After root formation, the growth of the apex gathered momentum through a brief exponential phase. Rooting started in about 7 days, and by 18 days the amount of root (and the resultant mineral and water uptake) was adequate to support the full amount of growth which the shoot apex could achieve, so that it settled down to a steady rate in which, under the uniform conditions used (in the greenhouse with relatively high night temperatures and full nutrient supply), new leaves and internodes appeared at a uniform rate

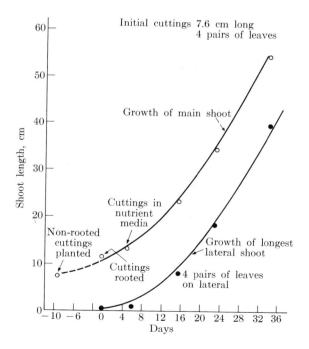

FIG. 9–7. Analysis of growth in length of detached and attached lateral shoots of *Mentha piperita* L. (After Crane, 1951; cf. Crane and Steward, 1962.)

which was linear with time; this continued for a relatively long period (e.g., 36 days). In due course the crop of leaves and the crop of roots was enough to support the growth of more lateral shoots. Although these appeared in very symmetrical fashion, only the growth of the lowest one, furthest from the suppression due to the dominance of the main shoot, was recorded. Again after the brief exponential increase to a maximum rate, the laterals also settled down to grow at *the same* rate as the apex, for this seemed to be the maximum rate that a mint apex could achieve when reasonably unlimited by neighboring plants and under the physical conditions of light, temperature, and nutrition that obtained. Moreover, the slope of this line, which relates shoot length to time, proved to be a good index of the effect of external nutrients on the growth of the rooted mint cuttings, and it was in every way as useful a criterion as the final weight of the entire crop of plants. By repeated cutting, or by control of day length, mint can be kept in the vegetative state so that the shoot growing point continues almost indefinitely to form its leaves and inernodes in regular sequence and at a steady rate. The average time between one pair of opposite leaves and the next (i.e., one plastochron) is 3.2 days. But this potentially unlimited behavior is subject to the morphogenetic stimuli which lead to the intervention of flowering (which is in turn determined by long days and high night temperatures) or of stolon formation (which is determined especially by short days).

Figure 1–14 shows a transverse section of the shoot apex of mint. From this one can visualize that each pair of leaves arises on the flanks of the growing point and, in so doing, they occupy a given percentage of the surface and utilize the growth capacity of a given number of cells. Unfortunately, one cannot yet deduce from the number of cells that comprise the leaf primordium the number of cell generations that are required to form a mature leaf. The demands of leaf formation are such that only two leaf primordia can normally be accommodated on the apex at a given level at a time, and these arise as far as possible from each other and consequently they are oppositely arranged (cf. Fig. 1–14). When these leaves have been completely initiated there is space available for the initiation of another pair, but these emerge as far as possible from the vicinity of the first pair, as in the decussate arrangement; but all these events take time (approximately 3.2 days under a given set of conditions). Thus the mathematical description of growth of a mint shoot should give some recognition to the fact that a given amount of the apical dome needs to be mobilized to form a leaf, and a given time interval is required for the growing point to emerge from one leaf-forming event and to embark upon the next.

Any biologically useful mathematical description of growth of a mint shoot should, therefore, represent it as the summation of these discrete and periodic events and, if possible, interpret them; this, however, seems beyond the capacity of any of the simple types of equation that have yet been used to analyze growth in terms of overall size or substance.

Growth Analysis after Glaser

It is a characteristic of most orderly growth processes that they proceed with gathering momentum along the curve of growth, in the exponential or compound interest phase, but eventually the growth achieved falls short of the requirements under the Compound Interest Law by amounts which become progressively more apparent. A type of analysis was designed by Glaser to account for this (Glaser, 1938). Although this analysis was first applied to the growth of animal embryos, which often begin their growth in almost unlimited supplies of nutrient, it has also some interest for any growth which may emanate uniformly from a single growing center, or cell.

Glaser utilized the fact that the regular polyhedron which fills space most effectively, without "leftovers," is a regular 14-sided figure, the tetrakaidecahedron. Around this, 14 more cells could be arranged in the first layer of cells, so that a system with one such layer would contain $1 + 14$ cells. If there are two cell layers, there would be 50 cells in the center layer; three layers, 110; four layers, 194, and so on. The general expression which gives the number of cells in a system which forms around one cell, and in a system in which the cells are uniformly close-packed around a single initiating cell, is $Sn = 4n^3 + 6n^2 + 4n + 1$; this expression is not significantly different from $Sn = 1 + (2n + 1)^3/2$ or, in a logarithmic form,

$$\log Sn = 3 \log (2n + 1) - 0.3010.$$

Glaser also points out that the growth of embryos in a uniform and excess supply of nutrient, as in an avian egg, soon falls short of the requirements of the Compound Interest Law by amounts which are themselves a function of time. The empirical relation is that on the fifth day the percentage increase that occurs by growth is proportional to $1/(6^2 - 5^2)$; on the sixth day it is proportional to $1/(7^2 - 6^2)$; and on the seventh day $\propto 1/(8^2 - 7^2)$; and at t days it would be $\propto 1/[(t + 1)^2 - t^2]$ or $\propto 1/(2t + 1)$. Therefore the rate of growth (d/Wdt) at any time t is, according to Glaser, given by the expression

$$dW/dt = k \, [1/(2t + 1)] \, W;$$

by integrating and putting $k/2 = K$, we obtain

$$\log W = K \log (2t + 1) + C.$$

Thus there are two equations which are of similar form:

$$\log Sn = 3 \log (2n + 1) - 0.3010; \qquad \text{(Equation 1)}$$

$$\log W = K \log (2t + 1) + C. \qquad \text{(Equation 2)}$$

Equation 1 describes the increase in the number of cells in a system in which the cells are uniformly close-packed in n layers around a single initiating cell.

Equation 2 describes the growth of a system which is well supplied by external nutrient but which grows in such a way that any falling off in the growth rate is an inherent function of the system as it grows. The formal similarity of Equations 1 and 2 would be satisfied if n were proportional to t, that is, if equal numbers of cell layers were formed in equal intervals of time. Were this so, the rate of cell divisions, conceived to be in the surface layers, would not continue at the maximum of which each single cell is capable, but only at a rate sufficient to multiply the number of *cell layers* at a steady rate. No doubt the rate of cell layer formation might then be interpreted in terms of the ability of exogenous nutrients to diffuse through the surface.

Plant systems in which a single initiating cell gives rise to a uniform, close-packed, tissue mass which grows uniformly in all directions, under uniform external conditions, are neither frequent nor easy to establish. Where initiating cells or groups of cells seem to exist in the growing point (cf. Fig. 1–23), their directive influence is definitely oriented; and the rapid onset of differentiation in the cells cut off from them superimposes other features to which Glaser's analysis would not apply. Whether the growth of massive, parenchymatous storage organs could be profitably analyzed from this standpoint is a moot point; whether the growth of palmella stages in certain algae may fit these concepts is also untested. A near approximation to this type of growth is furnished by small explanted pieces of tissue (e.g., carrot phloem) in a medium competent to support growth and under conditions such that external stimuli are balanced. In such a system 2.5-mg explants are, however, far from single cells (they contain about 25,000 to 28,000 cells), but for a limited period the growth does approximately satisfy the conditions required if it is the increase in number of cell layers that is uniform with time (Steward, 1958). However, a system as uniform as this soon tends to grow in a more localized manner by means of nests, or nodules, of more actively growing cells which are distributed around the surface of the cultured mass. When growth actually does begin from free cells suspended in a liquid medium, as in free cells of carrot (Steward, Mapes, and Smith, 1958), it does not at first follow the pattern described by Glaser. When cells are free of the constraints of the mature plant body, they grow in various ways which do not reflect their tendency to partition space uniformly. On the contrary, it seems that their growth is then subject to some intrinsic factors, yet unspecified, which become apparent when cells are freed from external limitations of nutrient, or limitations of the space in which they grow.

The potentialities of free parenchyma cells have only been appreciated recently. These potentialities include an otherwise baffling array of cell forms and modes of division which have been described, and are illustrated in the figures (cf. Chapter 5), and they even include the ability to grow in such a way that a pro-embryo-like structure is reformed and from this whole plants can develop. In this type of development organization occurs and polarity is established before many cell layers in the sense of Glaser have been laid down.

The Bertalanffy Equation

Beverton and Holt (1957) also advocated another, and apparently useful, growth equation which has been devised by von Bertalanffy. This is based on the concept that the metabolic processes of organisms are determined by the relationship between the active mass which undergoes catabolism and the necessary surface to support anabolism. The anabolism, or synthesis, is expressed as the product of the rate at which mass is created per unit area (H) and surface (S), where S is the physiologically effective surface through which exchanges take place. Thus,

$$dW/dt = HS - kW,$$

where H is a coefficient of anabolism, since anabolism is proportional to the surface area through which essential exchanges take place, and k is a coefficient of catabolism, since catabolism is proportional to the entire bulk of living material. Where S and W can be described in terms of l^2 and l^3 respectively (where $l = $ length), Beverton and Holt show that this model permits the length or the weight of an organism at any time t to be expressed as follows:

$$l_t = L_\infty - (L_\infty - L_0)\, e^{-kt}$$

or

$$W_t = [W_\infty^{1/3} - (W_\infty^{1/3} - W_0^{1/3})\, e^{-kt}]^3,$$

where $l_t = $ length at time t, $L_\infty = $ length at time ∞, $L_0 = $ length of time 0, and $W_t = $ weight at time t. These equations have been shown to give a very good fit of the characteristically sigmoid but asymmetrical growth curve for certain marine fishes, where the point of inflexion appears at less than one-third of the final or asymptotic weight.

It is now apparent that the earlier empirical formulation of growth analysis, after Blackman and Gregory, is really the Bertalanffy equation in another form. To show this, one needs to transpose the Bertalanffy equation as follows:

For $\dfrac{dW}{dt} = HS - kW$ write $\dfrac{dW}{dt} = \left(\dfrac{1}{A} \cdot \dfrac{dW}{dt}\right) A - kW;$

this replaces total surface (S) with leaf area (A) and converts the coefficient H to its derivative form. When growth rate dW/dt is expressed as relative growth rate $(1/W)\,(dW/dt)$, the "equation" becomes

$$\frac{1}{W} \cdot \left(\frac{dW}{dt}\right) = \frac{1}{A} \cdot \frac{dW}{dt} \cdot \frac{A}{W} - k,$$

which is virtually identical with the growth analysis equation presented on p. 418. The constant k may be interpreted to represent the discrepancy incurred by substituting leaf area for total surface.

TABLE 9–1
The common growth functions and their more important analytical properties. The symbol W may be read as "size"; it usually stands for weight. Logarithms are expressed to the natural

Function	Equation	Linear form	W $t = 0$	W $t \to \infty$
1. Exponential	$W = be^{kt}$	$\log W = \log b + kt$	b	—
2. Monomolecular	$W = a(1 - be^{-kt})$	$\log \dfrac{a - W}{a} = \log b - kt$	$a(1 - b)$	a
3. Logistic	$W = \dfrac{a}{1 + be^{-kt}}$	$\log \dfrac{a - W}{W} = \log b - kt$	$\dfrac{a}{1 + b}$	a
4. Gompertz	$W = ae^{-b \exp (-kt)}$	$\log \log \dfrac{a}{W} = \log b - kt$	ae^{-b}	a
5. Parabola	$W = bt^{k}$	$\log W = \log b + k \log t$	0	—

From Medawar, 1945 (by permission of the Clarendon Press, Oxford.)

The advantage of the Bertalanffy equation is that it is based on a model which has some physiological meaning, namely, the balance between anabolism and catabolism. Until Richards (1959) the equation had not been much exploited in the analysis of plant growth curves. However, Richards has deduced a more generalized form of the Bertalanffy equation, although he started from somewhat similar concepts. Richards made various choices of the value of the constant relationship between the body weight W and the metabolic rate (nW^{m}), where n and m are appropriate constants. The catabolism is equal to kW, where k is a constant of catabolism and the growth rate is the difference $(nW^{m} - kW)$ between anabolism and catabolism. From this starting point Richards (1959) deduced a more general form of the Bertalanffy equation in which, if $m = 2$, it reduces to the characteristics of the autocatalytic equation; if $m = 1$, to the characteristics of the Gompertz equation (see Table 9–1). The Gompertz equation, devised long ago (Gompertz, 1825) but ignored till it was revived by Sewall-Wright for its use in the analysis of population growth, is a "double integral" equation which has the maximum flexibility in the fitting of asymmetric sigmoid time curves of growth. The point of referring here to the Bertalanffy equation, and its more generalized form after Richards, is that it is based on an intelligible physiological model rather than empirical interpretations of observations on growth.

The Characteristics of Growth Curves and Their Derivatives

Medawar (1945) assembled the characteristics of the equations which have been most usefully applied in the interpretation of growth. The essentials of base e. Many of the analytical properties may be more simply expressed as functions of W rather than of age, *t*, but time has been chosen as the independent variable in order to illustrate the empirical rules later formulated.

Point of inflection (W, t)	Specific growth rate	Specific acceleration	References
—	k	0	—
—	$\dfrac{kbe^{-kt}}{1 - be^{-kt}}$	$-\dfrac{k^2be^{-kt}}{(1 - be^{-kt})^2}$	Putter (1920); Brody (1926); Bertalanffy (1934)
$(a/2, (\log b)/k)$	$\dfrac{kbe^{-kt}}{1 + be^{-kt}}$	$-\dfrac{k^2be^{-kt}}{(1 + be^{-kt})^2}$	Robertson (1908); Crozier (1926); Reed and Pearl (1927); Titus (1930)
$(a/e, (\log b)/k)$	kbe^{-kt}	$-k^2be^{-kt}$	Wright (1926); Weymouth, McMillin, and Rich (1931); Winsor (1932)
—	k/t	$-k/t^2$	Murray (1925); Schmalhausen (1926); Teissier (1937)

Medawar's table are reproduced as Table 9–1, which shows the characteristics of the parabolic, exponential, logistic (autocatalytic as a special case), and Gompertz expressions. Column 2 presents the integrated form of the growth equation which describes the change of size or total substance (W) with time. Column 3 shows the logarithmic functions of growth (W) which, under the conditions imposed by the equation in question, should give a linear relationship, so that it may be used as a test of the applicability of a given equation to a given case. The fourth and fifth columns express the starting size (W_0) and the final size (W_∞) of the system which grows in terms of the derived constants in the equation. In column 7, headed Specific Growth Rate, r is the quantity dW/Wdt and represents the rate of multiplication at any time t per unit amount of growing substance; and, in similar terms, column 8 relates the change in specific growth rate (acceleration when $+ ve$, deceleration when $- ve$) to time. The logistic and Gompertz equations show a point of inflection along the time course of growth, and the coordinates of these are given in column 6. From this table the criteria which determine the type of equation which best interprets a given set of growth data may be discerned.

At best the growth curves *describe* the growth which *has occurred;* the equations to growth curves are, however, of very limited use to *explain* the growth of an organism, for it is not always possible to ascribe biological significance to the constants they contain—still less has it proved to be possible to start with all the factors which determine, or limit, growth and devise an expression in which these factors are represented in a growth equation which will *foretell* growth. Growth results from the working of an organization which still seems far too complex for ready description in such mathematical terms.

Discontinuities in Growth

Of necessity, the mathematical analysis of growth curves assumes that growth occurs smoothly in time. It is, however, apparent that growth is a discontinuous process; it proceeds by discrete steps, and it only assumes the semblance of a smooth process in time when the units of observation become large and the time periods relatively long. The time sequence of growth from one mitosis to the next shows that a relatively protracted period in the metabolic state may culminate in cell and nuclear division which is completed in a very much shorter time. Some examples of the time sequence, showing the period of the cell "at rest" and in division, are shown in Table 9–2. As the two parts A and B of the Table 9–2 show, the discrete steps which comprise the whole process of cell generation divide the cell generation time into different intervals according as one concentrates upon the visible events of mitosis, or upon the underlying synthesis of DNA which makes the replication of self-duplicating structures possible. In either event, however, even the process of cell multiplication is a discontinuous, not a smoothly continuous, process in time.

TABLE 9–2
Duration of the events of mitosis in *Vicia faba* root cells at 25°C

	A
Stage	Time in hours
Cell generation time	22.9
Mitosis	1.9
prophase	1.1
metaphase	0.3
anaphase and telophase	0.5
	B
Total cycle	24 to 30
Interphase	
G_1 (pre-DNA synthesis)	12
S (DNA synthesis)	6
G_2 (post-DNA synthesis)	8

Data in A from Evans and Savage, 1959. Data in B from Howard and Pelc, 1952.
See also Woodard 1958.

The discontinuity in growth by day and by night, as shown by the effects of day length (or night length) and by the contrasted effects of night and day temperature, are evidence enough that any diurnal cycle is the summation of quite different effects by day and by night. Periods in which growth proceeds uniformly in time (shown by log/log plots of weight against time) have been called stanzas (cf. equation on page 438), and discontinuities in the growth may often be revealed by an abrupt change in the slope of such lines as one phase, or stanza, in growth gives way to another. Discontinuities in growth are perhaps more apparent in plants even than in animals. There is no essential continuity between growth in length and in girth, and as each new lateral organ (a bud or a lateral branch; a lateral root; new tillers; adventitious roots) bursts into growth, new centers are established which become, in large measure, independent. The formation of floral organs, the occurrence of meiosis and the onset of a sexual or gametophytic phase of growth, syngamy, and later the interacting effects of the embryo and the parent sporophyte, all represent discontinuities, or crises, in development which effectively interrupt the smooth time course of growth and effectively destroy any illusion that it can be uniform in its relationship to time. The occurrence of storage organs, and the phenomena of rest and dormancy (cf. Chapters 7 and 8) also show that growth does not bear a uniform, or consistent, relation to time and therefore any analysis of growth which assumes this must be to this extent inadequate.

Problems of Relative Growth

The concept of relative growth recognizes the unequal growth rates of different parts in the one body, and it measures the growth of one part in relation to the whole, or of one part in relation to another. In this way the variable time may be canceled. Dramatic examples of differences in relative growth occur in the animal kingdom, e.g., the weights of antlers in relation to body weight of deer, or the differences in the size of claws in lobsters.

Differential growth rates are apparent in the growth of many leaf laminae. The individual leaflets of a palmately lobed leaf such as that of *Aesculus* obviously grow in area and in length at different rates. (Gregory attempted to interpret the growth in area of cucumber leaves in terms of the factors that affect both cell division and cell expansion.) The shape of leaves such as those of *Nicotiana* is determined by the differential growth of the leaf in different parts of the lamina. Avery (1933) has analyzed, or rather described, this by the use of lines on the leaf surface to connect regions of similar relative growth rates. The results of an application of this method to the growth of a leaf are shown in Figs. 9–8 and 9–9, which are based on Avery's study of the tobacco leaf (cf. Richards and Kavanagh, 1945). A young leaf was marked with a rectangular network on its upper surface; as it grew to maturity, the network was deformed. Avery's figures give four growth stages. The corners of the rectangles are the reference points used in the analysis. For convenience the lines originally at right angles to the midrib have been numbered from 0 to 12, starting at the base of the leaf. Although growth in the neighborhood of the center of the leaf is continuous, the nature of the markings did not make it possible to use this fact in the analysis. Therefore, each half of the leaf was analyzed in turn and the midrib data were used with each half.

The distribution of values of the specific growth rate in *area* is indicated in each of the four stages of Fig. 9–8 by solid lines along which the rate is con-

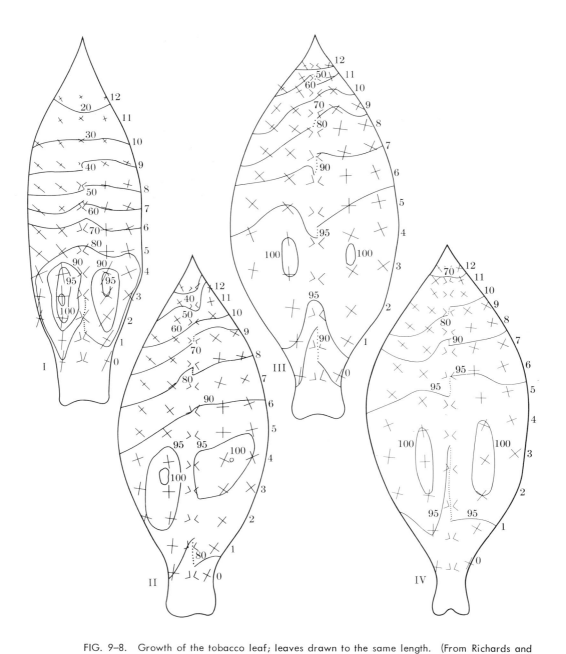

FIG. 9–8. Growth of the tobacco leaf; leaves drawn to the same length. (From Richards and Kavanagh, in *Essays on Growth and Form*, edited by W. E. Le Gros Clark and P. B. Medawar, Clarendon Press, Oxford, 1945, by permission of Clarendon Press and *American Naturalist*.)

FIG. 9–9. Growth of the tobacco leaf; size of leaves proportional to their length at each stage of growth. For the annotation of the contour lines see text. Crosses represent velocities and directions of growth shown as at the corners of the original grid. (From Richards and Kavanagh, in *Essays on Growth and Form*, edited by W. E. Le Gros Clark and P. B. Medawar, Clarendon Press, Oxford, 1945, by permission of Clarendon Press and *American Naturalist*.) ▶

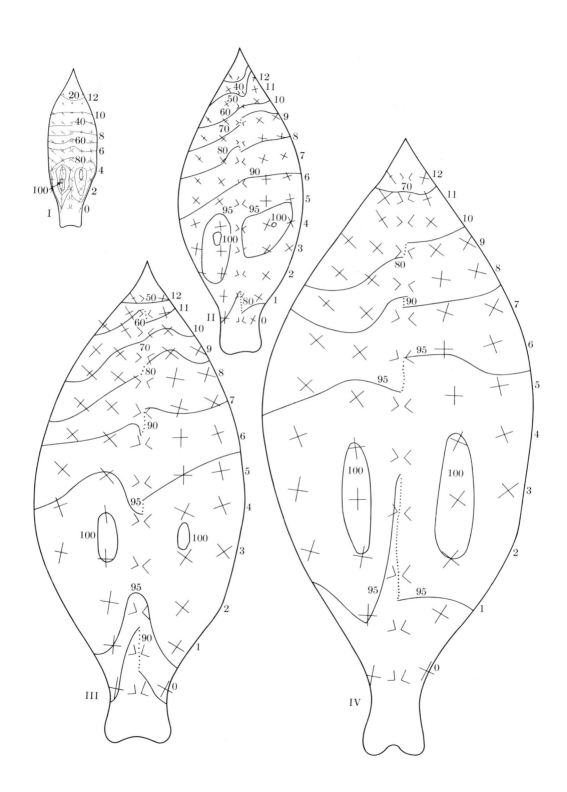

stant, just as isotherms are used on a weather map to indicate places of equal temperature. The curves marked 100 are those of approximately the maximum rate at each stage; the numbers 95, 90, etc., indicate that the rate on the corresponding region is 95 percent, 90 percent, etc., of the curve marked 100.

As a result of the separate analysis of two halves of the leaf, the curve for a given value is sometimes broken at the midrib; the two parts of each curve have then been joined by a dotted line.

The position of maximum growth rate in area remains fixed at all stages near the lateral marked 3. From these centers the rate falls off both towards the ends and the sides. However, as the leaf matures the gradient becomes less sharp; in the first stage (I) the rate near the lateral number 12 was less than 20 percent of the maximum, while on the fourth stage (IV) it was about 70 percent. A similar leveling off of the gradient is to be noted towards the sides and base of the leaf. It is therefore incorrect to hold that the ratio of the specific growth rates of two parts remains constant during the growth. The problem is one of determining the physiological factors which give rise to the gradient in the first place and which cause it to change as the leaf matures. Regulation is shown in Fig. 9–9 by the changes in size of the area of maximum rate of growth. Such changes conserve symmetry. The nature of the specific growth rate in *length* is shown at each point by a pair of crossed lines. The length of each line is proportional to the specific growth rate in length in that direction. The directions are respectively those of maximum and of minimum rate at each point and are at right angles to each other. Since the halves of the leaf were analyzed separately, two sets of values were obtained for each point at the midrib; these are shown by half-crosses slightly separated. Lengths of the lines at any one stage are comparable with each other, but are *not* to be compared directly with those in the other stages, since the scales are not the same.

In the early stages, especially in the left half of the leaf, the intensity of growth in length is much stronger in one direction than in the direction at right angles to it. As the leaf matures, this anisotropy tends to decrease, and the growth becomes more nearly isotropic. Again the inadequacy of the concept of specific growth rate ratio is evident. But this type of *description* of what occurs is far from an *explanation* of why it occurs. Pearsall has compared the relative growth of petiole and lamina in the garden nasturtium. The effect of factors which modify the relative growth of lamina and leaf base or petiole are very evident in the changes which accompany the progressive conversion of leaf primordia into bud scale primordia. This is well illustrated in such plants as *Ribes* (Fig. 9–10). While it is apparent that a change in the ratio of growth in leaf lamina to leaf base (petiole) is a necessary part of the description of the change in form, this is far from an explanation of how or why this change is brought about.

When an organ grows at a different rate from that of the rest of the body, the relation between them may be expressed by $y = bx^k$, or better by

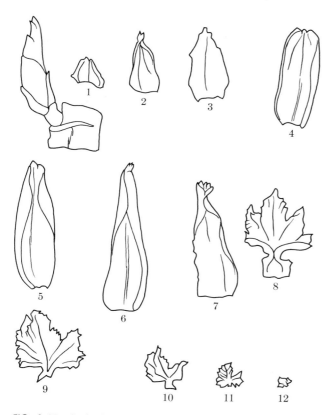

FIG. 9–10. Bud of *Ribes sanguineum* Pursh. (flowering currant). Comparison of bud scales (Nos. 1 to 7) with young foliage leaves (Nos. 8 to 12) shows clearly that only the leaf base is represented in the typical bud scales. (After Priestley and Scott, 1938.)

$y = b(x - y)^k$, where $y =$ the magnitude of the differentially growing organ, $x =$ the magnitude of the entire body of the organism in the same units, b and k are constants, and, whereas b has no biological significance, k is the ratio of the growth rate of the organ to that of the whole body. If $k = 1.0$, then the growth of the organ in question is directly proportional to that of the body as a whole, and growth is isogonic. If k is greater or less than 1.0, the organ is heterogonic and grows at a different rate than the whole body. If $k > 1.0$, then the part is positively heterogonic and grows more rapidly than the whole; if $k < 1.0$, then the part is negatively heterogonic and grows more slowly than the whole. The analysis of the growth of a leaf in terms of petiole and lamina may be made from this point of view, and the balance between shoot weight and root weight is also susceptible to similar analysis (cf. Figs. 9–11 and 9–12). A test of the heterogonic growth may be made by use of the relationship that describes

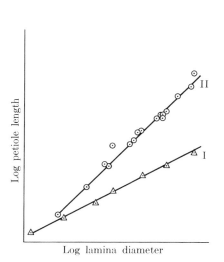

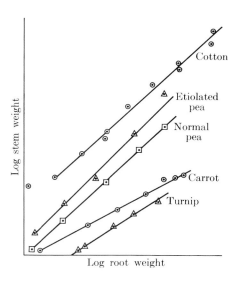

FIG. 9–11.   Relation between logarithms of lamina diameters and petiole lengths of *Tropaeolum majus* leaves.   I. A series of growing leaves.   II. All the leaves of a large plant grow-in the shade.   (From Pearsall, *Ann. Botany* 41, 549–556, 1927.)

FIG. 9–12.   Relations of logarithms of stem weights for various plants.   The vertical scale is reduced to one-half in the case of etiolated peas.   (From Pearsall, *Ann. Botany* 41, 549–556, 1927.)

their differential growth, namely, $\log y = \log b + k \log (x - y)$, where the symbols have the meaning described above. These double log plots give straight lines, the slope of which is a measure of the coefficient k, which is the ratio between the growth rate of the differentially growing organ and that of the rest of the body.

Quite early in the interpretations of relative growth rates, Pearsall (1927) pointed out that the constant k in the equation $y = bx^k$ involves a comparison of the respective efficiencies in growth of the differentially growing organs in question. If, as in the case of Fig. 9–12, growth is being measured for both shoots and roots by weight, then there are obvious differences between them. Shoots tend to emphasize surface (which contributes to fixation of light energy and of carbon dioxide) and they multiply their lateral organs superficially; roots, which are equally necessary to furnish salts and water, are relatively more efficient in producing length, their growth is more deep-seated, and when they do produce lateral organs, these originate endogenously. One can conceive, therefore, of a protracted phase in which the relative growth of shoot and root in weight would reflect these facts. But this otherwise uniform trend could profoundly change when, with the advancing season, the exponential growth of leaves is arrested, and, by a photoperiodic or other stimulus, an underground tuber or storage root develops. Thus, one type, or stanza, of growth would terminate and give way to another. One should, therefore, be able to see the effect of the morphogenetic stimulus in question by the change in the relative growth rates of the organs concerned and by the transition from one "stanza" of growth to another.

The treatments which are applied above to the dimensions of organs may also be applied to their content of chemical compounds. This is essentially the concept of chemical heterogony upon which Needham (1931) has written. The application of this form of analysis to the relative accumulation of water and dry matter during growth has already been mentioned (Chapter 1).

An interesting case in point is the progressive accumulation of dry matter relative to water during the growth of a potato plant. As related by Glaser (1938), this water/dry matter ratio of potato plants progressively declined as the season advanced from July 3. The new tubers, however, accumulated dry matter, relative to water, at a different rate from the plants. At the outset on July 3, the tubers had a dry matter content that the plants were not to emulate until August 28 (cf. Table 9–3). However, if the quiescent cells of the tuber are made to grow again (as, for example, by treatment with coconut milk and 2,4-D), they return to the very high water content (over 90 percent that is typical of embryonic plants (cf. Fig. 4–38).

TABLE 9–3
The ratio of water to dry matter in potato plants and tubers

Date	Potato plants	Tubers
July 3	9.06	5.20
August 4	6.16	4.21
August 28	5.22	4.37
September 20	3.61	3.25
October 23	3.36	3.36

Data from Glaser, 1938

The concepts of chemical heterogony could, it seems, be applied more widely to the interpretation of the effects of those morphogenetic environmental stimuli that cause such responses as photoperiodism, vernalization, etc. Changes occur in the soluble nitrogen compounds and in the keto acids of the leaves of mint which are caused by those variables which are known also to affect the growth of the shoot. More frequent use could, however, be made of these concepts to see whether there is any recognizable need to accumulate a given substance, or class of substances, as a prelude to a shift in the kind, as well as the rate, of growth which occurs. (Old work on carbohydrate/nitrogen ratios, though far in advance of the time when these distinct classes of compounds could be adequately separated and determined, was a move toward this end. However, it is now generally recognized that no really useful conclusion came from even the extensive application of these early ideas.)

Control Systems and the Analysis of Growth

The mathematical analysis of growth and growth curves is a convenient, often instructive, *description* of growth; it tells virtually nothing about the causation or control of growth, nor of its responses to stimuli, especially when the final yield of growth is a necessary constant in the equation.

It is now customary to conceive that the blueprint of the organism is impressed, like a carefully coded message, upon the DNA of the chromosomes. The message impressed on the DNA is conveyed through the appropriate enzymes to metabolism. (It is a debatable point whether all the effects of genes on morphology, i.e., effects of nature, not nurture, can be mediated simply in this way.) However, as the characteristics of the organism unfold during growth, innumerable relationships with the environment are involved, though, of necessity, these operate within limits set by the genetic information which is impressed upon the DNA of the nucleus. Therefore, factors inherent in the nucleus, the chromosomes, and the genes send the signals which, as it were, trip the switches that connect the circuits necessary for growth, but the power that is thus engaged resides in, or is generated by, the chemical processes of metabolism and nutrition which are thereby brought to bear. This situation has been likened (by Dr. J. T. Bonner) to a continuing system of "chemical conversations" between nucleus and cytoplasm which coordinate the processes of growth.

Intrinsic Versus Extrinsic Controls

Two types of message seem to engage, or control, the powerful thrust which sets a plant off upon its developmental journey. The one type of message is intrinsic to each cell and represents "its built-in capacity to grow," which emanates from the thousands of genes which interact with the cytoplasm to endow the cell with the ability to perform each of its separate reactions when appropriately nourished by the environment. The other type of message may be either intrinsic (though involving non-genic but nevertheless controlling nuclear effects in the sense of McClintock, 1951), or it may be extrinsic and operate on cells or centers through exogenous chemical regulatory substances. Through such regulatory substances (some known, others as yet unidentified) certain master adjustments are made, or directions given, in ways that "steer" the cell toward growth and cell division, or growth and cell enlargement, or even, when growth as such has ceased, to some particular form of differentiation. If all this information could be decoded at its source and then reassembled in such a way as to foretell what quantity and manner of growth would occur under a given set of environmental conditions, then a mathematical account of growth would indeed have emerged. The *post hoc* analysis of growth curves falls very far short of this ideal.

One may liken the growth and development of an organism to the voyage of an ocean liner. The predetermined course (i.e., the navigational instructions) is represented by the coded genetic information of the DNA, which is transmitted by the enzymes. To quote Waddington (1953):

> For the self-regulating feature of the embryo's development we can find models in the field of engineering: automatic ship's compasses, automatic pilots, and other feedback mechanisms for which the name cybernetics has recently become fashionable. In cell differentiation we must be dealing with chemical cybernetic systems.

But the directional signals that emanate from the bridge also need to be translated into operations that engage the great propulsive power of the ship's engines, and these adjustments may modify the originally charted course. The power which is generated by the fuel finds its analog in the various nutrients and metabolites which are converted at cytoplasmic centers (such as mitochondria and plastids) into energy, and, as metabolites are consumed, they are replenished from external sources. But the mere combustion alone is not enough. At the control panel of a ship's engine room the necessary adjustments are made that direct and engage the power, and these adjustments vary with the state of the environment. These latter operations, or controls, are analogous to the array of substances and morphogenetic stimuli which determine, within limits set by the previously charted genetic course, the power and drive behind the growth process in plants. Agents that promote growth by cell division, which cause cells to enlarge and tissues to differentiate, and which determine organic form through the operation of morphogenetic stimuli, seem to fulfill their role in the cytoplasm. These agents modulate the release of power through metabolism and so control the metabolic fires that their energy either runs to waste or is canalized toward growth; they need a name and their distinctive functions need to be recognized. But should these often extrinsic chemical agents merely be called hormones?

Growth Hormones

The word hormone is often held to mean a "messenger"—a chemical messenger that mediates action at a distance. But, as already stated in Chapter 3, the word "hormone" could more accurately relate to the message carried than to the messenger, for it more literally derives from a verb which means "to arouse into activity." The particular kind of activity implied by the Greek verb was that bustle of activity observed at a port when a vessel received its orders and was about to sail. This being so, it may well seem appropriate that the postulated, often extrinsic, controlling agents that determine plant growth might still be called plant hormones. However, the classical examples of animal hormones like thyroxine, insulin, and adrenaline each seem to act in a more specific and prescribed manner, and they do not necessarily operate through the overall control of growth. Each such action is highly specific at a specific center, and it brings about a particular, and usually known, chemical reaction.

Whereas older views of hormone action anticipated hormone-enzyme inter-actions, more current ones seek explanations via such intracellular regulatory substances or processes, common to most cells, as the generation of TPNH or the effect on glycogen breakdown of 3′, 5′-AMP. There are now, however, sug-gestions of more master controls, as in the action of ACTH, a peptide hormone of the pituitary, which in turn controls the steroid or thyroid hormones of glands which are its targets. But the way the larger peptide hormones, which do not enter cells freely, act may be quite different from the action of the steroid hor-mones which do enter cells and so may interact directly with enzymes, with RNA, or with other regulatory compounds (cf. Karlson, 1965, who has edited a work called *Mechanisms of Hormone Action*).

By contrast, the controls in plants often act in a more generalized way, and they seem to operate, *during growth*, to determine what the organism will be-come rather than to keep it in smooth operation *after it has developed*. It is true that it is currently fashionable to interpret the action of the known plant growth-regulatory substances (or hormones) in terms of their possible effects on DNA-promoted synthesis of RNA, thus leading to syntheses of characteristic pro-teins and enzymes by which their effects may be mediated. One must, however, recognize that all this is still more in the realm of hypothesis than of proof—somewhat justified, it is true, because the effects of plant hormones are more characterized by their general effects on growth than by the specific biochemical consequences which are more readily seen in the case of animals. This being so, it may therefore be unfortunate that certain chemical agents, that from the outset were seen to control and induce growth in plants, ever were called hormones in the sense that the term was first applied in animal physiology. To the extent that these substances perform functions over and above the known nutrients, but nevertheless harness those nutrients to growth, some inclusive term (like "nutrillite") which recognized this role might have been appropriate. Never-theless, the idea of "action at distance," which is so clearly involved in the tropisms and in floral induction, caused the phenomena in plants to be treated as in line with the classical "hormone" concept. In the animal body early dif-ferentiation into distinct predetermined organs, with specialized and limited functions, is much more conspicuous than in plants, where "totipotency" of the individual living cells of mature organs is much more frequent. Moreover, any single higher plant comprises few distinctive *kinds* of organs (e.g., root, stem, leaf, bract, sepal, petal, stamen, ovary with its ovules, etc.), although it may produce these in indefinite numbers of each kind, while the living cells of which the different organs are composed are often essentially similar (parenchyma cells and vascular tissue are very similar wherever they occur). By contrast, a higher animal may only form one, or a very few, organs of a kind, and their very distinctive nature may require that their constituent cells be uniquely dif-ferent from organ to organ. Thus the closely regulated control of the functions of animal organs (in which hormones play so large a part) is a very conspicuous and distinctive feature of the organization of animals, whereas in plants it is much less "organ-specific." Also, animal cells are maintained in strictly controlled, internal, ambient media in which they are very responsive, at their surfaces, to foreign bodies, namely, to foreign proteins as shown by antigen-antibody relationships. By contrast, it is the *internal* vacuolar fluids of plant cells that are stabilized against relatively wide changes in their immediate environment (cf. Chapter 6, and Steward and Sutcliffe, 1959). Thus preformed animal cells and organs often react sensitively to physiologically active substances brought to them in the blood stream, but the internal controls over the behavior of plants seem to act by determining the way the cells grow to form the organs in question, rather than by regulating the continued balanced physiological functioning of already developed cells and organs.

In short, the "growth-regulating substances" of plants are not really as comparable in their modes of action to the classical examples of animal hormones as the designation "growth *hormones*" implies; they are in fact much more closely and solely involved with growth than the classical examples of hormones in animals. Since growing, developing plants, unlike animals, constantly renew or multiply their growing centers (in buds, root tips, cambia, the growth of new appendages in shoot and root, etc.), such control mechanisms that regulate growing cells or organs may exert powerful and repetitive effects in plants in contrast to animals, which usually pass through their cycle of growth and development but once. Thus the behavior of plants is much more controllable by the stimuli that determine the use they make of their nutrients (including water) as they grow.

Genic and Non-Genic Control Systems

After the first great strides taken to link genetics and biochemistry, there is now increasing awareness of regulatory or control mechanisms that may be cytoplasmic rather than nuclear, or which may be due to controls that modify the action of genes. Thus it is now somewhat generally recognized that there is an extra chromosomal, even cytoplasmic, moiety in the machinery of inheritance (cf. Srb, Owen, and Edgar, 1965); this may even find its physical basis in plastids or other cytoplasmic inclusions which contain DNA.

However, the compelling need to consider non-genic, extra-nuclear control mechanisms is felt primarily by those who consider the problem of growth and development, i.e., those whose preoccupations are with problems of organization. Those who focus attention upon unit steps in metabolism can rightly point to the triumphs of biochemical genetics and the gene-protein-enzyme sequences which have been disclosed. However, by its very technique the nutritional approach, as in the use of minimal and supplemented media to detect mutations in heterotrophic plants, is not well adapted to the detection of other more graduated controls that may operate during the development of autotrophic plants.

McClintock (1951) conceives that there are non-genic centers, even in chromosomes, which modify the expression of genes, and that changes of these centers that occur through mitoses affect phenotypic expression in development. A few quotations from McClintock's writings illustrate this trend of thought:

[In gene mutation] a hereditable change of some nature has occurred at a particular locus in a chromosome and any one locus is somehow concerned with a certain chemical reaction, or with a certain phenotypic expression, or even with a complex pattern of differentiation in the development of a tissue or organ. . . .

The various types of known mutation, each showing unitary inheritance, obviously reflect various levels of control of reactions and reaction paths. . . .

The knowledge gained by the study of mutable loci focuses attention on the components in the nucleus that function to control the action of the genes in the course of development. . . .

This interpretation considers that the nucleus is organized into definite units of action and that the potentials for types of gene action in any one kind of cells differ from the potentials in another kind of cell. . . . the functional capacities of the nuclei in different tissues or in different cells of a tissue are not alike. . . .

Differential mitoses also produce the alterations that allow genes to be reactive. Other genes though present may remain inactive. This inactivity or suppression is considered to occur because the genes are "covered" by non-genic chromatin material. Genic activity may be possible only when a physical change in this covering material allows the reactive components of the gene to be "exposed" and thus capable of functioning. . . .

Our studies indicate that at least two classes of functional genetic units are carried by the chromosomes: one of them potentially capable of determining the course of cellular reactions, *the other associated with the control of this potential reaction.* . . . Our studies also suggest that many mutations may be expressions of changes in controlling systems, the potential capacities of the gene units remaining unchanged.

Whereas McClintock sees the modifying agents of genes in some extragenic influence that also resides in the chromosomes, is it not also possible that extranuclear effects due to chemical controls or morphogenetic stimuli may be superimposed upon such modifying influences?

Much attention has been given to accumulations ("knobs") of heterochromatin material in nuclei. These "knobs" of heterochromatin are in contrast to diffuse threads of euchromatin in metabolizing nuclei. The knobs of heterochromatin tend to be intimately associated with the inner surface of the nuclear membrane, and they may also be sites of control over the euchromatic areas where genes are located (cited from McClintock by personal communication). Knowing also that there are sieve-like areas on the nuclear membrane where pores exist (cf. Fig. 5–7), one may also speculate that the pattern of accumulations of heterochromatin might bear some relationship to the presence of the pores. If this were so, then stimuli might penetrate through open pores to activate the heterochromatic areas, whereas closed pores could as readily prevent this free access. Along lines like this one might visualize how the activity of given regions of chromosomes might be selectively called forth during develop-

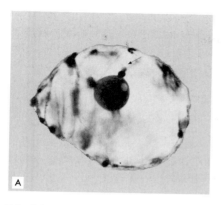
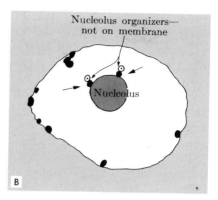

FIG. 9–13. Heterochromatic knobs in a maize endosperm nucleus and their relation to nuclear membrane. A. Photograph from Tschermak-Woess and Enzenberg-Kunz, *Planta* **64,** 149–169, Springer-Verlag, Berlin, Heidelberg, New York, 1965. B. Interpretive diagram showing location of "knobs" of heterochromatin adjacent to the membrane and of nucleolus organizers, shown by arrows.

ment. The sort of cytological evidence which relates to the "knobs" of hetero-chromatin and to the pattern of their distribution against the nuclear membranes is shown in Fig. 9–13, and reference may also be made to papers by Frenster *et al.*, 1963; Littau *et al.*, 1964; Tschermak-Woess and Enzenberg-Kunz, 1965; Frenster, 1965.

Epigenetic Controls in Growth and Development

Nanney (1958) expresses the idea that there are mechanisms that control growth and development which are not genetic in the accepted sense. Nanney recognizes two distinct types of control. One system of controls emanates from the nucleus, and this operates through DNA along now generally accepted lines. The other system is predominantly cytoplasmic, and is essentially not genetic, although it operates within the framework which is set by the direct genetic control. The non-nuclear control, termed "epigenetic" by Nanney, following the terminology of Waddington, is regarded as superimposed upon or tending to override the influence of the genetic control system. The epigenetic controls function mainly in those areas of growth and development in which cells with essentially the same nuclear constitution may yet be phenotypically distinct.

Waddington traces the term epigenesis to Aristotle, to whom it implied the progressive embryological development of organs from simpler constituents in the egg rather than their preformation in miniature. Waddington speaks in *The Strategy of the Genes* (1957) of what he terms the "Epigenetic Landscape." Epigenetics embraces all those discontinuities in development which lead to different cells, tissues, and organs within one genotype. The epigenetic landscape is thus the pattern of form and function which is laid upon and connected with the complex interactions of genes and the chemical reactions to which they give rise. But the strong tendency of embryonic development to resist deformation and to remain normal is also recognized by Waddington and described as a condition of "homeorhesis," i.e., of stable direction of flow. The stable or necessary path or trajectory which the organism takes during ontogeny Waddington terms its "creode" (literally, a necessary route or path, e.g., the prescribed route of a missile toward its target). However, in the consideration of plant growth there may be especial need for flexibility in these concepts, for the course of growth of plants is so subject to environmental control and to morphogenetic stimuli. The contrasted growth of gametophyte and sporophyte, juvenile versus adult forms, and periodicity in growth and development all call for regulatory mechanisms and stimuli which are superimposed upon the otherwise constant genetic information which is present in each living cell derived equationally from a zygote.

The term "epigenetic" may, however, suggest that stimuli of this nature must necessarily intervene in the cell at the same centers, and even use the same machinery as that which is normally controlled by the genetic apparatus. However, the distinguishing feature of these "epigenetic" controlling factors is that they work in cells even though the genes remain unchanged; thus they either exert their influence by intervening at points where genes normally act, and by so doing turn them "on or off," or they may work by means that are so remote from the normal scope of genes that an altogether different set of cytoplasmic controls should here be implied.

No discussion of the adequacy of current concepts of cell heredity and of molecular biological interpretations of biological diversity can afford to ignore the writings of Sonneborn, or his work on protozoa (Sonneborn, 1963; cf. also Srb, Owen, and Edgar, 1965, pp. 352 ff). Sonneborn clearly poses the dilemma. This is whether all higher levels of structure and behavior in cells, above those widely held to be attributable to the relationship between cistrons and polypeptides, between genes and proteins, are accountable solely by the further elaborations that may follow from the purely chemical and physical "self-assembly" of these primary products into cellular structures. The problem is the sufficiency of so simple a molecular hypothesis without the postulation or recognition of some form of organization in cells other than that inherent in their chromosomes. The point of Sonneborn's work and writing is that the cell cortex, by its specific organization, makes a decisive contribution to development and that there are, in protozoa, regionally diverse areas even within the cortex of a single cell. In short, Sonneborn (1963, p. 216) visualizes "an intricate intracellular coordination, the result of ruthless long selection," which "offers little hope that man could ever devise a noncellular milieu in which a nucleus could operate to make its own cell or any cell at all."

The Plant Protoplast: The Minimum Viable Unit of Growth

It now seems useful to return to the classical concept of the plant protoplast, i.e., a nucleus with its associated cytoplasm which comprises a complete living unit. The uniqueness of any such system may reside in the cytoplasm as well as in the genes with which it interacts. In fact, conventional genetics has really little to say about the unique qualities which distinguish the zygote of a mouse and a man, although it may have much more to say about the traits which distinguish different kinds of mice and men. If much of the basic biochemistry (glycolysis, Krebs cycle, protein synthesis, etc.) is common to all life, one might reasonably assume that the nuclear DNA by which the individual biochemical steps are controlled may also be the same. No doubt there is nuclear DNA over and above that which is preempted for this role of gene-enzyme determination, and this "extra" hereditary material may be that which is available to work through cytoplasm and to determine the overall characteristics of the organism —what Bateson is reputed to have called "catness" in contrast to genes for special characteristics in cats. But can one exclude the possibility that the organization of the cytoplasm itself contributes essentially to this dual system which constitutes the protoplast? Every zygote contains the cytoplasm from the female gamete; without this no egg could become a mouse or a man. Being committed to either a mouse or a man, the nuclear genes tell much about the characteristics of the organism that will emerge, but it may be asking too much to believe that they alone—composed of DNA on chromosome threads or by virtue of a number of base pairs—determine the whole pattern of growth and development. Obviously genes react with cytoplasm and cytoplasm with its environment. Nuclear transplants which have been successfully made in amoebae and in certain other animal cells (Lorch and Danielli, 1950; Danielli *et al.*, 1955) are so much more difficult to achieve in the cells of higher plants that the information on the behavior of a nucleus in its natural, or unnatural, cytoplasm which they might otherwise yield is lacking. (Incidentally, if isolated protoplasts can be more successfully studied by devices now being initiated by Cocking (1960), even culminating in claims by Binding (1964) that some naked protoplasts (moss) may fuse, the study of plant nuclei in their own and in different cytoplasms may become more feasible.) However, the effects which are mediated by exogenous substances and stimuli on plant cells seem to require that they affect the cytoplasmic moiety of the protoplast, for there is every reason to believe that the nuclei remain unchanged throughout development.

Therefore, in the determination of what constitutes the ability to grow, or the morphogenetic differences between cells of different organs, the organization of cytoplasm may—even must—play a key role. The transmission of genetic information in cells and tissues has been likened by Platt (1962) to reading out of a complex instruction manual. It is clear that the cell cytoplasm, through which the responses are mediated, also has the ability to transcribe, or to "read," the instructions in the DNA. Hence the cytoplasm is an integral part of the unit, or closed circuit, which responds in growth and morphogenesis. Therefore, the concept of the protoplast as the minimum organization and machinery has much to commend it. Thus the system which can grow must include both the *"information"* and *the means to transcribe it and put it to work*. We pay respect, perhaps exaggerated respect, today to the relations between genes, amino acids, and proteins because these readily permit one to relate all that happens metabolically in the cytoplasm to "information" that resides in the nucleus, even though it may only be evoked by devices which "uncover" or "unmask" the informative DNA center. (Conventionally the role of histones as agents which conceal or unmask this information is being stressed, notably by James Bonner, for plants.) Surely, however, this should not preclude the possibility of other effective controlling agents. Even potassium, which is necessary for all life, or light, which has morphogenetic effects on plants quite apart from photosynthesis, may determine the course of growth and development by means that relate to the organization as a whole; while these means assume the existence and working of genes, they are nevertheless "epigenetic" in the sense that they were not fixed and predetermined when the genetic information was laid down. To interpret these problems in the unfolding process of growth, the minimum unit that grows, i.e., a plant protoplast with its nucleus and cytoplasm, is the organization that needs to be considered. In this sense molecular biology is a contradiction in terms; for without the properties of a larger organization molecules have no biology. Isolated molecules, even if gene-determined, do not grow!

In 1917 Bottomley conceived of a category of growth substances which he termed "auximones." This concept fell into disfavor, and the term has fallen into disuse; although it is interesting that in the investigation of these effects purine and pyrimidine bases and nucleic acids were, even then, being implicated (Mockeridge, 1917). Bottomley's ideas, however, may well have been ahead of his time. The term "auximone" might now be revived to denote those chemical control substances, frequently exogenous to the cells on which they act, which control the direction or pace of growth but which are not intrinsic parts of the genetic control system. This term (auximone) emphasizes neither the connection with cell enlargement (as does the term auxin) or necessarily with cell division (as does kinin), nor does it emphasize that the agents of control are strictly to be classed as hormones. In fact, a degree of regulatory control can be exercised at the intracellular level by certain metabolites, for they may regulate the formation of certain enzymes involved in their synthesis. This principle is well illustrated in the work of Gorini and Maas (1958) by the effect of the level of arginine in *E. coli* upon the synthesis of ornithine transcarbamylase, which converts ornithine and carbamyl phosphate to citrulline. The cells possess a high enzyme-forming potential which is, as it were, "turned off or on" accordingly as the end product (arginine) is, or is not, present free in the cells.

Thus even metabolites of low molecular weight are here seen to regulate the enzymatic constitution by causing either "feedback inhibition" or "enzyme induction," and this is generally conceived to be an important mechanism for the regulatory control of protein synthesis and a step in the "series of reactions which are necessary to produce a differentiated cell." One could hardly call the effective agents (in this case an amino acid, e.g., arginine) hormones!

It is, however, in this area between genetics, which determines the hereditary traits, and their expression in the growth and development of the individual organism that some of the most important biological problems still exist.

Growth-Regulatory Substances: Some Thoughts on Terminology

Plant physiological terminology is now replete with terms that may be applied to the chemical agents that operate upon the control systems that must work through the plant protoplast—hormone, auxin, kinin, gibberellin, dormin, florigen, to mention but a few. In the most general sense the substances, effects, or mechanisms that control growth through the protoplast are perhaps best described without presuming that they will all, of necessity, fall within the conventional description of either a hormone, an auxin, or a kinin. When such control systems in the cytoplasm are brought into action by either external or internal stimuli, they either excite or modulate the pace and direction of growth within the overall genetic plan. Thus the agents which do this might be referred to quite generally as "excitants" or "modulants" of growth.

Although most of the terminology of growth substances derives from Greek, a Latin word expresses the ideas outlined above. The noun *moderamen* denotes a means of managing or governing, the means of moderating, or the management and control of direction, as in the control of a team of horses or the response of a ship to the helmsman. There is in this word *moderamen* an appropriate suggestion of *active* intervention, of a mechanism to control, govern, or regulate, as distinct from the more passive or remote control implied by the alternative word "moderator," which also suggests controls which only curb. It is when one recognizes that the organization of cells and organisms conveys properties that their several constituent parts do not alone possess that there is need of a term to designate where these consequences of organization reside and to describe the means by which they may become effective. Bertalanffy has ably shown that it is in recognizing the role of organization that the dilemma between a too strictly mechanistic philosophy (which does not alone suffice to explain the working of whole biological systems, even if it suffices for the several units of which they may be composed) and an outmoded vitalism may be resolved. It is not vitalism, for example, to recognize that the *de novo* accumulation of inorganic salts, or even of some organic solutes, in cells, or of the proteins they synthesize, occurs *pari passu* with the growth of the cells, for it is in that context that metabolic energy may be applied to bring these events to pass. It does, however, pose the question how and where the often exogenous stimuli that affect these events can be said to do their work. One needs, in short, to visualize a sort of central "control panel" where the whole organization is sensitively controlled. "Molecular biologists" may locate all these centers of control in the DNA of the nucleus, although the term *moderamen* as used above (to describe the means to control or govern) makes no such overriding commitment. The growth-regulating substances of plants certainly bring the diverse attributes of growing cells under regulated control, though whether only through DNA-RNA-protein-mediated syntheses (cf. Chapter 6) or by acts at some other points in the complex organization which enables cells to grow, is not yet settled. Waddington's "epigenetic landscape" and Nanney's "epigenetic" systems could therefore, correspond to the *moderamen* of the cell or organism, or the complex of agents and regulatory devices that operate to produce the variety of form and function that may exist within a single genetic complement. This term does not presuppose the kind of machinery or agent through which the management or the direction of growth is exercized, nor even whether it is wholly or partially nuclear, whether it may be cytoplasmic or even due to exogenous stimuli. When a cell cut off from the carrot cambium becomes a secondary phloem cell, its fate is locally directed *in situ* by some such system and when, through the intervention of coconut milk or other stimuli, the adult cells proliferate, this change of direction must again be motivated through the controlling system or *moderamen*. If and when the same cells are free and grow to re-form whole plants, some inherent restrictions are removed. The shift from normal growth to tumorous growth, as in crown gall tissue, must also involve a shift in the mechanism of control which determines how nutrition supports one habit of growth or another. These controls may be the equivalent, in the analogy between the development of an organism and a voyage of a ship, to the discretionary adjustments made in the engine room to link the motive power of the ship to the navigational instructions from the bridge. Thus many "moderaminals"—i.e., intrinsic factors, external chemical agents, and the results of excitation by environmental stimuli—may be expected to impinge upon and "overlay" the genetic control and thus will determine how fast and far growth proceeds and the ends to which it moves. Such effects would be "moderaminal" in contrast to genetic, nutritional, or metabolic effects, and any agent that achieves this effect could be described as a "moderaminal" without at this point presupposing that it belongs in one of the several classes already designated as due to hormones, vitamins, auxins, kinins, or gibberellins—or even amongst those catalytic effects on growth which are due to minute amounts of trace metals, i.e., the so-called "oligodynamic" effects.

This semantic excursion into the terminology of the agents which modify, modulate, excite, inhibit, or control growth in its pace and direction is, however, not without profit if it emphasizes the many aspects of growth and development which cannot yet be translated into the parameters of a growth equation, and if it stresses the importance of all those integrated controls which, collectively, regulate the system. This is essentially a consequence of, and a problem in, organization, for it is only when the system is more highly organized than mere molecules, or homogeneous reaction systems, that the need for, or the possibilities of, such regulation apply; but without this degree of complexity no system can grow.

A simpler example of control, because it is not drawn from the sphere of growth and development, may be helpful here. Cyanogenetic glucosides occur in many *Prunus* leaves. The glucoside (amygdalin) and the enzyme (emulsin) which hydrolyzes it may be present simultaneously. The presence of both the enzyme and its substrate no doubt reflects the controlling influence of some gene, or genes, and the extent to which these molecules are fabricated by the leaf will certainly involve the whole nutritional apparatus. But these considerations alone do not determine whether HCN will be released by the leaf, for the enzyme (emulsin) and the glucoside (amygdalin) may not even be in contact in the cells. It is necessary to cut the leaf, or to render its cells permeable, for the enzyme and its substrate to come into contact and to react. Thus the ultimate control *in vivo* is not here exercized by the genes that govern the course of synthesis of the amygdalin, nor through the nutrition that determines the quantity of it which is formed, but through features of the organization (the permeability of membranes and the maintenance of gradients across them) which "modulate" the action of the gene-determined enzymes upon its substrate. In fact, some current interpretations of metabolism in growing cells implicate the growth-regulating substances in metabolic turnover, and they recognize that metabolites may be segregated in isolated pools, which do not mingle, and in which the same substance (e.g., glutamic acid) may play distinctive roles. Such concepts are reinforced by modern knowledge of the fine structure of cells. All this suggests the extent of control over growth and the destinies of cells which is possible by the mutual adjustments between the parts of their complex machinery or organization.

Thus, the complete identification of these control systems and their role is one of the major problems of biology, for it is fundamental to an understanding of development and of normal and abnormal growth. In angiosperms much of this growth and development is already determined in the ovule, in part by the nutrients which are furnished by the parent sporophyte to the young embryo, although still further effects may be superimposed in response to the environment and to nutrition.

Physicists strive to achieve a unified theory which will embrace the fundamental properties of matter and energy. In the interpretation of growth, biologists may also move toward more broadly based and more general concepts. These concepts will ultimately embrace the effects, direct and indirect, due to genes, i.e., effects which are intrinsic to protoplasm as well as those which are extrinsic to cells and which, when superimposed upon the hereditary mechanism, modulate the effects of genes during development; such broadly based bio-logical concepts should also take account of the effects mediated by environ-mental and nutritional stimuli in the control of growth. Although fitted equa-tions to growth curves at best describe, but do not explain, growth, they were, and are, a necessary step toward a concept which will interpret all of growth and development. This challenge remains, for the stately march of an organism through time as it grows and develops is one of the majestic events and unsolved problems of the world in which we live.

Summary

Whether growth may be regarded as increase of size, substance, or complexity, it is essentially a process that occurs through time. Therefore, the course of growth may be described by curves that relate it to time and by the equations of these curves. The properties of the sigmoid curve of growth, which relates the increments due to growth to time, and of its first derivative, which relates the velocity of growth to time, and of the second which relates its acceleration or deceleration to time, are also described. Sachs' Grand Period of Growth shows how organs start growth slowly, gather momentum, and then slow down. Various types of auxanometers are used to measure such growth. Curves that relate specific growth (i.e., growth per unit of growing substance, or the multi-plication due to growth) to time are different in form and have their special uses. In its early phases growth bears an exponential relation to time: all parts are growing as rapidly as they can. The Compound Interest Law applies in this phase. The Compound Interest Law has been used to portray the growth of a seed plant, and the constant of relative growth (the rate of "interest") to mea-sure its rate or efficiency ("efficiency index"). In the attempt to relate the products of growth to their efficiency in bringing about new and further growth, growth has been analyzed in terms of relative growth rate (RGR), which equals net assimilation rate (NAR) times leaf area ratio (LAR). This form of growth analysis, which has its uses when applied to plants in the field, achieves some measure of success because growth in terms of dry weight is so dominated by photosynthesis which, when light is non-limiting, is a function of leaf area. The autocatalytic equation, which leads to a sigmoid growth-time curve which is symmetrical about its midpoint, can be used to describe growth *after it has occurred*, but when applied to the growth of shoots it leads to some untenable conclusions concerning the behavior of shoot apices. A vegetative shoot apex does not behave as if it had a reserve of substrate to expend and as if the prod-ucts of growth catalyzed the rate of its use until it is expended and the rate slows down. On the contrary, vegetative growing regions seem capable of po-tentially unlimited growth under proper nutritional and environmental condi-tions. Growth that starts from an embryo in an unlimited supply of food may be analyzed in terms of the ability of that growing embryo to partition space. As the embryo, or growing center, grows by adding new cell layers around the old, the growth falls progressively short of the requirements of the Compound Interest Law. Such systems add new cell *layers* in equal intervals of time and the cells that comprise the growing mass fall increasingly short of expressing their full capacity to grow. This, however, may be released when the cells are freed from the limitations that obtain in the organized mass of cells. The Gompertz, or double exponential, equation has the advantage that it may be fitted to asymmetrical sigmoid curves. Although the equation is complex, it is based on the simple model that the specific rate of growth (rate per unit mass) falls off in equal intervals of time by equal fractions of the rate. The Bertalanffy equation is based on a simple physiological concept, namely, that the rate of growth is due to the difference between the amount of anabolism (represented by a constant of anabolism multiplied by the surface area, proportional to l^2, for entry of substrates) and the amount of catabolism (represented as the product of a constant of catabolism and the bulk of metabolizing tissue, which is in turn proportional to volume or l^3). Richards has shown, however, that both these equations may be treated as special cases of a more general one. However, this requires the amount of growth at time $t\infty$ to be used as a constant in the equation and, therefore, like all other similar equations and curves it describes, it cannot foretell or explain the course of growth. Growth, however, is really a discontinuous, not a continuous, process in time though the discontinuities are commonly smoothed in the growth-time curves and equations. Also, all parts of the organism do not grow at the same rate and it is necessary to analyze the relative growth of different parts. Concepts of relative growth may be used to describe the different rate of formation of one type of substance compared with another. Since the mathematics of growth curves merely describes, but does not explain, growth, the attention is turned to control systems. There are both intrinsic controls, which supply the initial "built-in goal of growth" in the zygote, and also extrinsic ones. The course of the organism through time is here likened to the course of a vessel or a missile. It has a preset course or direction, and it requires an initial thrust and a means to maintain itself on course. However, in plants the directions may be modified as growth is modulated in response to nutritional and environmental factors. Genetic and epigenetic, nuclear and cytoplasmic, intrinsic and extrinsic controls and growth factors need to be considered. The plant protoplast, with interactions between nucleus and cytoplasm, is the minimum unit that grows, and stress is laid on the role of cytoplasm and non-genetic control factors. Among these extra-nuclear controls are a variety of chemical growth regulations which intervene to affect either cell division, cell enlargement, or cell differentiation. The terminology of these growth regulators which affect the pace and direction of growth and of the systems upon which they act needs to be considered, and the consequences of the historical parallels with animal hormones appreciated. Some misconceptions which may arise are stressed and also the many aspects of growth and development which cannot be treated as parameters of a growth equation. Much of the potentiality for growth is already "built-in" and predetermined in the zygote in the ovule; the way this unfolds in time in response to numerous intrinsic and extrinsic stimuli may be described empirically *after the event* by growth curves, but this will not *explain* growth until a unified and general theory can describe the organization of a fertilized egg, or a totipotent plant cell, implicitly and so give effect to all the factors that impinge upon it to regulate the behavior of the growing cells, the growing regions, and the embryos of plants. This is a goal for the future.

chapter ten

TOTIPOTENCY AND DIVERSIFICATION IN CULTURED CELLS: ORGANIZATION AND THE CAPACITY TO GROW

The discussion of growth and development now returns essentially to where it began, for it is here concerned with the potentiality which is inherent in an embryo and transmitted by successive equational cell divisions from the zygote to all its derivatives. Many of these derivatives will divide again, but many differentiate as their behavior is modified in accordance with the part they play in the controlled events of development and morphogenesis. It is useful, therefore, to take another look at these problems, to see them in restrospect and in the light of some more recent results.

Energy, Entropy, and the Capacity to Grow

The organic and the inorganic world—"the quick and the dead"—are basically distinguished by the capacity to grow, i.e., to incorporate the randomly distributed molecules of the environment into the stuff of which cells or organisms are made. This capacity to grow is most dramatic in zygotes which, though single cells, give rise to whole organisms. This does not mean, however, that when the first intensity of growing has subsided, death ensues—far from it— for some plant cells will persist for very long periods. Some parenchyma cells of trees may grow again even though they have remained quiescent for many years (estimated at 200 years for *Salix*; cf. Barker, 1953, and MacDougal *et al.*, 1926 and 1927). Spores of many organisms have great longevity; even the pollen grains of certain conifers do not produce fertilization until long after they are deposited on the nucellar surface. But a living, quiescent cell which is merely in a more or less protracted steady state, has previously passed through a more intensive phase of biological activity in which, as it grew, its organization also developed. And if quiescent cells return again to cell division and growth, to recreate facsimiles of themselves by equational division, they recapture briefly something of the property which so distinguishes the zygote of an angiosperm (which can develop and grow) from the gametes (which normally cannot). What is it then which distinguishes zygotes from gametes; or dividing cells from those which, though alive, have lost this propensity? Does the act of fusion bring into play mechanisms that were otherwise disconnected, as though many incomplete electrical circuits were being connected by the pairing of innumerable homologous sites?

We may say that the zygote has an innate, or "built-in," capacity to grow. A free cell which behaves like a zygote, because—like carrot cells—it is totipotent, has likewise retained, or recaptured, this "built-in" capacity to grow. But can these words, which are intelligible enough on descriptive morphological grounds, be given a physical meaning?

Any physical interpretation of the living state, of the capacity to grow, must ultimately conform to the two laws of thermodynamics. These have been expressed as follows: The First Law states that "The total amount of energy in Nature is constant"; and according to the Second Law "The total amount of entropy in Nature is increasing." The First Law requires that when work is done, energy is transformed from one form to another—heat may flow from a high temperature to a low; a gas may expand as its pressure declines, etc.; but the relations between the work done and the energy expended are equally rigid for both the living and the non-living state. The Second Law prescribes the convertibility of energy from one form into another, and the provision here is that in our universe the energy is becoming less and less available overall, as the system as a whole tends to run down. This is what is implied by saying that entropy is increasing, for entropy is a measure of the unavailability of energy. Entropy has been described as measuring the degree of "mixed-up-ness" or "run-down-ness"; in fact, all spontaneous changes are those which tend to increase the value of this property, i.e., which bring all matter to a uniform, random, equilibrium state. But the business of growing, under the influence of the sun and its light, of day versus night, and of the recurring seasons, produces order out of chaos. Therefore, to this extent, the spontaneous drift in the universe toward equilibrium and increased entropy is *locally* put into reverse, and entropy is reduced, although, within the restrictions set by the Second Law, this is only accomplished by the aid of some opposing change in the environment. As quoted by Oparin (1961, p. 15), Bergson saw life as a "struggle against entropy." And, of course, the ultimate driving force for all of organic nature is sunlight. But what we seek is some physical means by which the "growth energy" or "growth potential" of a system may be expressed.

Organic nature can exist on earth only because a not inexhaustible store of matter in the sun is being turned into energy, and to that extent the system as a whole is running down. But locally "free energy," i.e., energy capable of doing work, may be increased to produce organization and decreased entropy according to the formula $\Delta F = \Delta H - T \cdot \Delta S$. Even if the heat change ΔH reduces to zero it is still possible to achieve a positive change in free energy (ΔF), and a consequential ability to do work; by a reduction in entropy (i.e., ΔS is negative) the term $-T \cdot \Delta S$ then becomes positive. This is another way of saying that by the act of becoming more complex (as entropy is reduced) the system acquires a capacity to do work (free energy is increased). But how do these concepts work out in the more restricted context of the individual zygote, the individual cell and organism?

The gametes which cannot grow can nevertheless use nutrients to maintain their existing complexity. They may transform some metabolites into energy and do some work—as in the locomotion of spermatozoa or the absorption of solutes by an egg—but essentially and ultimately they can only run downhill, as their organization unwinds and a state of maximum entropy ensues. The free energy of these systems relentlessly declines. But when gametes fuse to form a zygote, this cell can grow into an organism, it can create order out of disorder, create morphology out of molecules, and absorb into itself the "negative entropy" which it obtains from its food and its environment, and entropy is reduced. Thus, the essential feature bestowed upon the zygote at fertilization, the feature which distinguishes the zygote from the gametes, is the "capacity to create or absorb negative entropy," i.e., to produce "new organization." In some way, the reservoir of this "bank or pool of the ability to reduce entropy, i.e., to store up negative entropy," is associated with that pairing of homologous structures in the nucleus of the zygote (which thus contains the "information") and the constitution of the cytoplasm of the cell (which receives, or puts the information to work). In each subsequent division self-duplicating structures are replicated. This is an increase of complexity—two sets of highly ordered structures appear where only one existed. But it is after their cleavage that the process can be repeated; each new protoplast is again able to "reduce entropy or to create negative entropy." As the daughter cells grow, they absorb and utilize energy-rich substances, they build up free energy to be expended in doing work, they form complex structures and molecules; but new form and new complexity are not again created as intensively until the cell and its organelles are recapitulated. And when, finally, the capacity for new growth by cell division subsides, or even departs, when even growth by cell enlargement slows down and stops, the cell—though living—approaches senescence and eventual death. In this mature state, cells can only expend their reserves of free energy; they may delay their eventual death (i.e., their approach to true thermodynamic equilibrium) if they compensate the gain of entropy they suffer by living (i.e., by breakdown of their own structure), or if they can attract to themselves a "stream of negative entropy" from their environment. This "stream of negative entropy" is only available in the form of substances which owe their energy content ultimately to photosynthesis. Whereas the zygote acquires its "capacity to reduce entropy or to create negative entropy" when homologous structures pair and fuse at fertilization, this capacity is transmitted to, and given expression in, every succeeding division by which new cells arise by equational division. Thus we need to say in physical terms what is really meant by the "built-in capacity to grow" which resides in the zygote, and what is meant by the ability of some cells to divide and of others merely to subsist. We need, in fact, to bridge the gap between the morphological and physiological language which describes a zygote as having an innate, or "built-in," capacity to grow and the recognition that a capacity to struggle against entropy in some way describes energetically the zygote and the cells of a growing embryo.

Autotrophic green plants, in a system which is not closed, inject into biology as a whole a "stream of negative entropy" from the sun, as energy is made available through photosynthesis and other heterotrophic cells and organisms draw upon the products of green plants. But to do this, the heterotrophs must be endowed with the capacity to grow—which is not merely determined by the supply of nutrients. Walker and Forrest (1964) have considered the entropy changes during the growth of bacteria. In the exponential phase of growth there is a rate of entropy decrease of the cells at the expense of the environment. (This means that the cells can turn nutrients into cells, randomness into order.) The exponential growth could continue indefinitely but it soon becomes limited by the environment and, in the nearly linear portion of the time-growth curve, the rates of entropy outflow and entropy inflow balance and, as the culture ages and the medium is exhausted, it gains in entropy. Thus, at the outset, bacterial cells in a nutrient medium have the ability to reduce entropy and this is transmitted through every equational division. To ask how this process began is to ask how life originated. But in a sexually reproduced plant (or animal) one can also say that this ability to reduce entropy, to create negative entropy or absorb it from the surroundings, is renewed at each fertilization; it is transmitted by equational cell divisions and may continue indefinitely through the vegetative propagation of a clonal stock. But it also seems to be the case that, unless so renewed, each organism in each life cycle can expend during its development a reserve or pool of that "capacity to reduce entropy or to create or absorb negative entropy," which must be the essential feature of the innate or "built-in capacity to grow" of the zygote. This decline of growth in a determinant organ, the working out of the life span of an organism or the approach to senescence and death of the constituent cells, is, however, a feature of the cells and organs *in their internal environment* in the plant body; it is the price that is to be paid for the organization of higher plants. Although the "built-in capacity to grow" in a zygote, like the ability to divide in a bacterium, is potentially unlimited, it could only be expressed indefinitely if the cells, *having divided*, separate and each has access to an unrestricted chemical and physical environment.

Schrödinger (1944) started from the concept that "entropy" is a measurable physical property which at absolute zero is also zero. For a given change in state, e.g., the melting of a solid in which entropy increases, the entropy change is calculated as the heat input (latent heat of fusion) divided by the absolute temperature at which the process occurs; i.e., the dimensions of the entropy change are calories per degree. In turn, the entropy can be calculated as the product of a physical constant (the Boltzmann constant,* in calories or ergs per degree) and a quantity (log W) which is a statistical measure of order and disorder. Thus, $-$ entropy $= K \log (1/W)$. In the analogy of melting a crystal the supply of heat destroys the orderly array of molecules, increases their turbulent motion, increases entropy, and increases the value of W. The term W is a measure of the "thermodynamic probability" that a given configuration or state exists. A completely random, disorderly state is more probable (W nearer to 1.0) than one of a high degree of order (W much less than 1.0), and for a highly organized system W becomes very small. Thus the negative log of W [that is, log $(1/W)$] becomes a positive measure of orderliness, i.e., of the inherent improbability of the system in question.

Therefore, the changes in this term [log $(1/W)$] may replace, or be the equivalent of, the concept of negative entropy. Thus, any change of state or any transformation which creates order out of disorder, i.e., which promotes organization, also reduces entropy; and the effect of that change (if it occurs within a closed system at, or near, equilibrium) should be reflected in a change in the value of W; if $1/W$ becomes larger, i.e., if W becomes smaller and the system inherently more improbable, then a *reduction* of entropy would occur.

One might therefore conceive (cf. Steward, 1966) of a scale of numbers [log $(1/W)$ or $-$ log W] analogous to the pH scale which is used for measuring acidity in terms of H ion concentration; such a scale could serve to measure morphological complexity in terms of "thermodynamic improbability" and the numbers would range from very high values for the complex systems which can grow and develop, down to zero for those which have reached true equilibrium with their environment and die. But it is one thing to visualize such a scale and it is another to know how to make appropriate measurements along it!

When gametes fuse, a new level of order is reached, for the resultant system can perpetuate itself by a series of replications. Thus the impact of fertilization (syngamy) on growth, i.e., the production of the innate or "built-in" capacity of the zygote to grow, increases what may be called "growth energy," which should be intelligible in terms of the Boltzmann equation, for it should take the form of an increase in the term $K \log (1/W)$ (measured in calories or ergs per degree). This is only another way of saying that the fusion product (with its paired, homologous chromosomes) has a greater value than the gametic units separately on some scale which reflects its organizing capacity, i.e., features that can be devoted to growth and development. And at each replication of self-duplicating structures, prior to cell division, a similar increase of complexity

---

* The Boltzmann constant K is the value of the gas constant R, not per mole, but per molecule, i.e., R/N where N is the Avogadro number.

and organization occurs with a renewal of the cell's overall capacity to grow. But when further self-duplication is either arrested or irretrievably lost, this reservoir of ability to build up negative entropy [i.e., to increase the value of the term $K \log (1/W)$] declines and disappears. When this occurs cells can only defer their final drift to equilibrium inasmuch as they are able to consume negative entropy in the form of already elaborated molecules. But it can also be shown that the ability of cells to divide also declines progressively as a consequence of their remaining attached in a multicellular mass.

Each zygote, or each freely suspended totipotent cell, having the full capacity to develop into an organism has maximal "morphogenetic propensity" (which might be expressed on a numerical scale of $-\log W$). If the first two cells which arise by division should separate, then each will have the same maximum "morphogenetic propensity," i.e., the numbers which measure this property per cell need not have changed. This state of affairs is obviously very common with microorganisms, for in the log phase of growth and until the environment becomes limiting each daughter cell can grow as rapidly as its predecessors. If, however, either a zygote or a freely suspended angiosperm cell divides into two cells which remain in organic contact, then the morphogenetic propensity per cell has actually declined because the cells as they are attached *are more limited in what they can do than if they were free.* And so, as this process is repeated, the measure of morphogenetic propensity *per cell* declines rapidly in a multicellular higher plant because, to use the language of an earlier era, "division of labor" ensues. In the outcome only a very few cells of the entire plant body individually participate in the procreation of new plants and even these, after meiosis, only do so as *isolated cells* by initiating a sexual phase of development. From this standpoint, therefore, the circumstance which limits the expression of the full morphogenetic propensity inherent in each living cell is *the fact of their remaining attached* and organically connected through plasmodesmata.

In other words the price that is paid for the morphological complexity of higher plants is the suppression of, or the masking of, or the control over the inherent totipotency of each living cell as it exists in the plant body. Thus to be a part of a higher plant each living cell must do less than all of which it is intrinsically capable, and the measure of its morphogenetic propensity must decline from the potential totipotency of the zygote, or of certain single free cells, to a low level as each cell becomes part of a more complicated structure and its behavior is brought under more stringent and regulated control.

This change, or trend, may be described in terms of the items of information that are necessary to make or define an organism. In the zygote all of these items of information are potentially effective; as differentiation proceeds, only a part of this total information is effective at any one time. The change in the number, or the statistical probability term $\log (I/W)$ or $-\log W$, may therefore be thought of as the changing (i.e., declining) fraction of the items of information which define the whole organisms that are active, or effective, in any given differentiated cell.

This trend, however, may be reversed by (a) returning free cells to the biochemical and nutritional environment of the embryo or (b) through meiosis and syngamy when new cycles of development commence with *free* single cells that can grow. Thus, in plants, a decisive landmark was passed when a small colony of cells, united by protoplasmic connections into an organic whole, emerged and, in consequence, every cell no longer expressed all the attributes of a complete organism.

But does all this mean anything tangible in terms of what we know about cells? The epitome of growth and development is the formation of new substance and new form, and this is traceable to the ability of DNA (a) to recapitulate itself and (b) to generate RNA which, in turn, can promote the formation of protein at active sites or templates. Or at least so runs the current dogma! The language of molecular biology and of the genetic code *tells us much about how this happens, but not why it all happens, and it certainly does not specify the driving force to make it go.* This may be only another way of saying that the molecules or strands of nucleic acid which can replicate, or the RNA templates at which protein is made, are in themselves only long fibrous molecules which, when in a test tube, are very dead. They lack the "something" which is conveyed by their environment within the cell, which is transmitted from previous cells, which is the essence of the organization within which they can do what they do. In part, this may be a matter of enzymes, without which no molecule may replicate, nor any DNA-RNA-protein sequence be effectuated. In part, no doubt, it is a property of the asymmetries which distinguish the milieu in cells in which, by contrast with the non-living world, the chemical reactions of life proceed. This is only another way of saying that nuclear genes and DNA are powerless without the cytoplasmic organization on which they act. But, if the innate or "built-in" capacity to grow is to be understood, we need to recognize it as an expendable "capacity to reduce, or store, negative entropy," to make energy available to organisms through the creation of their very form and complexity, and this needs to be translated into a model or concept that may be comprehended in physical terms.

This analysis, therefore, presents the following dilemma. How may one visualize in physical terms, i.e., as a model system, what we mean by "morphogenetic propensity"? What is the physical equivalent of the "thermodynamic improbability" of potentially growing cells which is symbolized by the term $\log (1/W?)$ How may measurements be so made that these abstract ideas can be expressed numerically? Admittedly these questions cannot now be answered satisfactorily.

One may visualize, however, that the innate capacity of the zygote to grow might be due to the creation of a large number of incipient sites or templates at which syntheses of essential structures (e.g., proteins) could occur. Every such site, or template, which is needed to form the whole organism must be represented in the zygote. Could we count them and their specific products (i.e., kinds of protein), the number would be very large. Even at the outset not all of these synthetic sites may be operative and, during development, differentiation, and morphogenesis, the number of such sites which are effective at any time runs down, or they are masked. If our methods were adequate to reduce all organs to cells we might then plate them out and measure—not a mere "plating efficiency," i.e., the viability of cells and their growth into colonies—but also their morphogenetic propensity as measured by the treatment needed to cause a given percentage of the cells to behave as totipotent and to grow into plants. We might then have a set of numbers running parallel to the "number of active sites or templates expressed as a percentage of all those that are needed for the full development of a zygote." Thus it is common for a zygote to cleave into separate cells, both of which grow into embryos. In young carrot embryos this ability certainly persists much later than had been suspected (cf. pp. 474 *et seq.*). But, as differentiation proceeds, the controls become tighter and fewer cells are able, easily, to release or express their totipotent qualities. Although the methods of free cell culture may eventually provide suitable observations to measure the "morphogenetic propensity" of cells from different organs and in different states of development, both the subject and the methods are yet too new to make this feasible. Nor does the conventional language of genetics present a ready solution. If each active site, or template, is under the control of, or is represented in the zygote, by a gene, or an even smaller unit where mutation can occur, then the scale of numbers we seek may reflect the essentially "epigenetic" means to bring these sites into effective action or, conversely, to suppress them. Therefore we need a measure of the number of DNA sites that were effectuated at fertilization and of the number which at various points during development remain unblocked (e.g., by histone; cf. pp. 488 *et seq.*) or which are otherwise free to interact with their cytoplasm.

Speculations on the Origin and Nature of Life:
Their Bearing on the Problems of Growth and Development

The state of current speculations on the origin of life (cf. Oparin, 1961) may clarify these problems somewhat. One should look, however, when considering the origin of life, not so much for something that is very similar to what we now know in biology, but for some more primitive beginning in the conversion of mere random molecules into purposive structures, i.e., in which like gives rise to like, and in which there is organization. Purely mechanistic ideas of the genetic nature of life visualize that "In the primitive and as yet lifeless solution of organic material there somehow arose particles . . . and these, suddenly, on their appearance had an intramolecular structure which was extremely well adapted to the accomplishment of self-reproduction and to the vital functions." But Oparin (1961, p. 96) sees the need to account for the prior origin of much less complicated systems which have ". . . the ability to carry out metabolic processes, even though only primitive ones, which will ensure their continued self-preservation and self-reproduction under the existing environmental conditions of the surrounding medium." This is only another way of saying that we still cannot say how the first biological organization began, although we can trace the much later subsequent history of its increasing complexity.

Oparin believes that the primitive precursors of life were anaerobic heterotrophs which would have used the ready-made range of compounds that, as we now know, could have formed from ammonia and hydrocarbons in a primitive atmosphere. He also sees in the widespread anaerobic degradation of organic molecules in contemporary organisms an indication that this may well be the more primitive mechanism which supported organization by metabolism; he also sees the autotrophic mechanisms as "mere superstructures upon this foundation." Oparin could not, however, assume that the design of all the strictly coordinated biochemical reactions of life as they are now known (glycolysis, aerobic respiration, protein synthesis, etc.) arose at the very outset, for he concedes that prolonged evolution of the original living things was required for the formation of these reaction sequences—for the evolution, in fact, of the very milieus in which these complex systems could work. He believes that the first thing which primitive living systems required was an envelope to separate them from the external medium and, after that, a means to mobilize the energy obtained from oxidoreductions for synthetic purposes. This formed a basis for the development of self-preservation and self-reproduction which was in turn based on a continual repetition of a particular set of reactions. And Oparin sees that neither the later and highly developed metabolic mechanisms (such as those which involve coenzymes, etc., like DPN, CoA, or ATP) nor the earlier ones, were closely related to DNA. The protein enzymes, and their particular contributions to molecular architecture in biology and the need for its regulation by RNA, all appear to Oparin to be later developments. It was even later still, when the organization of living things had greatly increased in complexity, that the role of DNA emerged. When the more or less accurate reproduction of the organization was not to be solved by a single reaction taking place constantly in the system, then DNA, with its stored information and its metabolic inertia, emerged to guarantee the continuity, i.e., "the essential conservatism," of living systems. Thus DNA only became necessary when the development of living things had already reached a high level and the means of maintaining a living versus non-living state was well established.

Thus the essential beginnings of life may not have been in the mere assembly of already prefabricated "modern" biochemical molecules and systems, but in circumstances that caused a primitive ability to mobilize energy to create structure or order—i.e., to defeat the general trend in the universe to increase entropy. Oparin (1961, p. 175) also pointed to the inevitability that a primitive living system "either grew and divided or it became old and died."

Thus speculations on the origins of life should hopefully have led to some specific feature, more than just the molecules which are its vehicles, that must be preserved as life continues through successive generations. This is the essential unanswered riddle of biological organization. This organization must have as its essential requirement the ability to create order out of disorder and the essential limitation that it must replicate in order to persist.

Morrison (1964) analyzed the thermodynamics of self-reproduction, or more strictly of self-duplication or self-replication. He visualizes a continuum of systems which range from those of a comparatively low order of ability to "reproduce" up to those which have this property to a high degree. Morrison designates this property by a series of numbers, for which he uses the symbol β, where β is a measure of the ability of a given system to duplicate itself. In Morrison's view there is a continuum from systems with low values of β, which have little in common with life (e.g., the ability of a solution to "reproduce" a crystal) to those with high values which characterize cells and organisms. Morrison's abstract, unitless parameter β is a ratio—the ratio of a free energy which is necessary to create the substance of the system in question to another free energy which makes that material specific. While the numerator of this ratio might be the free energy to create the DNA of the nucleus, the denominator would be the free energy which is necessary to make that DNA specific, or again it might be the free energy represented by the factors in the cytoplasm with which the DNA must interact to produce the system in question. So long as one is thinking only about equational division, then the characteristics of the system that multiplies itself by division are already defined. But for a sexually reproduced organism there is surely another component to be considered, for the system that can grow arises not from *one* preexisting structure but from two. Here the units that are capable of reproducing are the paired sexes (whether borne on monoecious or dioecious plants). This process of reproduction (as distinct from self-replication) must not only create, and recreate, the living substance which can replicate, but must also define its specific characteristics and must do so within the context of the kind of organism that is determined in the zygote.

In short, the egg, which is fertilized and then divides, absorbs from the environment the free energy of the substance of its daughter cells, and there is an energy component that ensures that this is according to the specific plan of the kind of organism in question. Therefore, at the formation of the zygote several energy-requiring components need to be considered; there is the innate or "built-in" capacity to grow which is expressed in the ability of the zygote to duplicate its substance (here free energy increases and entropy is reduced), but there is also the creation of that degree of order in the fertilized egg which also determines specifically what the organism will grow to be and, within that kind of organism, its minute characteristics.

In other words the egg and the zygote of a cat mobilize materials from the environment to build the intricate architecture of daughter cells, i.e., protoplasm which is specifically endowed with factors for "catness" as well as for the particular characteristics that identify that particular cat. Each of these steps in the reproductive and self-duplicating process represents a level which, in the language of Morrison, would seem to require greater and greater values of β and additional free energy components (even though these are small) that will relate in the overall equation to each degree of order, non-randomness, and thermodynamic improbability that the system entails.

But until these abstract terms can be measured, have we said anything more than that the living system which can grow, develop, and reproduce itself is highly complicated, it must be highly organized, and it is inherently (i.e., thermodynamically) improbable? The numerous restrictions imposed upon the matter that composes cells in order that they may function as they do is evidence enough of this; just a few examples will be mentioned. The DNA of the cell nucleus has a characteristic composition, it has a characteristic linear order of bases, and, to achieve a highly specific and asymmetric molecular architecture, its complementary strands are held by specific base-pair combinations. The proteins which function as enzymes have amino acids in specific linear order and a secondary and tertiary structure which determines their properties and which depends upon the proximity and linkage between functional groups. The protoplasm and its inclusions are highly organized into organelles, with elaborate intensely granular internal structure (e.g., chloroplasts, mitochondria, golgi bodies) with membranes, etc., and these carry out discrete and complementary processes in the cell. The entire cell system works by coupling catabolism to anabolism.

Thus, it is not enough to visualize life as a highly improbable self-induced assembly, or an intricate sort of clock assembled from its preformed parts. It has to be a clock *which can work,* and which works unidirectionally in time; perhaps only one out of the very many that might be made will achieve this, for, even though all the parts are present in a given clock, it may never run because of minor faults in their mutual balance. But the "cellular clock" also needs to be "wound up," as if by a raised weight or a taut spring, which gives it the means to turn energy into motion till its time span has elapsed. But here again the analogy is incomplete, for, by successive cell divisions and infrequent sexual fusions, the biological batteries are rechargeable (or the driving weights may be raised) and the machinery takes on a new lease of life. With our present lack of understanding of what is here involved, we are obviously unable to formulate a remotely satisfactory physical model.

Nevertheless, one must again recognize the very tangible events that lead to the "built-in capacity to grow" which exists in the zygote, which is usually lacking in the gametes, and which is renewed for a while at each self-duplication and cell division, although it may be expressed in vastly different ways according to where the "daughter" cells happen to be. Although the "built-in capacity to grow" is not yet understood, it may be represented in a mathematical model by the capacity to create negative entropy, and this is represented by an increase in a term $\log (1/W)$ (which in turn measures the degree of order in the matter of the cell) in the equation: Entropy $= K \log (1/W)$. This term or component, could it be measured, might also stand for J. Smuts's (1926) concept of holism in that it represents the something extra, the "whole being greater than the sum of its parts," which the cell or zygote derives from what we commonly call its organization. The 19th century idea of "vital force," or of some peculiar form of energy (entelechy) thought to be inherent in living cells, is universally discredited. Nevertheless it is idle to deny that the organization of matter in a living cell, i.e., its morphology, has consequences which cannot as yet be fully expressed in physical terms except that it is this, together with the interlocking events of anabolism and catabolism which it makes possible, that allows a given system to grow. This is shown most dramatically when free cells, without any other contact with their neighbors, can be made to grow and to form a fully mature organism. Such cells are termed totipotent.

Ultimately, this subtle totipotent quality of some cells may be measured, or evaluated, and interpreted in terms of the properties of molecules and of the mutual relationships of subcellular units. Until then, however, there is no other recourse than to use the essentially descriptive procedures of experimental morphology starting from a single cell which can grow, be it a zygote or a totipotent cell, as the minimum unit from which to study growth. By these means one may even now trace out the paths of growth and development and, hopefully, begin to prescribe the extrinsic conditions which first evoke, then modulate, and eventually suppress this intrinsic propensity as cells, which are essentially totipotent, are constrained to do what they do in the plant body.

Some present accomplishments and vistas ahead in this all-important problem of biological organization and in the understanding of growth and development of higher plants will now be presented. There need be no apology for doing this first in purely descriptive terms, for there is as yet no secure basis for any other approach.

Totipotency of Free Angiosperm Cells

Haberlandt first recognized the possibility of culturing plants from free cells, although the amount of actual growth and development which he then observed (1902) in free cells was, by modern standards, negligible. Nevertheless, Haberlandt had the remarkable insight to prophesy the growth of these cell cultures, not only into plants, but—he actually used the expression—"into embryos." Because of their historical interest, Haberlandt's actual figures (Fig. 10–1) are reproduced on the following page, and the words he used in 1902 are translated here (cf. Steward, Blakely, *et al.*, 1963). He says:

Without permitting myself to pose more questions, or to prophesy too boldly, I believe, in conclusion, that it will be possible to grow, in this manner, artificial embryos from vegetative cells [*aus vegetativen Zellen künstliche Embryonen zu züchten*]. In any case, the method of growing isolated plant cells in nutrient solutions could be a new experimental approach to various important problems.

In making this seemingly remarkable prophecy Haberlandt was clearly influenced more by his knowledge of many examples of adventitious embryo formation in plants by parthenogenesis and apomixis which he also studied (for references cf. Steward, 1966), than by any concrete evidence that the free cells he observed actually grew!

Whereas the evidence of Chapter 7 clearly pointed to the totipotency of free cells of carrot, more recent findings have established this conclusion in even more dramatic fashion. Certain essential features are now seen to determine the full expression of the inherent totipotency of the cells of the carrot plant. These are:

1. The living cells should first be set free from association with their neighbors and thus be able to grow independently, so that their behavior is unrestricted by the controls that operate in a preformed tissue mass that had developed within the plant body.

2. The physical sign of cell continuity in cells cultured *en masse* is the presence of protoplasmic connections. In some way these connections may superimpose the characteristics of the central core of cells upon those that divide and grow at the surface of the mass. These connections are, however, not present in the cells that grow free, though they do develop between the "daughter" cells to which the free cell may give rise (Fig. 10–2).

3. The free cells should be furnished with a medium which is fully competent to make them grow, and the best such medium is still a basal medium, such as that of White, supplemented by reduced nitrogen compounds (casein hydrolysate) and the contents from a developing ovule and embryo sac at the time when it nourishes the immature embryo, as in the special case of the coconut, or of immature corn grains, or *Aesculus* fruits. Additional synergists applied concurrently or sequentially may, in prior treatments, also release the cells from limitations acquired during their development in the plant body (Steward, Kent, and Mapes, 1966).

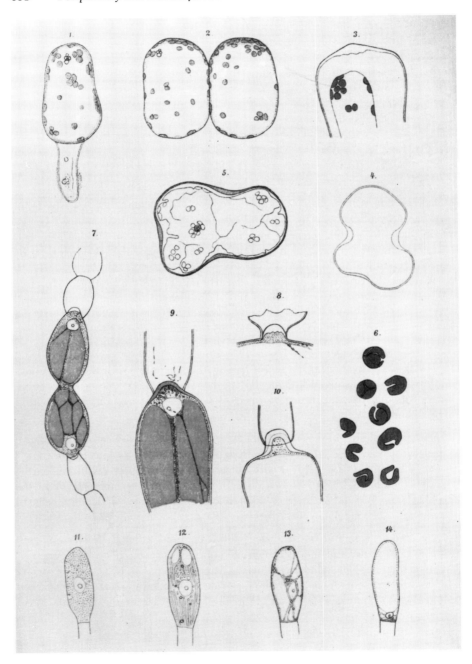

FIG. 10-1.

◀FIG. 10–1. Photograph from Haberlandt's paper, "Culturversuche mit isolierten Pflanzenzellen" (1902).

1. Palisade cell of *Lamium purpureum* after 8 days of culture in nutrient salt solution,
   nicely grown. Below is a dead palisade cell which was wounded in the isolation.

2. Two actively growing palisade cells of *L. purpureum* after 8 days of culture in nutrient
   salt solution.

3. Part of a palisade cell of L. *purpureum* after 11 days of culture in 1% cane sugar; plas-
   molyzed with dilute glycerin. The upper cell wall has become thickened.

4. A spongy parenchyma cell of *L. purpureum* after 12 days of culture in nutrient salt solution; cushion-like thickenings in the cell indentations; the cell content is not damaged.

5. Dead spongy parenchyma cell of *L. purpureum* after 16 days of culture in nutrient salt
   solution; the raised plasma membrane shows folding.

6. Chloroplasts from palisade cells of *L. purpureum* after 5 days of culture in 5% cane
   sugar; cultured in darkness.

7. Segment of a stamen hair of *Tradescantia virginica* after 12 days of culture in nutrient
   solution (2% glucose, 0.4% asparagine). Only 2 cells have remained alive; these have
   grown and have thickened on their cross walls adjacent to the dead cells.

8. End of a living hair cell after 8 days of culture; the cross wall has turned-up papillae
   and is quite thickened.

9, 10. The same after 12 days of culture. The wall thickening extends even up to the cross
   wall of the neighboring parts of the outer wall.

11. End cell of a glandular hair of *Pulmonaria mollissima* Kern. at the beginning of the cul-
    ture experiment.

12. The same after 1 day of culture in tap water. Vacuolization of the protoplast, which
    partly assumes a coarse fibrous structure.

13. The same after 3 days of culture in tap water.

14. The same after 7 days of culture in tap water. The protoplast is grown thin, and the
    cell nucleus has become much smaller.

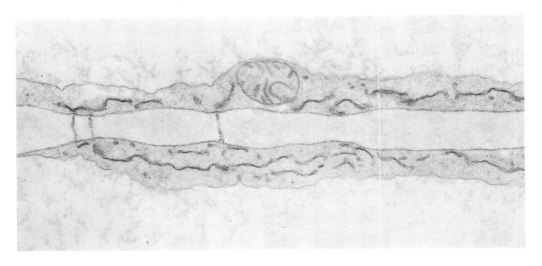

FIG. 10–2. The wall and parietal cytoplasm in quiescent carrot cells showing the plasmodesmata, or protoplasmic connections (X15,000). (From Israel and Steward, 1966.)

FIG. 10–3.

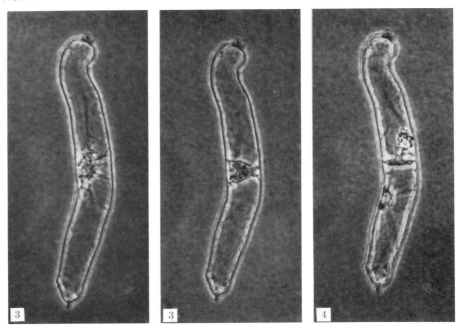

Two later techniques have, however, contributed to this field of work. Isolated angiosperm cells in a free cell suspension may now be distributed on the surface of a semisolid nutrient medium, with or without coconut milk. The fate of single cell isolates may thus be followed (Blakely, 1963; see Figs. 10–3 and 10–4). Secondly, free cell suspensions may be established from *relatively young embryos;* these may be grown in free suspension in liquid and then spread on agar plates. When this is done these free cells of embryo origin have been shown to develop into surprisingly faithful replicas of zygotic embryos and they do so with such frequency as to imply that virtually all of these carrot cells are totipotent.

By direct observation of free cell cultures on agar plates, the conclusion now is that isodiametric cells, or small densely granular and globular forms, have more success in growing into viable colonies than very elongate ones; that a cell in a small cluster may have a better chance of giving rise to a viable colony than cells that are entirely free; that growing tissue explants will actually release to a medium some stimuli that promote the growth of cells into clusters, and these are even more potent than the coconut milk itself. These effects were

FIG. 10–3. Septation divisions in free single carrot cells. Numbers on each photograph indicate days after plating. Four cells were formed by the sixth day. One cell burst between the sixth and seventh days, and all of the cells subsequently died on the seventh day. (From Blakely, 1963.)

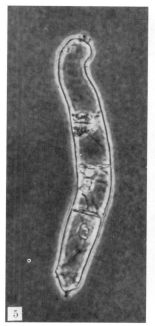
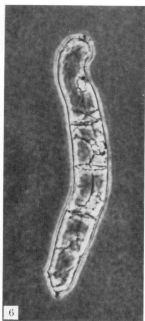
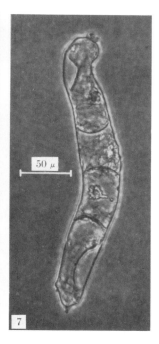

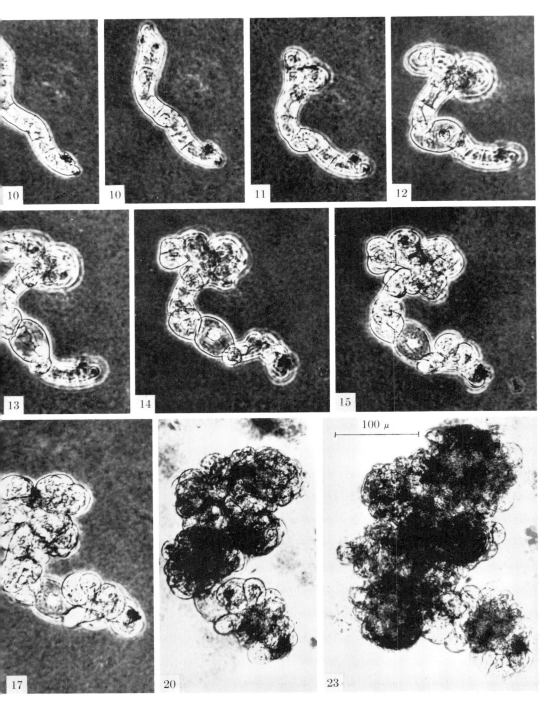

◀FIG. 10–4. Moderate cell enlargement in a septate cell, followed by the resumption of cell division. Numbers on each photograph indicate days after plating. Approximately three hours elapsed between the first two photographs, taken on the tenth day. In marked distinction to the course of events in the growth of some cells, only moderate cell expansion took place after septation, and, by 23 days, a small colony was formed consisting of over 100 tiny cells. (From Blakely, 1963.)

shown in the work of Blakely in the author's laboratory, on which Fig. 10–5 is based.

The many attempts to culture immature embryos, ovules, and ovaries of flowering plants (for references see Steward, Kent, and Mapes, 1966) and the production of callus tissue from embryos (e.g., in the very first work of Blakeslee and van Overbeek, and in later studies in Maheshwari's laboratory) prompted the idea that cell cultures established from embryos might be even more prone to undergo morphogenesis than cell cultures which are established from more differentiated tissue. The first free cell culture upon which this idea was tried was established from a callus culture of *Nicotiana rustica* of embryo origin that was obtained from Dr. Mohan Ram in Delhi. This culture grew very well (multiplying from about 5 cells/ml to over 10^5 cells/ml in about 40 days). Although this culture readily formed chloroplasts, it did not organize. In the belief that the capacity for organized growth might have been lost during the period of

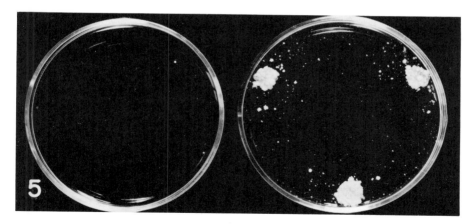

FIG. 10–5. Effect of cultured carrot explants placed in medium containing a rigorously filtered suspension of carrot cells. The photograph was made 45 days after plating. On the plate to the left, which received no explants, four visible colonies appeared. On the plate to the right, which received three explants, there were over 300 visible colonies. (From Blakely and Steward, *Am. J. Botany* **51**, 780–791, 1964.)

prior cultivation as a callus, a fresh embryo cell culture was established, first from an embryo of the wild species of *Daucus carota* and later from certain *Daucus* cultivars. The first and most outstanding result was obtained, however, with the common Queen Anne's lace. From a single embryo, taken from an immature seed, a free cell culture was established, and from an aliquot of this a dense growth appeared when it was spread over the surface of an agar medium containing the coconut milk supplement (Fig. 10–6A through D). On examination, it appeared that this growth consisted of thousands of minute clusters which organized readily into embryo-like forms.

Two things are remarkable about this experiment: first, the great number of embryos which were obtained (of the order of 100,000 organized structures on one Petri plate); second, the very faithful way in which the growth from the free cells could recapitulate normal embryogeny, with the formation of globular, heart-shaped, torpedo, and cotyledonary stages. This is illustrated in Fig. 10–6 (E through I) and its legend. Cell cultures freshly established from carrot root phloem, as distinct from those that have been subcultured, will readily regenerate plants directly—so much so that it has now become a routine operation in this laboratory to perpetuate the vegetative life cycle of the carrot plant by bridging the gap from one vegetative growth cycle to another through free cells (Steward and Mapes, 1963; Fig. 10–7).

Thus the totipotency of carrot cells is now established beyond question, and it is also very clear that the environment of the ovule and the embryo sac is dispensable if the proper nutrition and external conditions are furnished. Instead of the zygote being, developmentally speaking, a unique cell it is really to be regarded as a very general one; the zygote of an angiosperm now seems to be adequately described as a "diploid cell which can grow, in a medium which will make it grow, and in a space which will protect it and allow it to grow."

FIG. 10–6.   Development of carrot plants from freely suspended cells of embryo origin. A. Cultured carrot cells in liquid medium; the suspension is filtered through bolting silk.   B. Growth of a large number of embryoids on a Petri dish on which a suspension of carrot cells was dispersed. An estimated 100,000 embryoids were on this plate, and all of them were derived from part of the cells from one embryo of the wild carrot.   C. Higher magnification of the plate shown in B. D. Growth in a liquid medium of many units from a cell suspension similar to that shown in A. Many globular masses in various stages of development and one clear torpedo stage may be seen. In the second row of photographs are shown selected stages of carrot embryogeny developed from free cells: E. Globular stage. F. Heart-shaped stage. G. Torpedo stage. H, I. Cotyledonary stages.   In the bottom row are shown stages in development of plants reared from embryoids

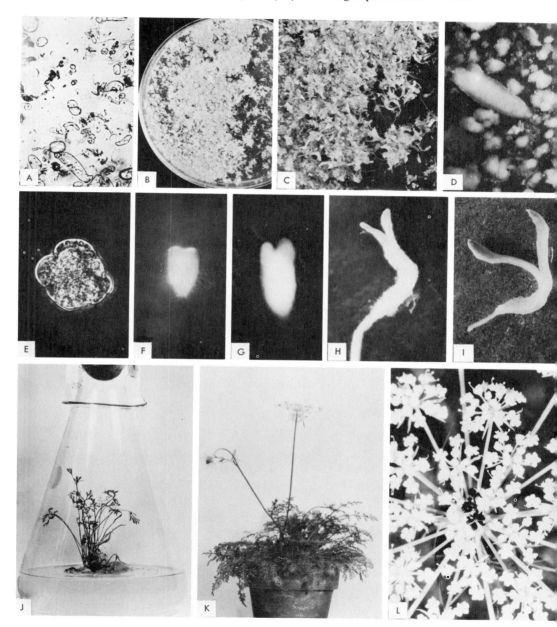

grown, in turn, from cells: J. Plant on agar. K. Plant bearing inflorescences after six months' growth. L. Detail of inflorescence of Queen Anne's Lace (*Daucus carota* L.) on a plant reared from cells of embryo origin (see A). Note the few typical red flowers at the center of the inflorescense. (From Steward *et al.*, *Science* **143**, 20–27, 1964.)

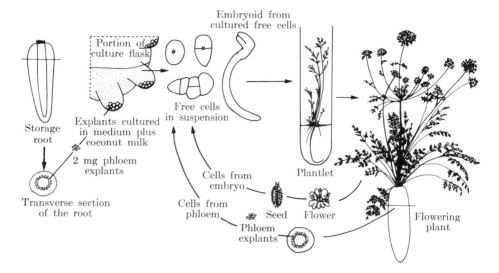

FIG. 10–7. Diagrammatic representation of the cycle of growth of the carrot plant; successive cycles of growth are linked through free, cultured cells derived from phloem, or from the embryo.

From this point of view, the early sequence of cell patterns in embryos seems not to be so peculiar to embryogeny as might otherwise be supposed. When the stages in growth of carrot embryoids from free cells are examined they are found to recapitulate normal embryogeny in a surprisingly faithful manner (Steward *et al.*, 1963). The similarity in form between some epidermal hairs (which grow from an initiating cell) and some young embryos, which was first noted by Sachs, and recalled by Steward and Mohan Ram (1961), is also very suggestive here. (In the growth of the hair, as of the zygote, an initiating cell has, for a while, the ability to grow and a free space into which it can grow unrestrictedly.) Indeed, it is now far easier to make previously differentiated cells of carrot, when they are free, grow and behave like embryos than it is to remove zygotes from ovules and to cultivate them separately! Furthermore, where one needs large numbers of embryos for experiments that must have a statistical basis the technique of free cell culture now makes this feasible.

Clearly, then, the genetic instructions, the blueprint, as it were, which entered the zygote at syngamy, are perpetuated in mature somatic cells, and they work themselves out very faithfully. This can be seen in the remarkable detail with which the floral structure of the Queen Anne's lace was reproduced in the flowers borne on plants that were grown from cells. An example of this is the presence of even a few anthocyanin-pigmented flowers at the center of the inflorescence, for this is a characteristic of the wild *Daucus carota* L. as it grows normally (Fig. 10–6L). Since free somatic cells of carrot can behave like zygotes and since all the morphological features of the adult plant may be so faithfully transmitted via free cells, can anything be said about mechanisms that permit so many diverse cell types to appear during development from cells which have the same genetic constitution?

Therefore, one should now ask what factors seem to control the embryonic growth of free cells, in contrast to their random proliferation, for this will create the internal environments which prompt cells *in situ* to do what they do. Occasionally this embryonic type of development occurs normally from cells within the plant body, as in apomictic development, but, as seen in Fig. 10–8, it may often be induced at will by appropriate chemical treatments of cultured free cells.

The Significance of Free Cell Cultures for Embryology and Morphogenesis

This question has been discussed elsewhere (Steward *et al.*, 1966) on the basis of the evidence first obtained in this and later in other laboratories. The observed totipotency of carrot cells and the ability to rear plants from free cells was rapidly succeeded by other examples. Two other umbellifers, the water parsnip (*Sium*) and the coriander (*Coriandrum*) and a crucifer (*Arabidopsis thaliana*) were shown to be capable of this behavior. A tobacco (*Nicotiana suaveolens*) and an orchid (*Cymbidium* sp.) successfully developed plants from cells (cf. also Steward, Kent, and Mapes, 1966; Steward, 1966). To these examples may now be added many others from other laboratories, especially from the Department of Botany at Delhi.

The comparative ease with which free cells of umbellifers have exhibited totipotency and have developed like embryos calls for some comment. It is hardly to be expected that this should arise from any unique affinity of umbelliferous cells for the coconut milk used—except insofar as it contains substances which foster cell divisions generally and also nourish embryos. It is known, however, that even carrot cells elaborate, from a coconut-milk-containing medium, substances which are more stimulatory than the coconut milk itself (cf. Fig. 10–5). A possible suggestion, therefore, is that plants with well-developed suspensors perform such functions for the proembryo in that organ, whereas plants (like umbellifers) with poorly developed suspensors absorb the active substances from their endosperms directly into the pro-embryos and then transform them, as in cotyledonary primordia, for their use.

Can any significance be attached to the kind of stimulants necessary to evoke embryological development in cells from different plants and different organs? This is a large topic. Briefly, it is very clear that many cells can be caused to grow vigorously and in the free state without spontaneous organization. In fact, the best conditions for organization and embryological development may not always coincide. The present picture is as follows.

Early in the development of zygotes, each cell if freed would readily become an embryo and polyembryony would result. Plants known to develop

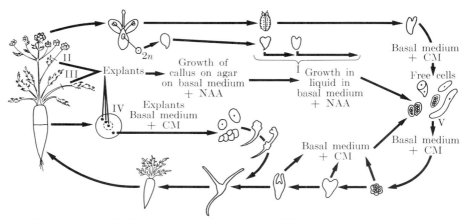

I. *Excised embryos:* In the later stages of embryogeny all isolated embryos grow and form
callus; in the earlier stages this is more difficult.

II. *Stem*

III. *Petiole* } With appropriate treatment these regions have
yielded free cells shown to be capable of growth

IV. *Root:* secondary phloem, cambium, and } and morphogenesis.
secondary xylem

V. *Free cells in suspension:* When derived from any young embryo they readily
recapitulate embryogeny on basal medium + coconut milk
(CM); when derived from mature organs they are more
restricted in response, requiring an intermediary or prior
growth stimulus.

FIG. 10–8. The morphogenetic responses of free cells of *Daucus carota* as determined by their
origin and culture.

embryos apomictically carry this propensity unrestricted into the cells in question (Maheshwari, 1950). The most potent source of somatic cells which develop
freely and in large numbers into plantlets is, in this laboratory, still a free cell
culture propagated from cells originating from young embryos removed from
ovules or immature seeds. Cells of carrot (*Daucus*) and water parsnip (*Sium*)
grown in this way develop plantlets in great profusion (cf. Steward *et al.*, 1964,
and Steward *et al.*, 1966). But as organogenesis proceeds and tissues and organs
become mature the control or restrictions over the behavior of the genetically
totipotent living cells may tighten. Therefore, it is not surprising, but is suggestive, that often more drastic devices are needed to evoke the totipotent growth.
Evidence of this is the needed interplay which has been observed of the factors
present in the coconut milk, on the one hand, and synergistically active substances, on the other.

A useful concept proves to be the following. Development, differentiation,
and morphogenesis as they normally occur represent sequential events in time.
These bring cells to their final condition in the plant body, in which their
capacity to grow and develop further is restricted, by steps which occur in a

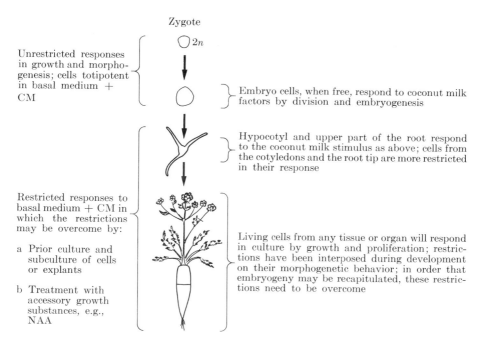

Zygote

Unrestricted responses in growth and morphogenesis; cells totipotent in basal medium + CM

Embryo cells, when free, respond to coconut milk factors by division and embryogenesis

Hypocotyl and upper part of the root respond to the coconut milk stimulus as above; cells from the cotyledons and the root tip are more restricted in their response

Restricted responses to basal medium + CM in which the restrictions may be overcome by:

a Prior culture and subculture of cells or explants

b Treatment with accessory growth substances, e.g., NAA

Living cells from any tissue or organ will respond in culture by growth and proliferation; restrictions have been interposed during development on their morphogenetic behavior; in order that embryogeny may be recapitulated, these restrictions need to be overcome

FIG. 10–9. Gradients of activity determined during development as expressed by growth and morphogenesis in cultured tissues and cells.

1. During development the totipotency of embryonic cells becomes restricted: this restriction can be viewed as due to a balance between factors that promote the growth of cells in the embryo and factors that control this during development.

2. The restrictions develop basipetally and may therefore be associated with the basipetal flow of auxin. Such gradients have been shown for the growth of phloem explants in relation to their position within the carrot root.

3. Mature tissue can be restored to the freely dividing state when placed in an environment like that of the zygote (CM). However, the restrictions on morphogenesis encountered in the mature organs still exist.

4. IAA and "unnatural" growth regulators (NAA, 2,4–D) may intervene by affecting this balance, freeing the cells from the previous restrictions which arose during development.

prescribed order. It is not, therefore, surprising that to reopen the doors of cell division and full morphogenetic propensity the appropriate steps need again to be taken in a prescribed order. The key to the renewed working of the full cellular organization is not a single one, but is in fact more like a combination lock—it is not enough to know the numbers and to apply them simultaneously or at random, they should be used not only in sequence but in the right order! Therefore, sequential treatments with growth-regulating combinations of substances have proved very useful in converting cells which merely grow in free culture, to cells with the maximum ability to develop. Briefly, it is often the case that combinations of growth factors (like coconut milk plus NAA or 2,4-D) will just place the cells in a very actively proliferating state which paves the way for a later, perhaps even less rapid, growth on a basal medium which, either unsupplemented (as in the case of *Arabidopsis*), or with only coconut milk added, now freely promotes the organized growth and development. By these means (growth on basal medium plus coconut milk plus NAA or 2,4-D followed by transfer to growth on basal medium plus coconut milk alone) an original carrot cell culture (laboratory strain, MIT 2) which, by very long cultivation in the free cell state, had lost its erstwhile power to organize (Steward *et al.*, 1967), was easily restored to organized growth. One may argue, therefore, that these sequential, exogenous treatments with regulatory substances which restore the totipotency of zygotes to differentiated cells reflect the converse controls or restrictions imposed upon the cells as they developed *in situ*. In the light of this one may now alter an earlier "life cycle" diagram (Fig. 10–7) for the growth of carrot plants from free cells to the form shown in Fig. 10–8. One may also illustrate the sequences of controls over unrestricted totipotency of cells, as they occur in differentiation or are released in dedifferentiation, in the schematic diagram of Fig. 10–9.

Essentially, therefore, the totipotency of cells is limited *in situ* by their associations with other cells and their behavior is subject to stimuli which are mediated by growth-regulatory substances. In this context ideas on the controlling effects of the environment, which Weiss called "molecular ecology," are relevant.

Concepts of Cellular and Protoplasmic Organization: Molecular Ecology

In his preoccupation with problems of growth, differentiation, and morphogenesis Weiss (1947, 1949a, b, 1950) has elaborated a concept of cellular and protoplasmic organization which he has termed "molecular ecology." Although this concept antedated much of the current chemical reaction schemes which comprise modern molecular biology, it still may be suggestive.

Weiss quotes, or formulates, certain aphorisms: "Growth is essentially an increase in protoplasm; differentiation is a transformation of protoplasm" (1950, p. 179); "The criterion of differentiation is the irrevocable restriction of potency" (1947, p. 263). From such starting points Weiss proceeded to speculate upon the nature of protoplasmic organization as the basis of an understanding of differentiation and of morphogenesis.

Weiss used the ecological simile as a "convenient device to describe the behavior of the molecular populations of cells." A cell is viewed as an organized mixed population of molecules and molecular groupings whose survival and orderly function is predicated on the presence of all essential members in definite concentrations, combination, and distributions; i.e., the various molecular species are not self-sufficient but depend in various degrees upon other members, as well as upon the physical conditions in the space they occupy.

Each such population is made up of molecular species of very different rank and stability ranging from trivial inorganic compounds to huge and highly organized protein systems. Some segments of the population occur in relatively constant groupings and constitute the cell particulates.

But the concept of molecular ecology replaces much of the former rigid morphological concepts of cell life—based upon internal static frameworks—with the more dynamic idea that what occurs in any part of a cell is the consequence of the statistical probability of its occurrence, rather than being prescribed by an absolutely fixed and stereotyped pattern exactly repeated in each cell specimen:

No two cells are precisely congruous . . . It is in the very nature of the cell that we can predict no more than the *probability* of the occurrence of a particular process in a given place . . . If each biochemical system requires highly specific conditions for its operation then obviously the probability of finding that system will be high at sites where the conditions are satisfied and low at others.

Preferential sites for the synthesis of certain compounds exist where "the necessary ingredients, templates, energy sources, and physical factors for that particular synthesis coexist." The "molecular ecology" concept of the cell places emphasis on local "conditions" meaning simply "*probabilities* that certain processes rather than others will occur with varying degrees of definiteness." In the operation of this dynamically, rather than statically, determined skeleton maintained by metabolic energy, Weiss gives particular attention to those "frontier populations" of molecules which function as membranes at boundary surfaces, for they "will play a unique role in the events in the interior." Weiss pursued this train of thought as he recognized the role of particular interlocking molecular configurations and the possible role of "stable layers of molecules with specially shaped ends firmly adsorbed to an interface" and able to "trap roaming molecules of complementarily fitting configuration." The following summary statement (Weiss, 1949b, p. 476) includes most of these salient ideas:

Each cell and organized cell part (nucleus, chromosome, etc.) consists of an array of molecular species whose densities, distribution, arrangement, and groupings are determined by their mutual dependencies and interactions, as well as by the physical conditions of the space they occupy. These species range from the elementary inorganic compounds to the most complex "key" species characteristic of a given cell. Chemical segregation and localization within the cell result from free molecular interplay, as only groups of elements compatible with one another and with their environment can form durable unions. The behavior of both developing and mature cells, as well as their restitution and regulation after disturbance, are faithfully described by this concept. . . . Among the principal segregative factors of molecular mixtures are interfaces.

Interfacial forces between partly immiscible molecular populations concentrate certain selected molecular species of the interior along the border.   By their surface positions, these border species acquire power over the further behavior of the enclosed system.   This is due partly to their common orientation relative to the interface, which increases their structural coherence and chemical combining faculty, and partly to their control over substance exchange across the border.   Various considerations suggest that in biological systems the fixation of a given molecular species in a surface is not due solely to unspecific factors such as surface tensions, adsorptions, etc., but that in addition, highly selective chemical affinities are involved.   These may be based on the steric interlocking of characteristically shaped groups of the surface molecules of adjacent systems.

But how do these ideas relate to the problems of differentiation and morphogenesis? As Weiss pointed out, the highest degree of invariance is assigned to the gene with a remarkably constant composition and arrangement, so that mutations are explained by the loss of a given member of it or by the loss of its controlling position. However, the rigid determination of chromosome structure is not matched by an equally rigid determination of cellular characters.

Cells in ontogenetic biochemical specialization assume characters which predispose them to make or break connections with other cells; these properties guide mobile groups of cells and determine their associations with others—cells come to rest only after they are contiguous with others of matching properties.

Antibody formation, in response to foreign antigens, shows that animal cells can acquire a new specific property not originally contained in their native endowment. Thus new specific characters may not be only *evoked* but actually *impressed* upon one cell type by another. This occurs in *specification* of neurons by their terminal organs, for "each muscle tunes in on the action systems operating in the nerve centers" and "specification may be in the nature of an antigenic reaction as the individually distinguishing protein groups of each terminal organ impressing its configuration on receptive protein groups in the nerve fiber where it would be passed on in similar manner down the line."

Higher plant morphology and organization is built upon, as we have seen, a greater degree of cellular totipotency and a lesser degree of organ specificity than exist in the higher animal body, and the "cell mobility" of which Weiss speaks is virtually non-existent. Nevertheless one needs some means by which the constituent cells respond and express their built-in genetic information in accordance with the "local conditions" or the milieu of the organs and tissues in which they exist. This effect "supervenes" or "modulates" the primary genetic instructions and it is here that a concept of molecular ecology seems useful. But the controlling factors of molecular ecology we need to know most about are those that impinge upon plant cells from without. Such factors which are present in the surroundings of cells, or are transmitted from organs of perception responding to environmental stimuli, determine the responses of that dynamic molecular system to which Weiss refers. Whether such stimuli must feed back into and operate through the genetic apparatus, or may operate more statistically upon the molecular populations which Weiss conceives in his ecological analogy, may be a moot point.

However, the significant point of difference between the animal systems (from which Weiss draws his illustrations) and the higher plants (with which we are here concerned) is the greater degree of organic connection which plant cells achieve through their protoplasmic connections. This may permit the conditions that require adjacent cells to be distinct, though genetically similar, to be dictated by asymmetrical distribution of some members of the molecular population and yet also retain a characteristic pattern throughout the cells of a uniform tissue mass. To this extent Weiss's concepts of "molecular ecology" still have their uses, although they need to be adapted to our greater present knowledge of the underlying fine structure of cells and of the more precise biochemical reactions by which genetic information may be transferred through protein and enzyme specificity than existed when his ideas were first formulated.

Genes and Development

Whereas genes clearly determine differences between individuals, the problem now faced by geneticists is to prescribe the means by which variations from cell to cell of the same individual may have a genetic basis. It is interesting to see how this problem is faced in a current genetical text book (Srb, Owen, and Edgar, 1965) and how this account fits with what is known about higher plants. Evidence is cited from sea urchins to show that identity of the nuclei in cells from a zygote is not incompatible with cytoplasmic differences that may correlate with their development. Evidence is cited from nuclear transplant experiments which led some zoologists to the view that differentiation involves nuclear changes that are not readily reversed, even when the modified nucleus is returned to the environment of unmodified egg cytoplasm. These reservations are, however, now set at rest by a dramatic demonstration of the maintained integrity of the cell's nucleus throughout development, which is due to Gurdon and Uehlinger (1966) and is referred to as "the fatherless frog of Geneva" by Adam (1966). These workers successfully transplanted nuclei from abdominal cells of *Xenopus* into enucleated eggs and showed that the eggs, with their transplanted nuclei, developed into mature organisms which reproduced sexually. Thus, although irreversible cytoplasmic changes during the development of animal cells may still occur, the maintained effectiveness of their nuclei is demonstrable. But in plant cells *both* nuclei and cytoplasm must remain fully competent since the cells retain their innate totipotency throughout development.

A later and very significant study by Graham, Arms, and Gurdon (1966) has shown that almost immediate (less than 90 minutes) DNA synthesis (detected by nuclear volume changes and H^3-thymidine labeling) in nuclei from a variety of quiescent cells (blood, liver, brain) is promoted when they are transplanted into enucleated eggs. Moreover, it is actual contact with normal egg cytoplasm that furnishes the stimulus and not any of the several alternatives considered. These authors now believe that "egg cytoplasm is capable of inducing all nuclei with unreplicated chromosomes to commence DNA synthesis" and observe that "the results on *Xenopus* . . . show that a very high percentage (over 75 percent) of adult cell nuclei can be induced within a very short time (1½ hours) to synthesize DNA by exposure to *entirely normal* cytoplasm."

Graham *et al.* do not speculate upon the nature of the cytoplasmic constituent in eggs which so effectively induces DNA synthesis in nuclei. They point out, however, that it does not discriminate between nuclei from different tissues of the same animal and nuclei which respond to alien egg cytoplasms (90 percent of mouse liver nuclei synthesized DNA in frogs' eggs!). All this reinforces what has already been emphasized (pp. 447–449), namely, the importance of the plant protoplast, i.e., of the nucleus in its cytoplasmic environment. The diverse environmental and developmental stimuli that control development must do this inasmuch as the small molecules, whether endogenous or exogenous, that mediate their effects do so via the cytoplasm and its organization, even though this, in turn, sets nuclear responses in train.

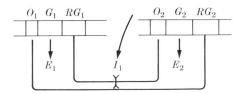

FIG. 10–10. An operon circuit that would switch the production of one enzyme off and another on. (From *General Genetics*, Second Edition, by Adrian M. Srb, Ray D. Owen, and Robert S. Edgar. W. H. Freeman and Company, San Francisco. Copyright © 1965.)

Inhomogeneity of the internal environment, which exposes some cells of a multicellular mass to different environments and gradients, seems to be as important in plants as it is in animals. The evidence obtained through chromosomal "puffing" of localized gene action, which may be activated by specific external stimuli, suggests that the events of development may coincide with triggers which turn given genes "on or off"—though which is "cause" and which is "effect" is a moot point. The favored model here is that of the operator-regulator genes, triggered by inducers (following the ideas of Jacob and Monod, 1961). If one assumes that morphological responses during development are mediated by different complements of enzyme proteins, then at least the operon concept, as conceived in the figure, enables one to visualize how a single exogenous substance might cause a switch from one morphogenetically determining enzyme protein to another. The diagram and its explanation are essentially quoted from Srb, Owen, and Edgar (see Fig. 10–10). The enzyme protein E_1, produced by the gene G_1, is active because its operon site O_1 is open and active, whereas its regulator gene (RG_1) represses the activity of the operon (O_2) which controls the action of G_2 and the formation of E_2. If the inducer substance I intervenes to block the R regulator gene G_1 it may release the operator site O_2, cause G_2 to form E_2, and simultaneously enable regulator gene G_2 to block operon O_1. These elaborate hypothetical formulations can at best act as models to guide thought; they do not in any way establish the reality of what they represent. In the last analysis the diagram, interesting as it is, expresses the dilemma of development in another way. It simply says that what the organism grows to be is determined by its genes; during development the genes, present in all nuclei, successively mediate their action through proteins as enzymes and some extranuclear agents (inducers or repressors) activate or suppress given genes as required. In other words morphogenetic stimuli act within an inherited gene-determined system which prescribes what the organism can grow to be! The puzzle still is that all the living cells of the higher plant body potentially have all the attributes of the organism even though, during development, they do not individually display them all.

Cell Diversification: Differentiation and Morphogenesis

Here the thought is that diversification results, not because of any inherent change in plant cells, since both nuclei and cytoplasm retain their integrity throughout development, but due to the position of cells in the plant body or their regulation by exogenous stimuli. In other words, the course of cell differentiation is due not so much to *what* the cells are as to *where* they are; and this effect should now be interpreted in terms of chemical and physical stimuli. These morphogenetic stimuli do not, however, elicit any new features or characteristics; they merely evoke, accentuate, or modulate certain of the characteristics which were all embodied in the zygote, but which are called upon (i.e., programmed) during development.

The modifying effects of position on the development of given primordia are illustrated by the existence of juvenile and adult forms in many plants. In fact, there are here examples of morphogenetic responses, difficult to identify with external morphogenetic stimuli, which were not dealt with in Chapter 7. The incidence of these juvenile and adult forms, often revealed by drastically different leaf shapes, in many plants (for example see Sinnott, 1960, or such older sources as Oliver's 1902 translation of Kerner's *Natural History of Plants*), has long suggested that sequential changes in the environment of developing primordia, which are associated with the time of their formation or their position on the axis, may greatly modify their development. (The old term "topophysis" designated this effect.) Two recent and contrasting examples cited from Marcavillaca and Montaldi (1967) suffice to show the different responses of buds regenerated from callus in relation to its point of origin. In the passion flower tree (*Passiflora caerulea* L.) a callus which has developed at the base of a petiole of the juvenile, rounded, entire leaves produces buds which, in turn,

 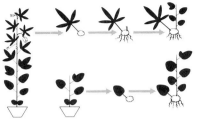

(a) *Nicotiana tabacum*   (b) *Passiflora caerulea*

FIG. 10–11.   (a) Regeneration of buds on callus formed at leaf bases of a photoperiodically insensitive strain of *Nicotiana tabacum*. It is to be noted that the leaves regenerated from the callus
retain the same form as the leaf by which the regeneration was stimulated. (b) Regeneration of buds
on callus formed at the base of leaves of *Passiflora caerulea* L. Note that the regenerated leaves
are always of the juvenile form uninfluenced by the juvenile or adult form of the leaf upon which
the regeneration occurred. (From a diagram supplied by Dr. Montaldi.)

reproduce juvenile leaves. Moreover, buds which develop on callus formed on
adult three- or five-lobed leaves also develop juvenile leaves. Therefore, the initiating cells from which these adventitious buds were formed behave as though
they were physiologically independent of, or isolated from, the biochemical environment on the main axis which first produced the leaf in question. By contrast, a photoperiodically indifferent strain of *Nicotiana tabacum* always regenerated from callus at leaf bases the same type of leaf (juvenile or adult) as
the leaf that produced the callus. Hence these primordia behave as though they
were still a part of the same environment, or subject to the same stimuli, which
governed the formation on the main axis of the leaves from which they were
regenerated. The diagram of Figure 10–11 illustrates these effects, and similar
phenomena are also encountered in other plants (e.g. *Citrus*). It would be interesting, therefore, to follow up these observations by converting each leaf
callus into free cells in ways which would indicate, indubitably, that the initiating cells from which the buds form were in fact totally isolated and, if so, by
determining what are the consequences for the subsequent leaf form. Enough
has been said, however, to illustrate that the development of a given leaf primordium may well be a function of the morphogenetic environment in which it
develops, which may also be, in turn, a progressively changing function of the
age of the shoot.

   Morphogenetic studies of insect larvae have produced the remarkable observations on the polytene chromosomes. These large structures display elaborate
chromosome morphology and show signs of local activity (called puffs), which
are typically associated with distinct stages of the development of the insect
(Fig. 10–12). It is as if at each developmental stage the activity of a particular
part of a chromosome is called upon and this accentuates a given gene or set of

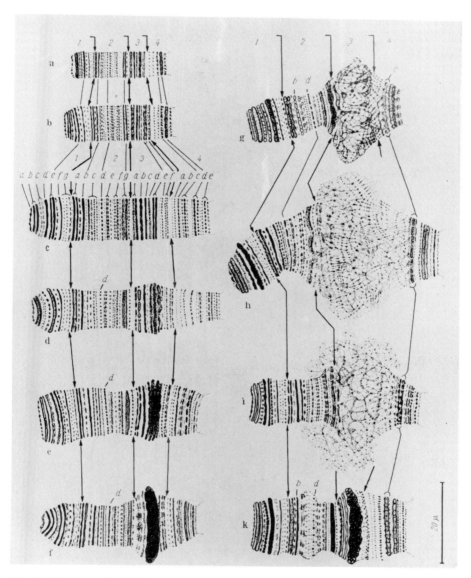

FIG. 10–12. Camera lucida drawings of the distal end of chromosome (c) of the salivary gland of *Rhynchosciara angelae* in different stages of larval development. Phase (c) is from a chromosome of a full-grown larva. Phase (a) is from a chromosome 16 days younger than the one in phases (h) and (i). Phase (b) is from a chromosome eight days older than the one in phase (a). Phases (c) through (k) represent eight days of larval development. The arrows and small letters indicate corresponding bands. The arabic numbers indicate sections into which this part of the chromosome was arbitrarily divided. (From Breuer and Pavan, *Chromosoma* **7**, 371–386, Springer-Verlag, Berlin, Heidelberg, New York, 1955.)

genes; these in turn pour out into the cytoplasm those RNA's that will lead to the enzymes and the metabolites which are needed. It is even now being claimed that the insect hormone "ecdysone" activates special regions of the chromosome (Breuer and Pavan, 1955; cf. Fig. 10–12). This sort of work presents the challenging possibility that plant growth-regulating substances (see Chapters 4 and 5) may act in a similar manner, even though the cytological evidence of the local activation of chromosome materials is lacking.

In this context, recent studies of soluble proteins by the technique of acrylamide gel electrophoresis show that development and morphogenesis in plants are accompanied by changes in the protein complement. This has been shown for two main systems; namely, the pea plant throughout its development and the tulip plant during morphogenesis in the bulb (cf. Figs. 7–18 and 7–19). Thus a specific stage in development emphasizes a given protein complement, while at another it may be de-emphasized. There must therefore be biochemical mechanisms for the "turning on or off" of the genetically determined metabolism; the plant growth regulators seem to be the exogenous agents which will do this. Histones are also being invoked (Bonner, 1965) as the endogenous agents that either "cover up" or "release" the action of the genes in the chromosomes.

Therefore, there is now hope that one may determine the means whereby the genetic instructions of the zygote are controlled or modulated during development to permit the cells to do in metabolism what, in fact, they do. But all these controls would be without effect were it not for the innate (or "built in") capacity to grow, which is conveyed to the zygote at fertilization along with the genetic instructions received from male and female gametes, and without the special stimuli which give to that zygote the initial nutritional and physiological stimulus, which acts as a "thrust" to start the embryo upon its way and lasts until it eventually becomes an autonomous, autotrophic, green plant.

The causal formation of organs in the outgrowth of the zygote is the crux of the great problems of embryogeny and morphogenesis. The means to the formation of tissues and cells adapted to special functions is the equally great problem of cellular differentiation. When all is said and done, we know much about *how* these events now occur but very little about *why* they occur as they do, except that the resultant organizations have proved to have selective advantages in evolution.

Organized growth in plants proceeds from free sporogenous cells or zygotes so that, from the outset, a single cell gives rise to a coordinated unit linked internally by protoplasmic connections (cf. Heslop-Harrison, 1963). If such connections link the endoplasmic reticulum of cells that are in organic connection (cf. Wardrop, 1965), the derivative cells are not to be regarded as autonomous units, behaving independently like soap bubbles, or liquid films in equilibrium which partition space efficiently as they multiply. On the contrary, polarity and "division of labor" in the cell mass occur almost from the outset, and thenceforward the behavior of cells within the mass is conditioned by their position and subject to the stimuli which integrate the growth of the organism as a whole. Where two cells are formed from one by equational division, neither of them is as externally unlimited in its behavior as was the mother cell, nor is it as free to express, unrestrictedly, its intrinsic potentialities. Commonly, therefore, the effects imposed upon each daughter cell are different. This may be seen in terms of the form of the two-celled stage in the development of carrot (cf. Fig. 10–8) and, in terms of biochemistry, by the often different pigmentation of adjacent attached cells in cultures of *Haplopappus*. There is here obvious evidence of cytoplasmic asymmetry between daughter cells. From such beginnings, and the resultant interdependence of cells which *en masse* and in organs and tissues acquire a specialization of function and "division of labor," the facts of epigenesis, of polarity, morphogenesis, and differentiation are eventually to be traced.

But all our evidence on the expression of genetic potentialities during development and the way these may be restrained or elicited relates to the biosynthesis of substances, not to the way the entire organization of cells is controlled during development. For that matter it is still obscure what in the protoplast constitutes the specificity of the protoplasm of any one organism. Therefore, it is not surprising that it is difficult to say what it is in the entire organization of a cell which "instructs" it to produce a whole plant, if it is free, or to grow in an organ into a tissue element. Some will take the view that the events that control morphogenesis are merely the summation of controlled events which determine the specific substances of which cells and tissues are made. Such views disclaim any distinctive role which is contributed by morphogenetic effects exerted through the organization of which the formative substances are but a part. Therefore, one should now ask what is known about the biochemical aspects of differentiation and ask what bearing this knowledge may have on morphogenesis. In asking this question one inevitably encounters the views of J. Bonner (1965) as expressed in *The Molecular Biology of Development*.

Development and Concepts of Molecular Biology

Bonner begins by stating that modern advances in biology began when biologists ceased their preoccupation with the differences between organisms and concentrated not only on cells, but on the similarities between cells. Out of this came the knowledge of the way likenesses are transmitted and of enzyme and protein synthesis as an information-requiring task. The modern idea is that the information contained in the cell's nucleus is, as it were, transcribed as though it were in the form of a message on a punched tape. The appropriate message conveyed in a four-letter, base-paired code, is transmitted via mRNA's from the DNA of the nucleus in the sequence "gene → mRNA → protein (enzyme)." This is all according to a general scheme which has already been illustrated (Fig. 3–20). Bonner now condescendingly dismisses all knowledge prior to these developments as "neo-classical biology"!

Bonner's thesis is simple, plausible, and vividly presented. Recognizing that the genetic constitution is preserved intact throughout all the living cells of plants, Bonner traces the problems of differentiation and development to the appropriate control of the extent to which the genetic information in cells is expressed. These controls, which operate in the living plant body, can be isolated from the cells in the form of their chromatin and shown (*with respect to a particular protein*) to operate *in vitro*. The isolated chromatin does not, however, so imprint its characteristics upon the protein-synthesizing system that virtually all the proteins of a given plant are simultaneously formed. On the contrary, in the cell-free state, even as in intact cells, the behavior of the chromatin is more restricted. This restriction is caused by histones which coat the genes and so control their action that, by covering or uncovering them, their activity may be "turned on" or "turned off" by the histone complement of the chromosomes. The general plan which has supported these views is summarized as Fig. 10–13.

It is an attractive hypothesis that the gene-controlled messages of development are either released and communicated to cells, or they are restrained, by the histones—even though this immediately poses the question: "What controls the histones?" The problem is thus being pushed, at best, one step further back.

The strongest justification for the histone concept of gene control is that histones are there, as prominent constituents of chromosomes and in close proximity to the DNA and the genes. A histone moiety is made along with DNA synthesis. The amino acid composition of histones is said to be very constant throughout the plant kingdom and, for the most part, they are not turned over in non-dividing cells. The histone concept of the sequential programming of gene action, which growth and development entails, clearly requires that the histone "coat" of chromosomes should be directly accessible to, and affected by, an array of small, often exogenous, molecules which affect development. These molecules must (as effector substances) affect the appropriate proteins which, in turn, should interact with specific areas of the chromatin to bring about its inactivation (when genes are repressed) or activation (when they are derepressed). The derepressed genes must then produce transient messenger RNA's which cause given protein-enzymes to be synthesized. As a working hypothesis this concept is so versatile that it is potentially equal to almost every demand that need be made upon it, provided only that one does not, perhaps prematurely, ask for rigorous proof at each crucial stage!

The experimental evidence is briefly as follows. The cotyledons of peas form characteristic protein(s) which do not exist elsewhere in the shoot—amongst them is a storage globulin which is detectable in small amounts serologically. In a reaction mixture which is said to contain all the requirements for both RNA and protein synthesis, the pea seed globulin is *not* appreciably made if the chromatin (DNA coated with histone) is extracted from pea buds. But, if the cotyledons are the source of the chromatin, then the pea seed globulin may be formed, but not if the chromatin is stripped of its histone coat.

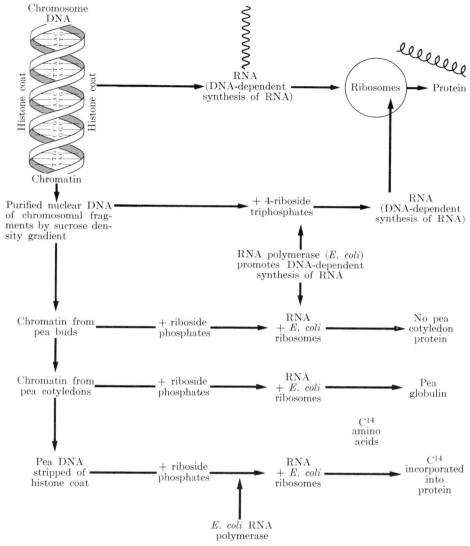

FIG. 10–13. Summary of current ideas on histone-regulated protein synthesis. See text for details. (Based upon Bonner, 1965.)

The criterion of synthesis of both general pea proteins and of the globulin in these experiments is the incorporation of C^{14}-leucine. However, the actual amounts of protein so synthesized are very small and the period during which the preparations remain active is very short (up to about 30 minutes). Therefore, although the protein in question (pea seed globulin, which furnishes most of the evidence) is sensitively detected by the serological test, it was not formed *in vitro* either continuously or in extractable quantities which permitted its analysis. It is in this respect that all the work with cell-free systems is so unsatisfying. The best of cell-free preparations have very brief and infinitesimal activity compared with active intact cells. Surely if we really know how the cell manufactures protein, as distinct from recognizing certain intermediate steps and catalytic arrangements that are feasible, we ought to be able to make pea seed globulin in bulk. It is still true that this can only be done by growing pea cotyledons! In the work of this laboratory, for example, cells of a few cotyledons have been cultured. Cells of peanut (*Arachis hypogaea*) cotyledons and jack bean (*Canavalia ensiformis*) have been grown successfully in culture, but their metabolisms (with respect to soluble nitrogen compounds, and probably also to proteins—e.g., urease in jack bean) are quite different from those of the intact cotyledons.

Nevertheless Bonner's argument really requires that the controls which cause the cotyledonary cells to develop as such, also control the formation of the pea seed globulin; presumably, it is by the formation of specific proteins and enzymes that the course of development is determined. These controls take the form of certain genes which are either activated or restrained by the histone moiety of the chromosomes.

These ideas are presented tersely and dramatically by James Bonner. As a contribution to a postulated mechanism of protein synthesis it has great interest. The salient question is, what do the observations tell about the control of development? The answer is still very little.

The particular pea seed globulin which provides much of the evidence is not itself part of the decision that causes cells to become cotyledons. The globulin is surely a symptom, not a cause. The essential decision that prompted pea cells to grow into cotyledons was obviously taken in their primordia *long before pea seed globulin was detected*. Pea seed globulin is a product of cells which have virtually stopped growing, not of those which comprise a system which is undergoing the morphogenetic response. Neither during the formation of the cotyledonary cells, nor later when the peas germinate and the globulin will disappear, does it enter into the constitution of the pea cells or contribute directly to their organization. The extent to which one is entitled to take the determination of pea seed globulin as an example of the way in which cotyledons are constrained to form from otherwise totipotent cells is the essence of the problem. Is it, in fact, credible that so simple a shift as between the formation, or not, of one kind, or even a succession of kinds, of protein, by effects upon a succession of genetic loci, could control the course of development of the whole cells in question? This does not seem plausible. The mechanism so ably discussed by Bonner deals with less important events, namely the formation of a protein which occurs in cells already committed to be cotyledons, not the behavior of cells which become cotyledons by virtue of the presence of that protein. We speak loosely of the "genetic control" of differentiation. Strictly, however, we could reverse the statement for it is the expression of the genes which is controlled during development. The biochemical evidence, cited by Bonner, could mean that the master switches which were engaged to turn a complex cell into a given course of development (e.g., to be part of a cotyledon) also created the circumstances in which certain proteins could now form. But that master switch did not merely activate the loci calling for the proteins in question, for it changed the cellular milieu in which they form.

Similar considerations apply, in greater or lesser degree, to the descriptions of soluble protein complements as they change (a) during differentiation along the axis of a root (cf. p. 367) or (b) as they exist in different regions of a tulip bulb (cf. p. 366). Again, specific protein complements in mice have been revealed by Markert. In fact, for lactic dehydrogenase Markert shows that this enzyme may occur as several isozymes (five in all). Each isozyme is composed of four polypeptide chains coded by two genes. The five possible isozymes provide for lactic dehydrogenase activity to be mediated in the different organs by combinations of isozymes which are specific and in the assembly of which the cytoplasm of given cells may play a role. Thus "the origin of specific proteins during development requires two basic interacting components—the genes and the cytoplasm" (cf. Markert, 1963).

The stable protein end products in mature organs are results, not causes, of the developmental trend; studies of them describe morphogenesis at a different level. The rapidly changing protein moieties along the axis of a growing pea root (Steward, Lyndon and Barber, 1965) may, however, be more causally related to the type of growth which occurs at any given point along the axis because the changes in question seem to affect many such proteins in relatively rapid succession. But evidence to suggest that there are gene-determined protein moieties concerned with a developmental shift comes from the observations on floral induction in the tulip (Fig. 8–14). In this case protein and enzyme changes have been observed in florally induced growing shoot tips so early in the development that floral organs had not yet formed: this arouses the hope that, eventually, specific proteins may be causally linked to the induction of the morphogenetic response, but this point has not yet been reached.

The basic decisions of morphogenesis seem to be of a more drastic and multiple kind than the activation of single genes. They concern the cellular organization—the way the essential units of the living system are compatibly put together and the way they function, whether as cells of the shoot, cortex, leaves, cotyledons, or roots. The various parts of the living system (nuclei, plastids, mitochondria, golgi bodies, ribosomes, reticulum, vacuoles, membranes) must in their interaction with each other constitute the cell's organization at work and, for the cell to act as it does, more multiple instructions must be given to determine development than merely the making of one or more proteins. In fact, the formation of distinctive proteins, especially if they are storage proteins, may well be determined by the changed milieu of the cell rather than the reverse.

The "instructions" to developing cells, comparable to the navigation instructions from a ship's bridge issued after the essential course has been charted, must result in many mutual readjustments of the cell's parts and of their interacting activities. Dr. James Bonner may well say that this takes the problem back to the discredited realms of "neo-classical biology"; nevertheless one can only repeat that this is where, essentially, the problem still stands. One cannot solve the problems of differentiation and morphogenesis solely by work on homogenates or cell-free preparations, on isolated enzyme systems—or even on *E. coli*—for these systems do not indulge in morphogenesis. Therefore, it is still important *where* a cell is in the intact plant body, for this determines what it will grow to be. While these variations may carry with them the formation of single proteins, biosynthetically determined in the manner visualized by James Bonner, the shift from one kind of developmental state to another may involve different consideration from those provided solely by the sequence "histone-regulated gene ⟶ mRNA ⟶ protein (enzyme)." There are obviously factors other than nuclear genes which are required to stipulate what an organism becomes, for its genes must exert their effect through the cytoplasmic organization. In fact, taken out of that context the genes, the DNA, the RNA, etc., are merely substances. Thus one should still recognize that differentiation and morphogenesis may be controlled as much by deep-seated changes in the non-nuclear, non-genic parts of the system as by the direct activation (i.e., derepression) or repression of the genes. In fact the events of development may be regarded as providing the cytoplasmic context, changing with time, in which specific genes can appropriately act.

Bonner (1965) has visualized the unfolding events of development from a zygote, or a primordial cell, in terms of a program in which cells, by virtue of their position, are faced with a series of yes and no decisions. At each cell division the daughter cells must respond to the new environment which they enter and, in so doing, bring into play some genes which are derepressed (by effector substances) while others remain repressed. In effect these decisions are responses to the fact of "where the cell is, not what it is" (cf. p. 365). These ideas readily evoke a picture of cells responding, as they develop, to a series of "commands" which are imposed by their respective locations in the plant body. A mechanical model of a "built-in" computer in cells, which can answer an almost infinite series of yes and no questions, may appeal to some as a description of developmental events; it should not, however, be raised to the level of an explanation. One major dilemma is to understand how, on this plan, the long series of apparently independent "switching acts" may be linked together in so orderly a developmental program. In the last analysis one has to admit that it is this program, with its numerous reasonable alternatives in plants, which the organism inherits. Indeed it is doubtful whether modern biology has yet said more than that the organism can grow to be what is inherent in a zygote, or in any totipotent derivative cell; inherent, that is, in its nucleus which transmits the genetic information and in the organization of its cytoplasm which will transcribe it and set the limits of its expression. But the proposed means by which all this is accomplished, the tenets of "molecular biology" notwithstanding, are still only crudely conceived.

All genetic, and even molecular-biological, approaches to problems of organization and of organism thus face the same dilemma. The tools of genetics are adapted to tell us about the inheritance of individual traits or characteristics of organisms or cells, provided these occur within a master plan, or design, which is necessary for their expression and which in turn prescribes what kind of system will be involved. The causal determination of differentiation and morphogenesis seems to be too intimate a part of the master plan to be subject only to genic control: on the contrary, growth and morphogenesis may in turn control, or invoke, the action of the genes. Morphogenesis cannot be conceived apart from the organization of the whole protoplast and its reactions to its environment.

Many attempts have been made to define the master plan of organisms in terms of units of biological organization in a general philosophical concept of living organisms. This literature is beyond the scope of this chapter. Nevertheless certain ideas may be noted.

Concepts of Organism: Units of Structure and Behavior

In the organization of higher animals the means of integration and control which lead to a concept of organism, over and above the mere summation of its constituent units, are more obvious than in plants. The brain, the central nervous system, the blood as a circulating tissue, the hormonal machinery, etc., all contribute to the unity of the organism as a whole. Though a tree lacks these obvious means of integration which a higher animal possesses, it is, nevertheless, an organic whole and something more than a mere colony of autonomous and independent living units. It is an individual organism, not a colony. All this raises the philosophic problem of the unity or wholeness of systems that are composed of separable parts. With these problems such authors as Smuts (1926) and Whitehead (1925) have dealt, and later Agar (1951) has attempted a philosophical approach to the concepts of a living organism. In two books, *Modern Theories of Development* (1962) and *Problems of Life* (1952), Ludwig von Bertalanffy develops an "organismical" philosophy. While Bertalanffy recognizes that "the history of biology is the refutation of vitalism," it is his avowed purpose to emphasize that "the characteristics of life are characteristics of a system arising from, and associated with, the organization of materials and processes" and, secondly, that "the actual whole shows properties that are absent from its isolated parts. The problem of life is that of *organization*." Bertalanffy recognizes that individual reactions in a living organism are indistinguishable from those in inanimate things or in a decaying corpse, and that many even complicated processes, like those of respiration and fermentation and nerve action, have been explained to a large extent physicochemically. Nevertheless, there is a fundamental contrast when we consider "not single processes, but their totality within an organism or a partial system of it, such as a cell or an organ," for then "we find that all parts and processes are so ordered that they guarantee

the maintenance, construction, restitution, and reproduction of organic systems."
From these premises Bertalanffy develops his "organismic" concepts, based on
the totality of the systems which, as organisms, comprise complexes of elements
in mutual interaction. Moreover, he shows that progressive analysis of individual
parts of that system, however necessary, is never sufficient, for there is still the
task of synthesizing the properties of the parts into a smoothly operating whole.
One has to recognize, also, that it is one problem to trace how these successful
biological organizations have evolved (and, in a recent book, Wardlaw (1965)
has essayed this task for plants), but it is still another to explain them in terms
of physics and chemistry and physiology.

From time to time living organisms have been regarded as made up of subject units which behave, perceive, and respond to stimuli. On these lines there
are units at different levels of organization and, in fact, a multicellular organism
is to be regarded (after Whitehead and Agar) as a complexity, or "nexus," of
such living subject units, each able to act as a distinct agent; but the whole
nevertheless acts as "a causal unit upon its own parts and upon other objects."
Even a single cell may need to be regarded as a "nexus" of living subagents or
organelles. An agent constituted as a nexus of subagents which in combination
give rise to a subject of a higher order is described, by Agar, as a Central
Agent, and the conspicuous example is that concerned with the organism as a
whole. In animals the locus of the Central Agent is the brain, in higher animals
the cortex of the brain. But one cannot similarly assign in plants the central
coordinating function solely to any cells or organs.

These attempts to produce a philosophy of biological organization have also
led to the concept of a biological "field," which is a region characterized by
some "community or organization of processes" distinguishing it from other
regions. The idea of morphogenetic or embryological fields has had its descriptive uses, particularly in the interpretation of animal development where specialization of organs is so marked. A "field" acts collectively as a causal unit.
A field may extend over but one cell, as for example where the factors responsible for development reside within a single tissue cell (e.g., the fertilized egg
or any cells which may apomictically behave like a zygote); or again, it may be
constituted as an intracellular field where local centers evoke special behavior.
But often a morphogenetic field extends over a large number of cells which are
characterized by some continuity which transcends cell boundaries (e.g., the
mouth- or eye-forming areas in animal embryos).

In higher plants it is obviously difficult to locate what could constitute a
central directing agent since the means of correlating behavior and activity are
not localized in any distinctive organ—there is no parallel for the brain or the
central nervous system. On the contrary, the lesson to be learned from free cell
cultures is that any free living cell may act like an egg, as a morphogenetic field.
But when such a cell is preformed in, and attached to, a fresh tissue explant, then
the explant as a whole acts as a unit (i.e., as a "nexus" of subject units) which

superimposes upon its parts the characteristics of the proliferating mass of callus. But the cells in the mass had potentialities for morphogenetic development not there exhibited. Even in animal systems this has also been noted. Holtfreter (1946) and Townes & Holtfreter (1955) have shown, for example, that isolated cells from embryos of amphibians reveal significant parallels to the behavior of free living simple organisms, and he came to a similar conclusion to that which was drawn from carrot cells, namely, that it is the act of isolation, or partial isolation, of the cells which provides the stimulus to their behavior. [Significantly Stephens (1960) has also shown the embryo-like behavior of cells of testicular teratomas of the mouse]. Conversely, in developing embryos the changes of environment upon which cellular differentiation depends are provided by the functioning *en masse* of the cells themselves. This provides the stimuli, chemical in nature, which provoke specific morphogenetic responses in the cells subjected to these stimuli. Along these lines one can comprehend, though not explain in detail, how the integration of distinct, totipotent parenchyma cells into a tissue, an organ, or an embryo is achieved by its tight organization via the protoplasmic strands, and how these in turn may represent sites where endoplasmic reticulum is also continuous from cell to cell. Conversely, cells, or cell aggregates, which must escape from conformity to the tissue masses in which they occur, may be expected to be isolated from their neighbor cells. In this connection it is significant that guard cells are said to be free from protoplasmic connections with the epidermal cells and so can behave, developmentally and physiologically, as isolated units. No doubt many cases of natural adventitious embryo formation will prove to be of a similar kind. One can also understand that a free living cell, giving rise by internal divisions to cell aggregates that are united by protoplasmic connections across new cell walls (cf. Fig. 10–2) will also give rise to a structure which behaves as an integrated whole. In the case of free carrot or other totipotent cells the derivative cells are clearly subjected to the same sort of stimuli that in normal embryogeny give rise to tissues and organs.

A theme that runs through all these considerations is the response of cells *in situ* to the controls to which they are there subjected. Figure 10–6, and its associated text, illustrates dramatically the effects that ensue when these controls are alternatively dislocated and restored. A similar effect was observed when large London plane trees in Lincoln's Inn Fields were exposed, in August of 1940, to the shattering shock equivalent to the pressure from about 1 ton of TNT at but a few feet from the highly blasting explosion of what were then known as "land mines" dropped by parachute. These "bomb-blasted *Platanus* of Lincoln's Inn Fields" then lost all their leaves and small twigs. The following spring the large gaunt branches unexpectedly sprang into growth. The living cells, within the periderm and on the "blasted side of the trees," freed from the integrated controls of the shoot which are normally mediated by the cambium, began independent growth and formed thousands of buds and sucker

FIG. 10–14. Controls over development: their dislocation and restoration in a tree. A, B, and C. Photographs taken in 1941, of London plane trees which had been exposed in August, 1940 to the force of a heavy explosion. Note the abundant sucker shoots on the side exposed to the explosion and that the longer shoots are at the base and the progressively shorter ones higher on the tree. D. A typical sucker shoot from near the base of C and a shorter shoot from much higher on the tree. E. Subsequent normal growth and appearance of the originally damaged trees.

shoots (Fig. 10–14A–C). Unlike the normal behavior, which decrees that the most vigorous shoot is nearest the apex, the graded activity was, in 1941, reversed so that the longest sucker shoots were at the base of the tree and the shortest ones nearest the apex (Fig. 10–14D). But the disoriented, liberated controls of the tree and of the cambium were eventually restored. Thus these otherwise freed cells and growing centers, which had developed independently in 1941, became resubjected to the normal integrated controls of the trees. Progressively from 1942, these otherwise affected trees re-assumed a normal pattern of behavior that is visible to this day (Fig. 10–14E). Hence, the responses of essentially totipotent cells of trees, as of the carrot plant, are restrained and controlled by the factors that operate *in situ* to produce the orderly integrated development of the plant body; when these controls are disrupted, each living cell may potentially behave as an independent unit. Often and by still other means, e.g. the indiscriminate use of growth substances, embryo-like forms (i.e. adventive embryos) may appear almost anywhere along the surface of some shoots. This was observed in this laboratory by Kent (1965) in carrot plantlets still growing under the influence of the growth-promoting stimulus of coconut milk, and somewhat similar structures, described as "neomorphs," have been reported by Waris (1959, 1962).

Similarly, in the apices of shoots and roots, initiating cells and cell aggregates behave within the organized growing region as initials and primordia, and function as units termed morphogenetic fields. In fact the differences between the plant growing regions are more implicit in their organization than in any innate characteristics of their growing cells. One can also recognize in the flow of stimuli from organs of perception, as of root and shoot tips, to regions of response, a basis for the control of activity and behavior that correlates and integrates the separate living units of higher plants. However, cells are still the ultimate units of structure through which growth and development are to be interpreted. The differences in their behavior which growth, differentiation, and morphogenesis require are superimposed upon, and concerned with, responses in the cytoplasm, and it is here, as well as in the consequences of protoplasmic contact via plasmodesmata, that one should look for the controlling mechanisms.

Chapters 4 and 5 have furnished ample evidence that there are chemical factors that both stimulate and suppress the division and enlargement of cells and, when neither of these aspects of growth continues, there are innumerable ways in which the form and metabolism of cells may be modified in response to their position and final role in the plant body. However, one cannot yet specify precisely the location and mode of action of the basic stimuli to growth by cell division and by cell enlargement, nor understand how these stimuli work together with the cytoplasmic apparatus which, in the plant protoplast, controls the destinies of cells, i.e., modulates and regulates the expression of their innate genetic constitution. Until this can be done factually, instead of by surmise, the philosophical concepts of a multicellular organism composed of agents, subjects, a "nexus" of subjects, of morphological or embryological fields, all lack the physical basis to give these terms concrete meaning.

The inescapable biological fact is the essential totipotency of cells in plants which are derived from the zygote by equational division; this totipotency implies the maintained integrity of their nuclei and the fully maintained competence of their cytoplasm. Thus there is need for exogenous agents, over and above the ordinary nutrients, to give effect to all this genetic information, and for the cytoplasmic means to transcribe it by creating an environment in which a totipotent cell can grow and develop. And it is when development proceeds from free cells in a medium fully competent to support their growth and development that the cell aggregate may follow paths similar to that of an embryo. In the development of adventive embryos from free cells, the limitations to the independent action of the derivative cells are all of similar origin (i.e., they are implicit in the differences which develop due to position in the cell mass) to those that cause differentiation and morphogenesis in the growth of zygotic embryos.

But the organism which develops from either a zygote or any other totipotent cell embodies in that cellular organization the following innate characteristics: (a) it is alive and can grow; (b) it has a history, for it has evolved and selectively adapted to its environment; (c) it has an identity which has been determined by a mechanism of hereditary control and which persists throughout its development; (d) it can give rise by differentiation and morphogenesis to the range of forms that its specialized functions require. These characteristics reflect what Stebbins has called Four Basic Questions of Biology (Stebbins, 1964), which he discusses in a masterly analysis under the following headings:

1. The nature of life.

2. The mechanism of heredity.

3. The mechanism of development.

4. The problem of evolution.

The salient features of organization to which Stebbins refers are evident from the following passages extracted from his paper, or merely paraphrased, because they are so applicable to the trend of this discussion.

Growth and Development:
Some Basic Biological Concepts (After Stebbins)

The basic property of life is organization but no simple property, present in all living things, distinguishes them from non-living systems. Life results from integration of various properties which at the individual level are principally replication of specific substances and response to stimuli. At the level of the population the most significant property is its ability to generate unprecedented systems of variability.

Heredity, based on the DNA-RNA-protein system, constitutes a single functioning unit even though its constituent elements are *separately functionless.*

Modern research on cell and culture methods is beginning to elucidate the nature of the alterations in the physicochemical conditions of cells which determine development without basic changes in their heredity.

The translation of the physicochemical differences to morphogenetic behavior is via four processes:

1. Differential rates of cell division and cell enlargement.

2. Orientation of the mitotic spindle by cell shape, cell growth, and cytoplasmic structure.

3. Intracellular mitoses across the gradient so produced.

4. Intercellular induction of mitoses.

(Parenthetically, one may note that points 1 and 2 outrank 3 and 4, for 4 modifies 1 and 3 underlies 2.)

All known *independent* living systems are based upon the three-fold interaction between DNA, RNA, and protein mediated by the activity of compounds containing high energy phosphate bonds.

The most remarkable feature about the organization of life (recently understood) is the code pattern on which it is based, i.e., a few kinds of units arranged into a linear sequence of order like letters of a word and words of a sentence—with the chemical relations between the basic substances (DNA, RNA, protein) depending upon specific correspondence between order sequences.

At all levels of organization the complexity of living organisms consists of a relatively small number of different kinds of elements arranged in an infinite number of ways or combinations— this confers properties not inherent in the elements themselves. It is a basic property of life that the whole is always greater than the sum of its parts.

One cannot understand the whole of life by studying a few simple organisms. One cannot understand the make-up or functioning of a complex animal or plant *solely* by tearing it apart and by analyzing its separate components.

The glamor surrounding the success of analytical studies of the biochemistry should not blind us to the fact that there are higher levels of organization which must be fully analyzed also before we understand larger animals and plants. At higher levels of organization differences may be more important than similarities.

It is a salient property of life to evolve new systems of complexity which would be entirely unpredictable on the basis of even a full knowledge of the systems of a lower order which preceded them. This point is illustrated by the system of cellular organelles, which evolved with "eukaryote," or truly nucleated, cells, which exists in the cells of all organisms other than viruses, bacteria, and blue-green algae. This system, in which each of the basic functions is carried out in a different compartment set apart by an elaborate system of membranes, contrasts with that of the "prokaryota" (i.e., bacteria, viruses, and blue-green algae) in which the intracellular membranes do not divide the cell into compartments so that its functions are performed in the same general medium. Thus the functions of the organelles of "eukaryote" are therefore more comparable to the entire cells of a bacterium or a blue-green alga. In bacteria the naked strands of DNA are about 25 A and they consist also of DNA bound into a complex with RNA, histone, protein, and protamine. Thus despite the diversity of blue-green algae *none* have evolved a system of progressive cellular differentiation. Therefore a system of membranes, organelles, and more complex chromosomal arrangements is seen to have been necessary for the evolution of multi-cellular organisms with well-developed cellular differentiation (i.e., to be externally more differ-entiated and complex, cells have also to be internally more complicated).

The regulation of gene action in plants occurs at four different levels: (a) by the genes them-selves (b) by the histone envelope of the chromosomes, (c) by the nucleolus, (d) by the cytoplasm.

The existence of a two-phase regulator system which acts simultaneously at the level of the cytoplasm and of the gene itself is exemplified by the "operator-regulator" system discovered by Jacob and Monod in 1961 in *E. coli*. The close similarity between this and the one worked out by McClintock (1961) in maize suggests this may be the most widespread system of gene regulation.

In two systems (Allfrey, Littau, and Mirsky, 1963, working on isolated calf thymus nuclei; and Huang and Bonner, 1962, on isolated pea nuclei) it has been shown that removal of the histone layer which lightly envelopes most of the DNA molecules in the eukaryote nucleus results in a many-fold increase in RNA synthesis which is the most direct measure of gene action.

From the fact that nuclei pass through a regular succession of states during a mitotic cycle and change their size and form in connection with the differentiation of various tissues, it is suggested that alterations of their synthetic activity and hence of gene-controlled RNA and protein synthesis exist.

The regulation of gene activity in the cytoplasm follows from fungi in which genes located in *different nuclei* of a dikaryon can interact in the same way as if they were in the *same* nucleus.

But why have organisms evolved such different means of regulating gene action? Some of the regulatory means in higher organisms may have resulted from their increased complexity, for to regulate this complexity different means became necessary. Whereas the control systems in genes and cytoplasm may be universal, those associated with histones and nucleolar regulation may be confined to eukaryotic organisms.

In higher plants adjacent cells of the same organ often have different metabolism rates or perform some particular function to an excessive or exclusive degree (many examples of this come to mind). Stebbins relates this to possible inhibition and activation of ATP synthesis and the general properties of a histone regulating system which could control different rates of metabolism in different cells.

Development is seen as the most important unsolved biological problem. How do cells with like genetics become such different entities? Stebbins cites examples of plants having been reared from cells; therefore, in the course of the development of the latter their genetics had not changed. He also shows that the $n/2n$ constitution is not now regarded as causally connected with gameto-phyte and sporophyte as formerly thought. The alternation of $m/2n$ nuclei and the form of gametophyte and sporophyte has evolved as expressing a genic combination adaptive to the particular environment and the developmental cycle concerned. Similarly the manifold increase of chromosome number and the polytene multiplication of chromosomal strands, which is charac-teristic of many differentiated cells and tissues (Tschermak-Woess, 1956; Sinnott, 1960), is not causally related to the differentiation but is part of the adaptation of these cells to their function (e.g., secretion!).

Cells with constant genetic constitution, of lower plants, are responsive to environment, etc., during growth and to nutrition; callus cultures of higher plants are more limited in their vari-ability. On the contrary the enucleated part of *Acetabularia* reacts to such substances as mer-captothioethanol etc.

What then, since genes are constant, are the internal states that determine cellular behavior? That this type of action results from the position of the cells in the organism seems clear from the work described in this book, some of which Stebbins cites. But what is the nature of the restricting forces which operate upon cells in a tissue? Here Stebbins cites:

a)   Feedback repression, as in bacteria, i.e., a mechanism by which an enzyme stops working because of the accumulation of the metabolites it produces.

b)   Enzyme induction—by which an enzyme is turned on by substances in the environment.

The hypothesis that the chemical basis of development lies in an orderly series of enzyme reactions mediated by precisely controlled feedback inhibitions and inductions has been developed in one form or another by several biologists and is referred to by Stebbins. That complex organic substances from outside cells can divert them into orderly sequences of development is known (e.g., the effects of certain galls, etc.). Therefore more should be learned about IAA, kinetin, gibberellin, etc., by studying their effects on nucleic acids and on proteins.

But Stebbins also asks, how is the chemical code of information, provided by sequences of enzymatic reactions, translated into a morphological code? Here he cites:

1.   The effect of cell elongation and mitotic division on the orientation of growth.
2.   Cytoplasmic differentiation through polarization of cell contents.
3.   Intercellular induction of mitosis.

The above represents an extensive précis from the summary of Stebbins.* It has been made to re-emphasize from another point of view and another author much of what has already been said. Whether one approaches the problems of growth from the standpoint of the organism and its units of structure, or from the standpoint of the cells and organelles which compose it, or the unit processes by which it functions, the essential problems can only be seen and understood in terms of organization. By isolating subcellular organelles and their constituent particles, or the membranes by which they are maintained discrete, or by describing the individual reactions and metabolic processes and seeking to determine their course and causation, one may learn much about how a cell or an organism is constructed. But one does not begin to understand its biology until one can visualize how, in the irreducible unit of cell or protoplast, below which the organism cannot function as such, its characteristics emerge from its coordinated, integrated, behavior as an organization.

Concluding Remarks: Physiology and Genetics

One may conclude therefore on the following note—paraphrased from an earlier paper (Steward, 1961, entitled "Vistas in plant physiology: problems of organization, growth, and morphogenesis") :

Biochemistry and enzymology have gone far to explain the course of metabolism; genetics and molecular biology have gone far to show how the individual characteristics of the organism

---

* G. L. Stebbins, Presidential Address to the Botanical Society of America, 1965.

are determined; knowledge of inorganic and organic nutrition goes far to show how plants are nourished. The outstanding gap in our knowledge of plants that needs to be closed is an adequate understanding of how they grow in terms of the organization of cells and of their growing regions.

Ultimately all the processes of metabolism occur at the level of molecules. The *kinds* of reactions of which the organism is capable are clearly prescribed by its genetic constitution, for they are responses to a genetic message transmitted by small entities which are composed of DNA. The smallest effective unit of DNA may be that which has the minimum size at which the effect of *changes* in it can be discerned. If this is the unit of genetic recombination (recon) or the unit of mutation (muton), to use the terminology of Benzer (1957) and of others, then the effect of one, or only a few, nucleotide base pairs may constitute a decisive enough message to be transcribed in the behavior of cells; a much larger number (of the order of 100 nucleotide pairs) may represent the classical unit of segregation, i.e., the gene (a term which is being replaced by the cistron), as a unit of function.

But metabolic reactions do not proceed in a homogeneous environment, they occur in a highly discrete and particulate and structured protoplasm. In fact the more that is known about the fine structure of cells, the more granular do the cytoplasm and its organelles seem to be. Therefore, what occurs in the different organelles is subject to other controls than the mere presence or absence of an enzyme, i.e., whether or not a given reaction is feasible. This is the difficult area in which cellular organization is all-important and in which the performance of the cell *in toto* is very difficult to stipulate from the behavior, or capability, of its individual parts. Here one needs to invoke, more than is often now done, the idea of the protoplast to suggest adequately the organization which is necessary to account for what a given cell does. The controlling machinery, however, may be epigenetic in the sense that it operates with (but is over and above) the hereditarily determined capacities of the cell, and is subject to a large measure of environmental and nutritional control. When a plant cell responds to the lack of, or the presence of, a given trace element or to a chemically or physically transmitted message from a photoperiodically or thermoperiodically stimulated organ, the ultimate site where the response is elicited may be the location on the DNA of the nucleus which imparts a given reaction to the organism. Thus the stimulus may act by covering or uncovering that site, i.e., by turning the genetic message on or off. In addition, however, to the control over biochemical reactions where they occur within cells, there is the still larger problem of controlling the behavior of cells in the aggregate in the organs in which they grow and develop.

So much of modern genetic work has been done with such simple organisms that morphogenesis is not obtrusive. But this fact should not be allowed to obscure the problem. Having evolved rather rigid means to transmit likenesses of biochemical behavior from cell to cell and from generation to generation, the price that has now to be paid for the complexity and "division of labor" of higher plants is the restriction and control over these otherwise genetically determined potentialities. In fact the next great advances must surely lead to much better understanding of these varied controls, to show how they are exerted and intervene during growth and differentiation and how they prescribe that many otherwise totipotent living cells shall do only what they do in the organs and tissues where they are. Genetics as such has little to say about the processes of growth and development; genetics may tell us why a particular tobacco plant has sectored areas in its flowers, but not why it has a flower or why a given leafy organ makes a carpel nor, in fact, why the plant is a tobacco plant in the first place!

The determination of such events needs a partnership between the nuclear DNA, upon which the genetic code is imprinted, and the cytoplasm without which the genetic code cannot be transcribed into meaningful biological language. One may here quote an aphorism which relates to the information theory that may underlie this biological language; this is to the effect that "whereas the words become the playthings of biochemists, the sentences remain always within the domain of the morphologist!" (For discussions on these lines see Waddington, 1957 and 1962.) But the complex organization without which such phenomena as growth and morphogenesis cannot be conceived is also the result of all the selective advantages and adjustments that have occurred through evolution and which have been preserved and maintained through hereditary control. It is appropriate, therefore, to conclude with an account of what a geneticist has to say on the problems of organization.

Mather presented to the International Botanical Congress at Edinburgh in 1964 a reasoned analysis of the problems of organization and discussed their genetical basis and determination. On the one hand, Mather stressed that organizations emerge through their selective advantage in evolution and that they are preserved by hereditary control. However, within the constancy so achieved, there is "built in" the flexibility demanded by differentiation and morphogenesis. To the constancy regulated by the nucleus is added a flexibility controlled by the cytoplasm. The following series of quotations from Mather's manuscript* summarizes the argument.

Physiology is concerned with the processes and the interrelations of the processes by which an organism develops and lives. Genetics on the other hand seeks to understand the determinants and determination of these processes . . .

Form and function can never, of course, be separated in any final sense. Nor ultimately can genetics and physiology: they are complementary in their aims, their approaches and their results. . . .

At the deepest level of organization within the cell, that of the gene and the active product for whose presence it is responsible, there must exist a simple and direct relation between the

---

* Kindly made available to the author and quoted by permission.

determinant and the determined. A given amino acid must stem from one characteristic nucleotide sequence. . . . But as we proceed up the ladder of organization, from nucleus and organelle, to cell, to tissue, organ, individual, and population, this simple correspondence is lost. The same structure or end may be achieved in a variety of ways and similar systems of determination may operate through quite different physiological pathways. . . .

The end is more important than the means, for it is by the end result that the system is judged in the court of natural selection. This is the final test of organization at any level. . . .

Equally, organization may be expected to break down when it no longer confers a selective advantage, whether because of the progress of development of the individual or of the transfer to an unfamiliar environment. . . .

It is obvious that the determinants of organization must be hereditary. . . .   So far as our evidence goes, these hereditary determinants are in the main nuclear genes. . . .

The role of the cytoplasm in fungi has been made clear by the work especially of Jinks and his associates [Jinks, 1963]. In *Aspergillus* species the cytoplasm has been shown to change characteristically during differentiation. . . .

Perhaps the most significant of all for our present consideration, the sexual cycle has been shown to involve a process of restandardization of the cytoplasm during which the cytoplasmic variants are eliminated and the cytoplasm brought back to a state which permits the development of a new colony or clone of the characteristic type to be initiated. . . .

The budding of new cytoplasmic organelles from the nucleus, such as has been described in ferns by Bell [Bell and Mühlethaler, 1964] might well be implicated in such changes. . . .

[However,] restandardization is achieved, at least in part, by cell selection within the colony . . . only those with a suitable cytoplasm initiating the development of sexual organs. Such cell selection might be expected in a fungus where the hyphae must be in a considerable measure independent of one another in their metabolism and development. . . . In higher plants, and even more so in animals, with their more complex and lightly knit somata, variation of this kind would be less tolerable. . . .

The cytoplasm [in fungi] is less a slave and more of a partner [than in higher organisms]. . . .

It is thus a general principle that organization exists at any of the levels we see in living things, only so far as selective advantage has depended on it and only to an extent sufficient to secure that advantage. . . .

The advantage of an organized system must lie in its ability to discharge the functions required of it and to meet the demands made on it, more adequately than could the entities of which it is composed were they acting as individuals in an unorganized way. This may require no more than an aggregation of like entities discharging the same functions but doing so simultaneously as a group. . . . Such is the case where neurons are aggregated into a ganglion, or muscle cells into a muscle, or palisade cells into a photosynthetic tissue. . . .

Such a colonial system, as we may term it, is organization at its simplest. The full advantages of organization are not reaped until the division of labor is among unlike, but mutually adjusted, entities each playing a special and limited role as an individual. . . .

In other words organization at its most effective necessarily involves differentiation. Now for differently specialized entities to cooperate efficiently, close limits must be set to competition between them . . . or, to put it the other way about, selective advantage at the higher level requires control of the selective situation at the lower. . . .

Every level of organization depends on control at the level below it, the population on the individual, the individual on the organ and the cell, the cell on its cytoplasmic elements and its nuclear genes. . . .

The unicellular organisms can afford to depend on directly reproducing determinants, such as kinetosomes outside the nucleus and therefore not closely coordinated with it in reproduction, for if the coordination fails only the single individual fails with it. . . .

We are thus led to the apparently paradoxical situation that greater change in development requires more rigorously controlled constancy in ultimate determination. The translation of the one into the other is the genetical problem of differentiation and morphogenesis. Its solution depends on the relationship of constant nucleus and changing cytoplasm, the changes of the cytoplasm springing from the action of the nucleus and in their turn affecting the outcome of that action. . . .

True, the differences in behavior between sister cells, to which differentiation of cell lineage must be traced, must themselves spring from differences within the cytoplasm of the parent cell. But these must be controlled differences springing from gradients initiated by the nucleus or *from characteristic differences in spatial relations of the cell to other cells* or to maternal tissues, or from determinatively acting forces of this kind.

Finally, one can sense from two recent summaries the bearing of current molecular biology upon problems of growth and development. The one by Watson (1965) presents a succinct detailed account of the facts approached from the standpoint of genetics. Nevertheless, and in the outcome, Watson is reluctant (1965, p. 438) to claim that those who study proteins and their synthesis *in vitro* have yet made a definitive interpretation of differentiation and morphogenesis. This is shown by the following quotation:

Virtually nothing is known about the molecular basis of the control of protein synthesis in the multicellular higher organisms. In particular little information exists as to mechanisms that bring about cell differentiation. Once a cell has become differentiated, all its descendants produce a specific group of unique proteins. There are hints that this selective protein synthesis, like that of microbial cells, is sometimes based on the selective synthesis of unique types of RNA. Thus differentiated cells must have mechanisms that control the rate at which specific DNA regions are read. A major difficulty that now hinders basic understanding is our current inability to study differentiation outside an intact organism. Though embryonic differentiation can be made to occur in tissue culture, it has not yet been possible to isolate the specific external factors that normally induce a cell to differentiate in a given direction.

Medvedev (1966) is also fully cognizant of the contributions of biochemistry and applies them to a range of biological systems, but, in doing so, he recognizes some of the present problems. For example, Medvedev admits, as is rarely done, that, despite all the assurances that DNA-RNA-mediated protein synthesis is the very basis of molecular biology, no one has yet made in a cell-free system a recognizable protein, with enzyme or other properties, or has "stripped off" a synthesizing template a product in which the amino acids were peptide bonded in a postulated linear array (1966, pp. 204, 248; cf. also the abstract of a paper by Steward, Holsten, and Krikorian, 1965). In fact, when "protein" is held to be measured by C^{14}, that is, incorporated in TCA precipitates, one has to remember that "all is not gold that glitters," for there is much binding of

C^{14}-amino acids that may pass for peptide bond formation. Medvedev is also to be commended for his recognition that all plant protein synthesis may not necessarily go via the postulated DNA-sRNA-mRNA template sequences. Plants are held to be endowed with a rigorous gene-determined mechanism for amino acid sequence, but also with the ability to put together, in different ways, the substantial fragments so made and thus enable the synthesis of different proteins as in roots, cotyledons, tubers, etc. The role of single- and double-stranded DNA is also discussed from the point of view that only one helix of double-stranded DNA contains the genetic information while the other is "blocked out" by combination with protein. Even more so than Watson, Medvedev ingeniously attempts to carry out the molecular biological interpretation of development, but in the outcome this is far from complete (1966, pp. 438–464).

Obviously, therefore, molecular biology has still a long way to go before it fully explains how any vital function really works, for example, how and why cell division, growth, differentiation, and morphogenesis occur. Biochemical work *in vitro* tells us descriptively what chemical resources cells have available in their molecules and the reactions they perform. Nevertheless, there is much more that needs to be known about the internal organization of cells, for this exploits these resources and turns the merely feasible into a smoothly operating, programmed, predictable, reproducible, but highly improbable system which obligates space and progresses through time as it grows.

Summary

In this concluding chapter an attempt is made to clothe the morphological and physiological concept of the "built-in capacity to grow" in the zygote with more meaning. Although the capacity to grow and develop is inherent in each diploid cell, it cannot be fully expressed in cells which form part of a tissue mass for they are then limited by their immediate environment. The loss of, or failure to express, the full totipotency of its constituent cells is the price paid for the complexity and "division of labor" of the higher plant body. When these controls are disrupted, or neutralized by the various means described, the individual cells may behave and grow as independent units, even recapitulating normal embryogeny and development. Philosophical organismal concepts and the relation of the whole to its several parts are therefore commented upon. These useful concepts, however, lack physical basis until one can locate in the cytoplasm the site, and also specify the mode of action, of those chemical, non-nutrient stimuli which govern the behavior of otherwise totipotent cells in their immediate environment in the plant body.

The concept of the capacity to grow is examined with respect to the increase of organization which occurs at fertilization, which is homologized with a decrease of entropy in a system which has thereby acquired a greater degree of improbability. Since entropy $= K \log (1/W)$, the negative logarithm of W could describe on an arithmetical scale (analogous to a pH scale for acidity) the morphogenetic propensity, which is high in the zygote and eventually declines to zero at senescence and death. How to measure this property of cells in their different states is difficult to say, but it is possible to visualize that these numbers might represent the number of effective sites or templates that are effectuated at fertilization, which are needed to determine a complete organism, which are replicated at each mitosis, but which are, as it were, "turned off and on" or "masked and unmasked" as development proceeds. The techniques of culturing free cells are still too new to make this a basis for measuring the frequency with which cells from different parts of the plant body form embryos and complete plants, but, in this or some other way, there is need to assign an arithmetical measure to the morphogenetic propensity of cells. These ideas are discussed against the background of current speculations on thermodynamics and life, of speculations on the origin of life and of the distinctions between the "quick and the dead"; the organization recognizable as life must fulfill an essential requirement to create order out of disorder and have the essential limitation that to persist it must replicate.

However, this chapter, which opened on a frankly speculative note, turns to a very factual one, for it sets out the evidence which shows that free cells of the carrot and other plants, especially those obtained from young embryos, can regenerate plants in very large numbers and in so doing they recapitulate embryogeny. This emphasizes the maintained genetic integrity of the nucleus throughout development and the maintained ability of plant cytoplasm to transcribe the information from the nucleus. What is now needed is a more intimate interpretation of the way flowering plants grow and develop which is more closely related to the organization of their cells and of their growing regions. To do this, we must know what determines the use a given cell makes of its inherent genetic information. Cells which have the same genes may be caused to do very different things during development as the genes are, as it were, turned "off and on." Ideas on the means by which this is achieved with respect to single substances (proteins) are discussed. However, it is a question how far such events describe or explain development and how far they are its consequences. This is the crux of the problem of differentiation and morphogenetic development. The extent to which explanations of morphogenesis have been sought in terms of molecular biology is touched upon.

The next great advances will surely require a much closer understanding of organization at all levels; at the level of fine structure, at the cellular level, and at the level of the plant growing regions. All this may be expected to involve much greater stress on the non-nuclear cytoplasmic machinery without which the genetic code cannot be transcribed. In short, the concept of the protoplast regains its earlier usefulness, for it can comprehend a cell's nucleus in contact with, and reacting to, a cytoplasmic organization that responds to the many small molecules which mediate the effects of environment, etc., during development. In conclusion, mention is made of the sort of views that are being formulated by geneticists as they contemplate the problems of organization. This constitutes that common ground from which, in partnership with cellular physiology and biochemistry, the causal explanations of growth, development, and morphogenesis will no doubt emerge.

EPILOGUE

In these chapters or essays many problems of growth and metabolism have been passed in incomplete review. Though much can be, and has been, said about growth, its ultimate interpretation cannot yet be made in any all-embracing aphorism or formula. Physicists may aspire to a comprehensive expression which embraces the salient properties of energy and matter, but no such goal is yet in sight for those who ask: How and why do plants grow? The properties of growth and development still distinguish "the quick from the dead."

The problem was approached with trepidation and, in the words of Albert Schweitzer, a certain "reverence for life." Despite all that has been accomplished in the understanding of the machinery of stimuli and response, of nurture and of metabolism, of the hereditary nature and development of plants as organisms, this spirit of reverence remains. Each advance in knowledge uncovers even greater complexity that should be interpreted.

The great advances of modern physics have been accomplished by investigating systems that are essentially simple—the lighter atoms with their nuclei and electrons in orbit; and even with the present baffling range of subatomic particles, it is still possible to conceive of the material universe as composed of relatively few entities whose properties and relations need to be understood. However, biology cannot yet be reduced to such simple terms. Although the science of genetics has probably gone farther than any other branch of biology in the attempt to explain in particulate and molecular terms the phenomena with which it is concerned, even in genetics this approach goes but part of the way. One may now see how the coded messages that blueprint what an organism will grow to be are impressed upon the DNA of the fertilized egg, but these messages are no more an explanation of how the organism grows and develops than is the blueprint of a skyscraper building or the landscape design of a great city an explanation of how these complex organizations came about. It is interesting to understand the commands that issue from the bridge to steer the ship, but these are not enough, if one aspires to know how an ocean liner really works and drives its way across the seas. An organism, like a liner, makes a journey, irreversibly, through time and space. A "built-in" drive to grow propels the

511

organism along its way, takes the inanimate stuff of which organisms are made and, within the overall design, creates the organized whole out of the disorderly, random substance of the environment. Neither genetics nor physiology has yet remotely explained these ultimate problems of growth and development, which are problems not of molecules but of organization. In a popular catchword it has become fashionable to speak of "molecular biology." Despite the laudable modern preoccupation with phenomena at the sub-cellular level, the term molecular biology nevertheless implies a confusion of thought. The properties of chemical substances may be interpreted at the molecular level, and the chemical reactions in cells likewise proceed at the molecular level. But the essential characteristics of biological systems occur through organization which is more complex than that of molecules.

It is permissible now to look forward, as well as backward, and to ask, What are some of the problems of plant growth and development that one would still like to see solved? And what kind of people should be trained for their solution?

In retrospect, some such problems are the following:

1) What is the essential difference between the living cell that can grow and that which cannot? What essential contribution is made by the fusion of gametes that causes the zygote to grow, whereas the gametes do so only rarely? How may the different morphogenetic propensities of different cells be measured and expressed in quantitative terms?

2) Can the fertilized eggs of angiosperms, already endowed with all it requires to control the course of development, be made to grow outside the ovule by the aid of known and specified nutrients and growth factors? Paradoxically it is now perhaps easier to restore some adult parenchyma cells, as of carrot and other plants, to the embryonic state than it is to isolate and grow true zygotes!

3) Can the essential differences between the shoot and root meristem cells be explained? How far are these differences the consequence of differences of position and environment in the existing organization of the plant body? Is not much of what the cells do determined not by *what* they are but *where* they are and, if so, how is this control expressed in chemical and physical terms?

4) Why are some cells endowed with the ability to transmit the capacity for growth and division almost in perpetuity, whereas others quickly lose this feature, even though they remain alive for long periods? What determines the working of the vascular cambium, which in a sequoia tree may recapitulate the same events now as it did three to four thousand years ago? Why is no such continuity evident in the procambial strand of monocotyledonous plants? Perhaps the vascular cambium as it occurs in a tree may come as close to eternal life as any plant structure we know, but what then is the feature that distinguishes it from many adjacent parenchyma, which irreversibly lose their capacity

to grow even as they differentiate? Why do some pericyclic cells grow and develop to form lateral roots, whereas in other plants (e.g., *Hyacinth, Narcissus*) the essentially similar cells never do this? These great questions lead naturally to the causation of abnormal or neoplastic growth, when normally mature cells virtually run amok and return to the persistent randomly growing state as in cancerous tissue. A start, but only a start, has certainly been made in the interpretation of the latter condition in plants on a biochemical basis in terms of the interactions between the regulatory substances that control cell division and/or cell enlargement, on the one hand, and the substances that act as their inhibitors, on the other. But there is still a long way to go. All this bears closely on current problems of aging, senescence, and death.

5) Granted cells with the overall ability to grow, the power to develop and to pass through the recurring phases of the life cycle, how can their growth, metabolism and development be maintained under regulatory control? Through the artificial control of photoperiodism, vernalization, and thermoperiodism, a measure of independence of the recurring seasons has already been achieved, so that seed time and harvest may, in some cases, be independent of the calendar. But can an ultimate chemical or physical control over the growth of higher plants be achieved and extended to embrace the phenomena of rest and dormancy in buds, the control of flowering and fruiting, as, for example, the alternate bearing of fruit trees, or the initiation at will of tubers and other storage organs, all with their specialized constituents, etc., etc?

6) At the sub-cellular level, the problem of carbohydrate synthesis is well on its way to solution. Emil Fisher's expressed ambition to make a lump of sugar can now be regarded as attainable though not without enzymes that only cells produce. But the growth of an organized cell wall still presents problems which are not yet solved, even in an age in which synthetic fibers and fabrics have become commonplace. But perhaps the greatest biochemical synthesis, readily performed in living plant cells, that still awaits solution is the synthesis of protein from inorganic nitrogen: this must eventually be comprehended in ways which show, not only how molecules of this order of complexity are reproducibly made, but also how their astonishing diversity and specificity is controlled. While great strides have recently been made to show how the genetic code is translated into protein structure it is still true to say that organized plant cells are the agents without which the vast bulk of primary protein synthesis in nature would not occur. The contribution made by this cellular organization still needs to be understood.

7) How does the organism take the solutes from its milieu and absorb these into its own body fluids and, in doing so, expend metabolic energy? How does this form part of the whole process of growth and development? While it is a partial explanation to see this accumulation of solutes as a process that requires

the expenditure of energy derived from respiration, the process still owes its initial impetus to the organism's innate capacity to grow. A full explanation of how plants absorb ions may well extend to an interpretation of how they grow. Even so, what sort of message passes from the shoot to induce the cells of the root to release their accumulated solutes? And how is the bafflingly rapid movement of organic solutes related to the cellular organization in which it occurs?

8) Once energy is released from compounds in which it is stored, how is it actually applied to the processes (synthetic or osmotic) in which useful work is done and the free energy of the system thereby increased? The various organic phosphorus compounds which can donate energy along with transphosphorylations tell us much about how the energy transactions are negotiated. They represent the "energy coinage" as in a financial transaction, and just as a flow of money (accumulated credit at one point and purchasing power at another) keeps the wheels of industry turning, so the phosphorylations and dephosphorylations keep the cellular machinery in motion. But these effects tell us only how the energy *transfers* are made and there is still much to learn about how energy is actually applied to achieve a given synthesis, or non-osmotic flow of water, or a movement of ions against a diffusion gradient, or even to do mechanical work (as in the streaming of protoplasm).

The solution of these and other great problems now requires the combined efforts and techniques of biophysicists, biochemists, and the students of plant behavior who understand the morphological setting in which the phenomena in question work. Perhaps as at no other period in science these goals are attainable, for modern instrumentation, technology, and analytical procedures permit work to be done and interpretations to be made at the submicroscopic and the molecular, or near-molecular, level.

But science is not advanced by instruments alone, but by people; people who even in this era of 8-hour days and 40-hour weeks should *live* and not merely *do* their work. Although science has become a complicated profession, instead of an avocation, the interpretation of plants still requires the dedicated spirit of inquiry which motivated the great pioneers like Stephen Hales, Joseph Priestley, de Saussure, Nageli, Hoffmeister and Pfeffer, Schulze, de Vries, and F. F. Blackman, to name but a few in a long and honorable progression. It is part of the responsibility and privilege of the teacher to hand on to those who will follow something of the pride and dignity which the search for biological truth inspires, in order that, here and there, another may be aroused to add his name to the long and distinguished succession. Indeed, this series of discussions was first addressed to those appointed to this task as teachers.

Truth may be expressed in numerous ways. To some, truth appears when succinctly expressed in mathematical equations and generalizations. To a chemist it may best be comprehended through the reactions and properties of particular molecules; to a physicist it may be all a matter of energy and of particles. Biological truth inevitably involves all of these, and more, for there is also the problem of biological organization, the incredibly beautiful way in which complex systems have been elaborated to do in a specific way what often seem to be simple jobs. How much of life is organized between the splitting of hydrogen from water, its use as a reductant, and its eventual release to combine again with oxygen to form water and, alternatively, between the reduction of carbon dioxide and the eventual return of the carbon by oxidation to carbon dioxide? But how long will it be before science can describe all that lies between these chemically comprehensible events?

Inevitably some philosophical questions arise. Is the whole indeed more than the summation of its parts? How does the organization that can grow super-impose the properties recognized as life upon the inanimate molecules from its environment? These and others can more easily be posed than answered. But where the man of science must approach the mystery of life step by step— with the limited techniques at his disposal—the poet, unfettered by the need to test and retest at each step of the way, can express by his words the essentials of truth. Tennyson did this in a few simple but familiar lines, which fittingly con-clude these essays on the problems of plant growth, plant metabolism, plant structure, and plant development:

> Flower in the crannied wall,
> I pluck you out of the crannies,
> I hold you here, root and all, in my hand,
> Little flower—but *if* I could understand
> What you are, root and all, and all in all,
> I should know what God and man is.

BIBLIOGRAPHY

ADAM, F. (1966), Die vaterlosen Frösche von Genf. *Die Weltwoche* (Sept. 30) No. 1716, 31 (Ch 10)

ADDICOTT, F. T., CARNS, H. R., LYN, J. L., SMITH, O. E., and McMEANS, J. L. (1964), On the physiology of abscissins. pp. 687–703. In J. P. Nitsch (ed.), *Régulateurs Naturels de la Croissance Végétale.* Centre National de la Recherche Scientifique, Paris (Ch 4)

AGAR, W. E. (1951), *A Contribution to the Theory of Living Organisms.* 2nd edition. pp. 235. Melbourne University Press, Carlton, Victoria (Ch 10)

ALLFREY, V. G., LITTAU, V. C. and MIRSKY, A. E. (1963), On the role of histones in regulating ribonucleic acid synthesis in the cell nucleus. *Proc. Natl. Acad. Sci. U.S.* 49, 414–421 (Ch 10)

ARDITTI, J. (1966), Orchids. *Sci. American* 214 (No. 1), 70–78 (Ch 2)

ASHBY, E. (1949), Hybrid vigour in plants. *Mem. Proc. Manchester Lit. & Phil. Soc.* 91, 1–18 (Ch 2)

ASHBY, E. and OXLEY, T. A. (1935), The interaction of factors in the growth of *Lemna.* VI. An analysis of the influence of light intensity and temperature on the assimilation rate and the rate of frond multiplication. *Ann. Botany* 49, 309–336 (Ch 9)

ASKENASY, E. (1896a), Über das Saftsteigen. *Verhandl. naturhist. med. Ver.* (Heidelberg) N.S. 5, 325–345 (Ch 6)

ASKENASY, E. (1896b), Beiträge zur Erklärung des Saftsteigens. *Verhandl. naturhist. med. Ver.* (Heidelberg) N.S. 5, 429–448 (Ch 6)

AVERY, G. S., JR. (1930), Comparative anatomy and morphology of embryos and seedlings of maize, oats, and wheat. *Botan. Gaz.* 89, 1–39 (Ch 2)

AVERY, G. S., JR. (1933), Structure and development of the tobacco leaf. *Am. J. Botany* 20, 565–592 (Ch 9)

AVERY, G. S., JR., BURKHOLDER, P. R., and CREIGHTON, H. B. (1937), Production and distribution of growth hormone in shoots of *Aesculus* and *Malus* and its probable role in stimulating cambial activity. *Am. J. Botany* 24, 51–58 (Ch 7)

BAILEY, I. W. (1919), Phenomena of cell division in the cambium of arborescent gymnosperms and their cytological significance. *Proc. Natl. Acad. Sci. U.S.* 5, 283–285 (Ch 5)

517

BAILEY, L. H. (1891), Some preliminary studies of the influence of the electric arc light upon greenhouse plants. *Cornell Univ. Agr. Expt. Sta. Bull.* No. 30, 83–122 (Ch 7)

BAILEY, L. H. (1892), Second report on electro-horticulture. *Cornell Univ. Agr. Expt. Sta. Bull.* No. 42, 133–146 (Ch 7)

BAKER, J. J. W. and ALLEN, G. E. (1965), *Matter, Energy, and Life.* pp. 180. Addison-Wesley Publishing Co., Inc., Reading, Mass. (Ch 2, 5)

BALL, E. (1948), Differentiation in the primary shoots of *Lupinus albus* and of *Tropaeolum majus. Symposia Soc. Exptl. Biol.* **2**, 246–262 (Ch 8)

BALL, E. (1960), Sterile culture of the shoot apex of *Lupinus albus. Growth* **24**, 91–110 (Ch 5)

BALL, E. (1963), Studies of living shoot apices. pp. 47–77. In J. C. O'Kelley (ed.), *Plant Tissue Culture and Morphogenesis.* Scholars' Library, New York (Ch 9)

BALL, E. and JOHRI, P. C. (1965), Observations on individual callus cells of *Nicotiana tabacum* in liquid culture. *Botan. Gaz.* **126**, 233–246 (Ch 9)

BALLS, W. L. (1912), *The Cotton Plant in Egypt. Studies in Physiology and Genetics.* pp. 202. Macmillan, London (Ch 7)

BARBER, J. T. and STEWARD, F. C. (1968), The proteins of *Tulipa* and their relation to morphogenesis. *Devl. Biol.* **17**, in press (Ch 8)

BARKER, G. A. and HASSID, W. Z. (1965), Synthesis of cellulose by enzyme preparations from developing cotton boll. *Nature* **207**, 295–296 (Ch 3)

BARKER, J. (1933), Analytical studies in plant respiration. IV. and V. The relation of the respiration of potatoes to the concentration of sugars and to the accumulation of a depressant at low temperature. *Proc. Roy. Soc.* (London) *B.* **112**, 316–358 (Ch 6)

BARKER, W. G. (1953), Proliferative capacity of the medullary sheath region in the stem of *Tilia americana. Am. J. Botany* **40**, 773–778 (Ch 10)

BARKER, W. G. and STEWARD, F. C. (1962a), Growth and development of the banana plant. I. The growing regions of the vegetative shoot. *Ann. Botany* N. S. **26**; 389–411 (Ch 7, 8)

BARKER, W. G. and STEWARD, F. C. (1962b), Growth and development of the banana plant. II. The transition from the vegetative to the floral shoot in *Musa acuminata* cv. Gros Michel. *Ann. Botany* N. S. **26**, 413–424 (Ch 8)

BARR, R. A. (1963), The nitrogen compounds of the banana plant: a comprehensive study. pp. 285. Ph.D. thesis, Cornell University (Ch 8)

BAYLISS, W. M. and STARLING, E. H. (1904), The chemical regulation of the secretory process. *Proc. Roy. Soc.* (London) **73**, 310–322 (Ch 3)

BEEVERS, H. (1961), *Respiratory Metabolism in Plants.* pp. 232. Row, Peterson and Co., Evanston, Illinois (Ch 6)

BEEVERS, H., STILLER, M. L., and BUTT, V. S. (1966), Metabolism of the organic acids. pp. 119–262. In F. C. Steward (ed.), *Plant Physiology, A Treatise.* Vol. IVB. Academic Press, New York (Ch 6)

BELL, P. R. and MÜHLETHALER, K. (1964), The degeneration and reappearance of mitochondria in the egg cells of a plant. *J. Cell Biol.* **20**, 235–248 (Ch 10)

BENNET-CLARK, T. A. (1956), Salt accumulation and mode of action of auxin. A preliminary hypothesis. pp. 284–291. In R. L. Wain and F. Wightman (eds.), *The Chemistry and Mode of Action of Plant Growth Substances.* Academic Press, New York (Ch 4)

BENNET-CLARK, T. A. and BEXON, D. (1939), Expression of vacuolar sap. *Nature* **144**, 243.

BENNET-CLARK, T. A. and BEXON, D. (1940), Water relations of plant cells. II. *New Phytologist* **39**, 337–361 (Ch 6)

BENNET-CLARK, T. A. and BEXON, D. (1943), Water relations of plant cells. III. The respiration of plasmolysed tissues. *New Phytologist* **42**, 65–92 (Ch 6)

BENTLEY, J. A. (1961), Chemistry of the native auxins. pp. 485–500. In H. Burström (ed.), *Handbuch der Pflanzenphysiologie*, Vol. XIV. Springer-Verlag, Berlin Ch 4)

BENZER, S. (1957), The elementary units of heredity. pp. 70–93. In W. McElroy and B. Glass (eds.), *Symposium on the Chemical Basis of Heredity.* The Johns Hopkins Press, Baltimore (Ch 10)

BERTALANFFY, L. VON (1952), *Problems of Life.* pp. 216. Watts, London (Ch 10)

BERTALANFFY, L. VON (1962), *Modern Theories of Development.* pp. 204. Harper, New York (Ch 10)

BEVERTON, R. J. H. and HOLT, S. J. (1957), *On the Dynamics of Exploited Fish Population.* pp. 533. H. M. Stationery Office, London (Ch 9)

BIDDULPH, O. (1959), Translocation of inorganic solutes. pp. 553–603. In F. C. Steward (ed.), *Plant Physiology, A Treatise.* Vol. II. Academic Press, New York (Ch 6)

BIDDULPH, O. and CORY, R. (1965), Translocation of C^{14} metabolites in the phloem of the bean plant. *Plant Physiol.* **40**, 119–129 (Ch 6)

BIDWELL, R. G. S., BARR, R. A., and STEWARD, F. C. (1964), Protein synthesis and turnover in cultured plant tissue: sources of carbon for synthesis and the fate of the protein breakdown products. *Nature* **203**, 367–373 (Ch 4, 6)

BINDING, VON H. (1964), Regeneration und Verschmelzung nackter Laubmoosprotoplasten. *Z. Naturforsch.* **19b**, 775 (Ch 9)

BIRNER, H. and LUCANAS, B. (1866), Wasserculturversuche mit Hafer. *Landwirtsch. Vers. Sta.* **8**, 128–134 (Ch 2)

BISBY, G. R. (1925), Zonation in cultures of *Fusarium discolor sulphureum.* *Mycologia* **17**, 89–97 (Ch 7)

BLACK, L. M. (1949), Virus tumors. *Survey Biol. Progr.* **1**, 155–231 (Ch 4)

BLACKMAN, F. F. (1905), Optima and limiting factors. *Ann. Botany* **19**, 281–295 (Ch 3)

BLACKMAN, G. E. (1961), Responses to environmental factors by plants in the vegetative phase. pp. 525–556. In M. X. Zarrow (ed.), *Growth in Living Systems.* Basic Books, Inc., New York (Ch 9)

BLACKMAN, V. H. (1919), The compound interest law and plant growth. *Ann. Botany* **33**, 353–360 (Ch 9)

BLAKELY, L. M. (1963), Growth and variation of cultured plant cells. pp. 298. Ph.D. thesis, Cornell University (Ch 10)

BLAKELY, L. M., (1964), Growth and organized development of cultured cells. VI. The behavior of individual cells on nutrient agar. *Am. J. Botany* **51**, 792–807 (Ch 10)

BLAKELY, L. M. and STEWARD, F. C. (1961), Growth induction in cultures of *Haplopappus gracilis:* I. The behavior of the cultured cells. *Am. J. Botany* **48**, 351–358 (Ch 5)

BLAKELY, L. M. and STEWARD, F. C. (1964), Growth and organized development of cultured cells. V. The growth of colonies from free cells on nutrient agar. *Am. J. Botany* **51**,780–791 (Ch 4, 5, 6, 10)

BOEGESEN, F. (1913), Chlorophyceae of the Danish West Indies. *Dansk botan. Ark.* **1**, 5–188 (Ch 5)

BOEHM, J. (1893), Capillarität und Saftsteigen. *Ber. deut. botan. Ges.* **11**, 203–212 (Ch 6)

BOKE, N. H. (1947), Development of the adult shoot apex and floral initiation in *Vinca rosea* L. *Am. J. Botany* **34**, 433–439 (Ch 8)

BOLLARD, E. G. (1956), Nitrogenous compounds in plant xylem sap. *Nature* **178**, 1189–1190 (Ch 6)

BONNER, J. (1959), The photoperiodic process. pp. 245–253. In R. B. Withrow (ed.), *Photoperiodism and Related Phenomena in Plants and Animals.* American Association for the Advancement of Science Publication No. 45, Washington (Ch 7)

BONNER, J. (1960), The mechanical analysis of auxin-induced growth. *Schweiz. Z. Forstw.* **30**, 141–159 (Ch 4)

BONNER, J. (1965), *The Molecular Biology of Development.* pp. 155. Oxford University Press, Oxford (Ch 10)

BONNER, J. and LIVERMAN, J. (1953), Hormonal control of flower initiation. pp. 283–303. In W. E. Loomis (ed.), *Growth and Differentiation in Plants.* Iowa State College Press, Ames (Ch 8)

BONNER, J., ORDIN, L., and CLELAND, R. (1956), Auxin-induced water uptake. pp. 260–270. In R. L. Wain and F. Wightman (eds.), *The Chemistry and Mode of Action of Plant Growth Substances.* Academic Press, New York (Ch 4)

BONNET, O. T. (1961), The oat plant: its histology and development. *Univ. Illinois Agr. Expt. Sta. Bull.* No. 672, 1–112 (Ch 2)

BORTHWICK, H. A., PARKER, M. W., and HENDRICKS, S. B. (1950), Recent developments in the control of flowering by photoperiod. *Am. Naturalist* **84**, 117–124 (Ch 7)

BOTTOMLEY, W. B. (1917), Some effects of organic growth-promoting substances (auximones) on the growth of *Lemna minor* in mineral culture solution. *Proc. Roy. Soc. (London) B.* **89,** 481–508 (Ch 9)

BOWER, F. O. (1935), *Primitive Land Plants.* pp. 658. Macmillan, London (Ch 1)

BOYSEN-JENSEN, P. (1936), *Growth Hormones in Plants.* pp. 268. McGraw-Hill, New York (Ch 4)

BRACHET, J. (1957), *Biochemical Cytology.* pp. 516. Academic Press, New York (Ch 1)

BRAUN, A. C. (1952), Conditioning of the host cell as a factor in the transformation process in crown gall. *Growth* **16,** 65–74 (Ch 4)

BRAUN, A. C. (1959), A demonstration of the recovery of the crown-gall tumor cell with the use of complex tumors of single cell origin. *Proc. Natl. Acad. Sci. U.S.* **45,** 932–938 (Ch 4)

BRAUN, A. C. and STONIER, T. (1958) Morphology and physiology of plant tumors. *Protoplasmatologia* **10,** 1–93 (Ch 4)

BRENCHLEY, W. E. (1912), The development of the grain of barley. *Ann. Botany* **26,** 903–928 (Ch 2)

BRENCHLEY, W. E. and WARINGTON, K. (1927), The role of boron in the growth of plants. *Ann. Botany* **41,** 167–188 (Ch 2)

BREUER, M. E. and PAVAN, C. (1955), Behavior of polytene chromosomes of *Rhynchosciara angelae* at different stages of larval development. *Chromosoma* **7,** 371–386 (Ch 10)

BRIAN, P. W., CURTIS, P. J., and HEMMING, H. G. (1946), A substance causing abnormal development of fungal hyphae produced by *Penicillium janczewskii* Zal. I. Biological assay, production and isolation of "curling factor." *Trans. Brit. Mycolog. Soc.* **29,** 173–187 (Ch 4)

BRIAN, P. W. and HEMMING, H. G. (1955), The effect of gibberellic acid on shoot growth of pea seedlings. *Physiol. Plantarum* **8,** 669–681 (Ch 4)

BROOKES, R. F., and LEAFE, E. L. (1963), Structure and plant growth regulating activity of some 2-Benzothiazolyloxyacetic acids and 2-oxobenzothiazolin-3-ylacetic acids. *Nature* **198,** 589 (Ch 4)

Brookhaven Symposia in Biology No. 19 (January, 1967), *Energy Conversion by the Photosynthetic Apparatus.* pp. ix, 514 (Ch 3)

BROOKS, S. C. and BROOKS, M. M. (1941), The permeability of living cells. *Protoplasma Monograph* **19,** 1–393 (Ch 1, 5)

BROWN, R. (1951), The effect of temperature on the duration of the different stages of division in the root tip. *J. Exp. Botany* **2,** 96–110 (Ch 5)

BROWN, R. and RICKLESS, P. (1948), A new method for study of cell division and extension with preliminary observations on the effects of temperature and nutrition. *Proc. Roy. Soc. (London) B.* **136,** 110–125 (Ch 6)

BUNNING, E. (1964), *The Physiological Clock.* pp. 145. Academic Press, New York (Ch 7, 8)

BURD, J. S. (1919), Rate of absorption of soil constituents at successive stages of plant growth. *J. Agr. Research* **18**, 51–72 (Ch 2)

BURG, S. P. and BURG, E. A. (1965), Ethylene action and the ripening of fruits. *Science* **148**, 1190–1196 (Ch 4)

BURG, S. P. and BURG, E. A. (1966a), Auxin-induced ethylene formation: its relation to flowering in the pineapple. *Science* **152**, 1269 (Ch 4)

BURG, S. P. and BURG, E. A. (1966b), The interaction between auxin and ethylene and its role in plant growth. *Proc. Natl. Acad. Sci. U.S.* **55**, 262–269 (Ch 4)

BURG, S. P. and BURG, E. A. (1967), Molecular requirements for the biological action of ethylene. *Plant Physiol.* **42**, 144–152 (Ch 4)

BURG, S. P. and CLAGETT, C. O. (1967), Conversion of methionine to ethylene in vegetative tissue and fruits. *Biochem. and Biophys. Research Commun.* **27**, 125–130 (Ch 4)

BURROWS, W. (1945), Periodic spawning of "Palolo" worms in Pacific waters. *Nature* **155**, 47–48 (Ch 7)

BUVAT, R. (1952), Structure, évolution et fonctionnement du méristème apical de quelques dicotylédones. *Ann. Sci. nat. Botan. et biol. végétale* **13**, 199–300 (Ch 5, 8)

CANNY, M. J. and PHILLIPS, O. M. (1963), Quantitative aspects of a theory of translocation. *Ann. Botany* N.S. **27**, 379–402 (Ch 6)

CANTINO, E. C. (1961), The relationship between biochemical and morphological differentiation in non-filamentous aquatic fungi. *Soc. Gen. Microbiol.* **11**, 243–271 (Ch 8)

CAPLIN, S. M. (1947), Growth and morphology of tobacco tissue cultures *in vitro*. *Botan. Gaz.* **108**, 379–393 (Ch 8)

CAPLIN, S. M. and STEWARD, F. C. (1949), A technique for the controlled growth of excised plant tissue in liquid media under aseptic conditions. *Nature* **163**, 920 (Ch 1, 4)

CARPENTER, W. G. and CHERRY, J. H. (1966), Effects of protein inhibitors and auxin on nucleic acid metabolism in peanut cotyledons. *Plant Physiol.* **41**, 919–922 (Ch 4)

CASPERS, H. (1951), Rhythmische Erscheinungen in der Fortpflanzung von *Clunio marinus* (Dipt. Chiron.) und das Problem der lunaren Periodizität bei Organismen. *Arch. Hydrobiol.* (Suppl.) **18**, 415–594 (Ch 7)

CHAILAKHIAN, M. KH. (1961), Principles of ontogenesis and physiology of flowering in higher plants. *Can. J. Botany* **39**, 1817–1841 (Ch 8)

CHERRY, J. H. and VAN HUYSTEE, R. B. (1965), Comparison of messenger RNA in photoperiodically induced and noninduced *Xanthium* buds. *Science* **150**, 1450–1453 (Ch 8)

CHRISPEELS, M. J. and VARNER, J. E. (1967), Gibberellic acid-enhanced synthesis and release of α-amylase and ribonuclease by isolated barley aleurone layers. *Plant Physiol.* **42**, 398–406 (Ch 4)

CLAYTON, R. K. (1965), *Molecular Physics in Photosynthesis.* pp. 205. Blaisdell Publishing Co., New York (Ch 3)

CLOWES, F. A. L. (1953), The cytogenerative centres in roots with broad columellas. *New Phytologist* **52,** 48–57 (Ch 5)

CLOWES, F. A. L. (1954), The promeristem and the minimal constructional centre in grass root apices. *New Phytologist* **53,** 108–116 (Ch 5)

CLOWES, F. A. L. (1961), *Apical Meristems.* pp. 217. F. A. Davis Co., Philadelphia (Ch 5, 8)

COCKING, E. C. (1960), Method for the isolation of plant protoplasts and vacuoles. *Nature* **187,** 927–929 (Ch 9)

CORNFORTH, J. W., MILBORROW, B. V., and RYBACK, G. (1965), Chemistry and physiology of "dormins" in sycamore. Identity of sycamore "dormin" with Abscisin II. *Nature* **205,** 1269 (Ch 4, 7)

CORNFORTH, J. W., MILBORROW, B. V., and RYBACK, G. (1966), Identification and estimation of (+)-Abscisin II ("dormin") in plant extracts by spectropolari-metry. *Nature* **210,** 627 (Ch 4)

CORRELL, D. L., STEERS, E., JR., SURIANO, J. R., and SHROPSHIRE, W., JR. (1966), Phytochrome: isolation from rye and partial characterization. *Plant Physiol.* (Suppl.) Vol. 41, xvi (Ch 7)

CRANE, F. A. (1951), Interactions between mineral nutrients and growth, develop-ment and metabolism with special reference to *Mentha piperita* L. pp. 308. Ph.D. thesis, University of Rochester (Ch 5, 8, 9)

CRANE, F. A. and STEWARD, F. C. (1962), The growth, nutrition and metabolism of *Mentha piperita* L. III. Growth and nutrition under experimental conditions. IV. Effects of day length and of calcium and potassium on the nitrogenous me-tabolites of *Mentha piperita* L. *Cornell Univ. Agr. Exptl. Sta. Mem.* No. 379, 41–67; 68–90 (Ch 8, 9)

CRICK, F. H. C. (1957), Nucleic acids. *Sci. American* **197** (No. 3), 188–200 (Ch 3)

CRICK, F. H. C. (1966), The genetic code III. *Sci. American* **215** (No. 4), 55–62 (Ch 3)

CROCKER, W. (1948), *Growth of Plants: Twenty Years' Research at Boyce Thompson Institute.* pp. 459. Reinhold Publishing Corp., New York (Ch 7)

CROCKER, W., HITCHOCK, A. E., and ZIMMERMAN, P. W. (1935), Similarities in the effects of ethylene and the plant auxins. *Contrib. Boyce Thompson Inst.* **7,** 218–231 (Ch 4)

CRONSHAW, J. and ESAU, K. (1967), Tubular and fibrillar components of mature and differentiating sieve elements. *J. Cell Biol.* **34,** 801–816 (Ch 6)

CURTIS, O. F. (1935), *The Translocation of Solutes in Plants.* pp. 273. McGraw-Hill, New York (Ch 6)

CURTIS, O. F. and CHANG, H. T. (1930), The relative effectiveness of the tempera-ture of the crown as contrasted with that of the rest of the plant upon the flower-ing of celery. *Am. J. Botany* **17,** 1047–1048 (Ch 8)

DANIELLI, J. F., LORCH, I. J., ORD, M. J., and WILSON, E. C. (1955), Nucleus and cytoplasm in cellular inheritance. *Nature* **176**, 1114–1115 (Ch 9)

DARWIN, F. (1916), On the relation between transpiration and stomatal aperture. *Trans. Roy. Soc. (London) B.* **207**, 413–437 (Ch 6)

DAY, P. R. (1959), A cytoplasmically controlled abnormality of the tetrads of *Coprinus lagopus. Heredity* **13**, 81–87 (Ch 1)

DE VRIES, H. (1920), Monographie der Zwangsdrehungen. *Opera E. Periodicis Collata* **5**, 232–420 (Ch 5)

DIXON, H. H. (1930), Über die Saugkraft. *Ber. deut. botan. Ges.* **48**, 428–432 (Ch 6)

DIXON, H. H. (1938), Transport of substances in plants. *Proc. Roy. Soc. (London) B.* **125**, 1–25 (Ch 6)

ENGARD, C. J. (1944), Organogenesis in *Rubus. Univ. Hawaii Research Publ.* No. 21, 1–220 (Ch 8)

ERICKSON, R. O. (1947), Respiration of developing anthers. Nature **159**, 275–276.

ERICKSON, R. O. (1948), Cytological and growth correlations in the flower bud and anther of *Lilium longiflorum. Am. J. Botany* **35**, 729–739 (Ch 6)

ERICKSON, R. O. and GODDARD, D. R. (1951), An analysis of root growth in cellular and biochemical terms. *Growth* **10**, 89–116 (Ch 5)

ESAU, K. (1960), *Anatomy of Seed Plants.* pp. 376. John Wiley & Sons, New York (Ch 6)

ESAU, K. (1966a), *Vascular Differentiation in Plants.* pp. 160. Holt, Rinehart and Winston, New York (Ch 6)

ESAU, K. (1966b), Explorations of the food conducting system in plants. *Am. Scientist* **54** (No. 2), 141–157 (Ch 6)

ESAU, K. and CHEADLE, V. I. (1965), Cytologic studies on phloem. *Univ. Calif. Publ. Botany* **36** (No. 3), 253–343 (Ch 6)

ESAU, K., ENGLEMA, E., and BISALPUTRA, T. (1963), What are transcellular strands? *Planta* **59**, 617–623 (Ch 6)

EVANS, H. J. (1963), Effect of potassium and other univalent cations on activity of pyruvate kinase in *Pisum sativum. Plant Physiol.* **38**, 397–402 (Ch 2)

EVANS, H. J. and SAVAGE, J. R. V. (1959), The effect of temperature on mitosis and on the action of colchicine in root meristem cells of *Vicia faba. Exp. Cell Research* **18**, 51–61 (Ch 9)

FITTING, H. (1909), Die Beeinflussung der Orchideenblüten durch die Bestäubung und durch andere Umstände. *Z. Botan.* **1**, 1–86 (Ch 4)

FLINT, L. H. and MCALISTER, E. D. (1937), Wavelengths of radiation in the visible spectrum promoting the germination of light-sensitive lettuce seed. *Smithsonian Inst. Publs. Misc: Collections* **96**, 1–8 (Ch 7)

FORWARD, D. F. (1965), The respiration of bulky organs. pp. 311–376. In F. C. Steward (ed.), *Plant Physiology, A Treatise*, Vol. IVA. Academic Press, New York (Ch 6)

Fox, S. W. (1960), How did life begin? *Science* **132**, 200–208 (Ch 6)

Frenster, J. H. (1965), Ultrastructural continuity between active and repressed chromatin. *Nature* **205**, 1341–1342 (Ch 9)

Frenster, J. H., Allfrey, V. C., and Mirsky, A. E. (1963), Repressed and active chromatin isolated from interphase lymphocytes. *Proc. Natl. Acad. Sci. U.S.* **50**, 1026–1032 (Ch 9)

Frey-Wyssling, A. (1953), *Submicroscopic Morphology of Protoplasm.* pp. 411. Elsevier Pub. Co., Amsterdam (Ch 3, 5, 6)

Frey-Wyssling, A. (1954), The fine structure of cellulose microfibrils. *Science* **119**, 80–82 (Ch 3)

Frey-Wyssling, A. (1959), *Die pflanzliche Zellwand.* pp. 367. Springer-Verlag, Berlin (Ch 3)

Frey-Wyssling, A. and Mühlethaler, K. (1965), *Ultrastructural Plant Cytology.* pp. 377. *Elsevier Pub. Co., Amsterdam* (Ch 3, 5, 6)

Friesner, R. C. (1920), Daily rhythms of elongation and cell division in certain roots. *Am. J. Botany* **7**, 380–407 (Ch 7)

Gaffron, H. (1960), Energy storage: photosynthesis. pp. 3–277. In F. C. Steward (ed.), *Plant Physiology, A Treatise,* Vol. IB. Academic Press, New York (Ch 3)

Galun, E. (1959), Effects of gibberellic acid and naphthaleneacetic acid on sex expression and some morphological characters in the cucumber plant. *Phyton* **13**, 1–8 (Ch 8)

Galun, E. and Gressel, J. (1966), Morphogenesis in *Trichoderma.* Suppression of photoinduction by 5-fluorouracil. *Science* **151**, 696–698 (Ch 7)

Garner, W. W. and Allard, H. A. (1920), Effect of the relative length of day and night and other factors of the environment on growth and reproduction. *J. Agr. Research* **18**, 553–606 (Ch 4, 7)

Garner, W. W. and Allard, H. A. (1923), Further studies on photoperiodism: the response of the plant to relative length of day and night. *J. Agr. Research* **23**, 871–920 (Ch 4)

Gates, L. F. (1964), The sources of amino acids used for synthesis of tobacco mosaic virus by illuminated tobacco leaves. pp. 366. Ph.D. thesis, Cornell University (Ch 6)

Gautheret, R. J. (1935), *Recherches sur la Culture des Tissus Végétaux.* pp. 279. Librairie E. le François, Paris (Ch 1)

Gautheret, R. J. (1942), *Manuel Technique de Culture des Tissus Végétaux.* pp. 170. Masson, Paris (Ch 3)

Gautheret, R. J. (1959), *La Culture des Tissus Végétaux. Techniques et Réalisations.* pp. 863. Masson, Paris (Ch 1)

Gibbs, M. (1966), Carbohydrates: their role in plant metabolism and nutrition. pp. 3–116. In F. C. Steward (ed.), *Plant Physiology, A Treatise,* Vol. IVB. Academic Press, New York (Ch 3, 6)

GIESY, R. M. and DAY, P. R. (1965), The septal pores of *Coprinus lagopus* in relation to nuclear migration. *Am. J. Botany* **52**, 287–293 (Ch 1)

GIFFORD, E. M., JR. and STEWART, K. D. (1965), Ultrastructure of vegetative and reproductive apices of *Chenopodium album. Science* **149**, 75–77 (Ch 8)

GLASER, O. (1938), Growth, time and form. *Biol. Rev.* **13**, 20–58 (Ch 9)

GODDARD, D. R. (1939), The reversible heat activation of respiration in *Neurospora. Cold Spring Harbor Symposia Quant. Biol.* **7**, 362–376 (Ch 7)

GODDARD, D. R. and BONNER, W. D. (1960), Cellular respiration. pp. 209–312. In F. C. Steward (ed.), *Plant Physiology, A Treatise*, Vol. IA. Academic Press, New York (Ch 6)

GOMPERTZ, B. (1825), On the nature of the function expressive of the law of human mortality. *Phil. Trans. Roy Soc. (London)* **36**, 513–585 (Ch 9)

GOODWIN, R. H. and GODDARD, D. R. (1940), The oxygen consumption of isolated woody tissues. *Am. J. Botany* **27**, 234–237 (Ch 6)

GOODWIN, R. and STEPKA, W. (1945), Growth and differentiation in the root tip of *Phleum pratense. Am. J. Botany* **32**, 36–46 (Ch 1, 6, 9)

GORINI, L. and MAAS, W. K. (1958), Feedback control of the formation of biosynthetic enzymes. pp. 469–478. In W. D. McElroy and B. Glass (eds.), *Symposium on the Chemical Basis of Development*. Johns Hopkins Press, Baltimore (Ch 9)

GOWING, D. P. (1956), An hypothesis of the role of naphthaleneacetic acid in flower induction in the pineapple. *Am J. Botany* **43**, 411–418 (Ch 8)

GRAHAM, C. F., ARMS, K., and GURDON, J. B. (1966), The induction of DNA synthesis by frog egg cytoplasm. *Develop. Biol.* **14**, 349–381 (Ch 10)

GREEN, P. B. (1963), Cell walls and the geometry of plant growth. *Brookhaven Symposia in Biol.* **16**, 203–217 (Ch 1)

GREEN, P. B. and KING, A. (1966), A mechanism for the origin of specifically oriented textures in development—special reference to *Nitella* wall texture. *Australian J. Biol. Sci.* **19**, 421–437 (Ch 1)

GREGORY, F. G. and PURVIS, O. N. (1936), Vernalization of winter rye during ripening. Devernalization of winter rye by high temperature. *Nature* **138**, 973–974; 1013–1014 (Ch 8)

GREGORY, F. G. and PURVIS, O. N. (1938), Studies in vernalization of cereals. II. The vernalization of excised mature embryos and of developing ears. *Ann. Botany* N.S. **2**, 237–251 (Ch 8)

GREGORY, F. G., SPEAR, I., and THIMANN, K. V. (1954), The interrelation between CO_2 metabolism and photoperiodism in *Kalanchoe. Plant Physiol.* **29**, 220–229 (Ch 8)

GROSSENBACHER, K. A. (1939), Autonomic cycle of rate of exudation of plants. *Am. J. Botany* **26**, 107–109 (Ch 7)

GURDON, J. B. and UEHLINGER, V. (1966), "Fertile" intestine nuclei. *Nature* **210**, 1240–1242 (Ch 10)

GUTTER, Y. (1957), Effect of light on sporulation of *Trichoderma virida*. *Bull. Research Council Israel* 5D, 273–286 (Ch 7)

HABERLANDT, G. (1902), Culturversuche mit isolierten Pflanzenzellen. *Sitzber. kais. Akad. Wiss., Math-naturwiss. Kl.*, Bd. CXI, Abt. I, 69–92 (Ch 3, 10)

HACKETT, D. P. (1952), The osmotic change during auxin-induced water uptake by potato tissue. *Plant Physiol.* 27, 279–284 (Ch 6)

HACKETT, D. P. and THIMANN, K. V. (1950), The action of inhibitors on water uptake by potato tissue. *Plant Physiol.* 25, 648–652 (Ch 6)

HAINES, F. M. (1935), Observation on the occurrence of air in conducting tracts. *Ann. Botany* 49, 366–379 (Ch 6)

HALDANE, J. B. S. (1928), On being the right size. In *Possible Worlds and Other Papers*. pp. 305. Harper and Brothers, New York (Ch 8)

HÄMMERLING, J. (1953), Nucleo-cytoplasmic relationships in the development of *Acetabularia*. *Intern. Rev. Cytol.* 2, 475–498 (Ch 1)

HÄMMERLING, J. (1963), The role of the nucleus in differentiation especially in *Acetabularia*. *Symposia Soc. Exptl. Biol.* 17, 127–137 (Ch 1)

HAMNER, K. C. (1940), Interrelation of light and darkness in photoperiodic induction. *Botan. Gaz.* 101, 658–687 (Ch 8)

HARADA, H. and NITSCH, J. P. (1964), Isolement et propriétés physiologiques d'une substance de montaison. pp. 597–609. In J. P. Nitsch (ed.), *Régulateurs Naturels de la Croissance Végétale*. Centre Nationale de la Recherche Scientifique, Paris (Ch 4)

HARLAN, H. V. (1920), Daily development of kernels of Hannchen barley from flowering to maturity at Aberdeen, Idaho. *J. Agr. Research* 19, 393–430 (Ch 2)

HARRISON, J. A. (1938), Indicators of salt accumulation and translocation. Ph.D. thesis, University of London (Ch 6)

HEATH, O. V. S. (1959), The water relations and mechanisms of stomata. pp. 193–250. In F. C. Steward (ed.), *Plant Physiology, A Treatise*, Vol. II. Academic Press, New York (Ch 6)

HENDRICKS, S. B. and BORTHWICK, H. A. (1954), Photoresponsive growth. pp. 149–169. In D. Rudnick (ed.), *Aspects of Synthesis and Order in Growth*. (13th Growth Symposium). Princeton University Press, Princeton, N.J. (Ch 7)

HESLOP-HARRISON, J. (1957), The experimental modification of sex expression in flowering plants. *Biol. Rev.* 32, 38–90 (Ch 8)

HESLOP-HARRISON, J. (1963), Ultrastructural aspects of differentiation in sporogenous tissue. *Symposia Soc. Exptl. Biol.* 17, 315–340 (Ch 10)

HEYN, A. N. J. (1931), Der Mechanismus der Zellstreckung. *Rec. trav. botan. Neerl.* 28, 113–244 (Ch 4)

HEYN, A. N. J. (1940), The physiology of cell elongation. *Botan. Rev.* 6, 515–574 (Ch 4)

HILL, A. V. (1928), The diffusion of oxygen and lactic acid through tissues. *Proc. Roy. Soc. (London)* B. 104, 309–396 (Ch 5)

HILLIS, W. E. (1955), Formation of leucoanthocyanins in *Eucalyptus* tissues. *Nature* **175**, 597 (Ch 4, 7)

HILLMAN, W. S. (1962), *The Physiology of Flowering.* pp. 164. Holt, Rinehart and Winston, New York (Ch 7, 8)

HOAGLAND, D. R. (1944), *Lectures on the Inorganic Nutrition of Plants.* pp. 226. Chronica Botanica, Waltham, Mass. (Ch 2)

HOAGLAND, D. R. and ARNON, D. I. (1938), The water-culture method for growing plants without soil. *Univ. Calif. Agr. Expt. Sta. Circ.* No. 347 (Ch 2)

HOAGLAND, D. R. and BROYER, T. C. (1936), General nature of the process of salt accumulation by roots with description of experimental methods. *Plant Physiol.* **11**, 471–507 (Ch 2)

HOAGLAND, D. R., HIBBARD, P. L., and DAVIS, A. R. (1926), The influence of light, temperature, and other conditions on the ability of *Nitella* cells to concentrate halogens in the cell sap. *J. Gen. Physiol.* **10**, 121–146 (Ch 2)

HOLLEY, R. W. (1966), The nucleotide sequence of a nucleic acid. *Sci. American* **214** (No. 2), 30–39 (Ch 3)

HOLMAN, R. M. and ROBBINS, W. W. (1924), *A Textbook of General Botany for Colleges and Universities.* pp. 590. John Wiley & Sons, New York (Ch 1)

HOLSTEN, R. D., SUGII, M., and STEWARD, F. C. (1965), Direct and indirect effects of radiation on plant cells: their relation to growth and growth induction. *Nature* **208**, 850–856 (Ch 4, 6)

HOLTFRETER, J. (1946), Structure, motility and locomotion in isolated embryonic amphibian cells. *J. Morphology* **79**, 27–62 (Ch 10)

HOPKINS, E. F. and WANN, F. B. (1925), The effect of the H ion concentration on the availability of iron for *Chlorella* sp. *J. Gen Physiol.* **9**, 205–210 (Ch 2)

HOWARD, A. and PELC, S. R. (1952), Synthesis of desoxyribonucleic acid in normal and irradiated cells and its relation to chromosome breakage. *Heredity (Suppl. to Vol. 6)*, 261–273 (Ch 9)

HOWE, H. M. (1965), A root of Van Helmont's tree. *Isis* **56**, 408–419 (Ch 2)

HOWE, K. J. (1951), The structure and development of the mint plant, *Mentha piperita* L., with special reference to the secretion of the essential oil. pp. 168. M.S. thesis, University of Rochester (Ch 5)

HOWE, K. J. (1956) Factors affecting the growth and development of *Mentha piperita* L. with special reference to the formation of essential oil. pp. 248. Ph.D. thesis, Cornell University (Ch 7, 8)

HOWE, K. J. and STEWARD, F. C. (1962), The growth, nutrition and metabolism of *Mentha piperita* L. II. Anatomy and development of *Mentha piperita* L. *Cornell Univ. Agr. Expt. Sta. Mem.* No. 379, 11–40 (Ch 1, 5, 7)

HUANG, R. C. C. and BONNER, J. (1962), Histone, a suppressor of chromosomal RNA synthesis. *Proc. Natl. Acad. Sci. U.S.* **48**, 1216–1222 (Ch 10)

HUTCHINSON, A. H. (1936), The polygonal presentation of polyphase phenomena. *Trans. Roy. Soc. Can.* **30**, 19–26 (Ch 9)

HUXLEY, J. S. (1932), *Problems of Relative Growth*. pp. 276. Methuen, London (Ch 1)

ISRAEL, H. W. and STEWARD, F. C. (1966), The fine structure of quiescent and growing carrot cells: its relation to growth induction. *Ann. Botany* N.S. **30**, 63–79 (Ch 3, 4, 5, 6, 8)

ISRAEL, H. W. and STEWARD, F. C. (1967), The fine structure and development of plastids in cultured cells of *Daucus carota*. *Ann. Botany* N.S. **31**, 1–18 (Ch 3, 4, 5)

JACOB, F. and MONOD, J. (1961), Genetic regulatory mechanisms and the synthesis of proteins. *J. Molecular Biol.* **3**, 318–356 (Ch 7, 10)

JENNINGS, A. C. and MORTON, R. K. (1963), Changes in carbohydrate, protein, and non-protein nitrogenous compounds of developing wheat grain. *Australian J. Biol. Sci.* **16**, 318–331 (Ch 2)

JINKS, J. L. (1963), Cytoplasmic inheritance in fungi. pp. 325–354. In W. J. Burdette (ed.), *Methodology in Basic Genetics*. Holden-Day, San Francisco (Ch 10)

JOHANSEN, O. A. (1950), *Plant Embryology*. pp. 305. Chronica Botanica, Waltham, Mass. (Ch 7)

JONES, E. R. H., HENBEST, H. B., SMITH, G. F., and BENTLEY, J. A. (1952), 3-indolyl-acetonitrile: a naturally occurring plant growth hormone. *Nature* **169**, 485 (Ch 4)

JOY, K. W. and FOLKES, B. F. (1965), The uptake of amino acids and their incorporation into the proteins of excised barley embryos. *J. Exptl. Botany* **16**, 646–666 (Ch 2)

KARLSON, P. (1965), *Mechanisms of Hormone Action*. pp. 275. Academic Press, New York (Ch 9)

KARTHA, G., BELLO, J., and HARKER, D. (1967), Tertiary structure of ribonuclease. *Nature* **213**, 862–865 (Ch 3)

KEFFORD, N. P., KAUR-SAWHNEY, R., and GALSTON, A. W. (1963), Formation of a complex between a derivative of the plant hormone indoleacetic acid and ribonucleic acid from pea seedlings. *Acta Chem. Scand.* **17**, 313–318 (Ch 4)

KENT, A. E. (1966), The totipotency of cultured plant cells: Its control during development and morphogenesis. Ph.D. Thesis, Cornell University, pp. 177 (Ch 10)

KENT, A. E. and STEWARD, F. C. (1965), Morphogenesis in free cell cultures of carrot as affected by sequential treatments with naphthaleneacetic acid and with coconut milk. *Am. J. Botany* (*Abstr.*) **52**, 619 (Ch 6)

KERNER, A. (1894), *The Natural History of Plants*, Vol. I. pp. 777. Translated by F. W. Oliver. Blackie & Son, London (Ch 2)

KERNER, A. (1895), *The Natural History of Plants*, Vol. II. pp. 983. Translated by F. W. Oliver. Blackie & Son, London (Ch 1)

KEY, J. L. and SHANNON, J. C. (1964), Enhancement by auxin of ribonucleic acid synthesis in excised soybean hypocotyl tissue. *Plant Physiol.* **39**, 360–364 (Ch 4)

KIDD, F. (1934), The respiration of fruits. *Proc. Roy. Inst. Gr. Brit.* **28**, 351–381 (Ch 1)

KIDD, F., WEST, C., and BRIGGS, C. E. (1921), A quantitative analysis of the growth of *Helianthus annuus*. I. The respiration of the plant and its parts throughout the life cycle. *Proc. Roy. Soc. (London) B.* **92**, 368–384 (Ch 1)

KIRKWOOD, J. E. and GIES, W. J. (1902), Chemical studies of the coconut with some notes on the changes during germination. *Bull. Torrey Botan. Club* **29**, 321–359 (Ch 1, 4)

KLEIN, R. M. (1953), The probable chemical nature of crown-gall tumor-inducing principle. *Am. J. Botany* **40**, 597–599 (Ch 4)

KLEIN, R. M. (1954), Mechanisms of crown-gall induction. *Brookhaven Symposia Biol.* **6**, 97–114 (Ch 4)

KLEIN, R. M. (ed.), (1961), *Plant Growth Regulation.* pp. 850. Iowa State University Press, Ames, Iowa (Ch 4)

KLEIN, R. M. and BRAUN, A. C. (1960), On the presumed sterile induction of plant tumors. *Science* **131**, 1612 (Ch 4)

KNUDSON, L. (1951), Nutrient solutions for orchids. *Botan. Gaz.* **112**, 528–532 (Ch 2)

KOK, B. (1965), Photosynthesis: the path of energy. pp. 903–960. In J. Bonner and J. E. Varner (eds), *Plant Biochemistry.* Academic Press, New York (Ch 3)

KRIKORIAN, A. D. (1965), The synthetic potentialities of cultured plant cells and tissues. pp. 492. Ph.D. thesis, Cornell University (Ch 6)

KRIKORIAN, A. D. and STEWARD, F. C. (1965), Nicholas of Cusa and the Van Helmont experiment: the facts of the case? *Am. J. Botany (Abstr.)* **52**, 631 (Ch 2)

KUHN, W., HARGITAY, B., KATCHALSKY, A., and EISENBERG, H. (1950), Reversible dilation and contraction by changing the state of ionization of high polymer acid networks. *Nature* **165**, 514–516 (Ch 6)

LABARKA, C., NICHOLLS, P. B., and BANDURSKI, R. S. (1965), A partial characterization of indoleacetylinositols from *Zea mays*. *Biochem. Biophys. Research Commun.* **20**, 641–646 (Ch 4)

LAMPORTE, D. T. A. and NORTHCOTE, D. H. (1960), Hydroxyproline in primary walls of higher plants. *Nature* **188**, 665–666 (Ch 4)

LANG, A. (1956), Induction of flower formation in biennial *Hyoscyamus* by treatment with gibberellin. *Naturwissenschaften* **12**, 284–285 (Ch 7)

LANG, A. (1958), Induction of reproductive growth in plants. pp. 126–140. In *Biochemistry of Morphogenesis.* Proceedings of the 4th International Congress of Biochemistry. Pergamon Press, New York (Ch 8)

LANG, A. and MELCHERS, G. (1947), Vernalisation und Devernalisation bei einer zweijährigen Pflanze. *Z. Naturforsch. Pt. b.* **2**, 444–449 (Ch 8)

LEAR, J. (1966), Man's first robot with muscle. *Saturday Rev.*, Dec. 3, 83–86 (Ch 6)

LECOMTE DU NOÜY, P. (1947), *Human Destiny.* pp. 289. Longmans, Green and Co., London (Ch 1)

LEDBETTER, M., and PORTER, K. R. (1964), Morphology of microtubules in plant cells. *Science* **144,** 872–874 (Ch 5)

LEHNINGER, A. L. (1964), *The Mitochondrion.* pp. 263. W. A. Benjamin, Inc., New York (Ch 2, 6)

LEHNINGER, A. L. (1966), Dynamics and mechanisms of active ion transport across the mitochondrial membrane. *Ann. N.Y. Acad. Sci.* **137,** 700–707 (Ch 2)

LEOPOLD, A. C. and GUERNSEY, F. A. (1953), A theory of auxin involving coenzyme A. *Proc. Natl. Acad. Sci. U.S.* **39,** 1105–1111 (Ch 8)

LEOPOLD, A. C. and PRICE, C. A. (1956), The influence of growth substances upon sulphydryl compounds. pp. 271–283. In R. L. Wain and F. Wightman (eds.), *The Chemistry and Mode of Action of Plant Growth Substances.* Academic Press, New York (Ch 8)

LETHAM, D. S. (1963), Isolation of a kinin from plum fruitlets and other tissues. pp. 109–117. In J. P. Nitsch (ed.), *Régulateurs Naturels de la Croissance Végétale.* Centre National de la Recherche Scientifique, Paris. (Ch 4)

LIEBERMAN, M. A., KUNISHI, A., MAPSON, L. W., and WARDALE, D. A. (1966), Stimulation of ethylene production in apple tissue slices by methionine. *Plant Physiol.* **41,** 376–382 (Ch 4)

LIST, A., JR. and STEWARD, F. C. (1965), An account of the nucellus, embryo sac, endosperm and embryo of *Aesculus* and of their inter-dependence during growth. *Ann. Botany* N.S. **29,** 1–15 (Ch 4)

LITTAU, V. C., ALLFREY, V. G., FRENSTER, J. H., and MIRSKY, A. E. (1964), Active and inactive regions of nuclear chromatin as revealed by electron microscope autoradiography. *Proc. Natl. Acad. Sci. U.S.* **52,** 93–100 (Ch 9)

LIVINGSTON, B. E. and LUBIN, G. (1927), The Askenasy demonstration of traction transmitted through liquid water. *Science* **65,** 376–379 (Ch 6)

LLOYD, F. E. (1908), The physiology of stomata. *Carnegie Inst. Wash. Publ.* No. 82, 1–142 (Ch 6)

LOEWY, A. G. and SIEKEVITZ, P. (1963), *Cell Structure and Function.* pp. 228. Holt, Rinehart and Winston, New York (Ch 3)

LORCH, I. J. and DANIELLI, J. F. (1950), Transplantation of nuclei from cell to cell. *Nature* **166,** 329–333 (Ch 9)

LOW, B. W. and EDSALL, J. T. (1956), Aspects of protein structure. pp. 378–433. In D. E. Green (ed.), *Currents in Biochemical Research*, Vol. II. Interscience Publishers, New York (Ch 3)

LUBIN, M. and ENNIS, H. L. (1964), On the role of intracellular potassium in protein synthesis. *Biochim. et Biophys. Acta* **80,** 614–631 (Ch 2)

LUND, J. W. G. (1942), The marginal algae of certain ponds, with special reference to the bottom deposits. *J. Ecol.* **30,** 245–283 (Ch 1)

LYNDON, R. F. and STEWARD, F. C. (1965), Growth, protein metabolism and solute uptake: the simultaneous absorption of proline and caesium by aseptically cultured tissue. *New Phytologist* **64,** 451–476 (Ch 6)

MacDougal, D. T. (1924), Growth in trees and massive organs of plants: dendro-graphic measurements. *Carnegie Inst. Wash. Publ.* No. 350, 1–116 (Ch 6, 9)

MacDougal, D. T. (1926), Growth and permeability of century-old cells. *Am. Naturalist* **60**, 393–415 (Ch 10)

MacDougal, D. T. and Long, F. L. (1927), Characters of cells attaining great age. *Am. Naturalist* **61**, 385–406 (Ch 10)

MacDougal, D. T. and Smith, G. M. (1927), Long-lived cells of the redwood. *Science* **66**, 456–457 (Ch 10)

Machlis, L. (1944), The respiratory gradient in barley roots. *Am. J. Botany* **31**, 281–282 (Ch 6)

Machlis, L. (1966), Sex hormones in fungi. pp. 415–433. In G. C. Dunsworth and A. S. Sussman (eds.), *The Fungi—An Advanced Treatise*, Vol. II. Academic Press, New York (Ch 7)

Maheshwari, P. (1950), *An Introduction to the Embryology of Angiosperms.* pp. 453. McGraw-Hill, New York (Ch 7, 10)

Marcavillaca, M. C. and Montaldi, E. R. (1967), Diferentes formas de lojas pro-ducidas por yemas adventicias inducidas experimentalmente en lojas aisladas de *Nicotiana tabacum* L. y *Passiflora coerulea* L. *Revista de Investigaciones Agropecuarias*, INTA, Buenos Aires, Argentina, Ser. 2, Vol. IV, No. 1, 1–7.

Markert, C. L. (1963), Epigenetic control of specific protein synthesis in differ-entiating cells. pp. 65–84. In M. Locke (ed.), *Cytodifferentiation and Macro-molecular Synthesis.* Academic Press, New York (Ch 8, 10)

Markert, C. L. (1963), The origin of specific proteins. pp. 95–119. In J. M. Allen (ed.), *The Nature of Biological Diversity.* McGraw-Hill, New York (Ch 10)

Markham, R., Frey, S., and Hills, G. J. (1963), Methods for the enhancement of image detail and accentuation of structure in electron microscopy. *Virology* **20**, 88–102 (Ch 5)

Mason, T. G. and Maskell, E. J. (1928a), Studies on the transport of carbohy-drates in the cotton plant. I. A study of diurnal variation in the carbohydrate of leaf, bark and wood, and the effects of ringing. *Ann. Botany* **42**, 189–243 (Ch 6)

Mason, T. G. and Maskell, E. J. (1928b), Studies on the transport of carbohy-drates in the cotton plant. II. The factors determining the rate and direction of movement of sugars. *Ann. Botany* **42**, 571–636 (Ch 6)

Mason, T. G. and Phillis, E. (1939), Experiments on the extraction of sap from the vacuole of the leaf of the cotton plant and their bearing on the osmotic theory of water absorption by the cell. *Ann. Botany* N.S. **3**, 531–544 (Ch 6)

Mazé, P. (1915), Détermination des éléments minéraux rares nécessaires au déve-loppement du maïs. *Compt. rend. Acad. Sci.* **160**, 211–214.

McClintock, B. (1951), Chromosome organization and genic expression. *Cold Spring Harbor Symposia Quant. Biol.* **16**, 13–14 (Ch 9)

McClintock, B. (1961), Some parallels between gene control systems in maize and in bacteria. *Am. Naturalist* **95**, 265–277 (Ch 10)

McClintock, B. (1965), The control of gene action in maize. *Brookhaven Symposia Biol.* **18**, 162–184 (Ch 9)

Medawar, P. B. (1945), Size, shape and age. pp. 157–187. In W. E. Le Gros Clark and P. B. Medawar (eds.), *Essays on Growth and Form.* Clarendon Press, Oxford (Ch 9)

Medvedev, Z. A. (1966), *Protein Biosynthesis and Problems of Heredity, Development and Aging.* pp. 584. Oliver and Boyd, Edinburgh (Ch 8, 10)

Meundt, W. J. and Galston, A. W. (1962), Binding of an indole-3-acetic acid metabolite to the RNA of peas. *Plant Physiol.* **37** (Suppl.), xiv (Ch 4)

Miller, C. O., Skoog, F., von Saltza, M. H., and Strong, F. M. (1955), Kinetin, a cell division factor from DNA. *J. Amer. Chem. Soc.* **77**, 1392 (Ch 4)

Miller, J. C. (1929), A study of some factors affecting seed-stalk development in cabbage. *Cornell Univ. Agr. Expt. Sta. Bull.* No. 488, 1–46 (Ch 8)

Mitra, J. and Steward, F. C. (1961), Growth induction in cultures of *Haplopappus gracilis.* II. The behavior of the nucleus. *Am. J. Botany* **48**, 358–368 (Ch 8)

Mockeridge, F. A. (1917), Some effects of organic growth-promoting substances (auximones) on the soil organisms concerned in the nitrogen cycle. *Proc. Roy. Soc. (London)* B. **89**, 508–534 (Ch 9)

Mockeridge, F. A. (1924), The formation of plant growth substances by micro-organisms. *Ann. Botany* **38**, 723–734 (Ch 9)

Mohan Ram, H. Y., Ram, M., and Steward, F. C. (1962), Growth and development of the banana plant. III. A. The origin of the inflorescence and the development of the flowers. B. The structure and development of the fruit. *Ann. Botany* N.S. **26**, 657–673 (Ch 4)

Mohan Ram, H. Y. and Steward, F. C. (1964), The induction of growth in explanted tissue of the banana fruit. *Can. J. Botany* **42**, 1559–1579 (Ch 6)

Mohr, H. (1962), Primary effects of light on growth. *Ann. Rev. Plant Physiol.* **13**, 465–488 (Ch 7)

Moor, H. (1959), Platin-Kohle-Abdruck-Technik angewandt auf den Feinbau der Milchröhren. *J. Ultrastructural Research* **2**, 393–422 (Ch 3, 4)

Moor, H. and Mühlethaler, K. (1963), Fine structure in frozen-etched yeast cells. *J. Cell Biol.* **17**, 609–628 (Ch 5)

Morel, G. and Wetmore, R. H. (1951), Tissue culture of monocotyledons. *Am. J. Botany* **38**, 138–140 (Ch 4)

Morrison, P. (1964), A thermodynamic characterization of self-reproduction. *Rev. Modern Phys.* **36**, 517–524 (Ch 10)

Mothes, K. and Engelbrecht, L. (1952), Über Allantoinsäure und Allantoin. I. Ihre Rolle als Wanderform des Stickstoffs und ihre Beziehungen zum Eiweissstoffwechsel des Ahorns. *Flora* **139**, 586–616 (Ch 6)

Mumford, F. E. and Jenner, E. L. (1966), Purification and characterization of phytochrome from oat seedlings. *Biochemistry* **5**, 3657–3662.

MÜNCH, E. (1930), *Die Stoffbewegungen in den Pflanzen.* pp. 234. Jena (Ch 6)

MURNEEK, A. E. and WHYTE, R. O. (1948), *Vernalization and Photoperiodism: a Symposium.* pp. 196. Chronica Botanica, Waltham, Mass. (Ch 7)

NANNEY, D. L. (1958), Epigenetic control systems. *Proc. Natl. Acad. Sci. U.S.* **44,** 712–717 (Ch 9)

NASON, A. and McELROY, W. D. (1963), Modes of action of the essential mineral elements. pp. 451–536. In F. C. Steward (ed.), *Plant Physiology, A Treatise,* Vol. III. Academic Press, New York (Ch 2)

NEEDHAM, J. (1931), *Chemical Embryology.* pp. 2021. Cambridge University Press, Cambridge (Ch 7, 9)

NELSON, C. D. (1964), The production and translocation of photosynthate-C^{14} in conifers. pp. 243–257. In M. H. Zimmerman (ed.), *The Formation of Wood in Forest Trees.* Academic Press, New York (Ch 6)

NEWCOMB, E. and BONNETT, H. T., JR. (1965), Cytoplasmic microtubules and wall microfibril orientation in root hairs of radish. *J. Cell Biol.* **27,** 575 (Ch 5)

NIELSON JONES, W. (1920), A simple root auxanometer. *Ann. Botany* **34,** 555–557 (Ch 9)

NIRENBERG, M. W. (1963), The genetic code. II. *Sci. American* **208** (No. 3), 80–94 (Ch 3)

NITSCH, J .P. (ed) (1964), *Régulateurs Naturels de la Croissance Végétale.* pp. 748. Centre National de la Recherche Scientifique, Paris (Ch 4)

NITSCH, J. P., KURTZ, E. B., JR., LIVERMAN, J. L., and WENT, F. W. (1952), The development of sex expression in cucurbit flowers. *Am. J. Botany* **39,** 32–43 (Ch 8)

NITSCH, J. P. and NITSCH, C. (1956), Studies on the growth of coleoptile and first internode sections. A new, sensitive, straight-growth test of auxins. *Plant Physiol.* **31,** 94–111 (Ch 4)

OLTMANNS, F. (1904), *Morphologie und Biologie der Algen.* pp. 733. Gustav Fischer, Jena (Ch 1)

OPARIN, A. I. (1961), *Life: Its Nature, Origin, and Development.* pp. 207. Academic Press, New York (Ch 3, 10)

ORDIN, L., APPLEWHITE, T. H., and BONNER, J. (1956), Auxin-induced water uptake by *Avena* coleoptile sections. *Plant Physiol.* **31,** 44–53 (Ch 4)

ORDIN, L., CLELAND, R., and BONNER, J. (1955), Influence of auxin on cell-wall metabolism. *Proc. Natl. Acad. Sci. U.S.* **41,** 1023–1029 (Ch 4)

ORDIN, L., CLELAND, R., and BONNER, J. (1957), Methyl esterification of cell wall constituents under the influence of auxin. *Plant Physiol.* **32,** 216–220 (Ch 4)

PALEG, L. G. (1965), Physiological effects of gibberellins. *Ann. Rev. Plant Physiol.* **16,** 291–322 (Ch 4)

PASTEUR, L. (1860), Mémoire sur la fermentation alcoolique. *Ann. Chem. Phys.* 3e. sér. **58,** 323–426.

PAULING, L. C. (1953), *General Chemistry.* 2nd edition, pp. 685. W. H. Freeman Co., San Francisco (Ch 2, 3)

PEARL, R. (1925), *The Biology of Population Growth.* pp. 260. A. A. Knopf, New York (Ch 9)

PEARL, R. and REED, L. J. (1923), Skew-growth curves. *Proc. Natl. Acad. Sci. U.S.* **11**, 16–22 (Ch 9)

PEARSALL, W. H. (1927), Growth studies. VI. On the relative sizes of growing plant organs. *Ann. Botany* **41**, 549–556 (Ch 9)

PENSTON, N. L. (1931), A study by microchemical methods of the distribution of potassium in the potato plant. *Ann. Botany* **45**, 673–692 (Ch 2)

PFEFFER, W. (1899), Physiology of Plants. Vol. I. pp. 632. Translated by A. J. Ewart. Clarendon Press, Oxford (Ch 3)

PHINNEY, B. O. (1956), Growth response of single-gene dwarf mutants in maize to gibberellic acid. *Proc. Natl. Acad. Sci. U.S.* **42**, 185–189 (Ch 4)

PHINNEY, B. O. and WEST, C. A. (1960), Gibberellins as native plant growth regulators. *Ann. Rev. Plant Physiol.* **11**, 411–436 (Ch 4)

PLATT, J. R. (1962), A "book model" for genetic information-transfer in cells and tissues. pp. 167–187. In M. Kasha and B. Pullman (eds.), *Horizons in Biochemistry.* Academic Press, New York (Ch 9)

POLLARD, J. K., ROCHOW, W. F., and STEWARD, F. C. (1958), The incorporation of C^{14} labelled substrates into tobacco leaf proteins. *Plant Physiol.* **33** (Suppl.), xii–xiii (Ch 6)

POLLARD, J. K., SHANTZ, E. M., and STEWARD, F. C. (1961), Hexitols in coconut milk: their role in the nurture of dividing cells. *Plant Physiol.* **36**, 492–501 (Ch 4)

POLLARD, J. K. and STEWARD, F. C. (1959), The use of C^{14}-proline by growing cells: its conversion to protein and to hydroxyproline. *J. Exp. Botany* **10**, 17–32 (Ch 4, 5)

POLLOCK, B. M. (1950), An investigation of the physiology of the rest period in trees, with special reference to *Acer.* pp. 235. Ph.D. thesis, University of Rochester (Ch 6, 7)

POLLOCK, B. M. (1953), The respiration of *Acer* buds in relation to the inception and termination of the winter rest. *Physiol. Plantarum* **6**, 47–64 (Ch 7)

POPE, D. T. and MUNGER, H. M. (1953a), Heredity and nutrition in relation to magnesium deficiency chlorosis in celery. *Proc. Am. Soc. Hort. Sci.* **53**, 472–480 (Ch 2)

POPE, D. T. and MUNGER, H. M. (1953b), The inheritance of susceptibility to boron deficiency in celery. *Proc. Am. Soc. Hort. Sci.* **61**, 481–486 (Ch 2)

POSTLETHWAIT, S. N. and NELSON, O. E. (1964), Characterization of development in maize through the use of mutants. I. The polytypic (Pt) and ramosa-1 (ra_1) mutants. *Am. J. Botany* **51**, 238–243 (Ch 8)

POUX, N. (1962), Nouvelles observations sur la nature et l'origine de la membrane vacuolaire des cellules végétales. *J. Microscopie* **1**, 55–66 (Ch 2)

PRANTL, K. (1873), Über den Einfluss des Lichts und das Wachsthum der Blätter. *Arbeiten Bot. Inst.* 1, pp. 371–384. Würzburg (Ch 7)

PRESTON, R. D. (1952), Movement of water in higher plants. pp. 257–321. In A. Frey-Wyssling (ed.), *Deformation and Flow in Biological Systems*. North-Holland Pub. Co., Amsterdam (Ch 6)

PREVOT, P. and STEWARD, F. C. (1936), Salient features of the root system relative to the problem of salt absorption. *Plant Physiol.* 11, 509–534 (Ch 2, 6)

PRIESTLEY, J. H. (1935), Sap ascent in the tree. *Science Progr.* 117, 42–56 (Ch 6)

PRIESTLEY, J. H. and PEARSALL, W. H. (1922), Growth studies. III. A "volumeter" method of measuring the growth of roots. *Ann. Botany* 36, 485–488 (Ch 9)

PRIESTLEY, J. H. and SCOTT, L. I. (1938), *Introduction to Botany*. pp. 615. Longmans, Green and Co., London (Ch 5, 9)

PRINGLE, R. B. (1961), Chemical nature of antheridogen A, a specific inducer of the male sex organ in certain fern species. *Science* 133, 284 (Ch 7)

PRINGLE, R. B., NAF, U., and BRAUN, A. C. (1960), Purification of a specific inducer of the male sex organ in certain fern species. *Nature* 186, 1066–1067 (Ch 7)

PROBINE, M. C. and BARBER, N. F. (1965), The structure and elastic properties of the cell wall of *Nitella* in relation to extension growth. *Australian J. Biol. Sci.* 19, 439–457 (Ch 3)

PROBINE, M. C. and PRESTON, R. D. (1958), Protoplasmic streaming and wall structure in *Nitella*. *Nature* 182, 1657 (Ch 1)

PROBINE, M. C. and PRESTON, R. D. (1962), Cell growth and the structure and mechanical properties of the walls in *Nitella opaca*. II. Mechanical properties of the walls. *J. Exptl. Botany* 13, 111–127 (Ch 1, 3)

RABSON, R. (1956), Some interactions of the environment and plant metabolism with special reference to the roles of the keto acids. pp. 292. Ph.D. thesis, Cornell University (Ch 8)

RABSON, R. and STEWARD, F. C. (1962), The growth, nutrition, and metabolism of *Mentha piperita* L. VI. The keto and amino acids of mint plants: interacting effects due to day length and to night temperature. *Cornell Univ. Agr. Expt. Sta. Mem.* No. 379, 130–140 (Ch 8)

RANDOLPH, L. F. (1950), Cytological and phenotypical effects induced in maize by X-rays and the Bikini Test Able atomic bomb. *J. Cellular Comp. Physiol.* 35 (Suppl. 1), 103–117 (Ch 8)

RAPER, J. R. (1940), Sexuality in *Achlya ambisexualis*. *Mycologia* 32, 710–727 (Ch 7)

RAPER, J. R. (1952), Chemical regulation of several processes in the thallophytes. *Botan. Rev.* 18, 447–545 (Ch 7)

RAPER, J. R. (1955), Some problems of specificity in the sexuality of plants. pp. 119–140. In E. G. Butler (ed.), *Biological Specificity and Growth*. Princeton University Press, Princeton, New Jersey (Ch 7)

RAPER, J. R. (1957), Hormones and sexuality in lower plants. *Symposia Soc. Exptl. Biol.* 11, 143–165 (Ch 7)

RAPER, J. R. (1966), *Genetics of Sexuality in Higher Fungi*. pp. 283. The Ronald Press Co., New York (Ch 7)

RAPER, K. B. (1960), Levels of cellular interaction in amoeboid populations. *Proc. Am. Phil. Soc.* **104**, 579–604 (Ch 1)

RAPER, K. B. (1962), The environment and morphogenesis in cellular slime molds. Harvey Lectures, Ser. 57, 111–141 (Ch 1)

RAULIN, J. (1869), Études chimiques sur la végétation. *Ann. Sci. Natur.* 5th sér. **11**, 93–299.

REED, H. S. (1920), Slow and rapid growth. *Am. J. Botany* **7**, 327–332 (Ch 9)

REINDERS, D. E. (1938), The process of water-intake by discs of potato tissue. *Koninkl. Ned. Akad. Wetenschap., Proc. C.* **41**, 1–14 (Ch 6)

RICHARDS, F. J. (1951), Phyllotaxis: its quantitative expression and relation to growth in the apex. *Trans. Roy. Soc. (London) B.* **235**, 509–564 (Ch 8)

RICHARDS, F. J. (1956), Spatial and temporal correlations involved in leaf pattern production at the apex. pp. 66–76. In F. L. Milthorpe (ed.), *The Growth of Leaves*. Butterworth, London (Ch 8)

RICHARDS, F. J. (1959), A flexible growth function for empirical use. *J. Exptl. Botany* **10**, 290–300 (Ch 9)

RICHARDS, O. W. and KAVANAGH, A. J. (1945), The analysis of growing form. pp. 188–230. In W. E. Le Gros Clark and P. B. Medawar (eds.), *Essays on Growth and Form*. Clarendon Press, Oxford (Ch 9)

ROBERTSON, T. B. (1908), On the normal rate of growth of an individual and its biochemical significance. *Arch. Entwicklungsmoch. Organ* **25**, 581–614 (Ch 9)

ROBERTSON, T. B. (1923), *The Chemical Basis of Growth and Senescence*. pp. 389. J. B. Lippincott Co., Philadelphia (Ch 9)

ROTHWELL, K. and WAIN, R. L. (1964), Studies on a growth inhibitor in yellow Lupin, *Lupinus luteus* L. pp. 363–375. In J. P. Nitsch (ed.), *Régulateurs Naturels de la Croissance Végétale*. Centre National de la Recherche Scientifique, Paris (Ch 4)

ROTOR, G. and MACDANIELS, L. H. (1951), Flower bud differentiation and development in *Cattleya labiata* Lindl. *Am. J. Botany* **38**, 147–151 (Ch 8)

RUSSELL, E. J. (1950), *Soil Conditions and Plant Growth*. 8th edition. pp. 635. Longmans, Green and Co., London (Ch 2)

SACHS, J. (1887), *Lectures on the Physiology of Plants*. pp. 836. Clarendon Press, Oxford (Ch 1, 5, 7, 9)

SALISBURY, F. B. (1963), *The Flowering Process*. pp. 234. Pergamon Press, New York (Ch 7)

SCARTH, G. W. (1929), The influence of H ion concentration on the turgor and movement of plant cells with special reference to stomatal behavior. *Proc. Intern. Congr. Plant Sci.* (1st Congr., Ithaca 1926), 1151–1162 (Ch 6)

SCHNEIDERMAN, H. and FEDER, N. (1954), A respirometer for metabolic studies at high gaseous pressure. *Biol. Bull.* **106**, 230–237 (Ch 4)

SCHRÖDINGER, E. (1944), *What is Life?* pp. 92. Cambridge University Press, Cambridge (Ch 1, 10)

SCHWENDENER, S. (1881), Über Bau und Mechanik der Spaltöffnungen. *Monatsber. kgl. Akad. Wiss.* Berlin **46**, 581–597 (Ch 6)

SHANTZ, E. M. (1966), Chemistry of naturally-occurring growth-regulating substances. *Ann. Rev. Plant Physiol.* **17**, 409–438 (Ch 4)

SHANTZ, E. M., MEARS, K., and STEWARD, F. C. (1958), Comparison between the growth-promoting effects on carrot tissue of coconut milk and of kinetin and certain of its analogs. *Plant Physiol.* **33** (Suppl.), xvi (Ch 4)

SHANTZ, E. M. and STEWARD, F. C. (1955), The identification of Compound A from coconut milk as 1,3-diphenylurea. *J. Am. Chem. Soc.* **77**, 6351–6353 (Ch 4)

SHANTZ, E. M. and STEWARD, F. C. (1957), The growth-stimulating substances in extracts of immature corn grain: a progress report. *Plant Physiol.* **32** (Suppl.), viii (Ch 4)

SHANTZ, E. M. and STEWARD, F. C. (1959), Investigations on growth and metabolism of plant cells. VII. Sources of nitrogen for tissue cultures under optimal conditions for their growth. *Ann. Botany* N.S. **23**, 371–390 (Ch 4)

SHANTZ, E. M. and STEWARD, F. C. (1964), Growth-promoting substances from the environment of the embryo. II. The growth-stimulating complexes of coconut milk, corn, and *Aesculus*. pp. 59–75. In J. P. Nitsch (ed.), *Régulateurs Naturels de la Croissance Végétale*. Centre National de la Recherche Scientifique, Paris (Ch 4)

SHANTZ, E. M., STEWARD, F. C., SMITH, M. S., and WAIN, R. L. (1955), Investigations of the growth and metabolism of plant cells. VI. Growth of potato tuber tissue in culture: the synergistic action of coconut milk and some synthetic growth-regulating compounds. *Ann. Botany* N.S. **19**, 49–58 (Ch 4)

SHANTZ, E. M., SUGII, M., and STEWARD, F. C. (1967), The interaction of cell division factors with *myo*-inositol and their effect on cultured carrot tissue. *Ann. N.Y. Acad. Sci.* **144**, 335–356 (Ch 4)

SHARMAN, B. C. (1945), Leaf and bud initiation in the Gramineae. *Botan. Gaz.* **106**, 269–289 (Ch 8)

SHIBAOKA, H. (1961), Studies on the mechanism of growth inhibiting effect of light. *Plant and Cell Physiol.* **2**, 175–197 (Ch 4)

SIMMONDS, N. W. (1959), *Bananas*. pp. 466. Longmans, Green and Co., London (Ch 6, 7)

SINNOTT, E. W. (1960), *Plant Morphogenesis*. pp. 550. McGraw-Hill, New York (Ch 1, 10)

SKOOG, F. (ed.) (1951), *Plant Growth Substances*. pp. 476. University of Wisconsin Press, Madison (Ch 4)

SKOOG, F., STRONG, F. M., and MILLER, C. O. (1965), Cytokinins. *Science* **148**, 532–533 (Ch 4)

SMITH, E. F., BROWN, N. A., and McCULLOCH, L. (1912), The structure and development of crown gall: a plant cancer. pp. 11–60. *U.S. Bureau of Plant Industry Bulletin* No. 255 (Ch 4)

SMUTS, J. C. (1926), *Holism and Evolution.* pp. 362. Macmillan, New York (Ch 5, 10)

SNELL, F. M., SHULMAN, S., SPENCER, R. P., and MOOS, C. (1965), *Biophysical Principles of Structure and Function.* pp. 390. Addison-Wesley, Reading, Mass. (Ch 3)

SNOW, M. and SNOW, R. (1947), On the determination of leaves. *New Phytologist* **45**, 5–19 (Ch 8)

SNOW, M. and SNOW, R. (1948), On the determination of leaves. *Symposia Soc. Exptl. Biol.* **2**, 263–275 (Ch 8)

SNOW, M. and SNOW, R. (1955), Regulation of sizes of leaf primordia by growing-point of stem apex. *Proc. Roy. Soc. (London) B.* **144**, 222–229 (Ch 8)

SNOW, M. and SNOW, R. (1959), Regulation of sizes of leaf primordia by older leaves. *Proc. Roy. Soc. (London) B.* **151**, 39–47 (Ch 8)

SNOW, M. and SNOW, R. (1962), A theory of the regulation of phyllotaxis based on *Lupinus albus. Trans. Roy. Soc. (London) B.* **244**, 483–514 (Ch 8)

SOMA, K. and BALL, E. (1963), Studies of the surface growth of the shoot apex of *Lupinus albus. Brookhaven Symposia Biol.* **16**, 13–45 (Ch 9)

SONNEBORN, T. M. (1963), Does preformed cell structure play an essential role in cell heredity? pp. 165–221. In J. M. Allen (ed.), *The Nature of Biological Diversity.* McGraw-Hill, New York (Ch 9)

SPYRIDES, G. J. (1964), The effect of univalent cations on the binding of sRNA to the template-ribosome complex. *Proc. Natl. Acad. Sci. U.S.* **51**, 1220–1226 (Ch 2)

SRB, A. M., OWEN, R. D., and EDGAR, R. S. (1965), *General Genetics.* 2nd edition. pp. 557. W. H. Freeman and Co., San Francisco (Ch 2, 9, 10)

STEBBINS, G. L. (1964), Four basic questions of plant biology. *Am. J. Botany* **51**, 220–230 (Ch 10)

STEBBINS, G. L. (1965), Some relationships between mitotic rhythm, nucleic acid synthesis and morphogenesis in higher plants. *Brookhaven Symposia Biol.* **18**, 204–221 (Ch 9)

STEINBERG, I. Z., OPLATKA, A., and KATCHALSKY, A. (1966), Mechanochemical engines. *Nature* **210**, 568–571 (Ch 6)

STEPHENS, L. C. (1960), Embryonic potency of embryoid bodies derived from a transplantable testicular teratoma of the mouse. *Dev. Biol.* **2**, 285–297 (Ch 10)

STEWARD, F. C. (1933), The absorption and accumulation of solutes by living plant cells. V. Observations upon the effects of time, oxygen and salt concentration upon absorption and respiration of storage tissue. *Protoplasma* **18**, 208–242 (Ch 2)

STEWARD, F. C. (1939), The growth of *Valonia ventricosa* J. Agardh. and *Valonia ocellata* Howe in culture. Papers from Tortugas Lab. XXXII, *Carnegie Inst. Wash. Publ.* No. 517, 87–98 (Ch 3)

STEWARD, F. C. (1958), Growth and organized development of cultured cells. III. Interpretations of the growth from free cell to carrot plant. *Am. J. Botany* **45**, 709–713 (Ch 5, 9)

STEWARD, F. C. (1961a), Vistas in plant physiology: problems of organization, growth and morphogenesis. *Can. J. Botany* **39**, 441–460 (Ch 10)

STEWARD, F. C. (1961b), Organization and integration: some problems of cells, their growth and nutrition. pp. 453–490. In M. X. Zarrow (ed.), *Growth in Living Systems.* Basic Books, New York (Ch 6, 7)

STEWARD, F. C. (1962), The growth, nutrition, and metabolism of *Mentha piperita* L. I. *Mentha* as a plant for physiological investigations. *Cornell Univ. Agr. Expt. Sta. Mem.* No. 379, 3–10 (Ch 1)

STEWARD, F. C. (ed.) (1963), *Plant Physiology, A Treatise*, Vol. III. *Inorganic Nutrition of Plants.* pp. 811. Academic Press, New York (Ch 2)

STEWARD, F. C. (1963), Effects of environment on metabolic patterns. pp. 195–214. In L. T. Evans (ed.), *Environmental Control of Plant Growth.* Academic Press, New York (Ch 2, 7)

STEWARD, F. C .(1964), *Plants at Work.* pp. 184. Addison-Wesley, Reading, Mass. (Ch 6)

STEWARD, F. C. (1966), Physiological aspects of organization. pp. 3–26. In E. G. Cutter (ed.), *Trends in Plant Morphogenesis.* Longmans, Green and Co., London (Ch 10)

STEWARD, F. C. and BARBER, J. T. (1965), Proteins in differentiation and morphogenesis. Studies with acrylamide gel electrophoresis. II. Application to the proteins of the tulip. *Am. J. Botany* **52** (Abstr.), 623–624 (Ch 8)

STEWARD, F. C., and BERRY, W. F. (1934), The absorption and accumulation of solutes by living plant cells. VII. The time factor in the respiration and salt absorption of Jerusalem artichoke tissue (*Helianthus tuberosus*) with observations on ionic interchange. *J. Exptl. Biol.* **11**, 103–119 (Ch 6)

STEWARD, F. C., BERRY, W. E., and BROYER, T. C. (1936), The absorption and accumulation of solutes by living plant cells. VIII. The effect of oxygen upon respiration and salt accumulation. *Ann. Botany* **50**, 345–366 (Ch 2)

STEWARD, F. C., BERRY, W. E., PRESTON, C., and RAMAMURTI, T. K. (1943), The absorption and accumulation of solutes by living cells. X. Time and temperature effects of salt uptake by potato discs and the influence of the storage conditions of the tubers on metabolism and other properties. *Ann. Botany* N.S. **7**, 221–260 (Ch 6)

STEWARD, F. C. and BIDWELL, R. G. S. (1966), Storage pools and turn-over systems in growing and non-growing cells: experiment with C^{14}-sucrose, C^{14}-glutamine and C^{14}-asparagine. *J. Exptl. Botany* **17**, 726–741 (Ch 4)

TORREY, J. G. (1958), Endogenous bud and root formation by isolated roots of *Convolvulus* grown *in vitro*. *Plant Physiol.* **33**, 258–263 (Ch 1)

TOWERS, G. H. N. (1954), The keto acids of plants: their identity, analysis and metabolic roles. pp. 271. Ph.D. thesis, Cornell University (Ch 8)

TOWNES, P. L. and HOLTFRETER, J. (1955), Directed movements and selective adhesion of embryonic amphibian cells. *J. Exptl. Zool.* **128**, 53–120 (Ch 10)

TSCHERMAK-WOESS, E. (1956), Karyologische Pflanzenanatomie. *Protoplasma* **46**, 798–834 (Ch 10)

TSCHERMAK-WOESS, E. and ENZENBERG-KUNZ, U. (1965), Die Struktur der hoch endopolyploiden Kerne im Endosperm von *Zea mays*, das auffallende Verhalten ihrer Nucleolen und ihr Endopolyploidiegrad. *Planta* **64**, 149–169 (Ch 9)

TULECKE, W. R. (1957), The pollen of *Ginkgo biloba: in vitro* culture and tissue formation. *Am. J. Botany* **44**, 602–608 (Ch 4)

VAN OVERBEEK, J., CONKLIN, M. E., and BLAKESLEE, A. F. (1941), Factors in coconut milk essential for growth and development of very young *Datura* embryos. *Science* **94**, 350–351 (Ch 4)

VAN OVERBEEK, J., CONKLIN, M. E., and BLAKESLEE, A. F. (1942), Cultivation *in vitro* of small *Datura* embryos. *Am. J. Botany* **29**, 472–477 (Ch 7)

VARNER, J. E. and RAM CHANDRA, G. (1964), Hormonal control of enzyme synthesis in barley endosperm. *Proc. Natl. Acad. Sci. U.S.* **52**, 100–106 (Ch 4)

VLIEGENTHART, J. A. and VLIEGENTHART, J. F. G. (1966), Reinvestigation of authentic samples of auxins A and B and related products by mass spectrometry. *Recueil des Travaux Chimiques des Pays-Bas* **85**, 1266–1272 (Ch 4)

WADDINGTON, C. H. (1953), How do cells differentiate? *Sci. American* **189** (No. 3), 108–117 (Ch 9)

WADDINGTON, C. H. (1957), *Strategy of the Genes*. pp. 262. Macmillan, New York (Ch 9, 10)

WADDINGTON, C. H. (1962), *New Patterns in Genetics and Development*. pp. 271. Columbia Univ. Press, New York (Ch 10)

WAGGONER, P. E. (1966), Decreasing transpiration and the effect upon growth. pp. 49–72. In W. H. Pierre, D. Kirkham, J. Pesek, and R. Shaw (eds.), *Plant Environment and Efficient Water Use*. Iowa State Symposium Monograph (Ch 4)

WAGGONER, P. E. and ZELITCH, I. (1965), Transpiration and the stomata of leaves. *Science* **150**, 1413–1420 (Ch 4)

WAIN, R. L. (1955a), A new approach to selective weed control. *Ann. Appl. Biol.* **42**, 151–157 (Ch 4)

WAIN, R. L. (1955b), Some chemical aspects of research on plant growth substances. *J. Sci. Food Agr.* **6**, 361–363 (Ch 4)

WAIN, R. L. and FAWCETT, C. H. (in press), Chemical plant growth regulation, in F. C. Steward (ed.), *Plant Physiology, A Treatise*, Academic Press, New York (Ch 4)

WAIN, R. L. and WIGHTMAN, F. (1953), Studies on plant growth-regulating substances. VII. Growth promoting activity in the chlorophenoxyacetic acids. *Ann. Appl. Biol.* **40**, 244–249 (Ch 4)

WAIN, R. L. and WIGHTMAN, F. (1954), The growth-regulating activity of certain ω-substituted alkylcarboxylic acids in relation to their β-oxidation within the plant. *Proc. Roy. Soc. (London)* B. **142**, 525–536 (Ch 4)

WAIN, R. L. and WIGHTMAN, F. (eds.) (1956), *The Chemistry and Mode of Action of Plant Growth Substances.* pp. 312. Academic Press, New York (Ch 4)

WALKER, D. J. and FORREST, W. W. (1964), Change in entropy during bacterial metabolism. *Nature* **201**, 49–52 (Ch 10)

WARDLAW, C. W. (1949a), XIV. Leaf formation and phyllotaxis in *Dryopteris aristata. Ann. Botany* N.S. **13**, 164–198 (Ch 8)

WARDLAW, C. W. (1949b), Further experimental observations on the shoot apex of *Dryopteris aristata. Trans. Roy. Soc. (London)* B. **233**, 415–451 (Ch 8)

WARDLAW, C. W. (1955), *Embryogenesis in Plants.* pp. 381. Methuen, London (Ch 7)

WARDLAW, C. W. (1965), The organization of the shoot apex. pp. 966–1076. In W. Ruhland (ed.), *Handbuch der Pflanzenphysiologie*, Vol. XV. Springer-Verlag, Berlin (Ch 5, 8)

WARDLAW, C. W. (1965), *Organization and Evolution in Plants.* pp. 499. Longmans, Green and Co., London (Ch 8, 10)

WARDROP, A. B. (1965), Cellular differentiation in xylem. pp. 61–97. In W. A. Cote (ed.), *Cellular Ultrastructure of Woody Plants.* Syracuse University Press, Syracuse (Ch 10)

WAREING, P. F. (1958), Interaction between indole-acetic acid and gibberellic acid in cambial activity. *Nature* **181**, 1744–1745 (Ch 7)

WARIS, H. (1959), Neomorphosis in seed plants induced by amino acids. I. *Oenanthe aquatica. Physiologia Plantarum* **12**, 753–766 (Ch 10)

WARIS, H. (1962), Neomorphosis in seed plants caused by amino acids. II. *Oenanthe lachenalii. Physiologia Plantarum* **15**, 736–752 (Ch 10)

WARMKE, H. E. (1946), Sex determination and sex balance in *Melandrium. Am. J. Botany* **33**, 648–660 (Ch 8)

WATSON, J. D. (1965), *Molecular Biology of the Gene.* pp. 493. W. A. Benjamin Inc., New York (Ch 10)

WATSON, J. D. and CRICK, F. H. C. (1953), Molecular structure of nucleic acids: a structure for deoxyribose nucleic acid. Genetical implications of the structure of deoxyribose nucleic acid. *Nature* **171**, 737–738; 964–967 (Ch 1, 3)

WEINSTEIN, L. H., NICKELL, L. G., LAWRENCE, H. J., JR., and TULECKE, W. (1959), Biochemical and physiological studies of plant tissue cultures and plant parts from which they are derived. I. *Agave toumeyana* Trel. *Contrib. Boyce Thompson Inst.* **20**, 239–250 (Ch 4)

WEISS, P. (1947), The problem of specificity in growth and development. *Yale J. Biol. and Med.* **19**, 235–278 (Ch 10)

WEISS, P. (1949a), Differential growth. pp. 135–186. In A. K. Parpart (ed.), *The Chemistry and Physiology of Growth.* Princeton University Press, Princeton (Ch 10)

WEISS, P. (1949b), Growth and differentiation on the cellular and molecular levels. *Exptl. Cell Research*, Suppl. 1, 475–482 (Ch 10)

WEISS, P. (1950), Perspectives in the field of morphogenesis. *Quart. Rev. Biol.* **25**, 177–198 (Ch 10)

WELLENSIEK, S. J. (1961), Leaf vernalization. *Nature* **192**, 1097–1098 (Ch 8)

WELLENSIEK, S. J. (1964), Dividing cells as the prerequisite for vernalization. *Plant Physiol.* **39**, 832–835 (Ch 8)

WENT, F. W. (1928), Wuchsstoff and Wachstum. *Rec. Trav. Botan. Neerland.* **25**, 1–116 (Ch 1)

WENT, F. W. (1957), *The Experimental Control of Plant Growth.* pp. 343. Chronica Botanica, Waltham, Mass. (Ch 4)

WENT, F. W. and THIMANN, K. V. (1937), *Phytohormones.* pp. 294. Macmillan, New York (Ch 4)

WETMORE, R. H. (1956), Growth and development in the shoot system of plants. pp. 173–190. In D. Rudnick (ed.), *Cellular Mechanisms in Differentiation and Growth* (14th Growth Symposium). Princeton University Press, Princeton (Ch 5, 8)

WETMORE, R. H., GIFFORD, E. M. and GREEN, M. C. (1959), Development of vegetative and floral buds. pp. 255–274. In R. B. Withrow (ed.), *Photoperiodism and Related Phenomena in Plants and Animals.* American Association for the Advancement of Science Publication No. 45, Washington (Ch 8)

WETMORE, R. H. and MOREL, G. (1949), Growth and development of *Adiantum pedatum* L. on nutrient agar. *Am. J. Botany* **36**, 805–806 (Ch 7)

WETMORE, R. H. and RIER, J. P. (1963), Experimental induction of vascular tissues in callus of angiosperms. *Am. J. Botany* **50**, 418–430 (Ch 8)

WHALEY, W. G., MOLLENHAUER, H. H., and LEECH, J. H. (1960), The ultrastructure of the meristematic cell. *Am. J. Botany* **47**, 401–450 (Ch 5)

WHETZEL, H. H. (1918), *An Outline of the History of Phytopathology.* pp. 130. W. B. Saunders Co., Philadelphia (Ch 3)

WHITE, A., HANDLER, P., SMITH, E. L., and STETTEN, DeW. (1959), *Principles of Biochemistry.* 2nd edition. pp. 1149. McGraw-Hill, New York (Ch 6)

WHITE, P. R. (1938), "Root-pressure"—an unappreciated force in sap movement. *Am. J. Botany* **25**, 223–227 (Ch 6)

WHITE, P. R. (1943), *A Handbook of Plant Tissue Culture.* pp. 277. The Jaques Cattell Press, Inc., Lancaster, Pa. (Ch 3)

WHITE, P. R. (1963), *The Cultivation of Animal and Plant Cells.* pp. 239. The Ronald Press Co., New York (Ch 1)

WHITEHEAD, A. N. (1925), *Science and the Modern World.* pp. 296. Cambridge University Press, Cambridge (Ch 10)

WILLIAMS, R. F. (1960), The physiology of growth in the wheat plant. I. Seedling growth and the pattern of growth at the shoot apex. *Australian J. Biol. Sci.* **13**, 401–428 (Ch 8)

WILLIAMS, R. F. and RIJVEN, A. H. C. C. (1965), The physiology of growth in the wheat plant. II. The dynamics of leaf growth. *Australian J. Biol. Sci.* **18**, 721–744 (Ch 2, 8)

WILSON, K. (1947), Water movement in submerged aquatic plants with special reference to cut shoot of *Ranunculus fluitans*. *Ann. Botany* N.S. **11**, 91–122 (Ch 6)

WITHROW, R. B. and BENEDICT, H. M. (1936), Photoperiodic responses of certain greenhouse annuals as influenced by intensity and wavelength of artificial light used to lengthen the daylight period. *Plant Physiol.* **11**, 225–249 (Ch 7)

WOODARD, J. W. (1958), Intracellular amounts of nucleic acids and protein during pollen grain growth in *Tradescantia. J. Biophys. and Biochem. Cytol.* **4**, 383–389 (Ch 9)

WOODHEAD, T. W. (1915), *The Study of Plants.* pp. 440. Oxford University Press, London (Ch 1)

WOODWARD, JOHN (1699), Some thoughts and experiments concerning vegetation. *Phil. Trans. Roy. Soc.* **XX**, 193–227.

YAMAKI, T., SHIBAOKA, H., SYŌNO, K., MORIMOTO, H., and OSHIO, H. (1966), Physiological activities of heliangine, its derivatives, and breakdown products. *Botan. Mag.* (Tokyo) **79**, 339–341 (Ch 4)

YOSHIDA, K. (1962), Some experiments as for the maintenance of natural shape of algal balls in the culture. *Bull. Japan. Soc. Phycol.* **10**, 23–27 (Ch 1)

YUNG, C. (1938), Developmental anatomy of the seedling of the rice plant. *Botan. Gaz.* **99**, 786–802 (Ch 2)

ZELITCH, I. (1963), Stomata and water relations in plants. *Connecticut Agr. Expt. Sta. Bull.* No. 664 (Ch 6)

ZELITCH, I. (1965), Environmental and biochemical control of stomatal movement in leaves. *Biol. Rev.* **40**, 463–482 (Ch 6)

ZIMMERMAN, M. H. (1960), Transport in the phloem. *Ann Rev. Plant Physiol.* **11**, 167–190 (Ch 6)

ZIMMERMAN, M. H .(1961), Movement of organic substances in trees. *Science* **133**, 73–79 (Ch 6)

ZIMMERMAN, M. H. (1963), How sap moves in trees. *Sci. American* (No. 3), 133–142 (Ch 6)

ZUBAY, G. (1963), Molecular model for protein synthesis. *Science* **140**, 1092–1095 (Ch 3)

ZWAR, J. A., BRUCE, M. I., BOTTOMLEY, W., and KEFFORD, N. P. (1964), A comparison of the kinins of apple and coconut milk and of the modifications produced by purification procedures. pp. 123–130. In J. P. Nitsch (ed.), *Régulateurs Naturels de la Croissance Végétale.* Centre National de la Recherche Scientifique, Paris (Ch 4)

INDEX

The index combines a subject index, an index of substances, and an index of plant names. The plant names are listed in the index by genus and are cross indexed to trivial names where these are used. The bibliography includes, after each citation, the chapter in which the reference occurs and, in this sense, serves as an index by authors.